A-LEVEL
AND AS-LEVEL

LONGMAN
REFERENCE
GUIDES

PHYSICS

Dr Stephen Grounds

LONGMAN A AND AS-LEVEL REFERENCE GUIDES

Series editors: Geoff Black and Stuart Wall

TITLES AVAILABLE
Biology
Chemistry
English
Geography
Mathematics
Physics

Longman Group UK Limited,
Longman House, Burnt Mill, Harlow,
Essex CM20 2JE, England
and Associated Companies throughout the world.

First published 1991

British Library Cataloguing in Publication Data

Grounds, Stephen
Physics.
1. England. Secondary schools. Curriculum subjects: Physics. G.C.E. (A–Level) examinations
I. Title
530.076

ISBN 0–582–06392–2

Designed and produced by
The Pen and Ink Book Company,
Huntingdon, Cambridgeshire.
Set in 10/12pt Century Old Style.

Printed in Singapore

ACKNOWLEDGEMENTS

The author wishes to record his thanks to Reg Ph... suggestions concerning the text of the book. The ... encouragement of Mrs Linda Webb is also warmly acknowle... author would like to thank his wife Pauline for typing the bulk o... of the manuscript and to thank her and the rest of his family for ... shown whilst this book was in preparation.

HOW TO

AUTHOR'S PREFACE

The aim of this book is to provide those studying physics to A-level, AS-level, Scottish Higher, or their equivalents, with a useful reference book. The advent of 'Balanced Science' and the decrease in numbers of candidates offering physics as a single subject at 16+, has meant that many candidates now lack much of the background knowledge when studying A-level that their predecessors would have had. So one of the purposes of this book is to provide entries which will help them make the transition to A-level work.

There are two other types of entries. The first involves substantial and detailed sections on important parts of the core syllabuses of the A-level boards. The emphasis here is largely on concepts. Appropriate mathematics has been included, although it is recognised that some readers may not need such level of detail. Secondly, there are short entries which are more in the nature of a glossary of terms. These are largely on topics which, whilst not part of the A-level syllabuses, are likely to be encountered in background reading. An obvious example is some of the terminology of elementary particle physics.

Finally an attempt has been made to provide entries which will be useful in a study of the many 'options' now offered by some boards. The syllabuses for many of these options are very extended and it would not be possible in a condensed book of this kind to cover everything in them. Instead, at least for those well established options, the author has concentrated on topics which appear most frequently in examinations. The principal topics in options such as telecommunications, optical instruments, astronomy, sound and music, fluids, rotational mechanics, medical physics, electronics, and nuclear physics are covered in this way.

O USE THIS BOOK

Throughout your A-level and AS-level course you will be coming across terms, ideas and definitions that are unfamiliar to you. The Longman Reference Guides provide a quick, easy-to-use source of information, fact and opinion. Each main term is listed alphabetically and, where appropriate, cross-referenced to related terms.

- Where a term or phrase appears in **different type** you can look up a separate entry under that heading elsewhere in the book.
- Where a term or phrase appears in **different type** and is set between two arrowhead symbols ◄ ►, it is particularly recommended that you turn to the entry for that heading.

ABSOLUTE MAGNITUDE

◀ Magnitude scale ▶

ABSOLUTE TEMPERATURE SCALE

◀ Temperature ▶

ABSORPTION SPECTRUM

An absorption spectrum is that of a substance, usually a **gas** or a **plasma**, which stands in front of a source of white light and 'filters' out certain wavelengths.

If a **continuous spectrum** (white light) is passed through a gas, certain photons within the white light with just the right energy will be absorbed by the atoms of the gas, with corresponding electrons in the gas atoms 'jumping up' to a higher **energy level**. These excited atoms will quickly emit photons of
the same energy as the electrons 'fall back' to their original levels. As a result for a short while the absorbing atoms will hold some of the energy of the original beam of light. However, the emitted photons will not necessarily travel in the original direction of the beam of white light. Hence the spectrum will show dark lines of absorption in the continuous white light spectrum.

This is a process which occurs in the outer regions of stars. A continuous spectrum is produced within the star which is selectively absorbed in the outer regions of the star. By studying the spectral lines astronomers are able to work out the temperature and composition of the star.

◀ Stellar classification ▶

A.C.

◀ Alternating current ▶

A.C. METERS

◀ Alternating current meters ▶

ACCELERATION

This is the term used in **kinematics** when something experiences a change in velocity. It is a **vector** quantity in physics, and is defined in terms of changes in **velocity**.

As with velocity it is useful to distinguish between average and instantaneous values:

$$\text{Average acceleration} = \frac{\text{change in velocity}}{\text{time taken for the change}}$$

$$\text{Instantaneous acceleration} = \lim_{\Delta t \to 0} \left(\frac{\Delta v}{\Delta t} \right) = \frac{dv}{dt}$$

Graphically $\frac{dv}{dt}$ is the slope of a v, t graph at the particular instant in time.

◀ Uniform acceleration in a straight line ▶

ACCOMMODATION

◀ Eye ▶

ACHROMATIC COMBINATION

◀ Camera ▶

ACTION AT A DISTANCE

◀ Fields ▶

ACTION OF POINTS

The charge density on the surface of a charged conductor is particularly high at pointed parts of its surface (see **Charge distribution**). The resultant very high charge density produces a strong electric field in the vicinity of the points. In the surrounding air there will always be a small number of positive ions. Those near the points are blown either way from or towards the conductor, depending upon the charge on the conductor. Electrons move in the opposite direction. This movement in the air is sometimes called an

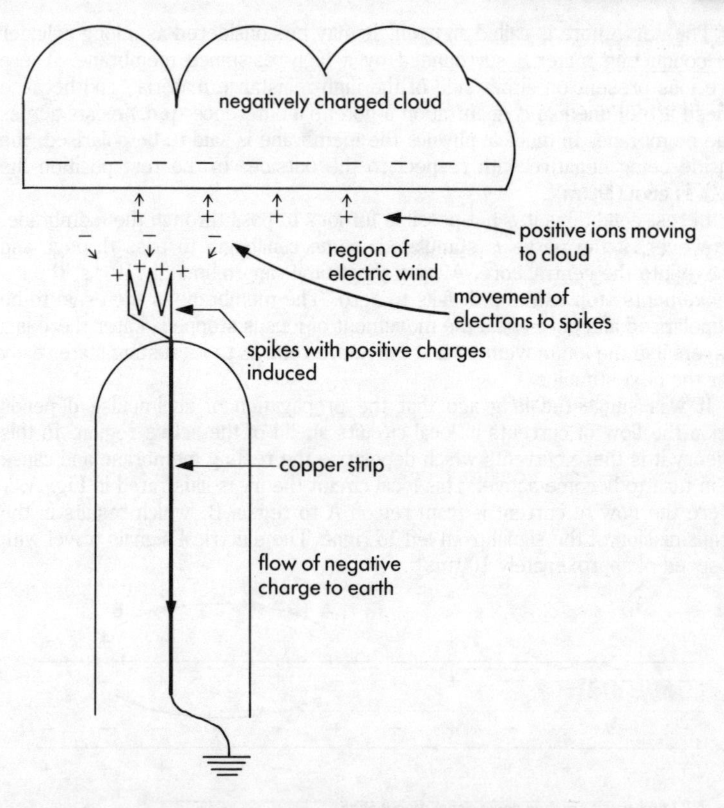

Fig. A.1 Action of points and electric wind with a lightning conductor

electric wind. Very quickly any charge on the conductor will be neutralised by the flow of opposite charges through the air towards it. The action of points forms the principle of the lightning conductor (Fig. A.1).

The action of a lightning conductor is to provide a preferred route to earth should there be an electrical discharge between a cloud and the ground. But the top of a lightning conductor is formed into an upward pointing set of points. A charged cloud above the conductor will induce charge on the conductor and particularly on the points. The electric wind which is then produced can lead to a safe and slow discharge of the cloud, thus avoiding the dangerous lightning flash of a sudden discharge.

ACTION POTENTIAL

This is the name in medical physics given to the changing electrical potential which is propagated along the nerves of the body and is used to 'trigger' the action of muscles.

The nerve fibre is called an *axon*. It may be considered as a long cylinder of conducting material surrounded by a high-resistance membrane. There are ions present on either side of the high-resistance material, and because these are of unequal concentration a potential difference (p.d.) exists across the membrane. In medical physics the membrane is said to be polarised, the inside being negative with respect to the outside. In the rest position the p.d. is about 90 mV.

In rest conditions it is not possible for ions to pass through the membrane. However, if the nerve is stimulated, some can begin to pass through and move into the central core. After a short time, approximately 10^{-3} s, the ion movements stop as the p.d. falls to zero. The membrane is then said to be depolarised and once again the movement of ions is stopped. Later there is a reversal in the ion movement and the nerve returns to its resting state ready for the next stimulus.

It was suggested long ago that the propagation of an impulse depends upon the flow of currents in local circuits ahead of the active region. In this theory it is these currents which depolarise the resting membrane and cause it in turn to become active. This local circuit theory is illustrated in Fig. A.2. Here the flow of current is from region A to region B, which results in the transmission of the signal from left to right. The electrical signals travel with a speed of approximately 100 ms^{-1}.

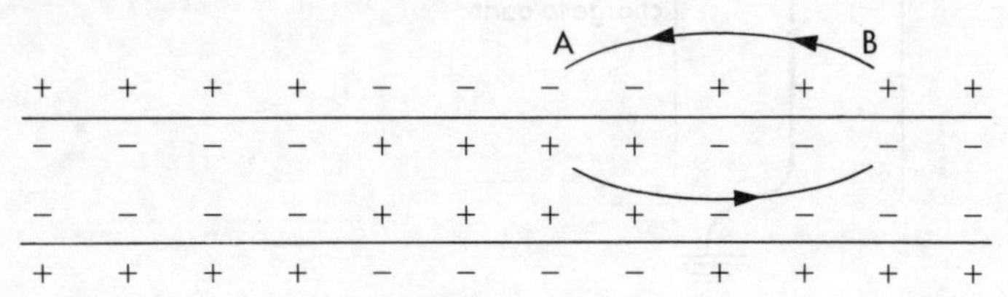

Fig. A.2 Local circuit action in nerve signal propagation

Fig. A.3 shows the record of a typical action potential for an axon in the heart of a frog. The signal before and after the action potential is called the resting potential.

ACTIVITY

◀ Radioactive decay law ▶

ADIABATIC CHANGE

An adiabatic change is a process which occurs in **thermodynamics** when no heat is lost or gained from a system. So for example if the air in a bicycle pump is compressed very rapidly the process is said to be adiabatic, because there is insufficient time for heat to flow in or out of the 'system', the system being the air inside the pump.

◀ Laws of thermodynamics ▶

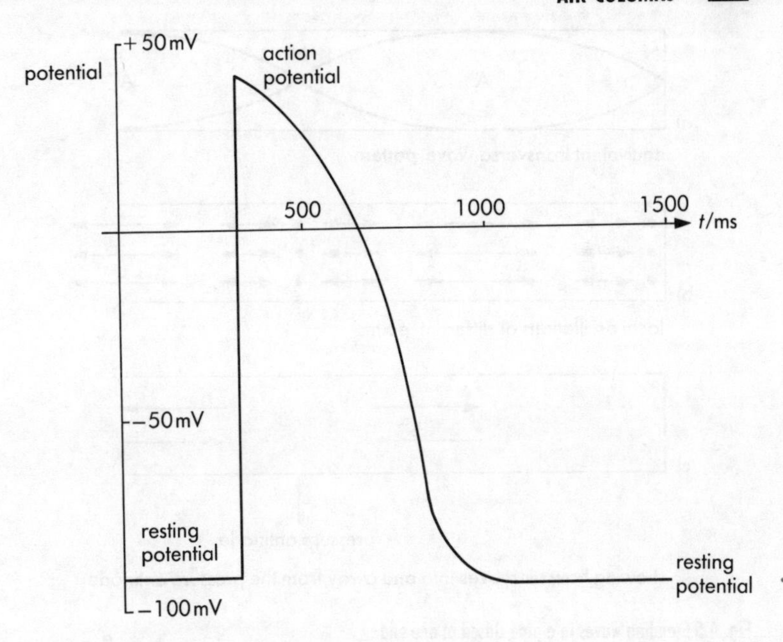

Fig. A.3 Resting and action potentials in the heart of a frog

AIR COLUMNS

A long column of air provides a system in which longitudinal **standing waves** can be set up in an example of **resonance.** Such columns form the basis of all musical instruments, such as organs, which use pipes to make their sounds.

A simple laboratory example of resonance in a tube closed at one end is obtained using the equipment shown in Fig. A.4.

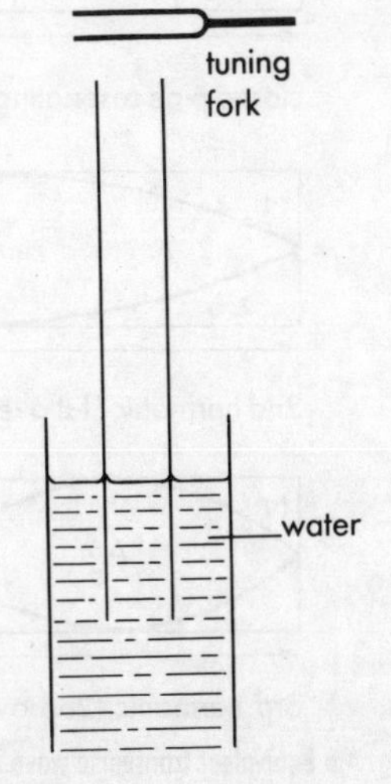

Fig. A.4 Resonance in tube closed at one end

A typical stationary wave pattern of nodes and antinodes of displacement is shown in Fig. A.5. Because sound waves are compressional it is common to show the equivalent pattern for a transverse system (Fig. A.5a). The open end is an antinode because the air can freely oscillate there. N is a node because there

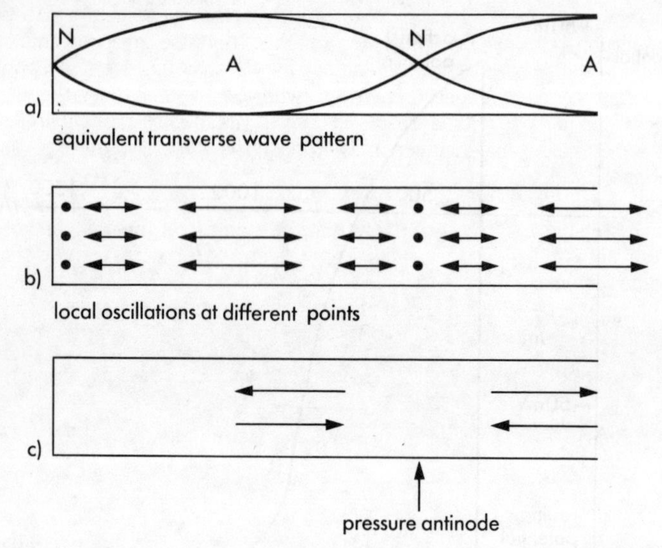

Fig. A.5 Standing waves in a pipe closed at one end

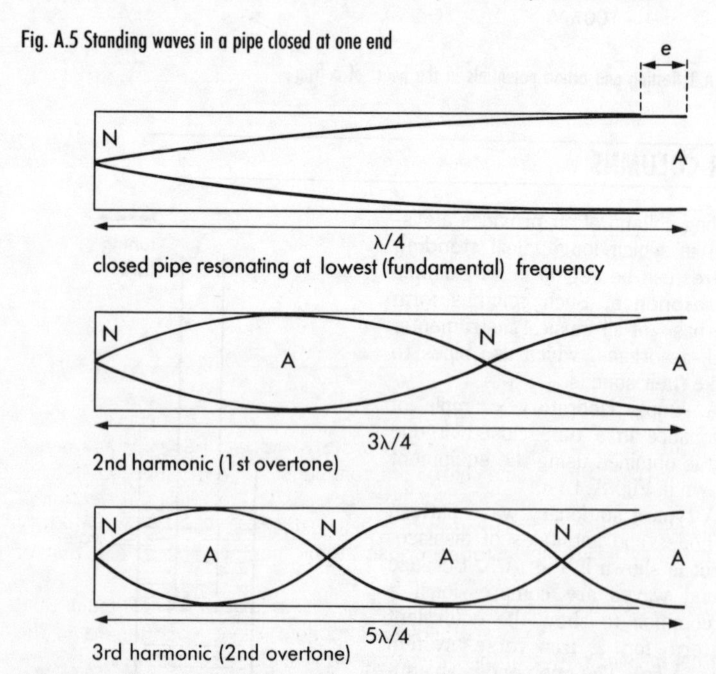

Fig. A.6 Equivalent transverse wave configurations for standing waves in a pipe closed at one end. The diagram shows three possible resonances

the oscillation is impeded by the end. Fig. A.5b shows the actual pattern of air oscillation at some intermediate positions. Because adjacent antinodes oscillate in antiphase the movement of air will sometimes be in opposite directions away from a node (Fig. A.5c), whereas at other times the air will converge on a node. As a result pressure variations have antinodes at displacement nodes and vice versa. Microphones will usually detect pressure variations, not displacements.

Typical equivalent transverse stationary wave patterns for a pipe open at one end are shown in Fig. A.6. Note that the antinode at the open end of the pipe will actually be a little way out from the end of the pipe, by a distance *e* called the end correction.

Similar patterns for a pipe open at both ends are shown in Fig. A.7.

◀ Musical instruments ▶

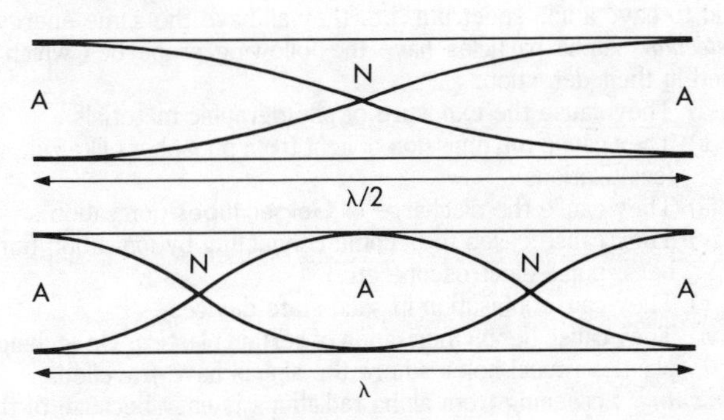

Fig. A.7 Two possible resonances for pipes open at both ends

AIR WEDGE

◀ Thin-film interference ▶

ALPHA RADIATION

The alpha particle is composed of two **protons** and two **neutrons** and hence has a mass of four units and charge of two units positive. It corresponds with the nuclei of helium atoms ^{4}He. Alpha radiation is the result of the ejection of an alpha particle at high speed from a heavy **nucleus**. Many alpha emitters are naturally occurring **isotopes** whose atomic number is between that of lead (82) and uranium (92).

All radiations can produce ionisation of the atoms of solids, liquids and gases; this is used as a method of detection. Alpha particles have the greatest ionising power of the three types of radiation because:

i) they have a two unit positive charge and hence strongly attract electrons;

ii) they are massive and hence travel relatively slowly for a given energy, consequently remaining a relatively long time in the vicinity of each atom near the path of the alpha particle.

Ionisation needs energy and each ion pair formed results in the loss of kinetic energy by the ionising particle. In the case of air the energy needed to form an ion pair is 34 eV, so an alpha particle of 5 MeV can produce 150,000 ion pairs, all in a distance of a few cm.

- *Penetrating power:* Penetrating power is the ability of radiation to penetrate matter. Alpha particles have low penetrating power and are stopped by thin metal foils, a sheet of paper or a few cm of air.
- *Energy spectrum:* From a given alpha emitter, the particles fall into a defined energy group and in air each group has the same range before being slowed down and becoming undetectable; these alpha particles are said to have a line spectrum, i.e. they all have the same energy.
- *Detection:* Alpha particles have the following properties which can be used in their detection:
    i) They cause the exposure of photographic materials.
    ii) They cause the emission of light from phosphors like zinc sulphide (scintillations).
    iii) They cause the discharge of **Geiger tubes** (ionisation).
    iv) They cause gases to become conducting by ionisation (ion chambers, pulse electroscope etc.).
    v) They cause ionisation in solid-state devices.
    vi) They cause depolymerisation of certain plastics. On etching, these plastics reveal holes where the alphas have travelled.
- *Screening:* Screening from alpha radiations is easy because of the poor penetrating power, but ingestion of alpha emitters may be dangerous.
- Typical alpha emitters:

Americium 241	5.5 MeV, half-life 458 y	+ low-energy gamma
Lead 210	5.3 MeV, half-life 21 y	+ low-energy gamma
Radium 226	4.5 to 7.7 MeV, half-life 1620 y	

ALTERNATING CURRENT (A.C.)

An alternating current is an electric current which changes direction periodically. Typically the current varies sinusoidally with time, as shown in Fig. A.8 below, but it is also possible to generate triangular and other waveforms, e.g. in a synthesiser. Alternating currents arise in two areas of engineering: the transmission of electrical power, and signal communication (telephones, radio, etc.).

POWER TRANSMISSION

In the transmission of electrical power alternating current is much preferred to direct current. This is because it can be very simply transformed from a high voltage/low current form to a low voltage/high current form, or vice versa, using a transformer. When power is sent along a transmission line the power loss due to transmission line heating is I^2R, where I is the current and R the resistance of the transmission cables. So it is better to transmit electricity, where possible, at very high voltages and small currents. Power is generated at relatively low voltages which are 'stepped up' for transmission purposes and finally 'stepped down' again for domestic consumption using transformers. Transformers have no moving parts, and small energy losses.

The electromotive force (e.m.f.) of an a.c. power supply varies sinusoidally according to the equation $E = E_o \sin \omega t$, where $\omega = 2\pi/T = 2\pi f$. Here ω is the angular frequency, f the frequency and T the period, as in simple harmonic motion theory. One complete alternation of the supply is called a cycle.

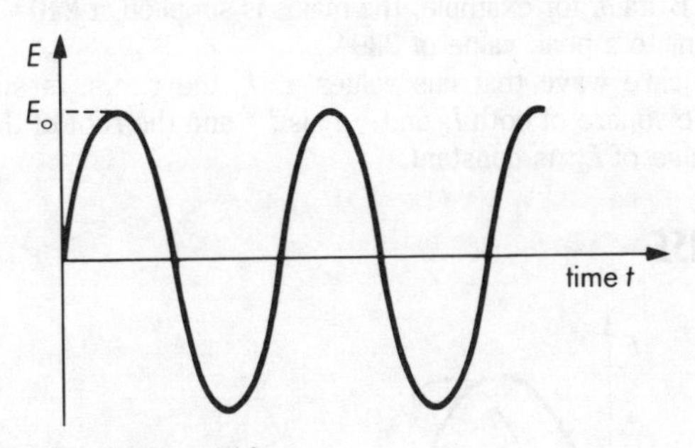

Fig. A.8 Alternating current of a sinusoidal form

COMMUNICATIONS

A.c. theory also has an application in telecommunications. Of course here waveforms other than sinusoidal ones are encountered (Figs. A.9 and A.10). By means of a technique called Fourier analysis each of these can be analysed into a series of simultaneous sinusoidal waveforms of different frequencies. The beauty of this is that the theory for sinusoidal signals can then be employed. See Fourier methods.

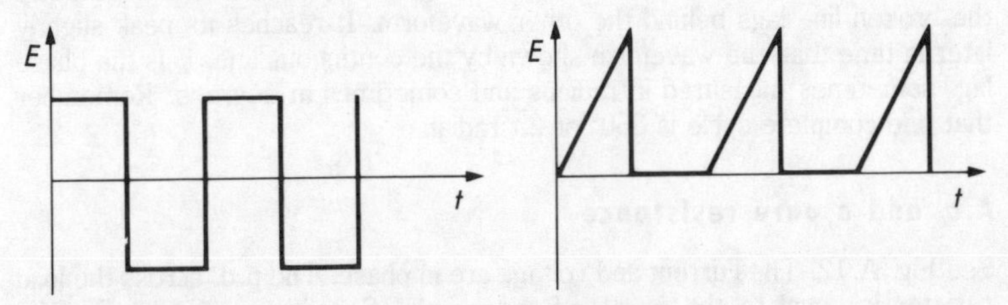

Fig. A.9 Square wave a.c.

Fig. A.10 Ramp and space a.c.

ROOT MEAN SQUARE (R.M.S.) VALUES

The r.m.s. value of an a.c. current is

i) the square root of the mean value of the square of the current, or

ii) that steady d.c. current which would convert electrical energy to internal energy (heat) and light in a resistance at the same rate as the a.c.

For a sinusoidal a.c. it is given by

$$I_{\text{r.m.s.}} = \frac{I_o}{\sqrt{2}} = 0.707\, I_o$$

where I_o is the peak value. This is because the average value of $\sin^2 \omega t$ is 0.5. Similar relationships hold for voltages. The r.m.s. value is the one usually quoted. In Britain, for example, the mains is supplied at 240 V (r.m.s.), which is equivalent to a peak value of 339 V.

For a square wave that has values $\pm I_o$ the r.m.s. is simply I_o (this is because the square of both I_o and $-I_o$ is I_o^2 and the root of this is I_o). So the average value of I_o^2 is constant.

PHASE

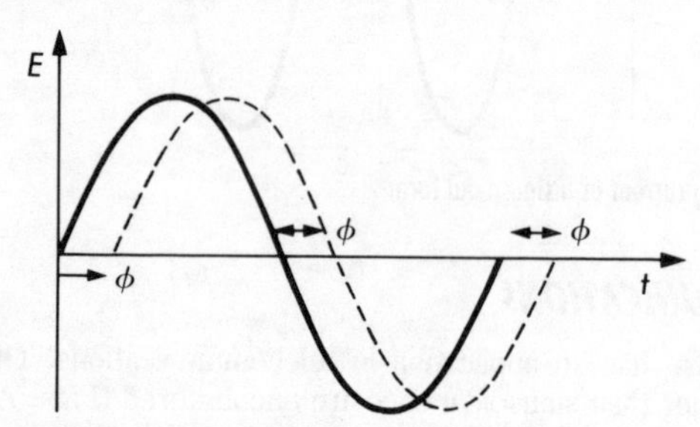

Fig. A.11 Phase difference between two alternating currents

In a.c., a voltage and the corresponding current may not be in step, or 'in phase', with each other. In the example in Fig. A.11 the waveform denoted by the broken line lags behind the other waveform. It reaches its peak slightly later in time than the waveform shown by the continuous line. ϕ is the phase lag, sometimes measured in radians and sometimes in degrees. Remember that one complete cycle is 360° or 2π radians.

A.c. and a pure resistance

See Fig. A.12. The current and voltage are in phase. The p.d. across the load resistor is equal to the e.m.f. of the supply. So with an e.m.f. given by $E = E_o \sin \omega t$ we have a p.d. given by $V = V_o \sin \omega t$ and $V_o = E_o$.

The current is given by $I = I_o \sin \omega t$, where $I_o = V_o/R$, V_o being the peak value of the p.d.

$$\text{The power delivered } P = \frac{V_o I_o}{2} = V_{\text{r.m.s.}}\, I_{\text{r.m.s.}}$$
$$= I^2_{\text{r.m.s.}}\, R$$

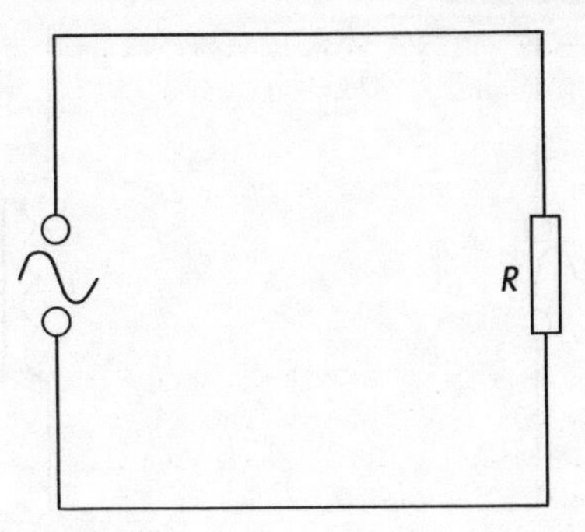

Fig. A.12 A.c. and a pure resistance

A.c. and a pure capacitance

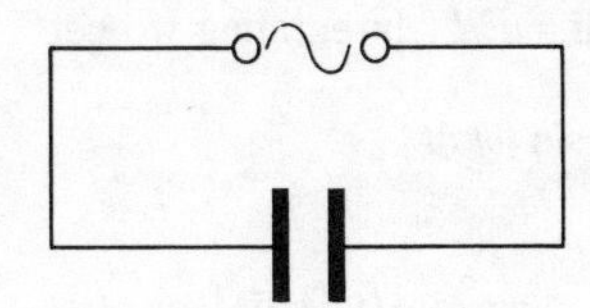

Fig. A.13

See Fig. A. 13. Here the current leads the voltage by 90°($\pi/2$); In this arrangement the e.m.f. of the supply equals the p.d. across the capacitor. For the capacitor the formula $Q = CV$ holds, and as $I = dQ/dt$ so $I = C\ dV/dt$. Then if the variation of voltage is given by $V = V_o \sin \omega t$ then
$I = C\omega V_o \cos \omega t = C\omega V_o (\sin \omega t + \pi/2)$.

Hence we can write I in the form $I = I_o \cos \omega t$, and in terms of magnitudes $I_o = V_o/X$, where X is the **reactance.** Reactance is measured in ohms like resistance, as it is a ratio of voltage/current.

Here $X = 1/\omega C$ or $X = 1/2\pi fC$

No power is delivered to the capacitor. In this circuit charge 'sloshes' in and out of the capacitor in a regular charge one-way-round, discharge, charge the other-way-round, discharge cycle. But as the electricity does not flow through a resistance no conversion of electrical energy to heat or light takes place. Another way of considering it is to plot V and I curves and note that over one cycle the net value of VI is zero.

A.c. and a pure inductance

In this arrangement (see Fig. A.14) there is a forward e.m.f. from the supply $E = E_o \sin \omega t$ and a back e.m.f. generated by the inductance L equal to $-L\,dI/dt$. The net e.m.f. in the circuit is zero, so that:

$$E + (-L\ dI/dt) = 0$$

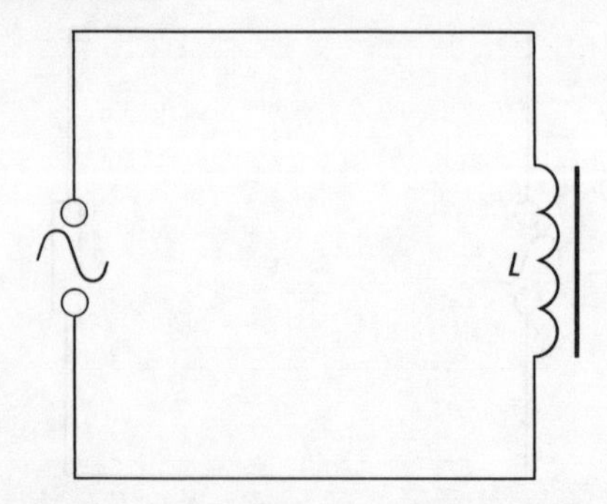

Fig. A.14 A.c. and a pure inductance

So $E = L\,dI/dt$, or, $dI/dt = E/L$. Integrating we get

$$\int dI = \int E/L\,dt = \int \frac{E_o}{L} \sin \omega t\,dt$$

$$\text{Hence} \quad I = -\frac{E_o}{L} \cos \omega t = \frac{E_o}{L} \sin(\omega t - \pi/2)$$

i.e. the current lags behind the voltage by 90° ($\pi/2$ radians).

As before we can write X for the reactance and here

$$X = \omega L$$

No power is delivered to the inductor. As with the capacitor circuit the net value of (voltage × current) over one cycle is zero.

The following points are worth noting

a) Reactances can also be expressed in terms of r.m.s. values

$$X = \frac{V_o}{I_o} = \frac{V_{r.m.s.}}{I_{r.m.s.}}$$

b) The reactance of both capacitors and inductors is frequency dependent. At low frequencies a capacitor has a large reactance and lets only a small current pass, but at high frequencies it has only a small reactance. The opposite is true of inductors.

In circuits containing resistance and reactance, voltage and current will generally be out of phase by an angle ϕ which is NOT ± 90° (= $+\frac{\pi}{2}$ radians). In this case $Z = E_o/I_o = E_{r.m.s.}/I_{r.m.s.}$, where E is the e.m.f. of the source. Z is called the **impedance**, and again, as a ratio of voltage/current, is measured in ohms. Note that the ratio can be in terms of either peak values or r.m.s. values.

◀ Phasors ▶

ALTERNATING CURRENT METERS

An a.c. meter uses a method of producing a deflection which depends on the magnitude but not on the direction of the electric current. Three methods are in general use:

a) Using the heating effect

In the past the hot-wire ammeter was used. This consisted of a length of resistance wire through which the current passed. The current caused the wire to heat and hence expand and a system of levers 'magnified' the expansion of the wire. With more modern technologies the current can be passed through a **resistor** to which is attached the junction of a **thermocouple**, or a tiny **thermistor**. In the former a very small voltage is produced which depends upon the temperature, and in the latter the resistance changes sharply with temperature. The heating method is mostly used for measuring very high-frequency a.c. because of the low inductance and capacitance of the resistor.

b) Using a moving-iron meter

Typically this consists of two soft-iron rods mounted inside a solenoid. One is fixed and the other is connected to a pointer. Current passing either way through the solenoid magnetises both rods the same way round. As a result they have similar poles next to each other and so repel each other. This repulsion is independent of the current direction and the meter can therefore measure a.c. or d.c.

c) Using diode rectification

In this method either a single **diode** or a bridge rectifier is used, the circuits being essentially those explained in the entry **alternator or a.c. generator**. A moving-coil meter or a digital meter is connected across an output circuit.

In all these cases the scale of the meter is calibrated to read r.m.s. values of currents and voltages, assuming these have sinusoidal wave forms.

Note that the scales on analogue meters may not necessarily be linear.

◀ Magnetic field configurations ▶

ALTERNATOR OR A.C. GENERATOR

The alternator or a.c. generator produces alternating electric current. In its simplest form it consists of a coil which rotates between the poles of a permanent magnet. Current is induced in the coil in a direction predicted by **Flemings right-hand rule**. In power stations and cycle dynamos, however, the coil (or coils) is stationary and the magnet is rotated.

Consider a coil of N turns and cross-sectional area A rotating at an angular speed ω (Fig. A.15) The component of flux through the coil $= B\cos\theta$.

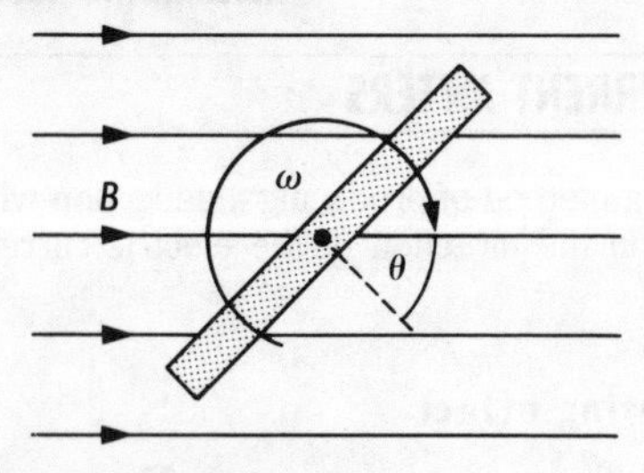

Fig. A.15 Coil rotating in field B at angular velocity ω

Hence the flux through one coil $= BA\cos\theta$, where A is the coil area. Hence, the flux linked by N turns, $\Phi = NBA\cos\theta$. As the coil turns, the induced e.m.f. $= -\mathrm{d}\Phi/\mathrm{d}t$

$$= \frac{-\mathrm{d}}{\mathrm{d}t}(NBA\cos\theta) = \frac{-\mathrm{d}}{\mathrm{d}t}NBA\cos\omega t = NBA\,\omega\sin\omega t.$$

Note that the e.m.f. is a maximum when the coil is perpendicular to the field (Fig. A.16).

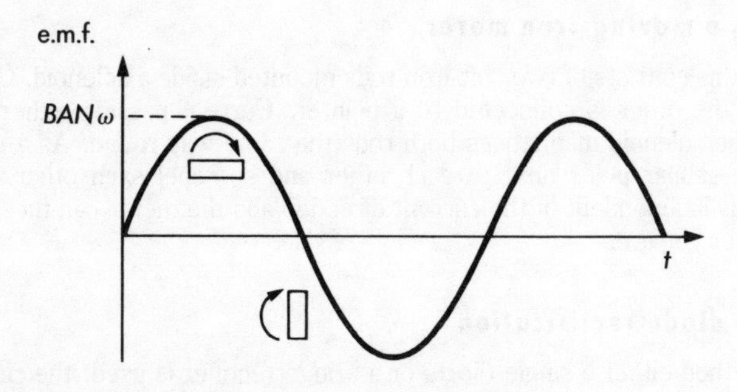

Fig. A.16 Induced e.m.f. in a rotating coil showing positions of the coil

In order to begin to turn such a system into a practical a.c. generator it is necessary to make connections to the external circuit using carbon brushes and two slip rings.

Such a device is called an a.c. *dynamo,* or more usually an *alternator* (Fig. A.17). If the angular velocity ω is increased, there are two effects:

i) an increase in the frequency of the voltage produced
ii) an increase in the amplitude of the e.m.f., since flux is now being cut more rapidly.

CONVERTING THE A.C. OUTPUT TO D.C. OUTPUT

The electrical circuitry of a motor car, for example, is a d.c. one. It is therefore necessary to convert the output of an alternator to d.c. There are two ways of achieving this:

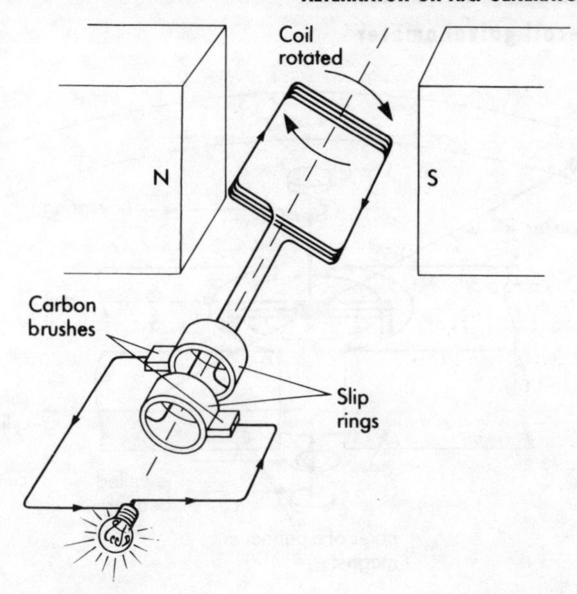

Fig. A.17 A.c. dynamo system

a) Using split rings

If split rings are used in place of slip rings then when the direction of induced e.m.f. from the coil changes, there is also an output contact change. In this way the output from the coil is always in the same direction, although the e.m.f. would still vary in magnitude. The output wave form is then a full wave rectified output.

b) Bridge rectifier

This uses four semiconductor diodes in order to rectify the a.c. current. In modern motor cars this is the most common arrangement for rectifying the output of the alternator.

◀ Direct current power supply ▶

AMMETERS AND VOLTMETERS

Ammeters measure electric current in a circuit. Voltmeters measure the potential difference across components in the circuit.

In a modern laboratory the meters used will essentially be of two types: meters based upon a moving-coil **galvanometer** system and meters based on electronic circuitry. The former will generally be analogue in form, i.e. with a needle moving over a scale, and the latter will be usually digital in form with a liquid crystal display of the kind commonly used with wrist watches.

Moving-coil galvanometer

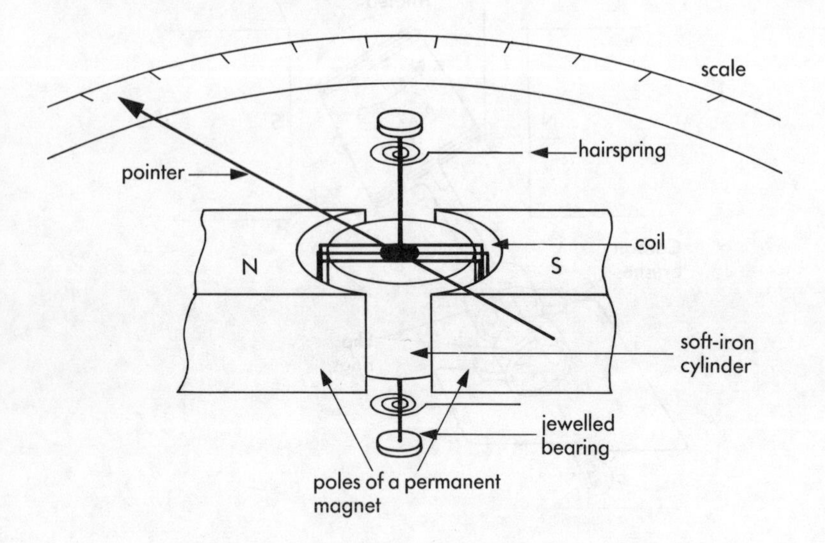

Plan view showing coil in radial magnetic field

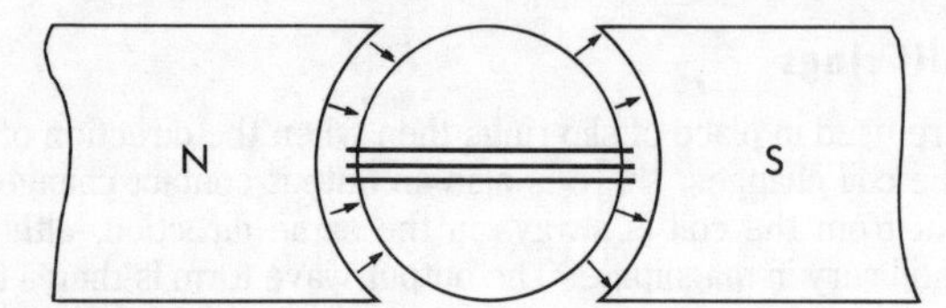

Fig. A.18 Moving-coil galvanometer

This device works on the principle that a current-carrying coil suspended in a magnetic field experiences a torque. A coil is suspended between the poles of a magnet on jewelled bearings and held in position by two very fine coiled springs (Fig. A.18). The current passes through one of these springs to reach the coil, passes through the coil, and then passes out to the other spring. The pole pieces are cut into a circular shape so that the magnetic field is radial, thus ensuring that the **torque** on the coil depends only on the current passing through it and not on the particular orientation of the coil. The radial geometry of the field results not only from the curved faces of the permanent magnet but also from the presence of a soft-iron cylinder in the centre of the coil. This concentrates the magnetic field through it because of the high value of the relative permeability of its material.

The electromagnetic torque exerted by the coil is given by $BANI$, where A is the mean area of the coil, N the number of turns of it, B the flux density of the field, and I the current. This torque is opposed by that of the spring, which is given by $k\theta$, where k is the moment of the couple needed to produce unit angular deflection (in newton metres per radian) and θ is the deflection. This gives

$$BANI = k\theta \text{ and hence } \theta = \frac{BAN}{k}.I$$

showing that the deflection is proportional to the current. Note that this type of meter is in essence a current-measuring meter which needs adaptation if it is to measure voltages.

Electronic meters

The basis of these is an analogue to digital converter **integrated circuit** (Fig. A.19). This i.c. generates, step by step, a series of steadily increasing voltages, each one a small amount greater than the previous. As this is done, a **comparator** assesses whether the voltage being measured is greater or less than the generated voltage. Suppose the voltage to be measured is 1.2 V, and the incremental steps are of magnitude 0.01 V. Then after 119 comparisons the generated voltage will be 1.19 V, and the comparator will record that this is less than the applied voltage. But after 120 or certainly 121 steps the comparator will register that the applied voltage is less than the internally generated voltage. At this point the analogue to digital converter stops and a read-out is given. As can be seen this instrument is basically a voltmeter which requires adaptation for it to be used as an ammeter.

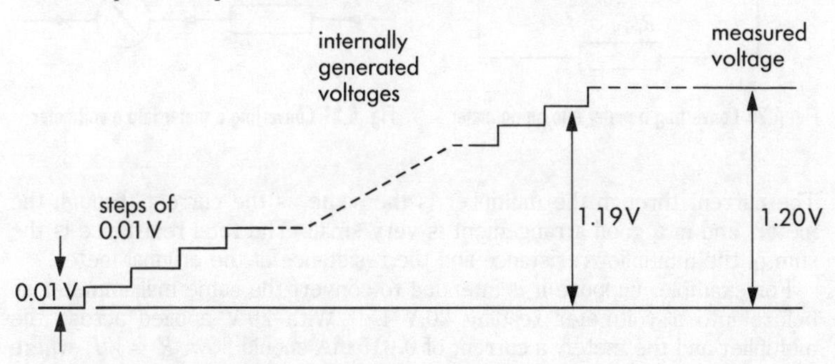

Fig. A.19 Principle of the analogue to digital converter

Ammeters

A moving-coil galvanometer of the kind described above will have a very small full-scale deflection (fsd). It can be converted into an ammeter with a larger fsd by adding a resistance in parallel. This is called a *shunt* resistance, and has to be very much lower than the resistance of the galvanometer itself. For example, if the galvanometer has a resistance of 5Ω and the shunt resistance is ⅑ of this, the total current will divide into two components in the ratio 9 : 1. So 90 per cent goes through the shunt and 10 per cent through the meter. Note that the p.d. across the shunt equals the p.d. across the meter.

Suppose it is intended to convert a milliammeter which has a resistance of 5Ω and a full-scale deflection current of 15 mA into an ammeter with an fsd of 1 A. At fsd it will be necessary to have a shunt which passes 0.085 A, while 0.015 A goes through the meter itself.

$$\frac{\text{Resistance of the shunt}}{\text{Resistance of the meter}} = \frac{0.015}{0.085} = 0.176.$$

Hence the shunt resistance is 0.882Ω

To convert a digital meter of the kind described above to an ammeter the current has to be passed across a standard resistance in order to generate a p.d., equal to IR, which can be measured (Fig. A.20).

Voltmeter

To convert a meter into a voltmeter with a larger fsd it is necessary to add a multiplier resistance in series (Fig. A.21).

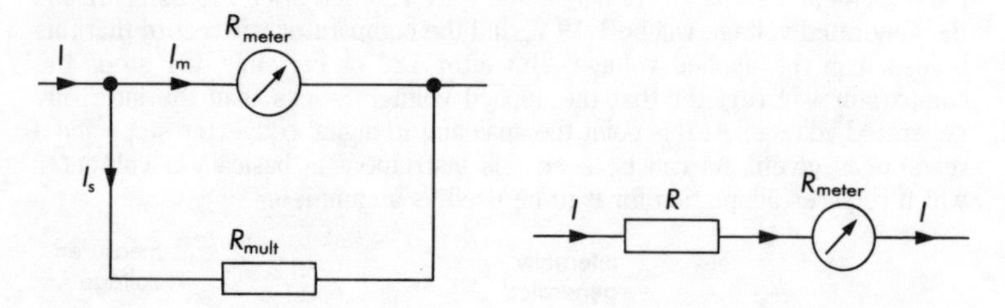

Fig. A.20 Converting a meter into an ammeter

Fig. A.21 Converting a meter into a voltmeter

The current through the multiplier is the same as the current through the meter, and in a good arrangement is very small. The total resistance is the sum of the multiplier resistance and the resistance of the original meter.

For example, suppose it is intended to convert the same milliammeter as before into a voltmeter reading 20 V fsd. With 20 V applied across the multiplier and the meter, a current of 0.015 mA should flow. $R = V/I$, where R is the total resistance. Hence $R = 20/0.015 = 1333.3\ \Omega$. The meter already has a resistance of 5 Ω, so the multiplier resistance must be $1333.3 - 5 = 1328.3\ \Omega$.

Such a voltmeter is still inferior to a perfect instrument which has a very high resistance and passes virtually no current. The entry Unity gain voltage follower explains how the meter can be adapted into a high-impedance instrument.

◀ Gold-leaf electroscope ▶

AMORPHOUS SOLIDS

◀ Solids ▶

AMPERE

◀ Permeability of free space ▶

AMPERE'S LAW

Ampere's Law is a general law about the intensity of **magnetic flux** in a path around the electric current producing the flux.

Lines of flux have no beginnings and no end; they are always loops. Alternatively one can think of magnetic field lines as being like whirlpools running round the flow of current which causes them. Ampere's Law states that the line integral of the flux density around a closed path is equal to the product of the current enclosed by the path and the permeability of the material, i.e.:

$$\int B \cos \theta \, . \, \mathrm{d}l = \mu I$$

where θ is the angle between a short length of path and the direction of the field at that point (Fig. A.22).

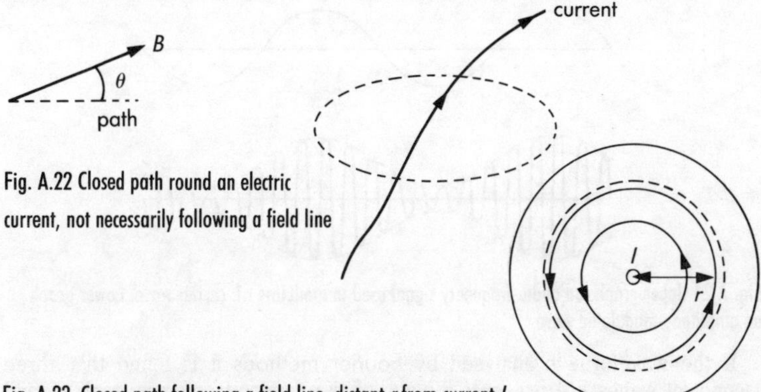

Fig. A.22 Closed path round an electric current, not necessarily following a field line

Fig. A.23 Closed path following a field line, distant *r* from current *I*

This law is an alternative to the **Biot-Savart rule** for determining expressions of the magnetic flux density of a field. The closed path referred to in the definition need not be a field line, but the law is particularly useful in simple symmetrical situations in which it is chosen to make the path a magnetic field line.

When this is done $\cos \theta = 1$ for all points along the path. Consider for example a circular field line distance r from a single current-carrying conductor (Fig. A.23). It is obvious that the flux density B is constant at all points on the line. Let this unknown flux density be B. The line integral becomes $B \int \mathrm{d}l$, and integrating round the whole circle we have $B[l]_{\mathrm{o}}^{2\pi r} = \mu_{\mathrm{o}} I$ giving $2\pi r B = \mu_{\mathrm{o}} I$. Hence $B = \mu_{\mathrm{o}} I / 2\pi r$, showing that B varies inversely with the distance from the wire.

◀ Magnetic field configurations ▶

AMPLITUDE

This is a term used in **oscillation** and wave theory to denote the maximum value of the **displacement** from equilibrium. If the form of an oscillation is given by $y = a \sin \omega t$, where y is the displacement, a is the maximum value of y and hence is the amplitude.

AMPLITUDE MODULATION

This is a term used in telecommunications to describe the way information is transmitted by varying the **amplitude** of a **radio** wave. The information to be transmitted might be an electrical signal of audio-frequency corresponding to speech or music. But it might also be a signal which controls the picture on a television tube. In amplitude modulation this signal is used to vary the amplitude of a radio wave, sometimes called a carrier wave, at a much higher frequency, f. Fig. A.24 shows the effect of this modulation process. The final waveform is called the modulated carrier.

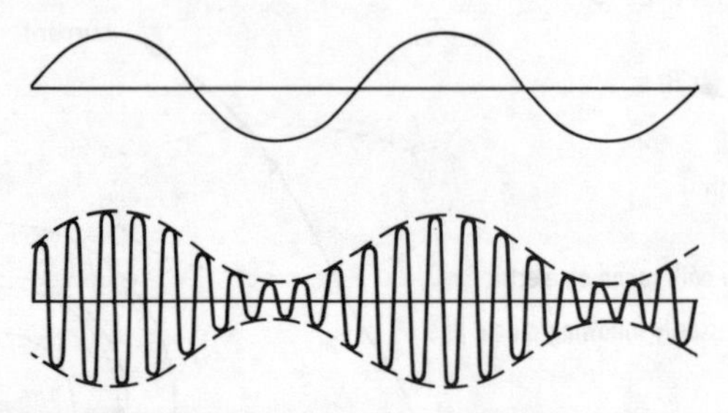

Fig. A.24 Upper graph: an audio-frequency signal used to modulate r.f. carrier wave. Lower graph: an amplitude-modulated wave

If the waveform is analysed by **Fourier methods** it is found that three sinusoidal waves are present: a wave of the carrier frequency itself, f, and two additional waves of frequencies $(f + f_m)$ and $(f - f_m)$, where f_m is the modulating frequency (Fig. A.25). If music is being transmitted the modulating frequency will be in a range from about 30 Hz to 16 kHz. The result therefore is a band of frequencies called the lower and upper side bands extending below and above the carrier frequency by the value of the highest modulating frequency, in this case 16 kHz. Thus when BBC Radio 4 is transmitted at 200 kHz the total band-width requirement is from 194 kHz to 214 kHz. Other stations will have similar band-width requirements, so that the number which can be crammed into a waveband is limited.

For intelligible speech a smaller band-width is necessary and this reduces the band-width requirement. Amateur radio enthusiasts use the fact that the information carried in the upper side band is the same as that carried in the lower side band and hence use special equipment to transmit with only one side band. This is called single side band transmission (ssb). By contrast

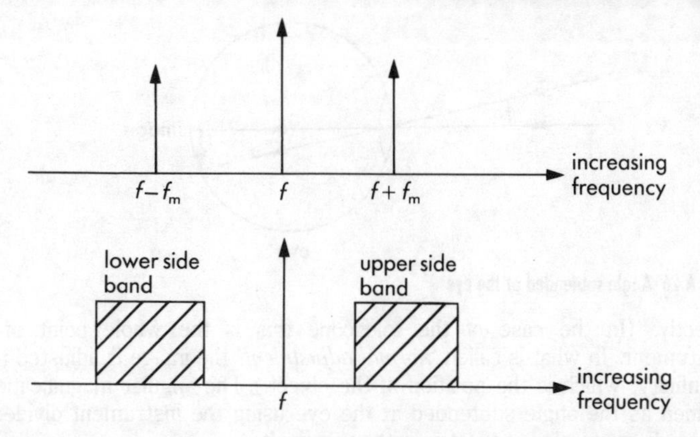

Fig. A.25

television signals require a band-width of 10MHz, and this is one of the reasons why very high-frequency (v.h.f.) carrier waves are required for this kind of transmission.

◀ Frequency modulation ▶

ANALOGUE TO DIGITAL CONVERTER

◀ Ammeters and voltmeters ▶

ANALOGUE ELECTRONICS

Analogue electronics is the branch of electronics dealing with inputs and outputs which can vary over a range of voltages and are not just at one of two fixed levels. A-level syllabuses have focused heavily on the operational amplifier integrated circuit (IC) because of its versatility. Most examination questions will focus on circuits using the operational amplifier

AND GATE

◀ Logic gates ▶

ANGULAR MAGNIFICATION

This is a term used in the optics of telescopes and microscopes.

Fig. A.26 shows that the size of the image of the retina of the eye depends upon the angle subtended at the eye. Both telescopes and microscopes change this angle from what it would be if the object were examined

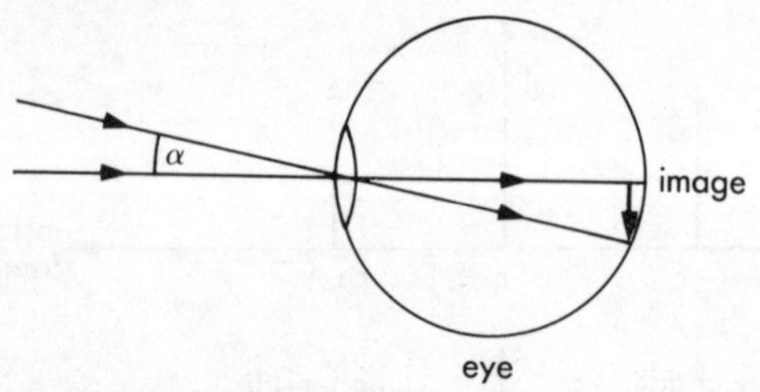

Fig. A.26 Angle subtended at the eye

directly. (In the case of the telescope this is the whole point of the instrument. In what is called '*normal adjustment*' the image is adjusted to be at infinity, which is the position of the object.) The angular magnification is defined as the angle subtended at the eye using the instrument divided by the angle subtended at the eye without using it.

◀ Astronomical telescope, Microscope ▶

ANGULAR MOMENTUM

Angular momentum is the quantity in rotational motion which is equivalent to momentum in straight-line motion. It is a conserved quantity in physics just like momentum.

Consider the angular momentum of a single mass, for example that of a planet moving round the sun. The angular momentum is defined in a similar way to that of a **moment** in **statics**. That is to say an axis, here a line through the sun, must first be specified and the angular momentum referred to that axis. The angular momentum L is then equal to the planet's momentum multiplied by the perpendicular distance from the sun to the velocity vector (Fig. A.27).

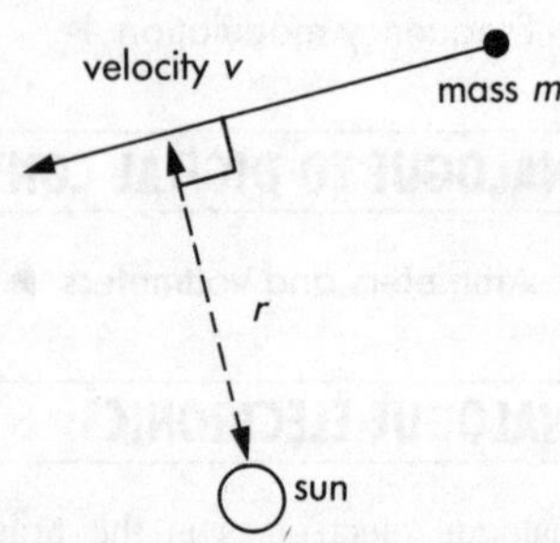

Fig. A.27 Angular momentum of a planet $L = mvr$

In **rigid body rotation** the angular momentum of all the elements of matter in the rotating body have to be considered. In this case it is convenient to use the concept of **moment of inertia**, defining angular momentum as the product of moment of inertia and angular velocity:

$L = I\omega$ (cf. momentum = mv)

This is equivalent to the definition introduced above in the description of a planet's angular momentum.

The conservation of angular momentum is then a principle which goes alongside the conservation of linear momentum (see **Conservation Law**). Provided no external **couple** acts on a system its total angular momentum remains constant.

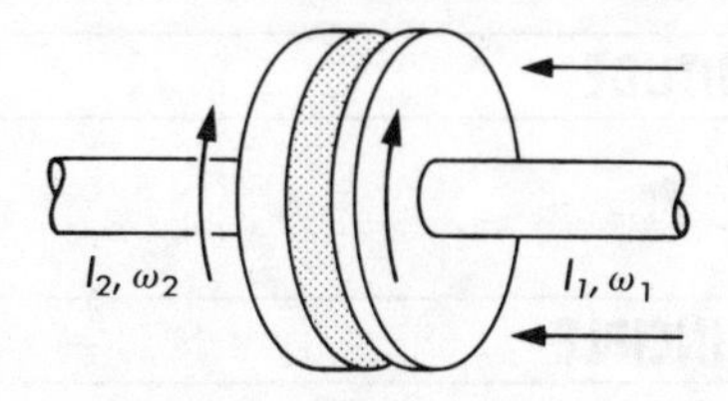

Fig. A.28 Activating clutch mechanism between two rotating discs

An example of something akin to a collision in straight-line motion is what happens when a clutch mechanism between two rotating discs is activated so that they come together and subsequently rotate together (Fig. A.28):

$$I_1\omega_1 + I_2\omega_2 = (I_1 + I_2)\,\omega_3$$

where ω_3 is the new angular velocity after the discs have come together.

In more advanced physics it is necessary to consider angular momentum as a **vector**, its direction being taken as the direction in which a right-handed screw thread advances when it is turned, i.e. the direction of L is normal to the plane of rotation. In A-level physics problems which involve a change in the direction of an angular momentum vector, such as the problem of a spinning top, will not be set.

ANHARMONIC MOTION

This is a type of oscillation where the period changes as the amplitude changes.

An example is that of one magnet suspended over another one, the latter being fixed. Opposite poles should be next to each other. If the top magnet is displaced it oscillates. When the amplitude is comparatively large the period is comparatively long. But as the amplitude diminishes the period gets shorter.

Anharmonic motion contrasts with **simple harmonic motion.**

ANTIMATTER

For every variety of sub-atomic particle there exists an anti-particle which has opposite properties. Among the opposite properties is the sign of electric charge. For example, the anti-particle of the electron is the positron, a particle with the same mass but with positive charge. When two such particles meet they can mutually annihilate and produce energy.

◀ Beta radiation ▶

ANTINODES

◀ Standing waves ▶

APPARENT MAGNITUDE

◀ Magnitude scale ▶

ARCHIMEDES' PRINCIPLE

◀ Upthrust ▶

ARMATURE

◀ Direct current electric motor, Relay ▶

ASTABLE

In electronics, pulses are useful for timing purposes. The first requirement is a device which will produce a continuous train of pulses. Such a circuit is called an astable multivibrator, or just an astable for short, and is made by coupling two logic switches with resistors and capacitors. The simplest way of making an astable uses two NOT gates, as shown in Fig. A.29. When the circuit is first connected it may not initially oscillate and produce a train of pulses. In this case it needs to be started by momentarily shorting across one of the capacitors.

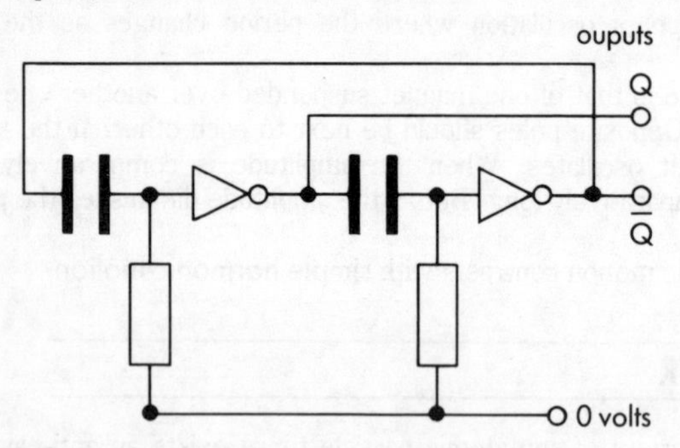

Fig. A.29

A more sophisticated circuit using NOR gates is shown in Fig. A.30. This circuit incorporates an 'enable' point, i.e. the oscillation will take place only if E is connected to the 0 volt rail (logic 0). If E is high the circuit is disabled. Note that in order to work CMOS chips have to be used in preference to TTL. This is because of the comparatively large currents with TTL chips which give the oscillator a very high frequency.

A low-frequency astable can be made with discrete transistors (Fig. A.31). This circuit is sometimes just called a *multivibrator*.

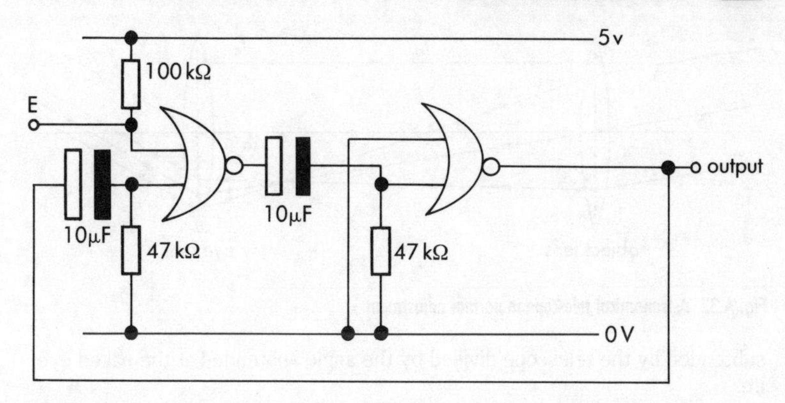

Fig. A.30

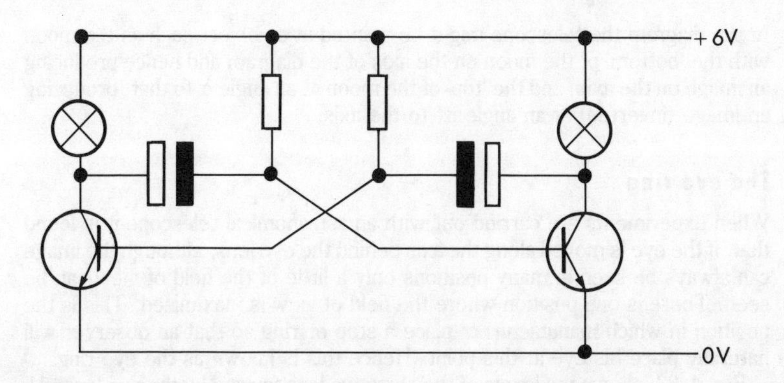

Fig. A.31

ASTIGMATISM

◀ Defects of vision ▶

ASTRONOMICAL TELESCOPE

Fig. A.32 shows a ray diagram of an astronomical telescope set in what is called normal adjustment. By this it is meant that the final image is at infinity. An intermediate image is formed at the common focal point of the two lenses. The effect of the arrangement is to increase the angular magnification which is provided. The angular magnification *M* is given by the angle

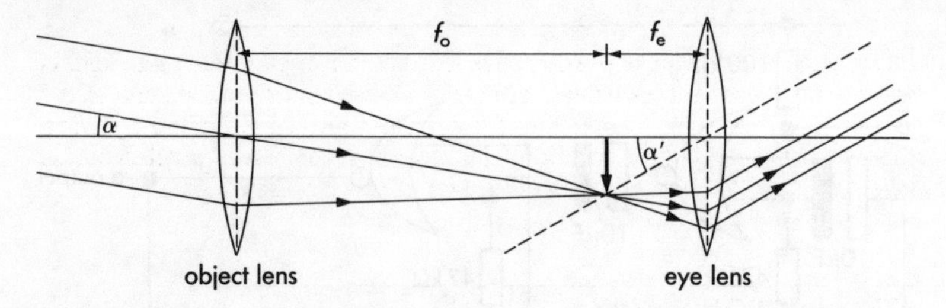

Fig. A.32 Astronomical telescope in normal adjustment

subtended by the telescope divided by the angle subtended at the naked eye, i.e.

$$M = \frac{\alpha'}{\alpha} = \frac{f_o}{f_e}$$

In the diagram the telescope might be pointed at an object such as the moon with the 'bottom' of the moon on the axis of the diagram and hence producing an image on the axis, and the 'top' of the moon at an angle α to that, producing an image (inverted) at an angle α' to the axis.

The eye ring

When experiments are carried out with an astronomical telescope it is found that, if the eye is moved along the axis behind the eye lens, although the image can always be seen in many positions only a little of the field of view can be seen. There is one position where the field of view is maximised. This is the position in which manufacturers place a stop or ring so that an observer will naturally place his eye at this point. Hence this is known as the eye ring.

Fig. A.33. shows the image of the objective lens formed by the eye lens. All the light which passes through both lenses must go through this image. The cone of rays produced by the instrument is smallest at this point and this is the best place to position the eye.

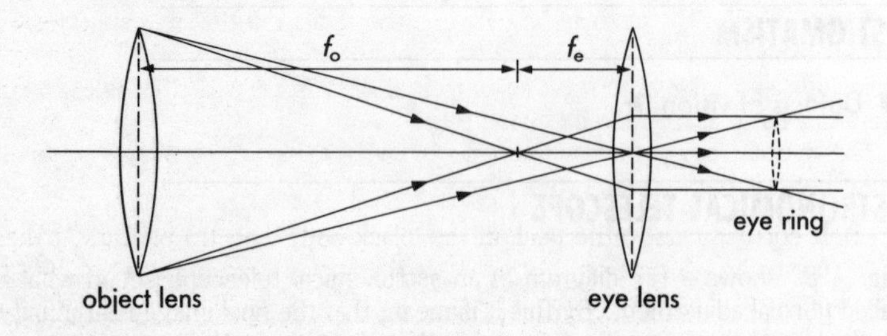

Fig. A.33 Image of the object lens formed by the eye lens

Resolving power

Increasing the diameter of the objective lens not only means that more light is collected and thus fainter objects are easier to see, but the resolution of the lens is improved. The resolution of a circular aperture is limited by wave theory. Using **Rayleigh's criterion**, the angular resolution of a telescope is given by $1.22\,\lambda/d$, where d is the diameter of the objective lens.

◀ Galilean telescope, Reflecting telescope ▶

ATMOSPHERIC WINDOW

Most astronomy is still done from the earth. Unfortunately the earth's atmosphere acts as a filter for electromagnetic radiation and some wavelengths are filtered out completely. The transparency of the atmosphere as a function of wavelength for wavelengths from 10^{-9} to 10^{3} m is shown in Fig. A.34.

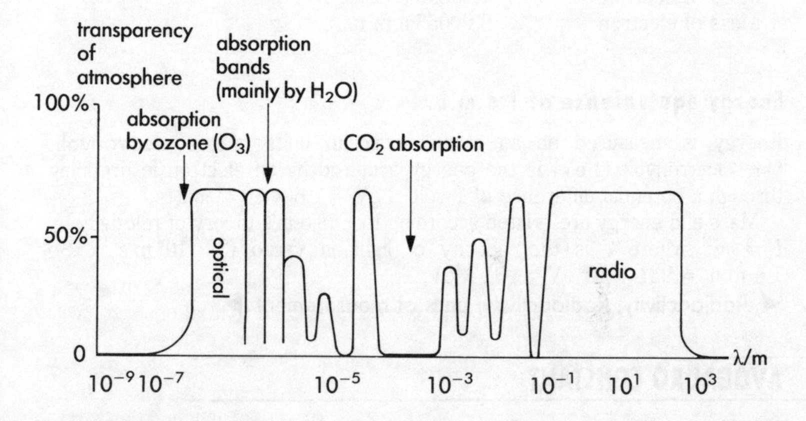

Fig. A.34 The atmospheric window

A good deal of the absorption between the radio and the optical regions is caused by water molecules in the atmosphere. Carbon dioxide and oxygen molecules also contribute to the absorption. In the blue and ultraviolet region there is a large absorption by ozone (O_3).

The optical region forms only one 'octave' of the electromagnetic spectrum, but it is of great importance because:

i) It corresponds to the peak of the 'black-body' spectra of stars at their normal temperatures. For example the sun at a temperature of 6000 K peaks at = 483 nm.
ii) The eye has its sensitivity in this waveband.
iii) There is comparatively little atmospheric absorption.
iv) There are many spectral lines emitted by stars in this waveband.

ATOM

Until the end of the nineteenth century the atom was regarded as the basic building block of matter. Discoveries at the end of the nineteenth century began to show that was not the case and the term atom is now used for a system of electrons orbiting a nucleus. It is the smallest piece of an element that can still be identified as that element.

◀ Elements, Nuclear model of the atom ▶

ATOMIC MASS UNITS

Atomic masses are measured relative to the mass of ^{16}O, which is defined as 16.000 atomic mass units (a.m.u.). 1 a.m.u. = 1.66×10^{-24} grams.

Mass of hydrogen atom	1.00814 a.m.u.
Mass of proton	1.00759 a.m.u.
Mass of neutron	1.00896 a.m.u.
Mass of electron	0.00055 a.m.u.

Energy equivalence of 1 a.m.u.

Energy is measured on an atomic scale in units of the **electronvolt**. One electronvolt (1 eV) is the energy acquired by an electron in dropping through a potential difference of 1 volt. 1 eV = 1.6×10^{-19} joules.

Mass and energy are related according to Einstein's theory of **relativity** by $E = mc^2$ where c is the velocity of light in vacuo (3×10^8 m s^{-1}). So 1 a.m.u. = 931×10^6 eV = 931 MeV.

◀ Radioactivity, Radioactivity: units of measurement ▶

AVOGADRO CONSTANT

The Avogadro constant is the proportionality constant connecting the number of entities (specified by a formula) to the amount of substance (expressed in moles). The value of the Avogadro constant, L, is 6.02×10^{23} mol^{-1}.

AXON

◀ Action potential ▶

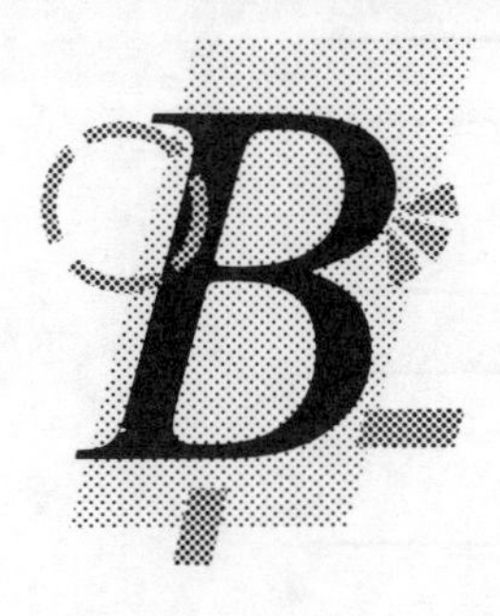

BALLISTIC GALVANOMETER

This is simply the name given to a **galvanometer** which is used in the so-called ballistic mode. This is a mode of operation in which a current passes for a very short time through the coil of the galvanometer giving it an impulse or 'kick' which sets it swinging. Usually **light-beam galvanometers** which have only small amounts of damping are used for this mode of operation. Provided the duration of the pulse of current is short compared with the period of oscillation of the coil, the amplitude of oscillation does not depend upon the manner with which the current varies during the pulse. It is simply proportional to the total charge, q, passed. The theory of operation is as follows: The *couple* C acting on a coil when a current i flows $= BAni$, assuming the current and field are perpendicular. The couple × time = change in angular momentum. Therefore $BAni.t = I\omega$, where I is the *moment of inertia* of the coil and ω is the angular velocity produced.

If i is not constant the equation is

$$\int BAni.\mathrm{d}t = I\omega \ (\text{cf.} \int F\mathrm{d}t = mv)$$

Now $\int i.\mathrm{d}t = q$, the total charge which flows.

Hence $BAnq = I\omega$. Kinetic energy $\frac{1}{2}I\omega^2$ is generated which twists the coil through an angle θ and eventually stores $\frac{1}{2}k\theta^2$ of potential energy. Here k is the couple per unit angle of twist which is provided by the spring.

Hence $\frac{1}{2}I\omega^2 = \frac{1}{2}k\theta^2$

giving $$\omega = \theta\sqrt{\frac{k}{I}}$$

and hence $$q = \frac{I\omega}{BAn} = \frac{I\theta}{BAn}\sqrt{\frac{k}{I}} = \frac{\theta\sqrt{kI}}{BAn}$$

This shows that the deflection θ is proportional to the charge which flows. Note that the galvanometer can be absolutely calibrated if BAn are known as well as k.

◀ Ammeters and voltmeters ▶

BALLISTICS

◀ Projectile motion ▶

BALMER SERIES

◀ Energy levels in hydrogen ▶

BAND SPECTRUM

This type of spectrum is characteristic of molecules. Molecules tend to have a very large number of energy levels which are very close together. These give rise to a characteristic spectrum which consists of a very large number of lines close together which appear as a 'band' when seen through a **spectrometer**, particularly when the individual lines cannot be resolved. It contrasts with a **line spectrum** and a **continuous spectrum**.

BAROMETER

This is a device used to measure the pressure of the atmosphere. The laboratory type works on the same principle as the **manometer**. In its simplest form it consists of a tube which has been filled with a liquid, sealed at one end and then inverted over a bath of the same liquid. Mercury is usually used.

In Fig. B.1, $p_A = h\rho g$ + pressure of a vacuum, i.e. $p = h\rho g + 0 = h\rho g$. Pressure is properly measured in pascals (Pa). $1\,\text{Pa} = 1\,\text{N m}^{-2}$. It is common for pressures to be expressed in liquid column equivalents, e.g. 760 mm of mercury, but they can always be converted to pascals using $p = h\rho g$.

The household barometer works on a different principle. It is called an aneroid barometer. It contains a partially evacuated can made of springy metal. As the external atmospheric pressure changes so does the shape of the can, albeit slightly. This movement is transferred to a dial by a series of levers which magnify the small movement.

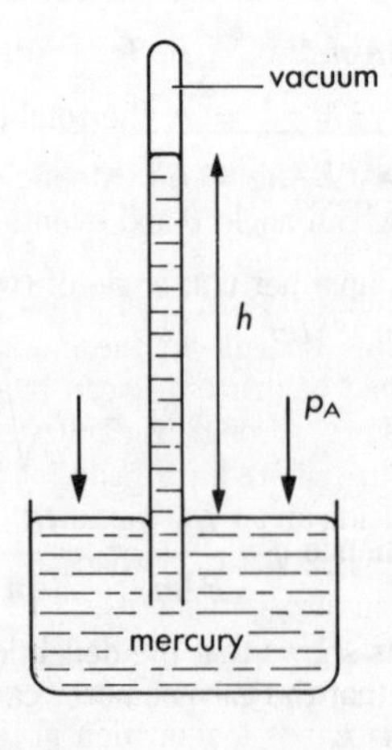

Fig. B.1 Barometer

BARYON

A particle of **elementary particle** physics which is constructed from three **quarks**. Both the **proton** and the **neutron** are baryons.

BEATS

If the waves from two sources of slightly different frequency are combined, the amplitude of the resulting wave will rise and fall at a much lower frequency called the beat frequency. If the frequency of one source is f and the frequency of the other is $(f + x)$, at some instant the two signals will be in phase and so produce a note of large amplitude. $1/x$ seconds later one source will have emitted $f(1/x) = f/x$ waves and the other $(f + x)\ (1/x) = f/x + 1$ waves. This means that the second source will have emitted one more complete wave and so the sources will be back in phase. The in-phase behaviour therefore occurs every $1/x$ second, or x times per second. So the beat frequency is x, the differences between the frequencies of the two sources.

◀ Doppler effect ▶

BECQUEREL

◀ Radioactivity: units of measurement ▶

BEL

◀ Loudness ▶

BERNOUILLI'S PRINCIPLE

This is sometimes known also as Bernouilli's theorem. It is a principle in the **streamline** flow of fluids which states that at a point along a streamline where the flow speeds up there is a reduction in the pressure in the fluid. An example of this effect can be demonstrated using a bunsen burner. As the gas flows through the nozzle it is forced to speed up. Consequently its pressure is reduced and so air is sucked in through the side air-hole, producing an air/gas mixture.

Fig. B.2 shows perhaps the most important application. When air passes over an aircraft wing it has to speed up over the upper wing because of the bunching together of the streamlines and the longer distance by the upper route compared with that for streamlines under the wing. The increase in speed causes a reduction in pressure above the wing which provides a net upward force.

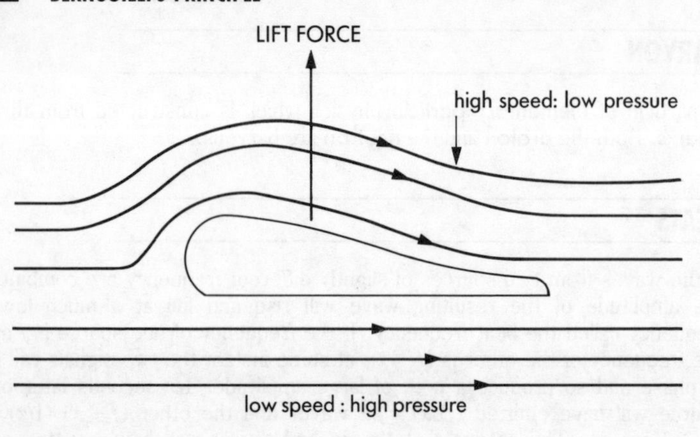

Fig. B.2 Bernouilli's principle at an aerofoil

The theorem which explains these effects is proved below. It is assumed that viscosity is negligible, i.e. there are no frictional forces to be considered.

Consider the flow shown in Fig. B.3. A pressure difference between the beginnings and the ends of the streamlines will cause work to be done, increasing both kinetic and potential energy. Let the work done be W.

Then W = force × distance moved
= pressure × area of cross section × distance moved
= pressure × volume of fluid moved.

Consider the movement of unit volume. At the beginning of the streamlines the work done on the fluid per unit volume = p_1, and at the other end the work done on the fluid per unit volume = p_2. Thus the net work done on the fluid per unit volume is $p_1 - p_2$

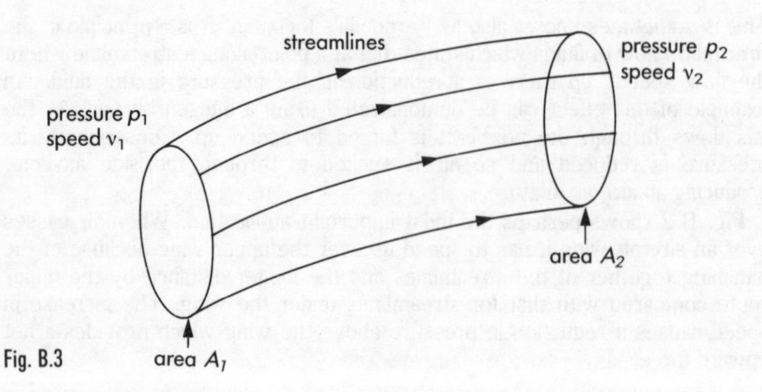

Fig. B.3

Suppose the velocities at either end are v_1 and v_2 and the heights at either end are h_1 and h_2. Then the kinetic energy gained per unit volume $= \frac{1}{2}\rho\,(v_2^2 - v_1^2)$ where ρ is the density, and the potential energy gained per unit volume is $\rho g\,(h_2 - h_1)$.

Applying the principle of the conservation of energy we have:

$$p_1 - p_2 = \tfrac{1}{2}\rho\,(v_2^2 - v_1^2) + \rho g\,(h_2 - h_1)$$

Therefore $p_1 + \frac{1}{2}\rho v_1^2 + \rho g h_1 = p_2 + \frac{1}{2}\rho v_2^2 + \rho g h_2$

Thus at any point in the streamline flow:

$$p + \tfrac{1}{2}\rho v^2 + \rho g h = \text{constant}$$

This is the formal statement of Bernouilli's theorem. For flow at a constant height h it simplifies to $p + \frac{1}{2}\rho v^2 =$ constant, showing clearly that an increase in velocity is offset by a reduction in pressure.

◀ Pitot static tube, Equation of continuity ▶

BETA RADIATION

Beta particles are either high-speed **electrons** or **positrons**. They are generated when a **nucleon** (proton or neutron) changes to a different form (neutron or proton respectively) with the ejection of a beta particle, the energy loss resulting in a more stable nucleus. The beta spectrum is a broad-band phenomenon, i.e. the particles are emitted with a range of energies. Beta emission is always accompanied by **neutrino** emission and is usually followed by **gamma** emission, usually immediately. The velocity of the beta particle often approaches the velocity of light; in this case its mass is much greater than its rest mass.

Beta particles are not so powerful as **alpha** particles in producing ion pairs. When the positron is reduced to rest by multiple ionising effects it combines with a negative electron and their combined mass is transformed into two electromagnetic photons of equivalent energy. This annihilation radiation is always present in the vicinity of positron emitters. Positrons are anti-matter. (Rest mass of the electron = 0.51 MeV.)

- *Penetrating power:* Beta particles are slowed down by causing ionisation and are scattered by encounters with nuclei and electrons. Their penetrating power is much more than alpha particles and, depending on their energies, they are stopped by a thin piece of metal or several metres of air. The amount of matter to reduce an incident beam of beta particles to half their number is referred to as the half-thickness.
- *Detection of beta particles:* Beta particles can be detected by:
  - i) **Geiger tubes** with thin windows;
  - ii) **ionisation chambers**;
  - iii) **scintillation counters**;
  - iv) photographic methods;
  - v) **solid-state detectors**;
  - vi) plastic or liquid scintillators and Cherenkov counters.

- *Screening of beta particles:* Beta particles are best screened by materials of low atomic number so that *Bremsstrahlung* is relatively weak, e.g. by polythene, perspex etc.
- *Typical beta-emitters:*

	Maximum energy	Half-life
^{3}H	0.018 MeV	12.26 y
^{14}C	0.158 MeV	5730 y
^{35}S	0.167 MeV	87 d
^{90}Sr	0.54 MeV	30 y
^{32}P	1.71 MeV	14.2 d

The usual energy range of beta particles from radioactive materials is from a few KeV to 3 MeV.

BINARY COUNTER

◀ JK flip-flop ▶

BINARY STARS

These are pairs of stars which are bound gravitationally and orbit round their common centre of mass. More than half the stars in the galaxy are binary stars or members of a multiple star system. Our sun is therefore in a minority class.

There are several types of binary stars:

i) Visual binaries: stars where both stars can be seen orbiting round their centre of mass
ii) Astrometric binaries: stars where only one star is bright enough to be seen but where the other can be inferred from its effect on the motion of the star that can be seen.
iii) Spectroscopic binaries: stars where the stellar motions are inferred from the Doppler shifts of the star's spectral lines.
iv) Eclipsing binaries: stars where one star orbits either completely or partially across the line of sight of the companion star, and hence as it does so there is an abrupt change in the light detected from the system.

BINDING ENERGY

This term is sometimes used in a general sense in physics to mean the energy that has been released when a composite particle fuses together from simpler ones, and hence is also the energy which needs to be given to the composite particle to separate it back into its component particles. For example, we can refer to the binding energy of a diatomic (two-atom) molecule. There will be an attractive force between the two atoms with an energy that has to be 'lost' (released) when they come together. This same energy has to be supplied if the two atoms are to be separated.

But the term is also sometimes used in a more specific sense in nuclear physics. The mass of the nucleus of the atom is less than the combined masses of all the separate **nucleons** (protons and neutrons). This difference is known as the mass defect. The mass defect is usually measured in atomic mass units (a.m.u.). This difference, converted into energy using Einstein's $E = mc^2$ formula, is called the binding energy. This is the energy that would have to be supplied to the mass to turn it into separate nucleons.

Fig. B.4 shows the binding energy per nucleon against nucleon number, A. The graph has a maximum at a nucleon number of about 80. If a nucleus of much larger mass splits into two nuclei of smaller mass, then as the total number of nucleons remains constant the total energy in the nuclei is less and the energy difference is released as kinetic energy of the fragments. This process of the disintegration of a nucleus of large mass into smaller fragments with the release of energy is called nuclear **fission**. It is one way of generating kinetic energy (heat) by the conversion of mass to energy in a nuclear process. The other way is the process of nuclear **fusion**, where two nuclei of small mass combine to produce a more massive nucleus, again with a mass loss and hence a conversion to kinetic energy (heat).

◀ Liquid-drop model ▶

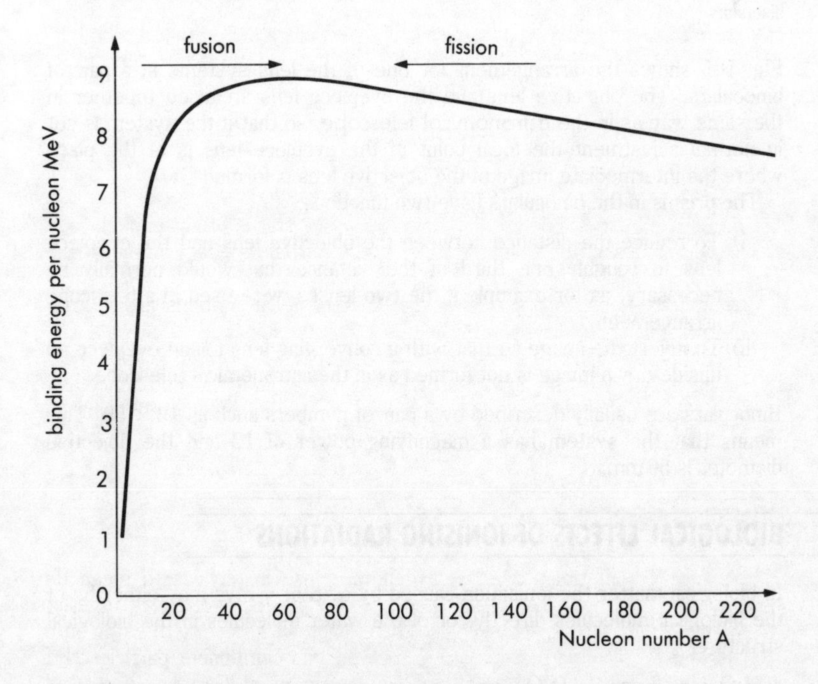

Fig. B.4 Graph of binding energy per nucleon against nucleon number

BINOCULARS

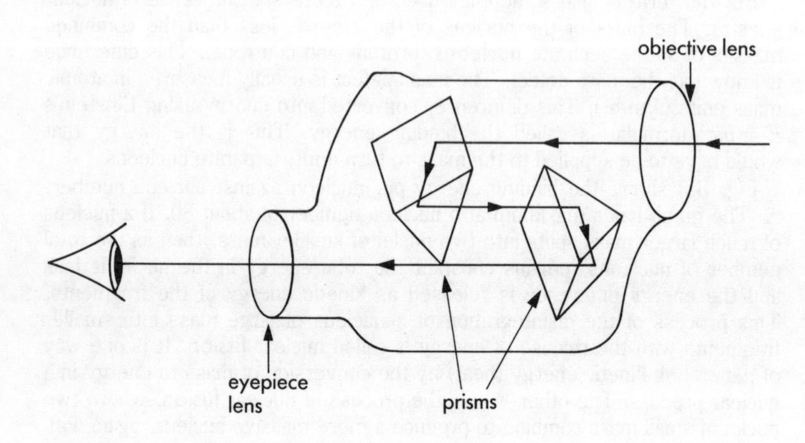

Fig. B.5 Use of prisms to extend the path between the objective lens and the eyepiece in a pair of binoculars

Fig. B.5 shows the arrangement for one of the lens systems in a pair of binoculars. The objective lens and the eyepiece lens are used together in the same way as in the **astronomical telescope**, so that if the system is set in normal adjustment the focal point of the eyepiece lens is at the place where the intermediate image of the objective lens is formed.

The prisms in the binoculars have two functions:

i) To reduce the distance between the objective lens and the eyepiece lens to roughly one third of the distance that would normally be necessary, as for example if the two lenses were used in a telescope arrangement.
ii) To invert the image so that with a converging lens for an eyepiece an upside-down image is not formed as in the astronomical telescope.

Binoculars are usually described by a pair of numbers such as 12 × 50. This means that the system has a magnifying power of 12 and the objective diameter is 50 mm.

BIOLOGICAL EFFECTS OF IONISING RADIATIONS

In biological matter the ionisation caused by α, β or γ rays may either be of the biological molecules directly, or of the water molecules in the biological structure:

$H_2O + \alpha, \beta \text{ or } \gamma \rightarrow H_2O^+ + e^-$
$H_2O + e^- \rightarrow H_2O^-$

Both of these may dissociate to give free radicals:

$H_2O^- \rightarrow H^* + OH^-$
$H_2O^+ \rightarrow H^+ + OH^*$

These are highly reactive. Thus ionisation can easily cause the breaking of a bond in a macromolecule, probably making it ineffective. Disruption of the chromosomes produces the most lethal effects, so that sensitivity to radiation is the greatest in the rapidly dividing cells of the body, the gonads, bone marrow and skin. The foetus is most sensitive of all, and children are more susceptible than adults. Old people are also more sensitive than younger adults because damage is less likely to be repaired.

Damage to the body may be of two types:

i) Somatic, which affects the exposed individual by producing malignant cancer or immediate cell damage.
ii) Genetic, which causes abnormalities in future generations by affecting the chromosomes of the exposed person.

■ **Permissible doses of radiation**

Basing itself largely on the effects on the Japanese people of the two atomic bombs exploded there at the end of the Second World War in 1945, the International Commission on Radiological Protection (ICRP) has assessed the possible risks to people from radiation. From these assessments it has laid down the maximum permissible doses that members of the public may receive, as follows:

Part of the body exposed	*Dose per year*	
	rem	*Sv*
Reproductive organs	0·5	5×10^{-3}
Bone marrow	0·5	5×10^{-3}
Skin, bone, thyroid	3·0	3×10^{-2}
Hands, ankles, feet, forearms, etc.	7·5	$7{\cdot}5 \times 10^{-2}$

The maximum permissible doses for workers in the nuclear industry are ten times larger than these values.

◄ Radioactivity: units of measurement ►

BIOT-SAVART RULE

Biot and Savart were two French physicists after whom is named a rule for determining the flux density B at a point P due to the current in a length of wire (Fig. B.6).

The flux density dB at P due to a short length dl is proportional to the current in the wire, the length of the element of wire considered, sin θ and inversely proportional to the distance, x, from the wire squared, i.e.

$$dB \propto I\,dl\,\frac{\sin\theta}{x^2}$$

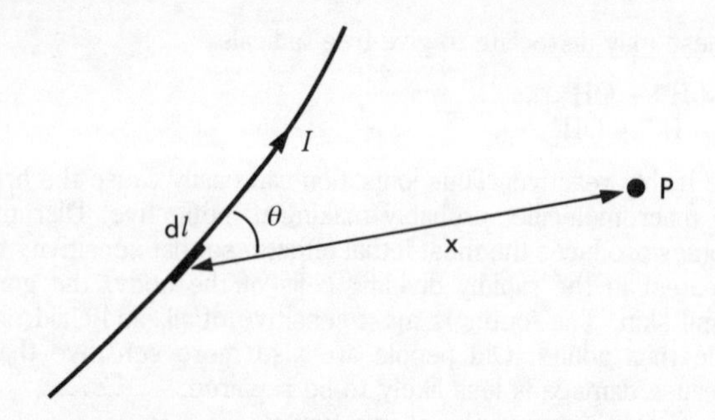

Fig. B.6 Field dB resulting from current at length dl

The constant of proportionality is the permeability of free space divided by 4π. Hence

$$dB = \frac{\mu_o}{4\pi} I dl \frac{\sin\theta}{x^2}$$

Using this formula, the fields due to various arrangements or currents in a vacuum can be found, e.g. the formula for the field at a distance r from the long straight wire, $B = \mu_o I/2\pi r$, or the field at the centre of a plain circular coil, radius r, of N turns and carrying a current I, $B = \dfrac{\mu_o NI}{2r}$

The Biot-Savart rule provides an alternative method to **Ampere's Law** of calculating B in certain situations.

BISTABLE

The bistable is an electronic device which can exist in one of two stable states, its most important property being that it can 'remember' the state it was last in.

It is sometimes called the set-reset (SR) flip-flop or the reset-set (RS) latch. It can be constructed from two NAND gates and two NOT gates (Fig. B.7). Note how the outputs of the NAND gates are cross-connected to their inputs. This is called feedback. The output depends upon the output as well as the input.

As the name suggests a bistable can exist in one of two stable states. These are $Q = 1$ $\bar{Q} = 0$, the so-called 1 stable state, the flip-flop being said to be 'set', and the $Q = 0$ $\bar{Q} = 1$ state, the flip-flop being said to be 'reset'.

The behaviour of the circuit can be worked out by going through the sequence of input conditions shown in the truth table (Table B.1).

For example if $S = 1$ and $R = 0$ then $\bar{S} = 0$ and $\bar{R} = 1$. Q must be 1, since one of the inputs, that from $\bar{S}$, is 0. Both inputs to the bottom NAND gate are 1 and so $\bar{Q} = 0$.

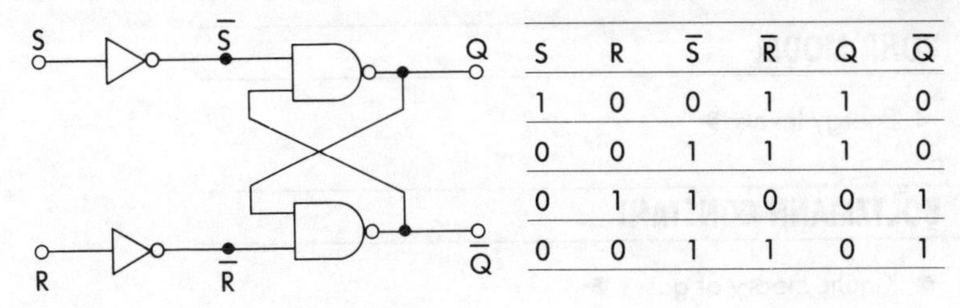

S	R	$\overline{S}$	$\overline{R}$	Q	$\overline{Q}$
1	0	0	1	1	0
0	0	1	1	1	0
0	1	1	0	0	1
0	0	1	1	0	1

Fig. B.7

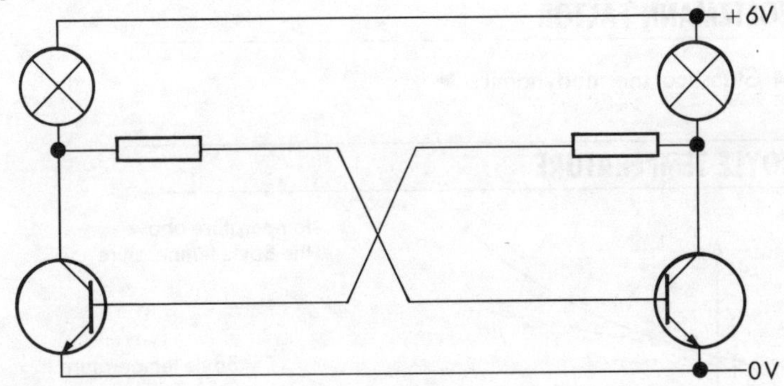

Fig. B.8

Note that when S = R = 0, Q can be either 0 or 1 depending upon what the state of the bistable was before this input condition existed. Note also that this type of bistable has an indeterminate state when S = R = 1, and this situation is best avoided.

The most important property of the bistable is that it 'remembers' the state it was last in. If S is made high momentarily, then Q = 1 and remains at l until either S or R are made high again.

A bistable can also be constructed from discrete transistors (Fig. B.8). It will sit permanently in either with either transistor 'on' and the other 'off'. It can be switched from one state to the other by shorting the base of the 'on' transistor to the 0 volt rail.

BIT RATE

◀ Pulse code modulation ▶

BLACK-BODY RADIATION

A hot body which is black and therefore a perfect absorber of radiation emits radiation with a characteristic distribution of wavelength and energy. Any radiation having this characteristic distribution is called black-body radiation.

◀ Thermal radiation ▶

BOHR MODEL

◀ Energy levels ▶

BOLTZMANN CONSTANT

◀ Kinetic theory of gases ▶

BOLTZMANN FACTOR

◀ Statistical thermodynamics ▶

BOYLE TEMPERATURE

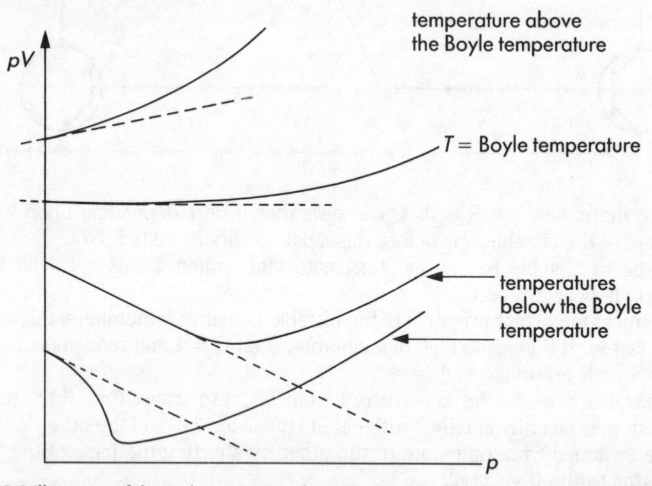

Fig. B.9 Illustration of the Boyle temperature for real gases. The dotted lines represent tangents to the curves at $p = 0$

Real gases show some differences from the behaviour which would be expected if they behaved like the model of an **ideal gas**. Fig. B.9 shows a graph of pV against p where p is the pressure and V the volume of a fixed mass of gas. If the gas behaved like an ideal gas, pV would be a constant proportional to the absolute temperature T. The Boyle temperature is the temperature at which pV is most nearly constant over a wide range of pressures. In particular a tangent to the pV curve at $p = 0$ is horizontal. The departures from ideal gas behaviour are due to repulsive and attractive intermolecular forces which are not accounted for in a model of ideal gases. The Boyle temperature is the temperature at which these opposing effects almost completely cancel each other out.

BOYLE'S LAW

◀ Gas laws ▶

BREAKING STRESS

◀ Stress ▶

BREMSSTRAHLUNG

This is a German word meaning 'braking radiation', a term used for electromagnetic radiation produced by the deceleration of electric charges.
◀ X-rays ▶

BREWSTER'S ANGLE

Light which is reflected from a surface is partially polarised parallel to the surface. At a particular angle p known as Brewster's angle the reflected light is completely polarised parallel to the surface The angle p is given by the equation $\tan p = n$, where n is the refractive index.
◀ Polarisation ▶

BRIDGE RECTIFIER

◀ Power supply ▶

BROWNIAN MOTION

This is the name given to the microscopic movements of particles in fluids. These can be seen when a sample of smoke is illuminated and observed with a microscope. The movements are random and are caused by the random bombardments of the smoke particles by the much smaller, lighter and faster-moving invisible air molecules.

The phenomenon was originally first observed with pollen grains by the botanist Robert Brown in the early nineteenth century. He originally thought it was motion due to living organisms. Only later was it recognised as part of the common motion matter has as a result of its temperature.
◀ Kinetic theory of gases ▶

BUBBLE CHAMBER

The bubble chamber is like the **cloud chamber** in that its main use is to show the tracks of radioactive particles rather than to measure the intensity of radiation. The bubble chamber usually contains liquid hydrogen at a temperature and pressure just below its boiling point. The pressure is suddenly lowered so that boiling can take place provided there is something to 'trigger' the growth of bubbles. As an ionising particle passes through the hydrogen the ions it produces act as centres on which the hydrogen can start to boil, and so a line of bubbles is formed along the track of the particle. These are photographed and the photographic records are subsequently analysed. Unlike the cloud chamber, the bubble chamber is a very large and expensive device which is normally used for measuring events in nuclear and particle physics in a high-energy physics laboratory such as that at the Brookhaven National Laboratory in the USA or at CERN in Geneva.

BUOYANCY

◀ Upthrust ▶

CALLIPERS

Callipers are used to measure the sizes of items up to several centimetres in length, usually to an accuracy of 0.1 mm.

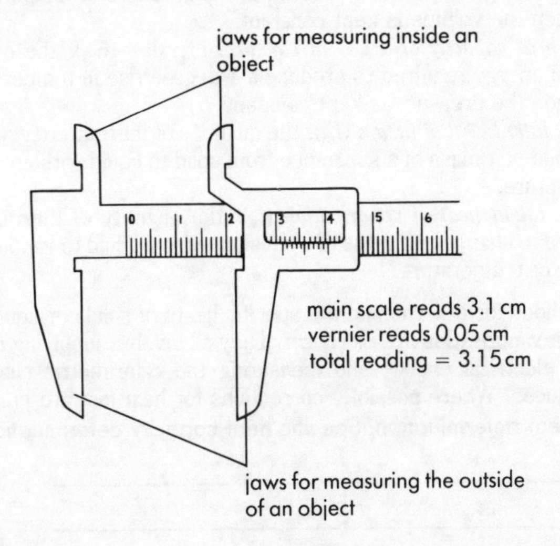

Fig. C.1

Fig. C.1 shows a pair of callipers used for measuring inside or outside distances on solid objects. They normally have a **vernier scale**, as shown. This is the short scale of ten divisions on the sliding jaw. It enables the accurate determination of the second decimal place without having to estimate fractions of the division by eye.

CALORIMETRY

Calorimetry is the somewhat old-fashioned name given to the science of making heat measurements by experiment. Calorimetry is all about measuring the amount of heat required for things to become hotter or colder or for them to change state, i.e. go from solid to liquid.

Like any science it has its own vocabulary, the main terms of which are:

- *Thermal capacity* (C): the quantity of heat required to raise the temperature of a body by 1 degree.
- *Specific heat capacity* (c): the heat capacity per unit mass, i.e. per kg. So $C = mc$ and $\Delta Q = mc\,\Delta\theta$, where ΔQ is the heat or thermal energy supplied and $mc\Delta\theta$ the increase in internal energy, and where $\Delta\theta$ is the change in temperature. Hence if $\frac{d\theta}{dt}$ is the rate of temperature rise, $\frac{dQ}{dt}$, the rate of supply of thermal energy, is given by

$$\frac{dQ}{dt} = mc\,\frac{d\theta}{dt}$$

For gases, molar heat capacities may be used.

- *Molar heat capacity of a gas at constant volume* (C_v): the quantity of thermal energy required to produce a 1 degree rise in temperature of a gas when the volume is kept constant.
- *Molar heat capacity of a gas at constant pressure* (C_p): the quantity of thermal energy required to produce a 1 degree rise in temperature of a gas when the pressure is kept constant.
- *Specific latent heat of fusion* (l_m): the quantity of thermal energy required to change unit mass of a substance from solid to liquid without change of temperature.
- *Specific latent heat of vaporisation* (l_v): the quantity of thermal energy required to change unit mass of a substance from liquid to vapour without change of temperature.

Most methods for determining the specific heats of solids or liquids or the latent heat of vaporisation are electrical. They all involve supplying measured amounts of electrical energy and measuring the calorimetric changes the energy produces. Where possible, corrections for heat lost are employed.

◀ Latent heat determination, Specific heat capacity determination ▶

CAMERA

The camera is used for recording photographs on to photographic film or, with specialist cameras, plates. The name derives from the term *camera obscura*, meaning dark chamber, of which there is an example in Edinburgh. It consists of a darkened room with a lens which casts a real inverted image of the city on to a white-painted wall.

In the camera the lens may contain several elements of **converging** and **diverging lenses** as shown in Fig. C.2. Usually within the lens system is a stop to control the amount of light reaching the film during an exposure. On many cameras, particularly single-lens reflex cameras (s.l.r.), the shutter which opens and closes to admit light to the film is essentially a black blind with a hole in it which moves rapidly across a plane at right angles to the principal axis. The lens is focused by turning it on a screw thread so that the distance between it and the film can be varied according to the distance of the object. In order to take photographs of objects which are very close up it

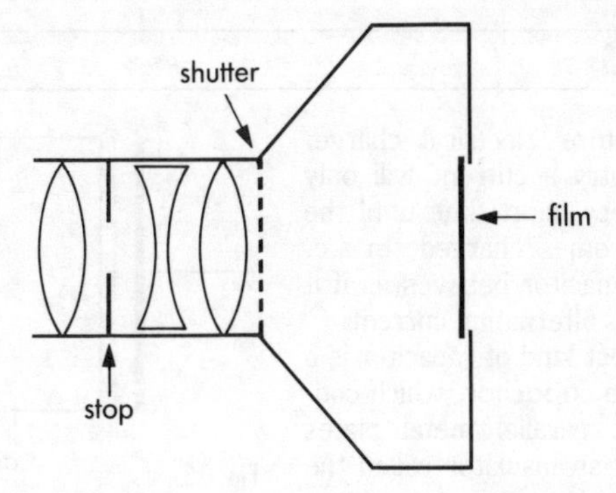

Fig. C.2 Camera

may be necessary to use extension tubes to increase this distance.

The camera has its own terminology:

- f-*number:* For example 2.8, 4, 5.6 etc. This is the ratio of the focal length *f* to the diameter of the lens. Thus when the lens is at an 'aperture' of 2.8 the diameter of the stop is *f*/2.8. If the f-number is changed from 2.8 to 4 or 4 to 5.6 the area of cross-section of the lens is reduced by half and the exposure time has to be doubled.
- *Depth of focus:* Although the image is focused in the plane of the film, small movements of the film away from this plane can still result in an acceptable degree of sharpness. This range of movement is called the depth of focus.
- *Depth of field:* The lens will be focused on a particular object. However, objects closer to the lens and further away from the lens than this object may still produce an acceptably sharp image. The range of distance over which objects can be in reasonable focus is called the depth of field. Both the depth of focus and the depth of field depends upon the degree to which enlargements from the film are to be made. Both depth of field and depth of focus are increased by stopping down the lens, i.e. having a large f-number.
- *Spherical aberration:* A single converging lens does not have perfect focusing properties. That is to say rays passing through the lens near its centre are not focused to precisely the same point as rays passing near the rim of the lens. The lens surfaces are spherical and an ideal lens would have no spherical surfaces. This defect is called spherical aberration and can be reduced by using a combination of lenses as shown in Fig. C.2 and by stopping down the lens so that only rays near the **principal axis** can pass through the axis.
- *Chromatic aberration:* A single converging lens will focus light of different wavelengths, and therefore different colours, at different points. That is to say each colour will have its own focal length. This is because the *refractive index* of glass varies with wavelength. This is overcome in a lens by using several lenses (again as shown in Fig. C.2) converging and diverging, made of glasses of different refractive indices. A combination of lenses like this is called an *achromatic combination*.

◀ Telephoto lens ▶

CAPACITORS

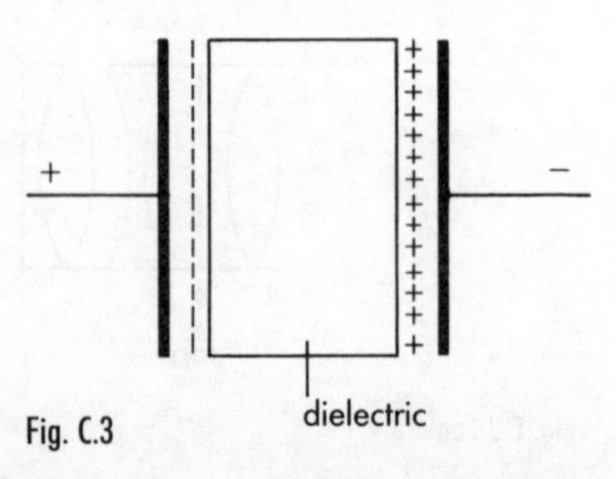

Fig. C.3

Capacitors store electrical charge. In d.c. circuitry a current will only flow for a very short time until the capacitor becomes charged. In a.c. circuitry a capacitor behaves as if it is able to pass alternating current.

The simplest kind of capacitor is a **parallel-plate capacitor**, which consists of two parallel metal plates separated by an insulator called the dielectric (Fig. C.3).

The capacitance C of a capacitor is a measure of its ability to store charge and is the ratio of the charge stored on one of the plates divided by the voltage between the plates. The unit is the farad (F). In practice the farad is a very large unit of capacity and the microfarad ($1\ \mu F = 10^{-6}$ F), the nanofarad ($1\ nF = 10^{-9}$ F) and the picofarad ($1\ pF = 10^{-12}$ F) are commonly used.

 FIXED CAPACITORS

Capacitors come in two types, polarised and non-polarised. Polarised types must be connected so that conventional current enters their positive terminal. Several materials are used for constructing polarised fixed capacitors:

a) Mica

Mica is an insulator found in a mineral form which can be split into very thin sheets. A capacitor can be made by interleaving sheets of aluminium foil or depositing a metal film on both surfaces. The tolerance of capacitors made in this way is small, but they are stable and can be used for high working voltages. They are suitable for uses where high stability is required, as in tuned circuits, filters, etc.

b) Polyester

Polyester film forms the dielectric between two strips of aluminium foil which form the plates of the capacitor (Fig. C.4). In another version, films of metal are deposited on the plastic and these act as the plates. The tolerance on stated values is about ±20 per cent.

c) Polycarbonate

This is an alternative to polyester. Polycarbonate provides for smaller leakage currents and better stability.

d) Polypropylene

This has a very low loss dielectric suitable for continuous use at high a.c.

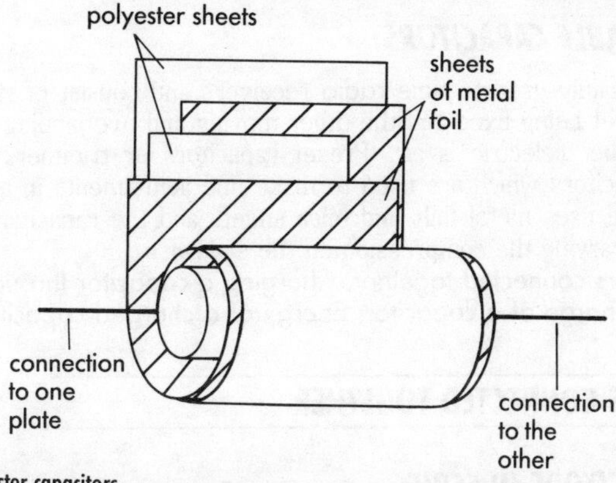

Fig. C.4 Polyester capacitors

voltages. It is capable of withstanding high-voltage fast rise-time pulses and is suitable for use in high-frequency circuits.

e) Ceramic

Like mica this forms a good dielectric with good stability and a high working voltage. These capacitors are used in situations where exact values are not important.

f) Electrolytic (polarised)

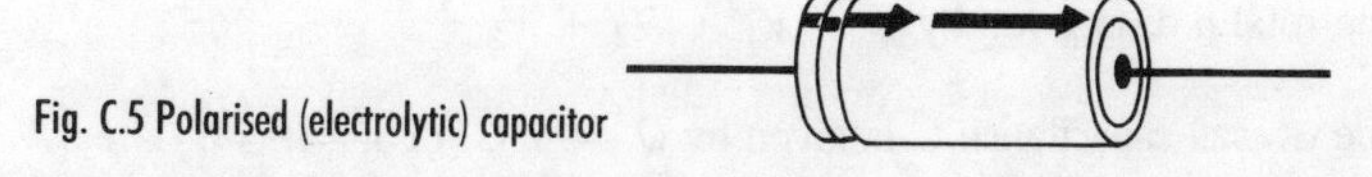

Fig. C.5 Polarised (electrolytic) capacitor

These are capacitors in which the dielectric is an extremely thin layer of aluminium oxide formed electrolytically (Fig. C.5). The advantage of a thin layer is that very high values of capacitance can be produced in a small volume. Unfortunately such capacitors have a big tolerance, high leakage current and poor stability. The leakage current in these capacitors is important in order to maintain the oxide layer. Lack of use will cause the layer to deteriorate, reversed polarity will destroy it.

The table below summarises the properties of these types of capacitor.

Type	*Typical values*	*Stability*	*Working voltage*	*Leakage current*
Mica	2 pF → 10 nF	high	typically 300 V	very small
Polyester	0.1 μF → 2 μF	poor	typically 300 V	small
Polycarbonate	100 pF → 10 μF	high	typically 200 V	small
Polypropylene	1 nF → 0.1 μF	high	typically 1000 V	very small
Ceramic	10 pF → 1 μF	good	typically 100 V	small
Electrolytic	1 μF → 10000 μF	poor	typically 25 V	large

VARIABLE CAPACITORS

These are mainly used to tune radio receivers and consist of two parallel plates, one set being fixed and the other moving and overlapping within the fixed set. The dielectric is air. Preset capacitors or trimmers are small variable capacitors which are used to make fine adjustments in a circuit. A common type uses metal foils and mica sheets and the capacitance can be changed by varying the compression on the sandwich.

◀ Capacitors connected together; Charging a capacitor through a resistor; Discharge of a capacitor; Energy of a charged capacitor ▶

CAPACITORS CONNECTED TOGETHER

CAPACITORS IN SERIES

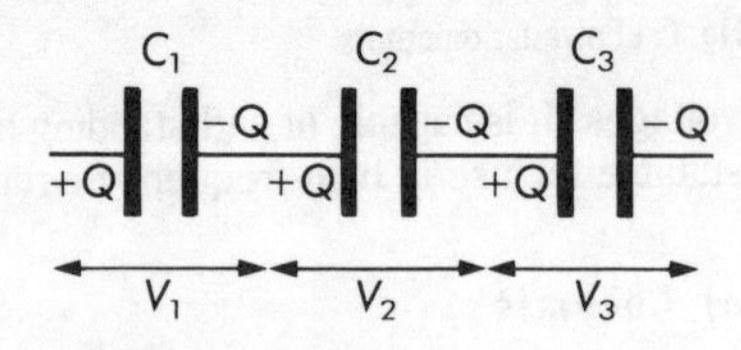

Fig. C.6 Capacitors in series

Fig. C.6 shows three capacitors in series. When such an arrangement is charged from an external source, the plates at the extreme ends of the arrangement have opposite charges. The net charge on each pair of inner plates is zero. Each behaves as a polarised conductor with charge $+Q$ at one end and $-Q$ at the other. We note therefore the following points:

a) The charge stored on each capacitor is the same.
b) We can use this value of charge to calculate the voltages on each capacitor. We get $V_1 = Q/C_1$, $V_2 = Q/C_2$, $V_3 = Q/C_3$.
c) The total p.d. is given by $V = V_1 + V_2 + V_3$.
d) The overall capacitance C is given by $Q = VC$, or $V = \dfrac{Q}{C}$.

V is given by

$$V = \frac{Q}{C_1} + \frac{Q}{C_2} + \frac{Q}{C_3} = Q\left(\frac{1}{C_1} + \frac{1}{C_2} + \frac{1}{C_3}\right)$$

Hence we have $$\frac{1}{C} = \frac{1}{C_1} + \frac{1}{C_2} + \frac{1}{C_3}$$

CAPACITORS IN PARALLEL

Because the capacitors are connected in parallel (Fig. C.7) the p.d. across each capacitor is the same. Charge supplied from an external source spreads itself out over the three capacitors. These can be replaced by a single capacitor with the same total charge, i.e. $Q = Q_1 + Q_2 + Q_3$, and because $Q = VC$ and $Q_1 = VC_1$, $Q_2 = VC_2$, $Q_3 = VC_3$, we get $Q = V(C_1 + C_2 + C_3)$, and hence $C = C_1 + C_2 + C_3$.

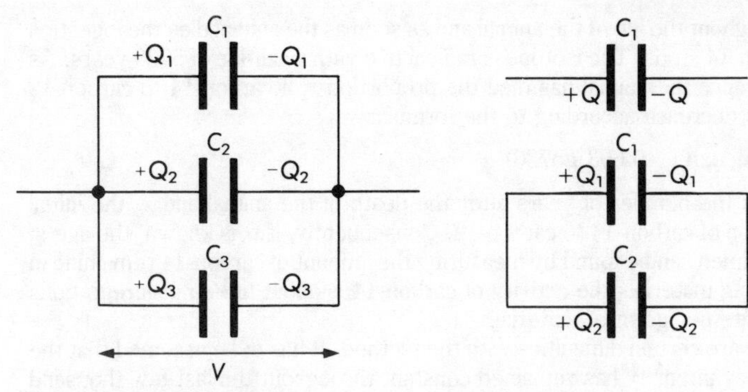

Fig. C.7 Capacitors in parallel

Fig. C.8 Sharing charge

SHARING CHARGE

When a capacitor C_1 shares its charge Q with an uncharged capacitor C_2, the charge is shared in the ratio of the capacitances (Fig. C.8).

$$V = \frac{Q_1}{C_1} = \frac{Q_2}{C_2} \qquad \therefore \frac{Q_1}{Q_2} = \frac{C_1}{C_2} \text{ and } Q = Q_1 + Q_2$$

The original charge is of course conserved. If $C_1 < C_2$ then $Q_1 < Q_2$ and $Q_2 \approx Q$. In this case almost all the original charge is transferred from C_1 to C_2. The p.d. across C_2 is now

$$\frac{Q_2}{C_2} = \frac{Q}{C_2}$$

If the p.d. across C_2 is measured, the original charge on C_1 can be measured. This is the basis of the coulomb meter.

◀ Unity gain voltage follower ▶

CARBON DATING

Carbon dating is a method used by archeologists to date historical and pre-historical specimens which have ages up to a few thousand years. The method uses the radioactivity of a carbon isotope.

The **isotope** carbon-14 is continually being formed in the atmosphere. This is because cosmic rays from outer space can produce **neutrons** which then react with nitrogen-14 in the following reaction.

$$n + {}^{14}_{7}N \rightarrow {}^{14}_{6}C + {}^{1}_{1}H$$

7.5 kg per year of carbon-14 are produced. This combines with oxygen to produce carbon dioxide which is chemically indistinguishable from CO_2 containing carbon-12.

The carbon-14 is then absorbed by plants which are in turn eaten by animals and hence the carbon is absorbed into the animal structure. This process goes on throughout the life of the animal and as soon as the animal dies the ingestion of carbon-14 stops. The isotope is radioactive with a half-life of 5730 years. As a result once the animal has died the proportion x of carbon-14 to carbon-12 starts to decrease according to the formula:

$$x = x_o \exp(-0.693\, t/5730)$$

Here t is the number of years after the death of the animal and x_o the initial proportion of carbon-14 to carbon-12. Consequently, if x_o is known, the age of the specimen can be found by measuring the amount of carbon-14 remaining in it. In living materials the activity of carbon-14 is about fifteen disintegrations per minute per gram of material.

There are certain difficulties with the method. It has to be assumed that the cosmic ray intensity has remained constant throughout the last few thousand years, so that when archaeological samples were formed they too had an initial radioactivity of fifteen disintegrations per minute per gram. Cosmic rays, being charged particles, are deflected away from the earth by the earth's magnetic field. The strength of the earth's field is considered to have varied and this could have caused variations in the annual production of carbon-14.

◀ Radioactive decay series ▶

CATAPULT FIELD

The catapult field is the name given to the resultant magnetic field when a current-carrying conductor is placed in a uniform magnetic field, such as that produced by a horseshoe magnet.

Fleming's left-hand rule considers the direction of the current and the direction of the magnetic field, from N to S. It predicts that the wire drawn in Fig. C.9 will move inwards. The left-hand rule is only a **direction rule** and does not offer an explanation of why this occurs. It also gives an unnecessary prominence to one of the magnetic fields, when in fact two are present simultaneously and nature does not consider one 'more important' than the other.

Consider the two fields in Fig. C.10. The left-hand diagram shows the field of the magnet alone, viewed from above. The right-hand diagram shows the field of the current alone. If the two fields are superimposed on each other, they add vectorially, and the result is that shown in Fig. C.11.

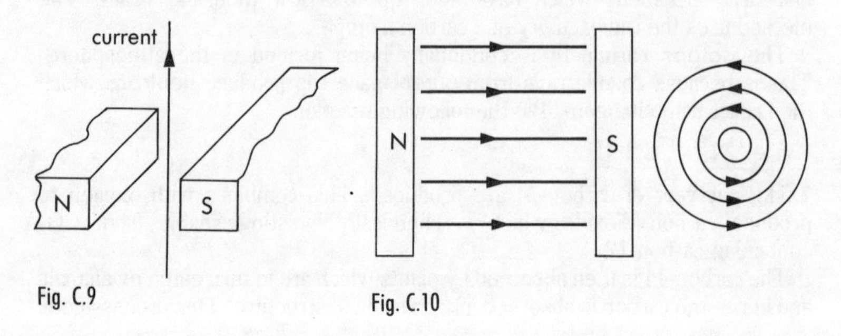

Fig. C.9

Fig. C.10

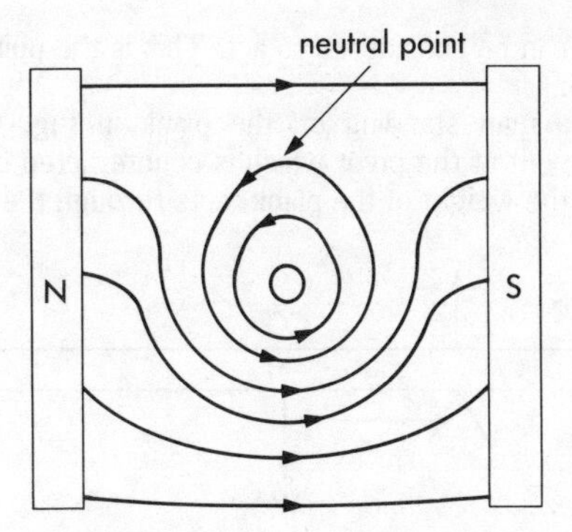

Fig. C.11

Beneath the wire the two sets of flux combine in the same direction, whereas above the wire they are opposing. If a card is placed in this plane and iron filings are scattered on it, this resultant magnetic field is illustrated fairly clearly. The stronger field lines beneath the wire remind one of a piece of stretched elastic, as in a catapult. The fact that the wire is propelled upwards in the diagram increases the suggestion that the magnetic field lines are behaving in a similar way to stretched pieces of elastic. Hence the name 'catapult field'.

Michael Faraday was the first to consider that the field had real properties He considered that the field lines had two properties:

i) They behaved like pieces of stretched elastic.
ii) They repelled each other sideways.

The field would always set itself in a way in which the system was in a kind of equilibrium, with the energy stored in the field at a minimum. Later in the nineteenth century James Clerk Maxwell provided a sound basis for field theory in magnetism, that is a theory in physics which describes a real existence and physical properties to the magnetic field.

◀ Ampere ▶

CATHODE RAY TUBE

This is an old-fashioned name for any evacuated glass tube in which beams of electrons are produced.

The electrons are generated by an **electron gun**. Most **oscilloscopes** and televisions use a form of a cathode ray tube.

◀ Deflection tube, Maltese cross apparatus ▶

CENTRE OF GRAVITY

The weight of an object behaves as if the object was a point of mass, with the weight acting at that point. For an object with a distributed mass the centre of gravity is the point at which, for the purpose of calculations, all the mass of the body can be considered to act. This is the point which is used in moment calculations.

For example, a man standing on the plank in Fig. C.12 produces an anticlockwise moment at the pivot which is counteracted by the moment Wx of the plank if W, the weight of the plank, acts through the centre of gravity.

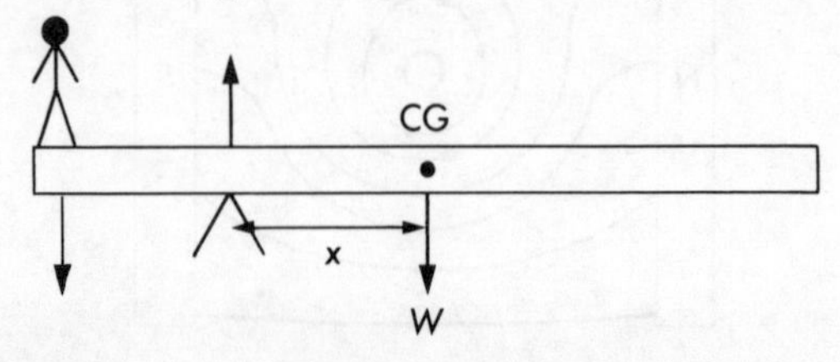

Fig. C.12

CENTRE OF MASS

The centre of mass of a body is that point where the mass of the body can be thought to be concentrated.

◀ Centre of gravity, Solving problems of several forces acting on a body ▶

CENTRIFUGAL AND CENTRIPETAL FORCES

Centrifugal force is the term used in everyday language to describe the effect of being thrown outwards when moving in a sharply curved circle. By contrast centripetal force is the term used in physics to measure the inward force needed for **circular motion**.

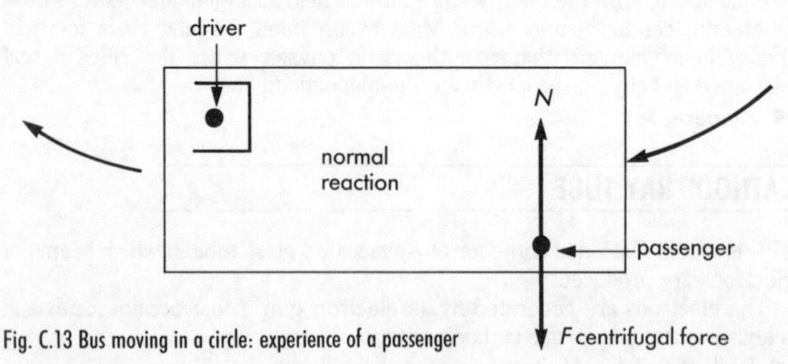

Fig. C.13 Bus moving in a circle: experience of a passenger

Students are often confused by the use of these two terms. A simple example will clarify the point. Consider a bus going round a roundabout (Fig. C.13). Many buses have sideways-facing seats. Consider a passenger sitting in one of the seats on the outside of the circle. The passenger seems to experience an outward force F tending to throw him/her out of the bus, and is only restrained by the normal reaction N of the seat. He/she would say that the force F is a centrifugal force, and that $F = N$. Such a description is a valid one, but we have to note that this is made from a moving 'reference frame', i.e. the moving environment of the bus. The bus is actually accelerating towards the centre of the roundabout. From the non-accelerating standpoint of the landscape we would say that the only force present is the reaction force N, and it is this which is a centripetal force causing the passenger to move in a circle.

We might actually go further and say that the passenger deceives himself/herself in saying there is an outward force F. This is just his/her experience of the reaction of the seat, in the same way as someone standing on the ground doesn't actually experience their weight (which isn't suddenly switched off when they jump off the ground), but the reaction force of the ground.

Now in Newtonian mechanics it is necessary for a description of motion to be made in a non-accelerating system. Physicists call this an 'inertial reference frame'. The bus clearly will not do for this. So the proper Newtonian description is that with reference to the landscape and using the term centripetal force. If a rotating reference frame is used by mistake, it is found that Newton's First Law of Motion does not work and a body may seem to be subject to otherwise unexplained forces of which the centrifugal force is one. Physicists call these forces 'fictional' forces.

◀ Coriolis force, Newton's Laws ▶

CEPHEID VARIABLES

Cepheid variables are a special type of star whose light output varies periodically over a time-scale of days. They are thought to pulsate. Their main use in astronomy is in distance determination. Their name comes from the star δ-Cephei, the fourth star in the constellation Cepheus, the magnitude–time curve of which is shown in Fig. C.14.

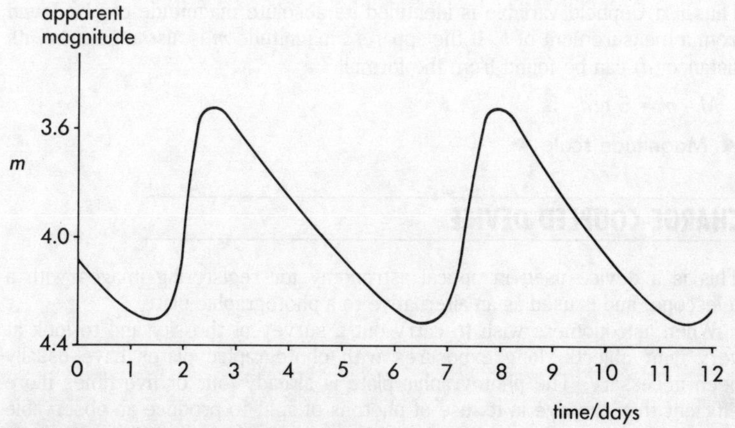

Fig. C.14 Magnitude–time curve for the star δ-Cephei

Stellar **parallax** can be used for distance determination only with comparatively close stars. So other methods have to be employed for stars much further away. In 1908 Henrietta Leavitt discovered that there was a relationship between period p and mean brightness for Cepheid variables. She explored stars in the Lesser Magellanic Cloud, now known to be a companion galaxy of our galaxy. The pattern of results is shown in Fig. C.15. Mathematically this can be expressed by the formula

$$M = -(1.8 + 2.4 \lg (p/\text{day}))$$

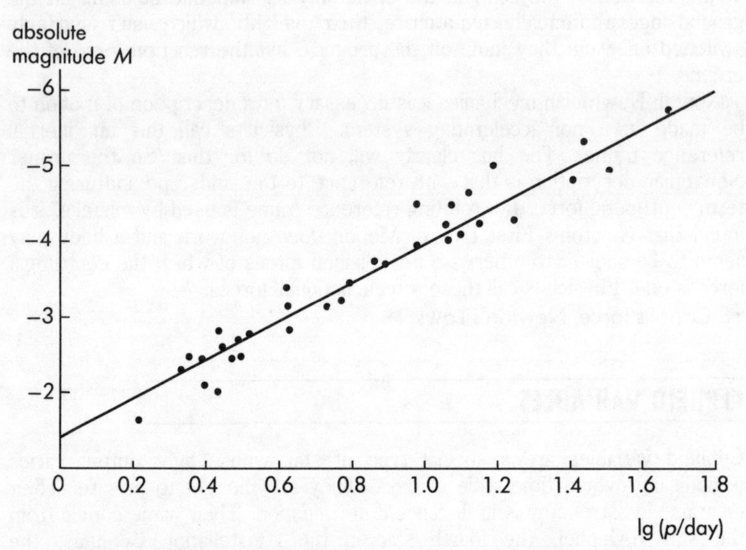

Fig. C.15 Graph of absolute magnitude *M* against the logarithm of the period *p* in days for the Cepheid variables in the Lesser Magellanic Cloud

Thus if a Cepheid variable is identified its absolute magnitude can be found from a measurement of p. If the apparent magnitude m is also measured, its distance (d) can be found from the formula

$$M - m = 5 \lg d - 5.$$

◀ Magnitude scale ▶

CHARGE-COUPLED DEVICE

This is a device used in optical astronomy for registering images with a telescope, and is used as an alternative to a photographic plate.

When astronomers wish to carry out a survey of the sky and to look at very faint objects, long exposures with photographic plates have usually been necessary. The photographic plate is already four or five times more efficient than the **eye** in its use of photons of light to produce an observable image. The charge-coupled device is better still, being about sixteen times more efficient in the use of light than a photographic emulsion. Hence its use considerably shortens the time needed to carry out a survey with a telescope if very faint objects need to be detected. Another way of describing it is to say that it allows the detection of objects several **magnitudes** dimmer than would otherwise be possible, without having to use a larger telescope aperture as a means of increasing the number of photons per second.

The device itself is a silicon chip with an array of electrodes dividing the chip into a large number of picture elements called pixels. The mechanism is that a single photon releases a charge which is held in the pixel by voltages applied to the electrodes. Charges are 'read out' by being moved along in sequence by applying appropriate voltages to the electrodes.

◀ Photographic film ▶

CHARGE DISTRIBUTION

The sharper the curvature on the surface of a charged conductor the greater the density of charge. If a conductor has a sharp point on its surface most of the charge resides there.

As the surface is an electrical conductor the electrical potential in volts is the same at all positions on its surface. If this were not the case there would be a **potential difference** over its surface and the charge would move over the surface, giving rise to small electric currents, until equilibrium was established.

There is, however, a potential difference, in volts, between the conductor and the earth. By this we mean that a certain amount of work has to be done to transfer negative charge to the conductor. Likewise if the conductor loses charge to the earth a certain amount of energy is released. (This is part of the reason why discharging a high voltage through the body can be painful.) If we bring a negative test charge from the earth to the conductor at Q by route 1 (Fig. C.16), a certain amount of work is done as an external force overcomes the forces of repulsion of the charges as Q is approached. The charge could also be moved by route 2. If the charge distribution were the same all over the conductor, a smaller force would be encountered in the region of P and less work would be done. Once on the conductor it could be moved to Q, because as the surface is at constant potential no work is gained or lost in moving charges over the surface. But the work done must be the same by both routes and so there must be a greater repulsive force than this at P and hence more charges.

◀ Action of points, Inverse square law fields ▶

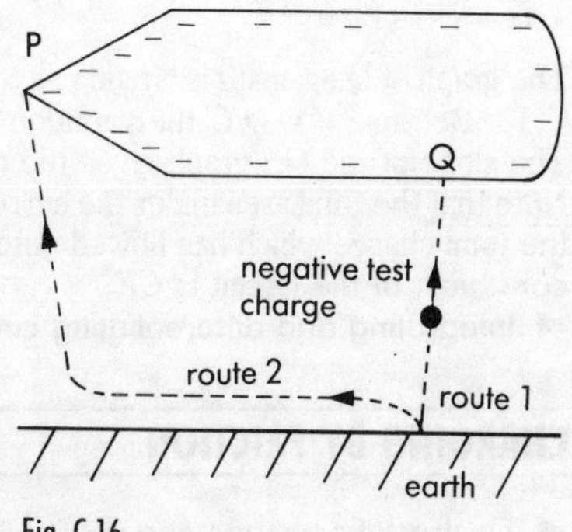

Fig. C.16

CHARGING A CAPACITOR THROUGH A RESISTOR

If a **capacitor** is initially uncharged, the e.m.f. E of the battery in Fig. C.17 causes current to flow when the switch S is closed. As the charge arrives at the capacitor a potential difference V_C builds up on the capacitor. This is in the opposite sense to the e.m.f. E and thus reduces the current flow. As V_C increases the current decreases and when the capacitor is fully charged the current is reduced to zero.

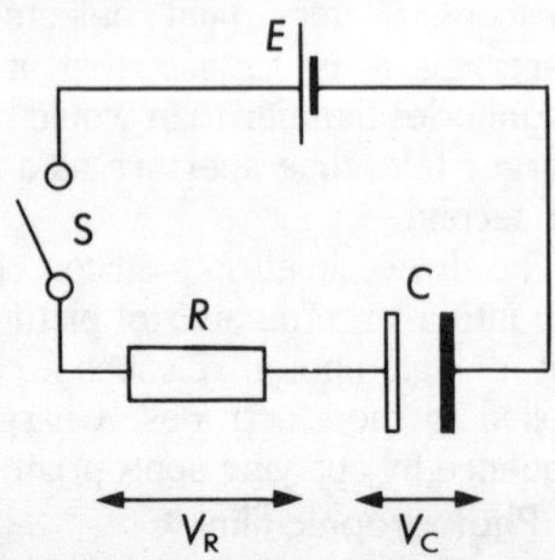

Fig. C.17 Charging a capacitor through a resistor

Mathematically, once the switch, S, is closed the circuit contains an e.m.f. E at the battery, and two potential differences, V_R across the resistor and V_C across the capacitor. By **Kirchhoff's** Second Law $E = V_R + V_C$. At $t = 0$, the capacitor is uncharged, so $V_C = 0$ and $V_R = E$. The current is given by V_R/R. The capacitor therefore is charging, and as the charge accumulates on the plates of the capacitor V_C increases. Eventually $V_C = E$ and $V_R = 0$. When this occurs the current has stopped flowing and the capacitor is fully charged.

We can take the above expression for Kirchhoff's Second Law at time t and substitute IR for V_R and Q/C for V_C, where Q is the charge at time t. The equation then becomes

$$E = IR + Q/C$$

Writing $\dfrac{dQ}{dt}$ for I we get the following differential equation for Q:

$$\frac{dQ}{dt} + \frac{Q}{C} = E$$

This has the solution

$$Q = EC\,(1 - e^{-t/CR})$$

The graph of Q against t is a rising exponential graph of the form shown in Fig. C.18. Because $V = Q/C$ the variation of V with time is similar to the above. The slope of the Q,t graph gives the current, which is plotted in Fig. C. 19. Note that the total area under the current graph is given by $\int I dt$, which equals the total charge which has flowed onto the capacitor. Note also that the **time constant** τ of the circuit is CR.

◀ Integrating and differentiating circuits, Discharge of a capacitor ▶

CHARGING BY FRICTION

◀ Electrostatic phenomena ▶

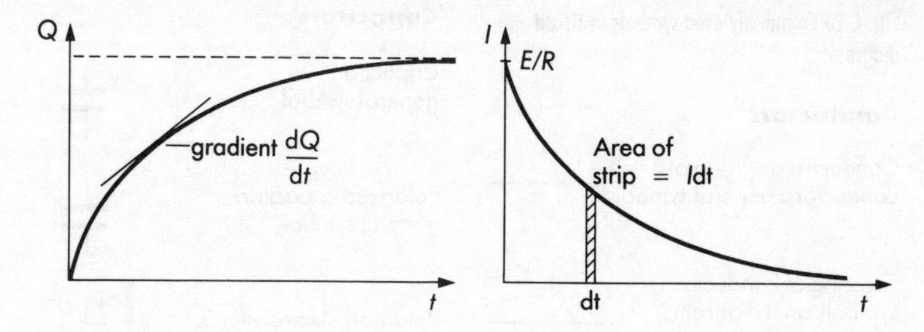

Fig. C.18 Graph of charge against time

Fig. C.19 Graph of current against time

CHARLES' LAW

◀ Gas laws ▶

CHARM

This is a term of **elementary particle** physics. It is a property of matter possessed by all material which contains a charmed **quark**.

CHIP

◀ Integrated circuit ▶

CHROMATIC ABERRATION

◀ Camera ▶

CIRCUIT SYMBOLS

Some of the commonly used symbols used in circuit diagrams are shown in Fig. C.20.

Note that in the logic problems in digital electronics it is quite usual to leave out the power supply rails altogether on circuit diagrams. Attention is then focused on the logic. In operational amplifier problems it is also common to leave out the connections to the power rails. The British and American symbols for logic gates are found in the entry **Logic gates**.

Fig. C.20 Commonly used symbols in circuit diagrams

Conductors

Conductor or group of conductors: general symbol

Crossing of conductor symbols on a diagram (no electrical connection)

Junction of conductors

Resistors

Fixed registor: general symbol

Alternative general symbol

Variable resistor: general symbol

Resistor with moving contact (rheostat)

Voltage divider with moving contact (potentiometer)

Resistor with pronounced negative resistance-temperature coefficient, e.g. thermistor

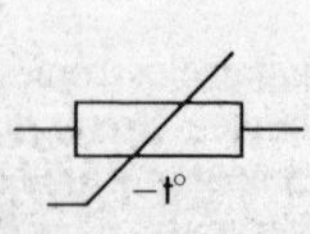

Capacitors

Capacitor: general symbol

Polarized capacitor: general symbol

Polarised electrolytic capacitor

Variable capacitor: general symbol

Impedance

Impedance

Inductors and transformers

Winding i.e. of an inductor, coil or transformer): preferred general symbol

Inductor with core (ferromagnetic unless otherwise indicated)

Transformer with ferromagnetic core

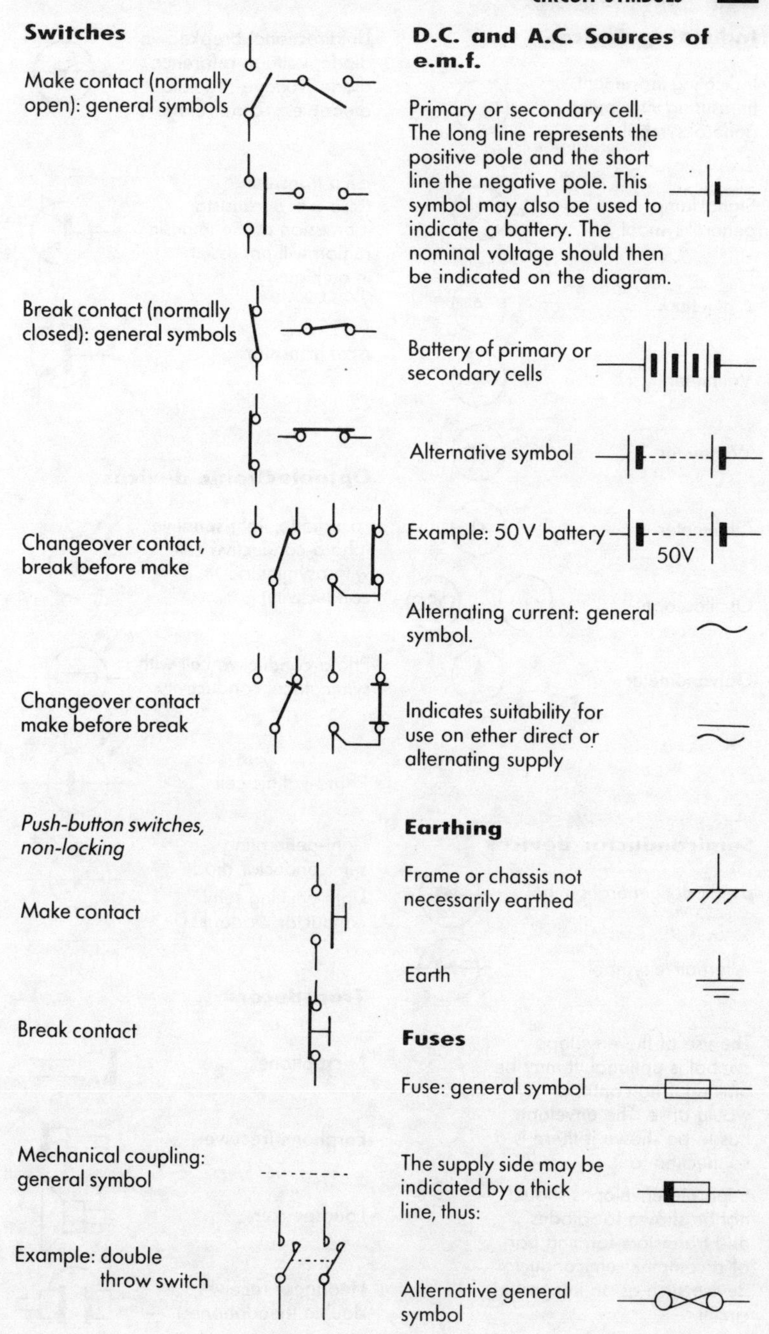
Switches
Make contact (normally open): general symbols
Break contact (normally closed): general symbols
Changeover contact, break before make
Changeover contact make before break
Push-button switches, non-locking
Make contact
Break contact
Mechanical coupling: general symbol
Example: double throw switch
D.C. and A.C. Sources of e.m.f.
Primary or secondary cell. The long line represents the positive pole and the short line the negative pole. This symbol may also be used to indicate a battery. The nominal voltage should then be indicated on the diagram.
Battery of primary or secondary cells
Alternative symbol
Example: 50 V battery
50V
Alternating current: general symbol.
Indicates suitability for use on ether direct or alternating supply
Earthing
Frame or chassis not necessarily earthed
Earth
Fuses
Fuse: general symbol
The supply side may be indicated by a thick line, thus:
Alternative general symbol

Indicating devices

Indicating instrument, or measuring instrument: general symbol

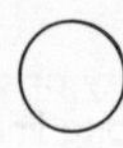

Signal lamp: general symbol

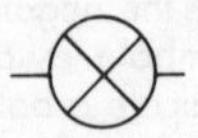

Ammeter

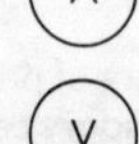

Voltmeter

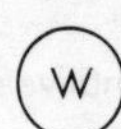

Wattmeter

Ohmmeter

Oscilloscope

Galvanometer

Semiconductor devices

p n diode: general symbol

Alternative symbol

The use of the envelope symbol is optional. It may be omitted if no confusion would arise. The envelope has to be shown if there is a connection to it.

Separate envelopes should not be shown for diodes and transistors forming part of a complex semiconductor device such as an integrated circuit.

Unidirectional breakdown diode, voltage-reference diode (voltage-regulator diode), e.g. Zener diode

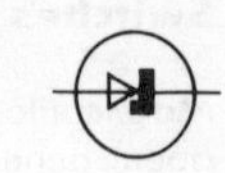

p n p transistor (also *p n i p* transistor if omission of the intrinsic region will not result in ambiguity)

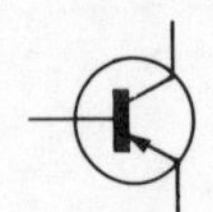

n p n transistor

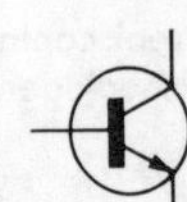

Optoelectronic devices

p n diode, light-sensitive (photo-conductive cell with asymmetric conductivity)

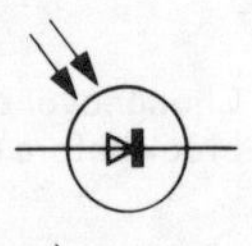

Photo-conductive cell with symmetrical conductivity

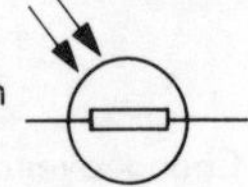

Photo-voltaic cell

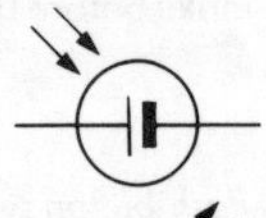

Light-generating semiconductor diode
Light-emitting semiconductor diode, LED

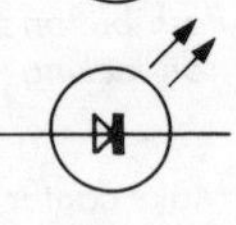

Transducers

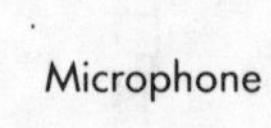

Microphone

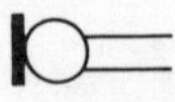

Earphone (receiver)

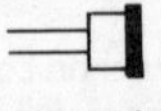

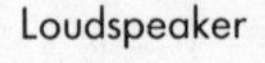

Loudspeaker

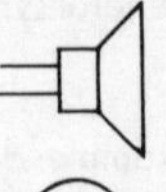

Headgear receiver, double (headphones)

Other symbols

Electric buzzer: general symbol

Filament lamp

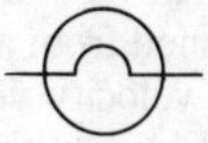

Cold cathode discharge lamp (e.g. neon lamp)

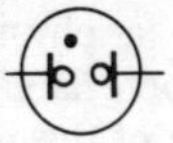

Electric bell: general symbol

Thermocouple (the negative pole is represented by the thicker line)

NOT gate

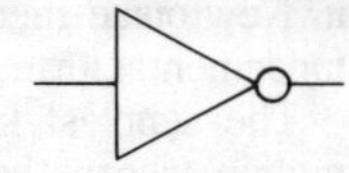

OR gate

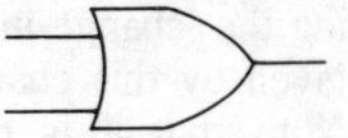

NOR gate

AND gate

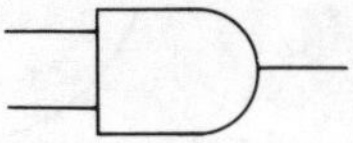

Electronic circuit symbols

Amplifier

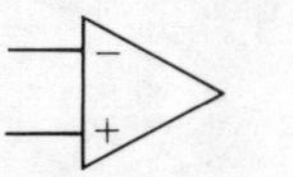

Operational amplifier

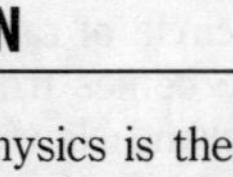

NAND gate

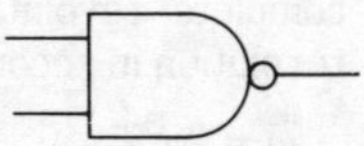

Exclusive OR gate

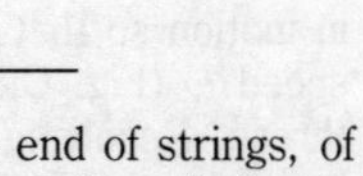

CIRCULAR MOTION

Circular motion in physics is the motion of stones on the end of strings, of whirling machinery, and, approximately at least, of the motion of planets around the sun. Before Newton's time circular motion had a special status in physics. It was considered to be one of nature's fundamental forms of motion because of the apparent motion of the stars. But we now know that the daily motion of the stars is an apparent motion caused by the earth's rotation and in Newtonian mechanics it is steady motion in a straight line which is the fundamental form of motion.

The simplest kind of circular motion is uniform circular motion. This is motion where the magnitude of the velocity vector is constant while the direction steadily changes. Fig. C.21 shows two positions, P and P′, of a particle when it is moving in a circle. The vector diagram shows how the velocity at P′, the 'final velocity', is obtained from adding a vector representing the 'change in velocity' to the initial velocity vector. The acceleration is given by this change in velocity divided by the time taken for the change. Note that it is directed inwards, towards the centre of the circle. By Newton's Second Law there must be a physical force inwards that is responsible for this acceleration. This force is called a centripetal force. It always has a physical cause. In the case of the planets revolving round the sun it is gravitational attraction.

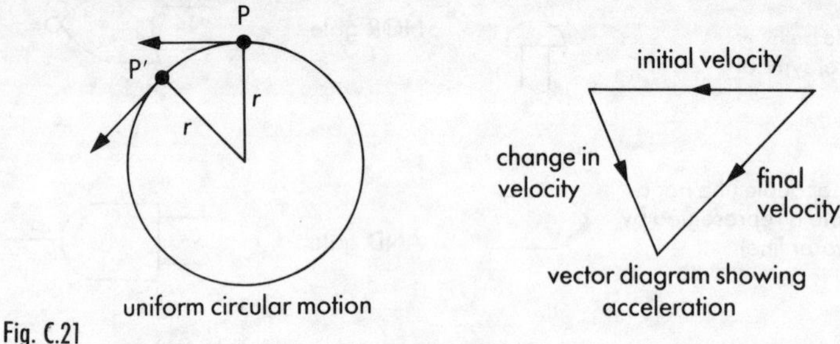

Fig. C.21

The angular speed ω of a particle in a circle is equal to the angle of a complete revolution in radians divided by the time T for a complete revolution in seconds, so

$$\omega = 2\pi/T$$

The velocity v of the particle is given by

$$v = \omega r$$

The inward acceleration is

$$a = v^2/r = \omega^2 r$$

and the centripetal force is $m\omega^2 r$.

Note that because motion is at right angles to the force the force does not act in the direction of the motion and so no work is done by it.

As an example of circular motion consider a mass hanging on a thread set in motion so that it moves in a horizontal circle of radius r with an angular speed ω (Fig. C.22). The centripetal force comes from the tension in the thread. Resolving forces vertically and applying Newton's Second Law we have

$$F \cos \theta = mg$$

(i.e. the net upward force is zero as the mass doesn't have vertical acceleration).

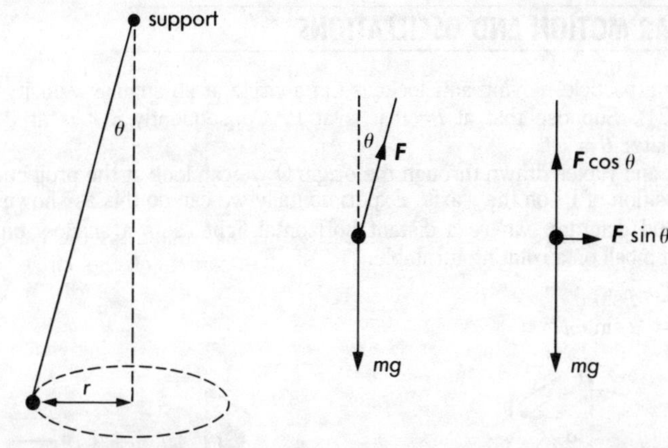

Fig. C.22 Conical pendulum

Resolving horizontally

$F \sin\theta = m\omega^2 r$

Dividing the second equation by the first we get

$\tan\theta = \omega^2 r/g$

i.e. the angle θ is related to the angular speed ω.

The periodic time T is $2\pi/\omega = 2\pi\sqrt{\dfrac{r}{g\tan\theta}}$

A second example is the motion of the bobsleigh in Fig. C.23. Here, in order to go round a circle, the bobsleigh has to ride up the slope so that the normal reaction to the ice surface has a sideways component. This sideways component is the centripetal force which is needed. Because the bobsleigh is on an ice surface there is no frictional force available as a centripetal force. Thus we have:

$R\sin\theta = mg$
$R\cos\theta = mv^2/r$

noting that θ is defined differently from the case of the mass on the string. Hence

$\tan\theta = gr/v^2$

As v increases, the bobsleigh rides higher up the curve.

◀ Centrifugal and centripetal forces, Newton's Laws of Motion, Resolution of vectors ▶

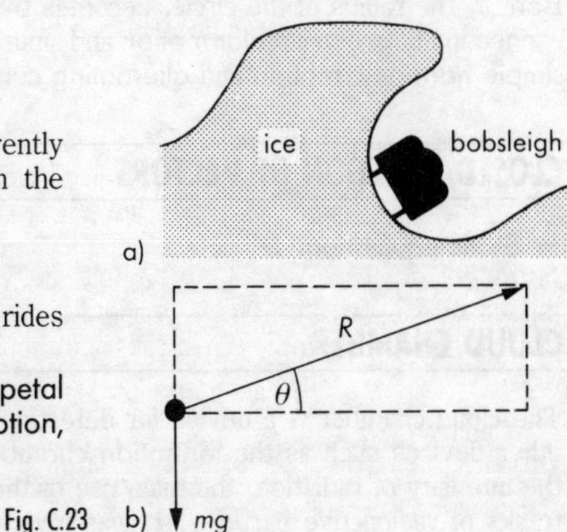

Fig. C.23

CIRCULAR MOTION AND OSCILLATIONS

Consider a particle moving anticlockwise in a circle at an angular velocity ω (Fig. C.24). Suppose that at $t = 0$ it is at P. Consequently if it is at P′ t seconds later $\theta = \omega t$.

With x and y axes drawn through the origin O we can look at the projection of the position of P′ on the y axis. Experimentally we can do this as shown in the second diagram, where a distant horizontal light casts a shadow on a screen of a ball on a rotating turntable.

$$y = a \sin \theta$$
$$\text{so } y = a \sin \omega t$$

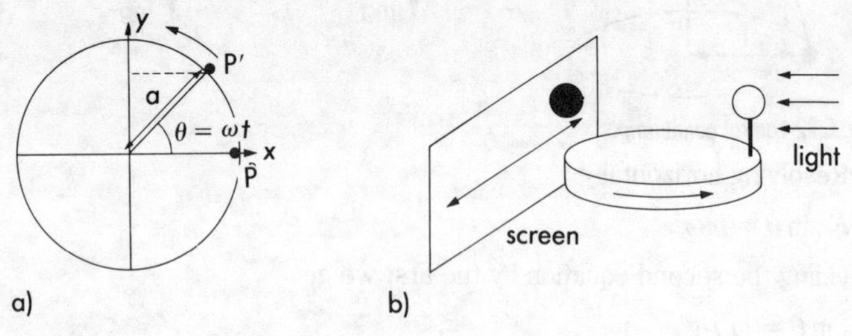

Fig. C.24 Particle moving anticlockwise in a circle

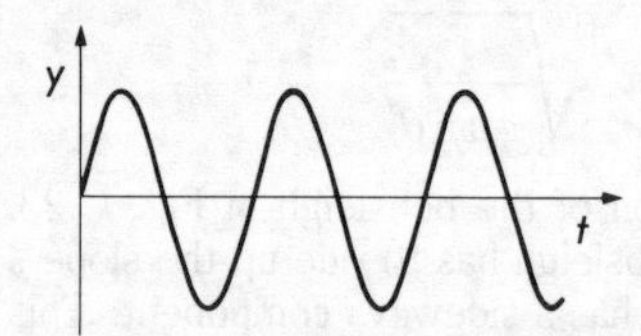

Fig. C.25

The graph of y against t (Fig. C.25) is sinusoidal with a period $T = 2\pi/\omega$. Here a, the radius of the circle, becomes the amplitude of the motion. This connection between **circular motion** and sinusoidal motion is important both in **simple harmonic motion** and **alternating current** theory.

CLOSED POLYGON OF VECTORS

◀ Static equilibrium ▶

CLOUD CHAMBER

The cloud chamber is a device for detecting radioactive particles. Whereas other devices such as the **ionisation chamber** and the **Geiger tube** detect the intensity of radiation, the main use of the cloud chamber is to show the tracks of radioactive particles. It was invented in 1911 by C.T.R. Wilson, and the first experiments which showed radioactive particles colliding with other particles were made with the cloud chamber. The principle of the cloud chamber is that when a radioactive particle passes through a supersaturated vapour, the ions it produces act as centres on which liquid condensation can occur. As a result a line of liquid droplets is formed along the trajectory of the particle. The liquid condenses more readily on the ions because they are larger than the uncharged gas molecules. Roughly speaking the length of the track produced is proportional to the energy of the particles.

There are two types of cloud chamber: the expansion type and the diffusion cloud chamber (Fig. C.26). In the expansion cloud chamber the supersaturated state is produced by suddenly lowering the pressure inside the chamber. By contrast in the diffusion cloud chamber solid carbon dioxide keeps the chamber cold at the bottom and produces a temperature gradient through the vapour above it. As a result at one level the air is supersaturated. Methylated spirits is used in both cloud chambers.

The tracks seen in a cloud chamber vary in appearance with the particles. The tracks of **alpha radiation** are straight because they are massive particles which are not easily deflected. They also produce very dense tracks because of the large amount of ionisation they cause. **Beta radiation** produces less dense tracks which are less straight. **Gamma radiation** is not detected directly: instead a track occurs where the particle gives up all of its energy injecting an electron from an atom in the chamber. This electron produces a

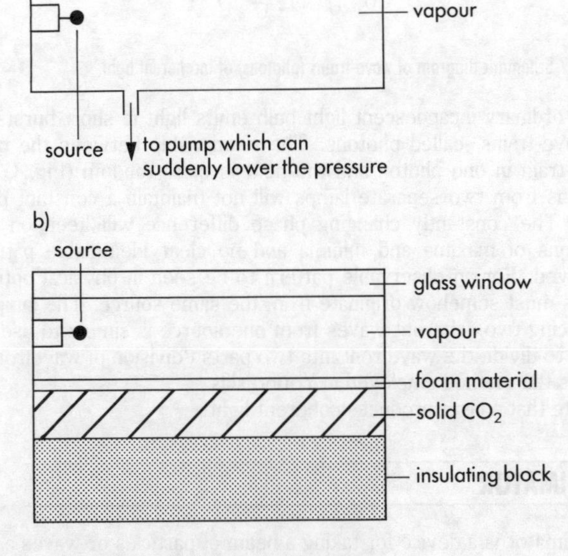

Fig. C.26 a) Expansion cloud chamber b) Diffusion cloud chamber

short beta track in mid-air away from the source. This is a consequence of **quantum mechanics** whereby the energy of the gamma photon must be all given up at once or not given up at all.

◀ Bubble chamber ▶

CMOS

◀ Digital logic ▶

COHERENCE

Coherence is the requirement in physical optics that two interfering wave-trains of the same frequency must have a constant phase difference between them in order for an observable **interference** pattern to be seen.

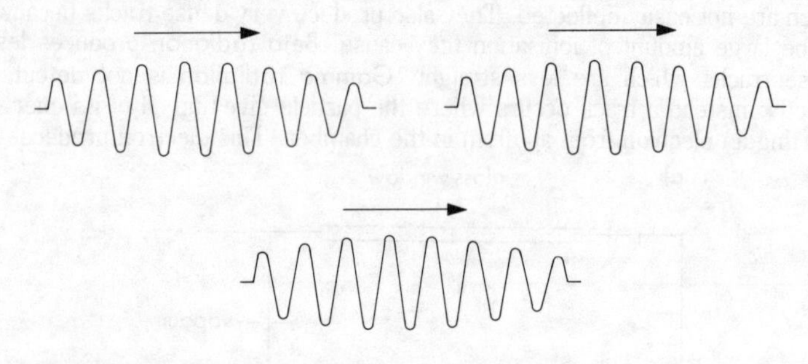

Fig. C.27 Schematic diagram of wave-trains (photons) of incoherent light

An ordinary incandescent light bulb emits light in short bursts of energy, or wave-trains, called photons. The relationship between the phase of the wave-train in one photon and the next is quite random (Fig. C.27). Hence photons from two separate lamps will not maintain a constant phase difference. The constantly changing phase difference will keep on moving the positions of maxima and minima and no clear identifiable pattern will be observed. For an observable pattern to be seen in physical optics, the two waves must somehow originate from the same source. The simplest way of producing two coherent waves from one source is simply to use two slits in order to divide the wavefront into two parts ('division of wavefront' method). This is the method employed in **Young slits**.

Note that a laser produces coherent light.

COLLIMATOR

A collimator is a device for taking a beam of particles or waves and making it parallel.

For example, in the **spectrometer** there is a collimator which is used to make a beam of light parallel. It uses a lens system. In **gamma radiation** and **X-ray** physics a collimator is more often a series of slits in pieces of lead metal arranged in a line so that only particles passing in one particular direction can pass through.

◀ Zartman's experiment ▶

COLLISIONS

◀ Energy in collision problems ▶

COLOUR

This is a term used in elementary particle physics. It has nothing to do with the day-to-day meaning of colour. It is a property similar to electrical charge which is possessed by the sub-elementary particles the **quarks** and the gluons. Unlike electrical charge, which comes in two types, there are three types of charge in colour theory. This charge is believed to be the source of the strong force between quarks in theories of the strong interaction (see **Nucleus**). At the elementary particle level, that is at the level of particles which are actually seen in experiments, colour is not observed.

COLOUR INDEX

The colour index is a number used in astronomy to indicate a star's temperature. When photographs of the sky (sky surveys) are taken using a telescope the light is filtered using certain standard filters. Commonly these are known as 'U', 'V' and 'B' filters. The 'U' filter allows an ultraviolet part of the spectrum. The 'V' is called a 'visual' filter because its response is close to that of the eye. The 'B' or 'blue' filter allows light from the blue end of the spectrum plus light from the blue end of the ultraviolet spectrum. When the photographic magnitude of a star is quoted, that is its magnitude as determined from the photographic plates of sky surveys, the filter which is used should be quoted: e.g. one should write m_B or m_V instead of just m. It is common to just write B for m_B and V for m_V.

The colour index of a star is defined as $m_B - m_V$, often written as $B - V$. (Note that $m_B - m_V = M_B - M_V$.)

As a rough approximation stars can be treated as black bodies (see **Black-body radiation**). Hot stars are bluer than cold ones, which are redder in colour. So the difference between B and V gives an indication of the stellar temperature. In fact, assuming black-body characteristics, the temperature T is given by

$$B - V = \frac{(7260)}{T} - 0.64$$

T is the surface temperature of the star, not that of the interior.

COMBINATIONAL LOGIC

◀ Digital logic ▶

COMMUTATOR

◀ Direct current electric motor ▶

COMPARATOR

◀ Operational amplifier, Voltage comparator ▶

COMPONENTS OF VECTORS

◀ Resolution of vectors ▶

COMPOSITION OF ERRORS

This is the procedure which has to be adopted in experimental physics when a number of measurements have been made to obtain and an estimate of the final uncertainty of the quantity is needed. For example the Young modulus of a quantity is given by $E = \dfrac{4\,Fl}{\pi\, d^2 e}$

where F is the measured force, l the unstretched length of the sample, d the diameter of the sample and e the extension. Each of these quantities will have uncertainties. Some people call them errors, but this word implies a 'mistake' when in fact there are limits to the precision of the measurements that can be made, even with a due amount of care. The simplest rule to obtain an estimate of the overall error or uncertainty is to compute the percentage errors for all the component errors. The percentage uncertainty in E is the sum of the percentage uncertainties in F, l and e plus twice the percentage uncertainty in d.

The rule invoked here is that if:

$$Q = \frac{xyz\ldots}{abc\ldots}$$

$$<Q> = <x> + <y> + <z> \;. \;. \;. + <a> + <b> + <c>$$

where $<x>$ is the percentage uncertainty of the quantity x. This is a useful 'first order' rule which is worth knowing, even if it is rarely assessed in exams.

Notice that in this case, as d occurs as a squared term, its contribution to the percentage uncertainty of E is doubled.

◀ Errors ▶

COMPOUND MICROSCOPE

As a small object is brought closer and closer to the eye the angle it subtends at the eye increases. However, an eye is unable to focus on very close objects. The distance from the eye to the nearest point that it can focus is called the least distance of distinct vision. The compound microscope employs two lenses, an object lens of very short focal length and an eye lens of longer focal length, in order to produce an increase of angular magnification, with the final image arranged to be at the near point.

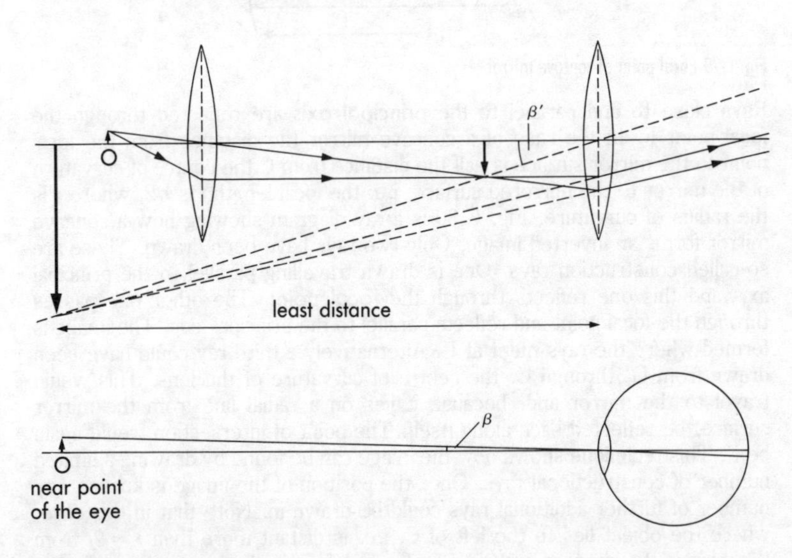

Fig. C.28 Compound microscope

In Fig. C.28, M, the angular magnification, is given by

$$M = \frac{\text{angle subtended by final image}}{\text{angle subtended by object at near point}} = \frac{\beta'}{\beta}$$

◀ Astronomical telescope ▶

COMPRESSIVE STRESS

◀ Stress ▶

COMPTON EFFECT

◀ Gamma radiation ▶

CONCAVE MIRROR

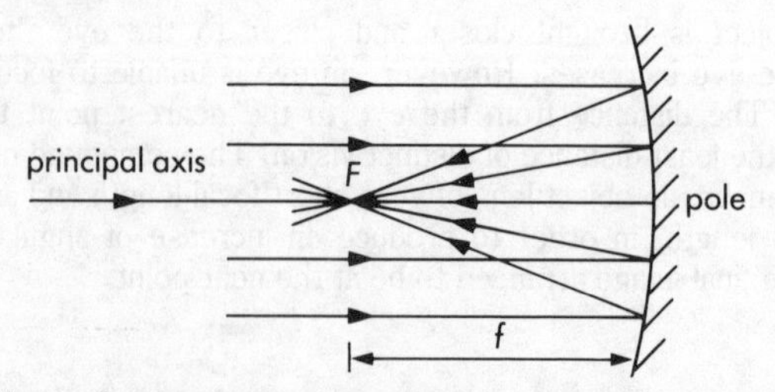

Fig. C.29 Focal point of concave mirror

Rays close to and parallel to the **principal axis** are reflected through the focal point F. In the case of a concave mirror the distance from the focal point to the mirror surface is half the distance from C the centre of curvature of the mirror to the mirrored surface, i.e. the focal length f is $r/2$, where r is the radius of curvature. Fig. C.30 is a ray diagram showing how a concave mirror forms an inverted image. Only two rays have been drawn. These are so-called construction rays. One is drawn travelling parallel to the principal axis and this one reflects through the **focal point**. The other one passes through the focal point and reflects parallel to the principal axis. The image is formed where the rays meet at I′. Alternatively a third ray could have been drawn from O′ through C, the centre of curvature of the lens. This would travel to the mirror and, because it lies on a radial line from the mirror surface, be reflected back along itself. The point of intersection would again be I′. This technique shows how the image can be found by drawing a limited number of constructional rays. Once the position of the image is known, any number of further additional rays could be drawn in. Note that in this case, where the object lies to the left of C, i.e. is distant more than $r = 2f$ from the mirror, the image is real, upside down and diminished.

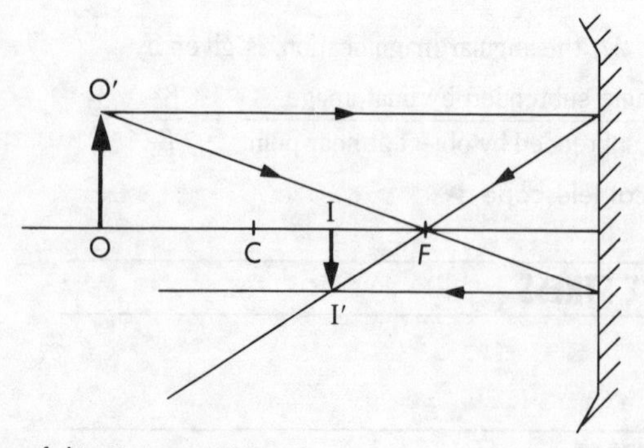

Fig. C.30 Image of object in concave mirror

The table summarises the properties of images for different object distances.

Object distance	*Image distance*	*Nature of image*
infinity	f	real, inverted
greater than $2f$	between f and $2f$	real, inverted, diminished
$2f$	$2f$	real, inverted, same size as object
between f and $2f$	greater than $2f$	real, inverted, enlarged
f	infinity	no image: parallel rays produced
less than f	greater than object distance	virtual, upright, enlarged image on opposite side of mirror to object

◀ Lens formulae, Real image, Virtual image ▶

CONDUCTIVITIES OF METALS

Metals which are good conductors of electricity are also good conductors of heat. Likewise those which conduct heat comparatively poorly conduct electricity comparatively poorly. The term comparatively is used because all metals conduct electricity reasonably well.

Both electrical conduction and thermal conduction are examples of what engineers and physicists call transport phenomena. They have the same kinds of equations. So thermal conduction, described by the equation

$$\frac{\mathrm{d}Q}{\mathrm{d}t} = kA\frac{(\theta_1 - \theta_2)}{l}$$

can be compared with electrical conduction. In the electrical case the familiar Ohm's Law equation is

$$I = V/R$$

V is the potential difference between the ends of the wire and can be written $\phi_2 - \phi_1$, where ϕ_1 and ϕ_2 are the potentials at the ends. $R = \rho l/A$, where ρ is the resistivity , and $I = \mathrm{d}q/\mathrm{d}t$, where q represents the charge. With these substitutions Ohm's Law becomes:

$$\frac{\mathrm{d}q}{\mathrm{d}t} = \frac{1}{\rho}A\frac{(\phi_2 - \phi_1)}{l}$$

Often this is written in the form: $$\frac{\mathrm{d}q}{\mathrm{d}t} = \sigma A \frac{(\phi_2 - \phi_1)}{l}$$

where σ is defined as $\frac{1}{\rho}$, the electrical conductivity.

The similarity with **thermal conductivity** is then clear:

θ is similar to ϕ and k is similar to σ.

CONDUCTIVITY

Conductivity, σ, is the reciprocal of **resistivity** and has units $\Omega^{-1}\,m^{-1}$.

◄ Conductivity of metals, Electrical conductivity, Thermal conductivity ►

CONDUCTORS AND INSULATORS

For an electric current to flow a conducting material is required. All metals have a low resistivity, making them good conductors, silver and copper being particularly good examples. Materials which have a high resistivity do not conduct electricity and are called insulators. These are usually non-metals or non-ionic materials. The division into conductors and insulators is of course a simplified one. Glass, after all, a good insulator, conducts well near its melting point. Note the position of carbon and the so-called semi-conducting substances on the resistivity chart below.

◄ Conductivity, Resistance, Resistivity ►

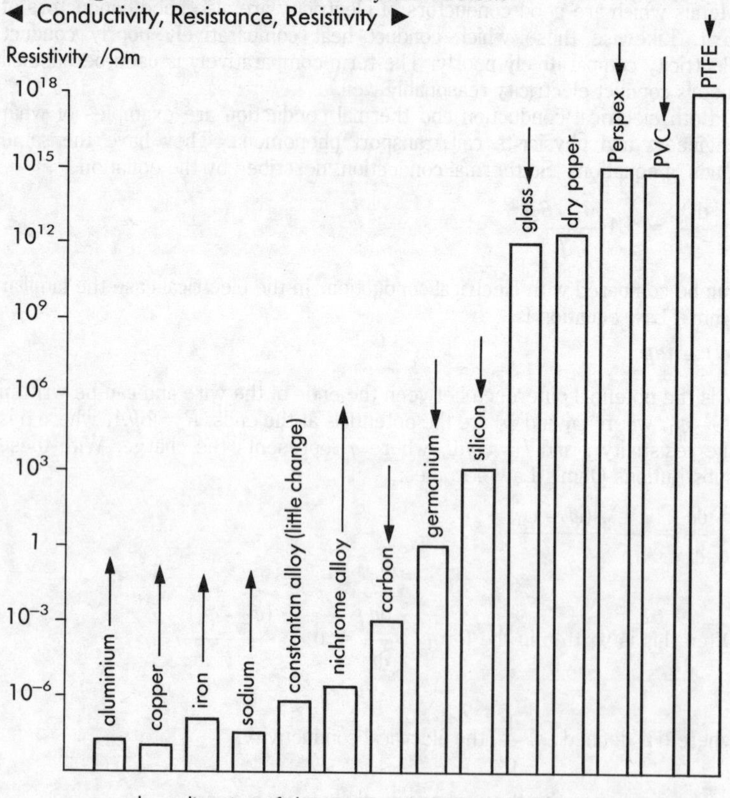

Fig. C.31 The resistivities of different substances

CONSERVATION LAW

A conservation law is a general law in physics which enables us to perform some kind of 'accountancy' to a particular process. Certain physical quantities or attributes of a physical system have to be identified. A conservation law is a general statement about the numerical value of those attributes before and after some physical process.

For example, when a number of particles collide the principle of the conservation of linear **momentum** applies. That is to say we can define an attribute of the particles in the system, namely their linear momentum, and state that the sum of the momenta before the collision process is the same as the momenta after the collision process, provided no external force acts.

The usefulness of a conservation law is that it enables us to make quantitative statements about a physical process even in situations where our detailed knowledge of the interaction may be hazy. There are many examples of conservation laws in physics, e.g. energy, electric charge, **mass**, **angular momentum**, etc. High-energy particle physics has invoked some new conservation laws such as those of strangeness and **charm**.

CONVECTION

Convection is one of the three ways in which heat is transferred from one place to another in a substance. The other two ways are by conduction (see **Conductivities of metals**), and by **radiation**.

Convection is a bodily movement of matter from one place to another carrying heat with it. A good example is the heating of water in a test-tube. If the test-tube is heated near the top of the tube, little heat gets to the bottom. Any that does gets there by the process of conduction, either through the glass of the tube or through the water. But if the bottom of the tube is heated, a great deal of heat is quickly transferred to the top. This is because as water gets hotter at the bottom it expands, becomes less dense than its surroundings and so moves upwards as it has more **buoyancy** than colder water around it, and as it moves it carries its heat with it. This is an example of an upward convection current. (Note however that this doesn't always happen. From 0°C to 4°C water contracts as it gets warmer, so in this temperature range as water is heated there will be downward convection currents, with the coldest water forming at the top.)

Convection currents are important in a wide range of situations: domestic heating, the weather, physical geography, the structure of stars, etc.

CONTINUOUS SPECTRUM

This type of spectrum is that emitted by a very hot body, for example the filament of an incandescent light bulb. It contrasts with a **line spectrum** and a **band spectrum**.

◀ **Emission spectrum** ▶

CONVERGING LENS

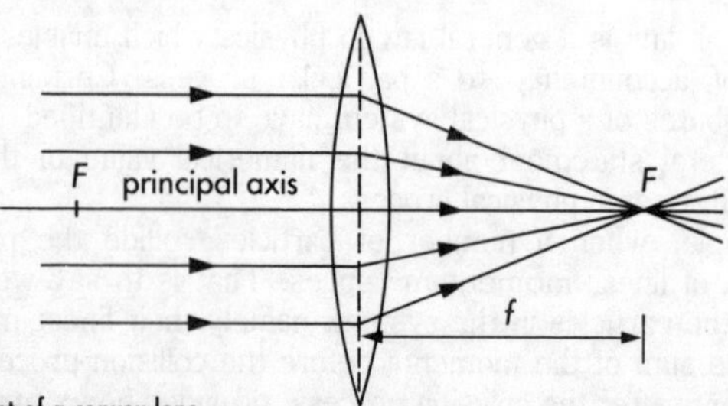

Fig. C.32 Focal point of a convex lens

Rays close to and parallel with the **principal axis** can converge to the focal point (Fig. C.32). The distance from this point to the centre of the lens is the focal length *f*.

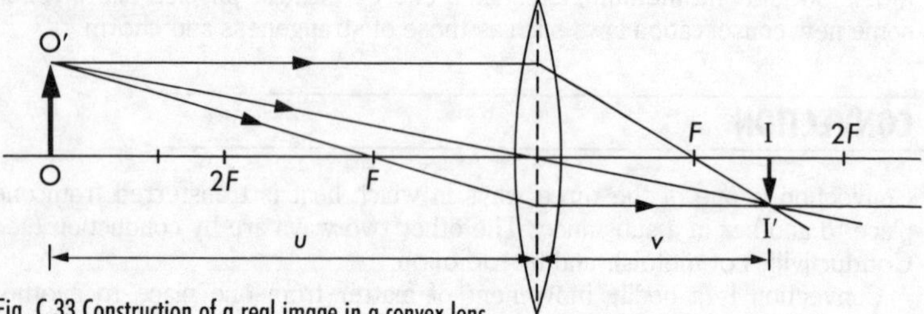

Fig. C.33 Construction of a real image in a convex lens

Fig. C.33 shows the construction of an image I′ formed from an object OO′. Three construction rays have been drawn, one parallel to the axis which is refracted through the **focal point** F on the far side of the lens, one through the focal point on the nearside of the lens which is then refracted parallel to the axis, and one which passes through the centre of the lens and is not refracted at all. All these rays meet at I′, thus defining the image point. Further rays could then be drawn in.

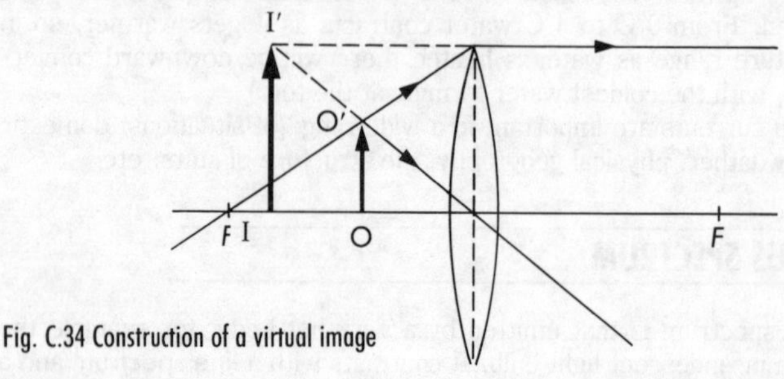

Fig. C.34 Construction of a virtual image

Fig. C.34 shows what happens when an object OO′ is nearer the lens than one focal length. Two constructional rays are drawn and it is seen that this time there is a **virtual image** produced. That is to say that the rays on the far side of the lens are still diverging, and they diverge as if they are coming from an image I′.

The table below summarises the properties of the image of a converging lens for various object distances.

Object distance	*Image distance*	*Nature of image*
infinity	f	real, inverted
greater than $2f$	between f and $2f$	real, inverted, diminished
$2f$	$2f$	real, inverted, same, size as object
between f and $2f$	greater than $2f$	real, inverted, enlarged
f	infinity	no image: parallel rays produced
less than f	greater than object distance	virtual, upright, enlarged image on same side of lens as object

◀ Lens formulae, Real image ▶

CONVEX MIRROR

Rays close to and parallel to the **principal axis** are reflected away from the mirror as if they are coming from a point known as the focal point F (Fig. C.35). The distance between this point and the mirror is called the focal length, f. In the 'real is positive' convention of mirror formulae, such a mirror is said to have a negative focal length.

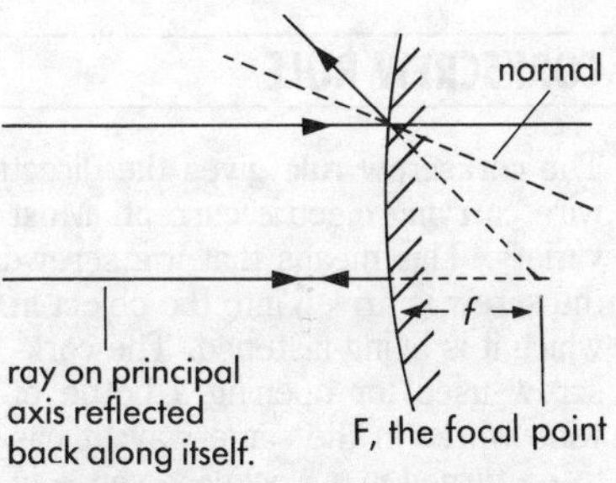

Fig. C.35 A convex mirror and parallel rays

CORIOLIS FORCE

This is the force responsible for the rotation of wind systems round a weather depression. Physicists regard it as a 'fictional force' which results from the rotation of the earth.

Newton's Laws of Motion are applicable only in a frame of reference which itself is not accelerating. A rotating reference frame such as that of the earth is an accelerating reference frame. If a rotating reference frame is used by mistake, it is found that when an attempt is made to apply Newton's laws of motion to a body there are otherwise unexplained forces. An example of such a force is the centrifugal force, which all bodies, whether still or moving in the rotating reference frame, experience. The Coriolis force is a force which only moving bodies experience. It acts at right angles to the direction of motion. For example, in the northern hemisphere winds would simply move towards the centre of a depression if the earth were not rotating. But because it is rotating, as soon as the air starts to move it experiences a force to the left as shown in Fig. C.36 and the net effect is a rotational air movement in a clockwise sense. In the southern hemisphere the force is to the right, giving anticlockwise motion.

◀ Centrifugal and centripetal forces ▶

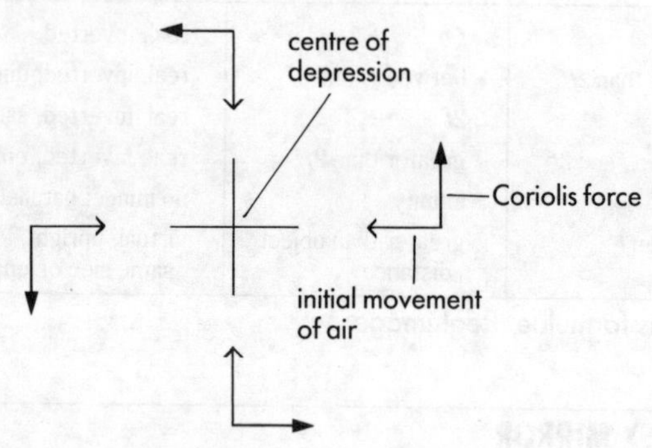

Fig. C.36 Coriolis forces in an air depression (in the northern hemisphere)

CORKSCREW RULE

The corkscrew rule gives the direction of the magnetic field round a single wire carrying electric current. Most screw threads are of the right-handed variety. This means that if a screwdriver is turned in a clockwise direction the screw is driven into the object in which it is being fastened. The cork-screw used for opening a bottle of wine works in the same way: it has to be turned in a clockwise sense in order for the corkscrew to engage the cork. All this is analogous to the behaviour of a magnetic field round an electric current. If the circulation of magnetic field lines is clockwise, current direction is downwards (Fig. C.37).

An equivalent statement is in the form of the right-hand grip rule. This states that you should point your thumb of your right hand in the direction of the electric current, and curl your fingers. The direction of your fingers give the direction of the lines of flux.

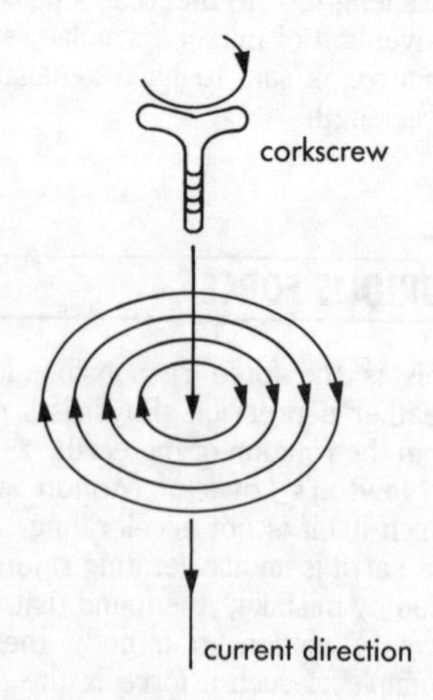

Fig. C.37 Corkscrew rule

COSMIC RAYS

Cosmic rays is a term used to refer to high-energy particles and nuclei arriving at the earth from outer space. Some of these particles interact with matter in the upper atmosphere and give rise to daughter products which penetrate down to the earth's surface. So radiation detected at the earth's surface may itself not have come directly from outer space but be the result of interactions in the upper atmosphere.

COULOMB'S LAW

◀ Inverse square law fields ▶

COULOMB METER

◀ Electrometer, Unity gain voltage follower ▶

COUPLE

This is defined as two equal and opposite parallel forces whose lines of action do not coincide. The moment of a couple is always the same about any fixed point and is always equal to the product of one of the forces and the distance between them (Fig. C.38).

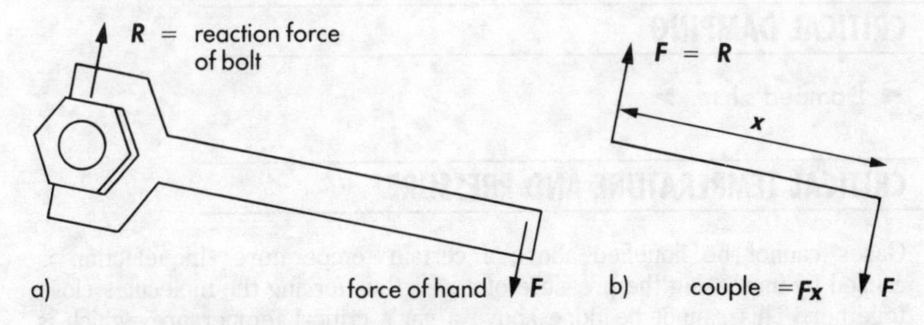

Fig. C.38 Example of a couple: turning a nut on to a bolt

COVALENT BONDING

◀ Solids ▶

CREEP

◀ Solids, properties of ▶

CRITICAL ANGLE

This is a term used in ray optics and wave theory generally. In ray optics if light travels into a medium which is said to be less dense optically, the ray bends away from the normal (Fig. C.39). This is a result of **Snell's Law**. By less dense optically it is meant that the medium into which it is travelling has a higher refractive index than the one from which it has come. The critical angle is reached when the ray emerges just along the boundary. Then:

$$n_2 \sin c = n_1 \sin 90°, \text{ giving } \sin c = \frac{n_1}{n_2}$$

At angles greater than the critical angle the ray cannot emerge and so it is totally internally reflected.

◀ Total internal reflection ▶

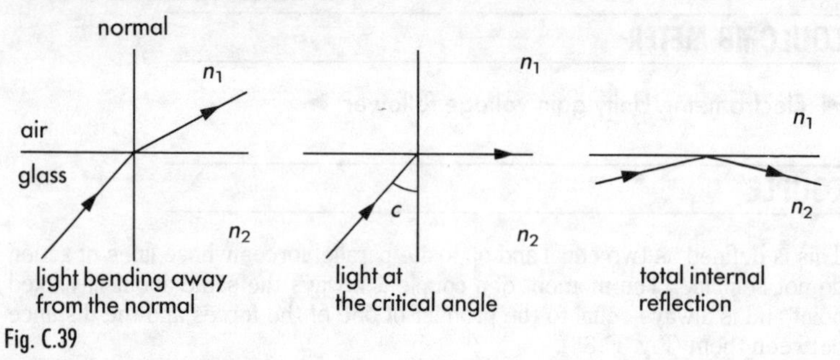

Fig. C.39

CRITICAL DAMPING

◀ Damped s.h.m. ▶

CRITICAL TEMPERATURE AND PRESSURE

Gases cannot be liquefied above a certain temperature. Liquefaction is caused by increasing the pressure of a gas, thus forcing the molecules close together. This cannot be done above a gas's critical temperaure, which is therefore defined as the temperature above which the gas cannot be liquefied by increasing the pressure.

The critical temperature of helium and hydrogen is very low, for helium 5 K and hydrogen 33 K. But gases such as carbon dioxide and ammonia can be liquified at room temperatures, as the critical temperature is much higher.

At the lowest temperature a gas can be liquefied, the critical temperature, the pressure necessary to produce liquefaction is called the critical pressure. For most gases this is several times normal atmospheric pressure.

An **ideal gas** would never liquefy. This ought not to be surprising, as in the model of an ideal gas there is no mechanism by which molecules might join together in a loose arrangement to form a liquid.

CRYSTALS

◀ Solids ▶

CURIE

◀ Radioactivity: units of measurement ▶

CURRENT BALANCE

A current balance uses the fact that adjacent current-carrying conductors exert forces on each other to obtain an absolute measurement of current by weighing.

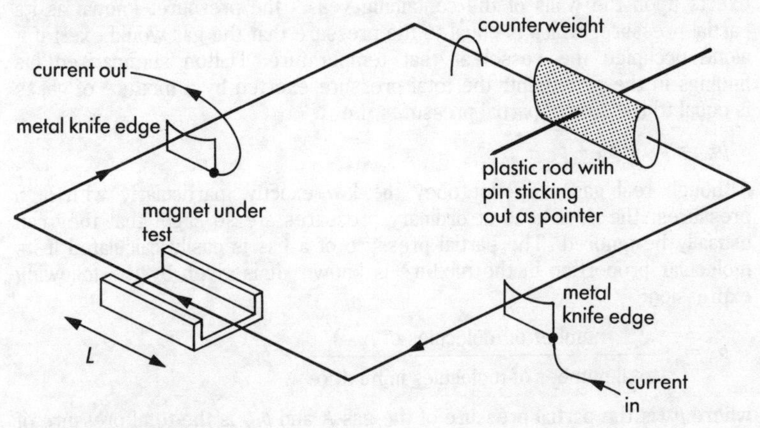

Fig. C.40 Current balance

The kind of current balance used in A-level physics is shown in Fig. C. 40. it consists of a balanced wire frame which is placed in the magnetic field to be measured. The field exerts a vertical force on this side of the frame, which is then rebalanced by placing a counterweight on the frame. In equilibrium the gravitational force which has to be applied is equal to BIL. It is necessary to measure the length of the frame in the field.

The method is suitable only for steady magnetic fields.

◀ Magnetic flux density measurement ▶

DALTON'S LAW OF PARTIAL PRESSURES

This law applies to mixtures of gases. As a result of his experiments on mixtures of gases in 1801, Dalton concluded that each gas in a mixture exerts upon the walls of the containing vessel the pressure, known as its partial pressure, which is equal to the pressure that the gas would exert if it alone occupied the vessel at that temperature. Dalton summarised his findings in the statement: the total pressure exerted by a mixture of gases is equal to the sum of partial pressures, i.e.

$$p_{\mathrm{tot}} = p_{\mathrm{A}} + p_{\mathrm{B}} + p_{\mathrm{C}} + \ldots$$

Although real gases do not obey the law exactly, particularly with high pressures, the deviations at ordinary pressures are so slight that they can ususally be ignored. The partial pressure of a gas is easily calculated if its molecular proportion in the mixture is known. It is given by the following expression:

$$p_{\mathrm{A}} = \frac{\text{number of molecules of A}}{\text{total number of molecules in mixture}} \times p_{\mathrm{tot}}$$

where p_{A} is the partial pressure of the gas A and p_{tot} is the total pressure of the mixture.

◀ Kinetic theory ▶

DAMPED S.H.M.

Most real oscillators are damped, i.e. there is a steady loss of energy as this is converted to other forms, and the amplitude dies away.

Usually the loss of energy is to **internal energy** through the action of frictional or viscous forces, but energy may also be radiated away. A mechanical case of this is the case of a vibrating tuning fork, which loses energy by sound radiation.

An important case of damped **simple harmonic motion** (s.h.m.) occurs when the damping forces are proportional to the velocity, v. This is called *velocity-dependent damping.* In this special case the period remains constant as the amplitude diminishes, a behaviour which is called isochronous. A graph of displacement (x) against time is as shown in Fig. D.1. The dotted curve is of an exponentially diminishing form. This kind of behaviour is very common. An example is the damping of a **ballistic galvanometer**. Unless the damping is considerable, the frequency is not appreciably different from what it would be without any damping.

With heavier damping there are no oscillations and the displacement exponentially diminishes to zero (Fig. D.2). $x = x_o e^{-t/\tau}$ where τ is the time-constant of the system. τ is the time taken for the displacement x to fall to x_o/e, i.e. $0{\cdot}37\ x_o$.

A *critically damped* oscillator is one where the time constant τ takes the minimum value it can without oscillations taking place (Fig. D.3).

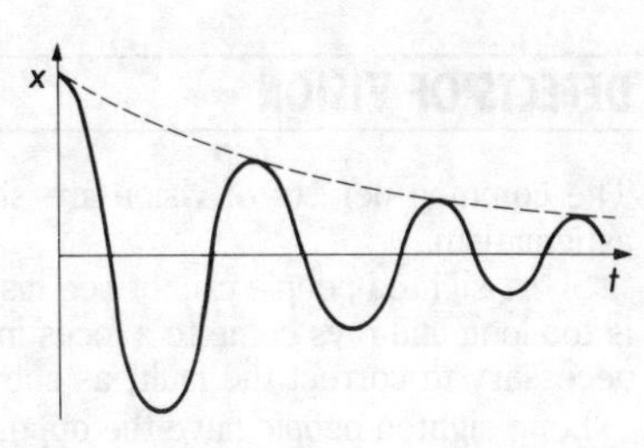

Fig. D.1 Small damping

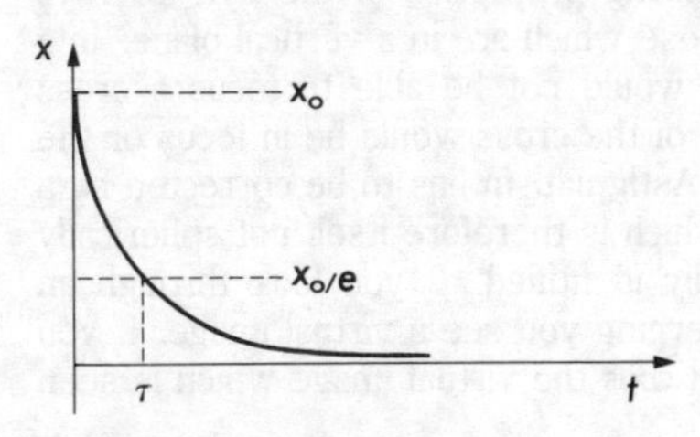

Fig. D.2 Heavy damping showing the significance of the time constant τ

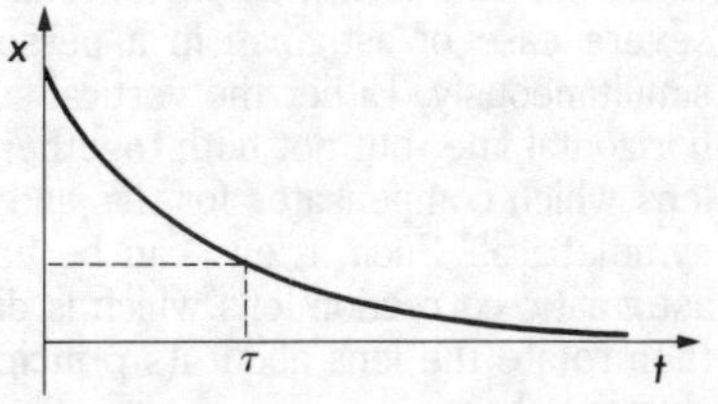

Fig. D.3 Critical damping

DATA LATCH

◀ D-type flip-flop ▶

DAUGHTER PRODUCT

A daughter product, a term used in nuclear physics, is an **isotope** which is produced by the radioactive decay of another, parent, isotope.

D.C. ELECTRIC MOTOR

◀ Direct current electric motor ▶

D. C. POWER SUPPLY

◀ Direct current power supply ▶

DECIBEL

◀ Loudness ▶

DEFECTS OF VISION

The common defects of vision are short-sightedness, long-sightedness and astigmatism.

Short-sighted people cannot see distant objects clearly because the eyeball is too long and rays come to a focus in front of the retina. A **diverging lens** is necessary to correct the fault, as shown in Fig. D.4a).

Long-sighted people have the opposite problem and a **converging lens** has to be placed in front of the eye to correct the fault (Fig. D.4b)).

Astigmatism is caused by the cornea not being perfectly round. As a result there is a difference in the focusing properties of the eye for rays which are in a horizontal plane from those which are in a vertical plane. In a severe case of astigmatism a person would not be able to focus a cross simultaneously. Either the vertical line of the cross would be in focus or the horizontal line, but not both together. Astigmatism has to be corrected by a lens which compensates for this and which is therefore itself not spherically symmetrical. Such a lens can be easily identified. If you look through an astigmatic correction lens which is diverging you see a virtual image. If you then rotate the lens about its **principal axis** the virtual image which is seen changes shape.

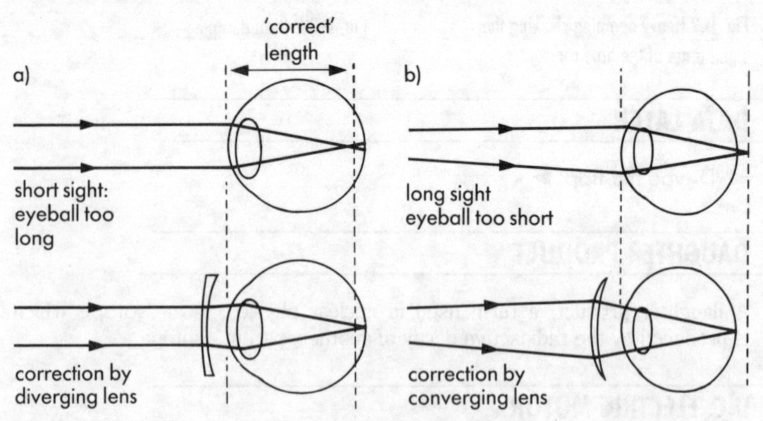

Fig. D.4 a) Short sight is corrected using a diverging lens b) Long sight is corrected using a converging lens

DE BROGLIE

◀ Quantum mechanical model of the atom ▶

DEFLECTION MAGNETOMETER

◀ Magnetic flux density measurement ▶

DEFLECTION OF CHARGED PARTICLES

Charged particles such as high-speed electrons or the alpha and beta emissions of radioactive substances are deflected by both electric and magnetic fields. In experiments on fundamental particles in nuclear and particle physics, say in a **bubble** or **cloud chamber**, measurements of the deflection are made. This is one of the principal ways in which otherwise unknown particles can be identified. The least massive charged particle in nature is the electron and so it is with this particle that the most pronounced deflections occur.

Deflection by electric fields

We shall consider the case of the deflection of an electron by an electric field. Other negatively charged particles, e.g. the μ-meson, will be deflected in a similar way but by a smaller amount because of the greater mass. Positively charged particles, e.g. the proton, will be deflected in an opposite direction. In the school or college laboratory the deflection tube is used to illustrate electron deflection. The treatment of the problem is similar to that of a projectile travelling in a uniform vertical gravitational field in which the horizontal velocity is constant and the vertical motion is subject to a constant downwards acceleration resulting in a parabolic path (see **Projectile motion**).

In Fig. D.5, the electron arrives at the end of the deflecting plates having travelled horizontally with a component of velocity v. While it is between the plates it is in a uniform electric field which exerts a constant force perpendicular to the plates. The field, E, is given by V/d, where V is the p.d. between the plates and d the plate separation. The vertical force experienced by the electron is therefore $Ee = eV/d$. It has a constant vertical acceleration therefore of eV/md while it passes between the plates. As it has initially no velocity perpendicular to the plates we can use the formula for the distance travelled $s = \frac{1}{2}at^2$. This distance s is the vertical deflection which we shall call y.

Thus we get

$$y = \frac{1}{2}\frac{eV}{md}t^2$$

Deflection by magnetic fields

Again we shall consider the case of an electron (Fig. D.6). More massive negatively charged particles will be deflected less but in the same sense, and positively charged particles will be deflected in an opposite direction. As the force is always perpendicular to the direction of travel, the situation is that of

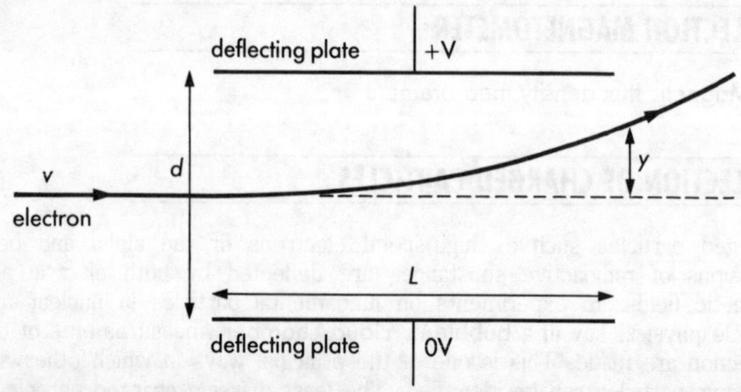

Fig. D.5 Deflection of an electron by an electric field

circular motion in which the acceleration and the force which causes it is perpendicular to the instantaneous direction of travel. An electron thus moves at a constant speed, v, experiencing throughout the whole time a constant force Bev.

Applying Newton's Second Law in the form Force = mass × acceleration, we have $Bev = mv^2/r$. Thus r, the radius of the circle, is given by mv/Be.

An important experiment is that in which the electron is subject to both electric and magnetic fields whose forces are equal and opposite. In such situations the electron is undeflected. This method can be used to measure the charge to mass ratio (specific charge of the electron).

◀ Deflection tube, Force on a charge in a magnetic field ▶

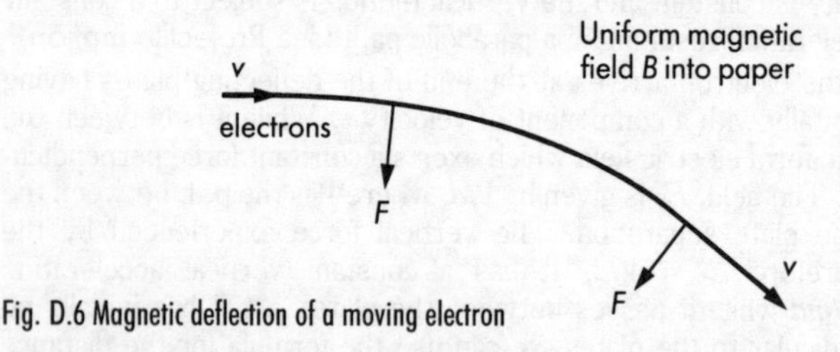

Fig. D.6 Magnetic deflection of a moving electron

DEFLECTION TUBE

The deflection tube is a type of **cathode ray tube** commonly used in schools and colleges to show the way in which an electron can be deflected by an electric field.

Fig. D.7 shows the arrangement of the circuits. The tube itself consists of an evacuated glass vessel at the left-hand end of which are two parallel plates across with a uniform electric field can be applied. These plates are connected up to the terminals of an extra high tension (e.h.t.) supply. The cathode and the anode form an **electron gun** which shoots high-speed electrons into the region between the two plates. The apparatus will show very clearly how the electron is deflected parabolically in the uniform field.

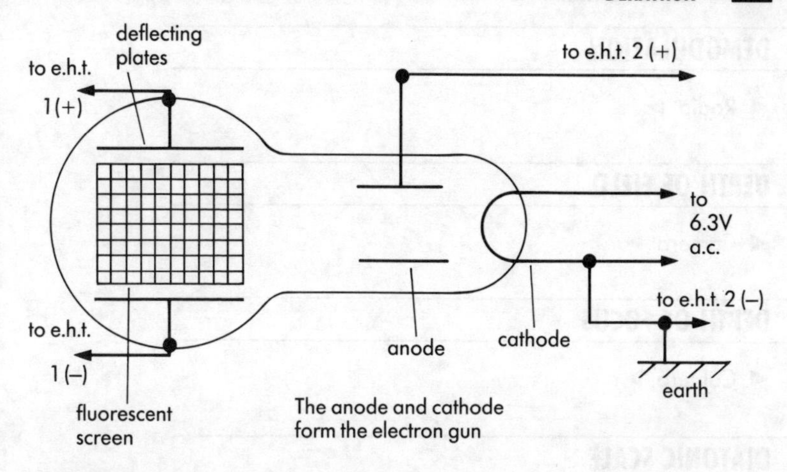

Fig. D.7 Deflection tube

To produce simultaneous deflection by electric and magnetic fields, the beam of electrons is subjected to the electric field applied by the two deflecting plates and an almost uniform field provided by two Helmholtz coils (see **Magnetic field configurations**). The strengths of the two fields are adjusted until the force due to the magnetic field (Bev) must equal the electric field force ($Ee = eV/d$). When this occurs we have $v = V/Bd = E/B$. Here v is the speed of the electron, V the voltage between the plates, and B the strength of the magnetic field provided by the Helmholtz coils. This arrangement enables the velocity v of the electrons to be calculated. But the velocity v of the electrons is given by

$$v = \sqrt{\frac{e}{m} . 2 V_A}$$

where V_A is the potential difference used to accelerate the electron in the electron gun. Hence e/m, the charge to mass ratio of the electron, sometimes called the specific charge of the electron, can be found.

The measurement of the charge to mass ratio of the electron is one of the classic experiments of modern physics, and was first performed by J. J. Thomson. The value of the charge on the electron, e, was found in an another celebrated experiment devised by Millikan. When the results of these two experiments are combined the mass of the electron can be deduced.

DEKATRON

◀ Scaler ▶

DEMODULATION

◀ Radio ▶

DEPTH OF FIELD

◀ Camera ▶

DEPTH OF FOCUS

◀ Camera ▶

DIATONIC SCALE

This is the scale used for most European music.

For musical purposes notes are arranged in groups. Each group lies between upper and lower limits which differ in pitch by an octave. If the frequencies of two notes are in the ratio 1 : 2 the interval between those notes is one octave. For example, Middle C on a piano has a frequency 256 Hz and C one octave above Middle C has frequency 512 Hz.

A group of notes spanning an octave and taken in order constitutes a scale. The selection of the number of notes in the scale and the intervals between them is quite arbitrary. There is an enormous number of scales in use in various parts of the world and clearly an infinite variety is possible. In any scale the group of notes upon which it is based repeats itself in each octave, that is, the interval between any two notes in one octave is the same as that between corresponding notes in another octave.

The diatonic scale between 256 Hz (the keynote) and 512 Hz is shown in the following table. Any frequency could be used for the keynote.

Note	*1 (keynote)*	*2*	*3*	*4*	*5*	*6*	*7*	*8*
		Second	Major third	Fourth	Fifth	Major sixth	Seventh	Octave
Interval from keynote	$\frac{1}{1}$	$\frac{9}{8}$	$\frac{5}{4}$	$\frac{4}{3}$	$\frac{3}{2}$	$\frac{5}{3}$	$\frac{15}{8}$	2
		Major tone	Minor tone	Semi-tone	Major tone	Minor tone	Major tone	Semi-tone
Interval from preceding note	$\frac{1}{1}$	$\frac{9}{8}$	$\frac{10}{9}$	$\frac{16}{15}$	$\frac{9}{8}$	$\frac{10}{9}$	$\frac{9}{8}$	$\frac{16}{15}$
Frequency/Hz	256	288	320	$341\frac{1}{3}$	384	$426\frac{2}{3}$	480	512

Notice that the first two intervals are large, $\frac{9}{8}$ and $\frac{10}{9}$; these are followed by a smaller one $\frac{16}{15}$; the next three intervals are large and the last one small. The small interval, $\frac{16}{15}$ is a semitone; of the large intervals, the bigger, $\frac{9}{8}$, is called a major tone, the lesser, $\frac{10}{9}$, a minor tone.

Suppose a musician wished to change the keynote from 256 Hz to 288 Hz. Remembering that the intervals must remain the same the frequencies of the succeeding notes on the new scale will be 324, 360, 384, 432, 480, 540 and 576 Hz. Apart from the keynote and its octave, the only notes in the second scale having the same frequencies as notes in the first are those at 384 Hz and 480 Hz. With a violin or a sliding trombone, where the player actually makes his own notes, the intervals may be produced just as accurately in one key as in another. But using an instrument in which the notes are made for the player, such as a piano or a harp, it would appear that additional notes ought to be provided for every fresh key. This would render the instrument impossibly complicated and in order to overcome the difficulty many modifications to the scale have been suggested. The one which is normally used is the *equitempered scale*, in which the octave is divided into twelve equally spaced, or equitempered, semitones. The ratio of the frequencies of two notes a semitone apart will be $1 : \sqrt[12]{2}$ or 1 : 1·0594. The distinction between a major and minor tone is waived; they are both regarded as full tones and the interval between them is $\sqrt[6]{2}$.

The pattern of notes is shown below with frequencies, assuming a keynote of 256 Hz.

Note	*1 (keynote)*	*2*	*3*	*4*	*5*	*6*	*7*	*8*
Interval from keynote . .	1	$\sqrt[6]{2}$	$\sqrt[3]{2}$	$\sqrt[12/5]{2}$	$\sqrt[12/7]{2}$	$\sqrt[12/9]{2}$	$\sqrt[12/11]{2}$	2
Interval from preceding note	1	Full tone $\sqrt[6]{2}$	Full tone $\sqrt[6]{2}$	Semi-tone $\sqrt[12]{2}$	Full tone $\sqrt[6]{2}$	Full tone $\sqrt[6]{2}$	Full tone $\sqrt[6]{2}$	Semi-tone $\sqrt[12]{2}$
Frequency/Hz	256	287.3	322.5	341.7	383.5	430.5	483.2	512

DIFFERENCE GATE

◀ Logic gates ▶

DIFFERENTIAL AMPLIFIER

◄ Operational amplifier ►

DIFFRACTION

When a wave meets an obstacle it does not simply go straight past, it bends round the obstacle. The same type of effect occurs at an aperture: the waves spread out the other side of the hole. This phenomenon is known as diffraction. The effects of diffraction become appreciable if the size of the object is small. By small we mean approximately the same size as the wavelength of the waves. A given size of obstacle will diffract a wave of long wavelength more than the shorter one.

One of the most powerful pieces of evidence for light being some form of wave motion is that it shows diffraction. The problem with light which led Newton to reject the wave theory is that the wavelength is very small, approximately 600 nm, and therefore diffraction effects are hard to observe. In spite of this, diffraction phenomena are common experiences: examples are the pattern of a street light when it is seen through the fabric of a stretched umbrella and the spreading of light round your eyelashes.

Physicists define two distinct types of diffraction:

i) *Fresnel diffraction*, produced when light from a point source meets an obstacle, the waves being spherical. The pattern observed is a fringed image of the object.

ii) *Fraunhofer diffraction*, which occurs with plane wavefronts, the object being effectively at infinity. The pattern is in a particular direction and is a fringed image of the source. In A-level physics all the examples of diffraction are those of Fraunhofer diffraction.

At a simple level diffraction can be understood using Huygens' method of secondary wavelets. This is shown in Fig. D.8. The idea of Huygens is that each point on a wavefront acts as a point source of waves. Consequently in a uniform medium each point source acts as a source of circular waves. Huygens proposed that to find the wavefront resulting from such a collection of secondary sources all that was necessary was to draw the circular waves and find the geometrical 'envelope' of them. The geometrical envelope is the line which runs through the region where all the circular waves come together. This is done in Fig. D.8, which shows that the wavefront is almost plane in front of the aperture but bends round into the region of geometrical shadow. In mathematical physics Huygens' method is replaced by calculations in which the disturbance at any point is found by integrating mathematical expressions for the waves, starting from each of the secondary 'point' sources.

◄ Diffraction from a circular aperture, Diffraction from a single slit, Diffraction from multiple slits ►

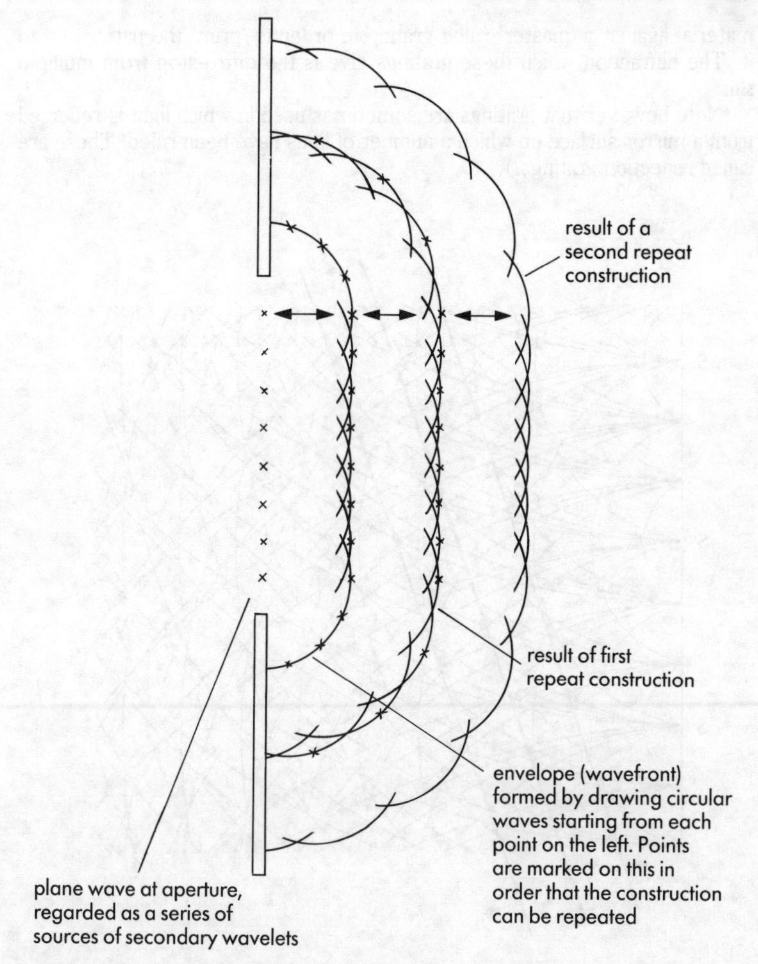

Fig. D.8 Huygens' construction for diffraction at an aperture

DIFFRACTION GRATING

A diffraction grating consists of many thousands of equally wide and equally spaced parallel slits (typically 300 per mm) at which radiation undergoes **diffraction**. The most usual kind of grating used in school is a transmission grating, where the incident beam is usually directed along a normal to the grating, and the radiation passes through it.

Gratings like this are made on a ruling machine. Cheaper gratings, sometimes called replica gratings, are made by pressing a piece of plastic material against a 'master' ruled grating in order to 'print' the pattern on to it. The diffraction which these gratings give is the **diffraction from multiple slits.**

(Note however that gratings are sometimes used in which light is reflected from a mirror surface on which a number of lines have been ruled. These are called reflection gratings.)

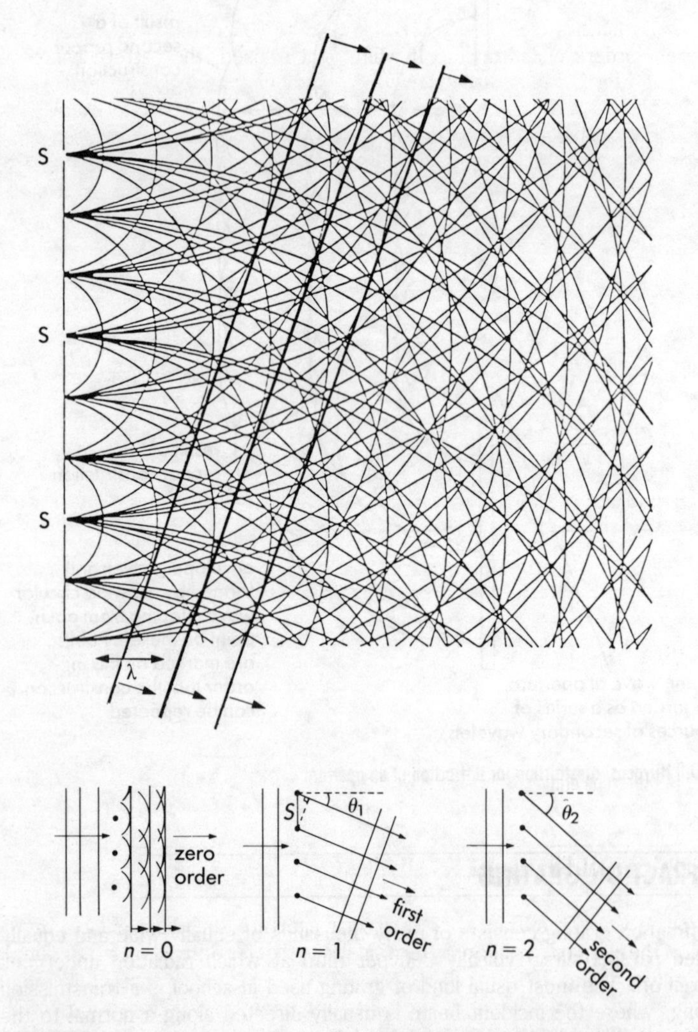

Fig. D.9 The working of a diffraction grating. Circular waves of wavelength λ have been drawn from each slit. Three straight lines have been drawn where all the wavefronts are in step. This gives the direction of first-order diffraction. Further changes of angle should reveal the other orders as below

TERMINOLOGY

The positions of the maxima of interference are governed by the equation

$\sin\theta = n\lambda/s$

Where s is the slit separation, and these maxima are known as orders (n).

When $n = 1$, the path difference between adjacent slits in the grating is one wavelength. This is known as first-order diffraction (Fig. D.9). If monochromatic light is used, very bright and sharp images will be seen at the different orders of diffraction. If white light is used, the pattern will be as shown in Fig. D.10, and there may be overlapping between the ends of the spectra of adjacent orders.

The principal use of the diffraction grating is for the accurate determination of wavelengths of light sources using a **spectrometer**, and for the analysis of the spectra of light from a particular source, e.g. the light from stellar sources.

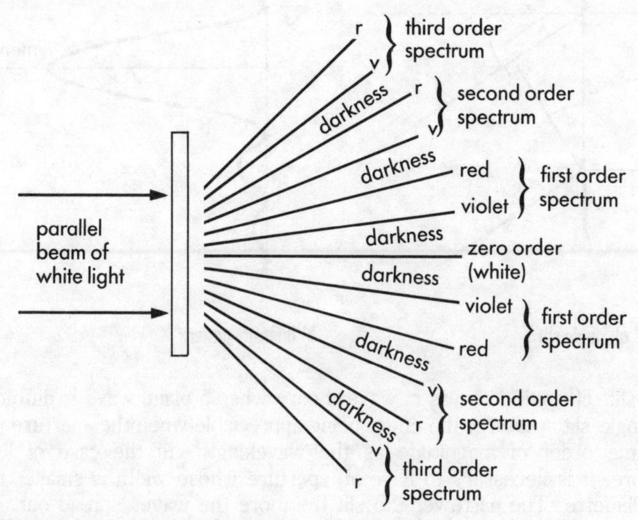

Fig. D.10 Diffraction grating and white light

DIFFRACTION FROM A CIRCULAR APERTURE

If a plane wave is diffracted by a circular aperture such as a pinhole or the pupil of the eye, a **diffraction** pattern similar to that for **diffraction from a single slit** occurs. The difference is that instead of a series of parallel fringes a bright central circular patch is seen, surrounded by alternate dark and bright rings. The slightly different geometry gives the formula for the first diffraction minimum to be at an angle θ given by $\sin\theta = 1{\cdot}22\,\lambda/d$, where λ is the wavelength and d the hole diameter.

This has an application in the theory of vision. The image of a 'point' object on the retina of the eye is not a point but a circular patch surrounded by rings. So if the eye is looking at two point objects close together their images will be close together on the retina and the circular patches will overlap. As a result, if they are very close together the observer may appear to see them as only one object.

◀ Diffraction from a single slit, Rayleigh's criterion ▶

DIFFRACTION FROM A SINGLE SLIT

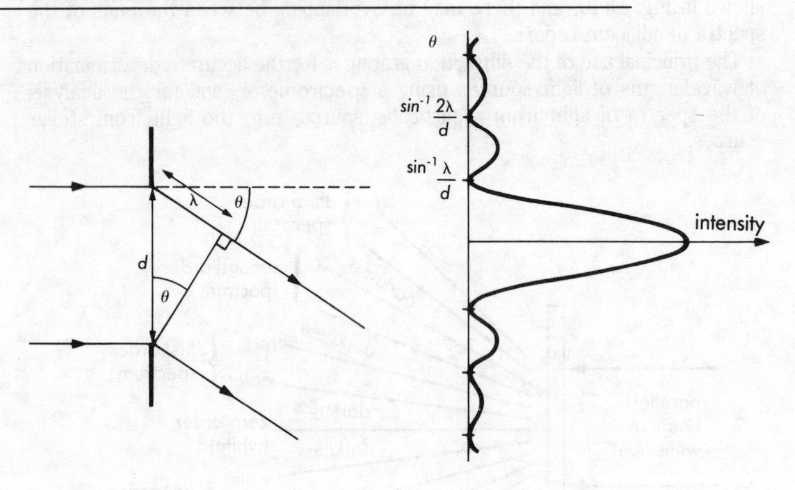

Fig. D.11 a) Single slit b) Intensity pattern

Single-slit **diffraction** occurs in wave theory when a plane wave is diffracted by a single-slit aperture, the effect being appreciable when the aperture is of the same order of magnitude as the wavelength. In the case of light, therefore, it is necessary to have an aperture whose width is smaller than 0·1 millimetre. The narrower the slit the more the waves spread out. The resulting intensity pattern is shown in Fig. D.11b). Zeros of intensity are found at angles θ described by the equation

$$\sin\theta = n\lambda/d$$

where n is an integer. The characteristic feature of the pattern is one of a central broad band which has twice the width of the secondary bands on either side.

The intensity distribution of the light is described by the formula

$$I = I_{\max}\left(\frac{\sin\alpha}{\alpha}\right)^2$$

where $I_{\max}$ is the maximum intensity (at the centre of the pattern), I is the intensity at an angle θ from the central maximum and $\alpha = \frac{\pi d \sin\theta}{\lambda}$, where d is the width of the slit, and λ is the wavelength.

This shows that the first 'secondary' maximum has an intensity of less than 10 per cent of that at the centre of the pattern.

◀ Diffraction from a circular aperture, Rayleigh's criterion ▶

DIFFRACTION FROM MULTIPLE SLITS

Fig. D.12 shows plane waves of light, i.e. parallel rays incident upon a grating with a number of slits laid out with a regular spacing. At each slit the light undergoes **diffraction,** the intensity of the light being sent in any direction being determined by the formula for the pattern of **diffraction from a single slit.** The light diffracted from any individual slit at a particular angle then interferes with the other diffracted beams from other slits at that same angle, and a characeristic interference pattern of alternate maximum and minima results. The net effect is an interference pattern which is characteristic of the number of slits and the spacing between them modulated by the diffraction pattern of a single slit with the same width of the slits used.

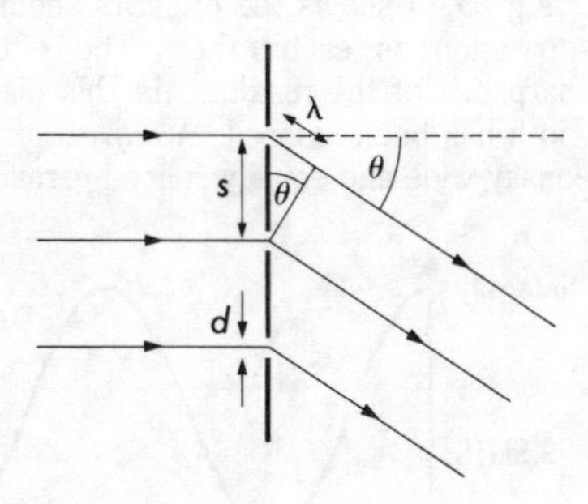

Fig. D.12 Several slits

Fig. D.13 shows this pattern. The condition for the maxima is that the path difference between the waves passing through adjacent slits is a whole

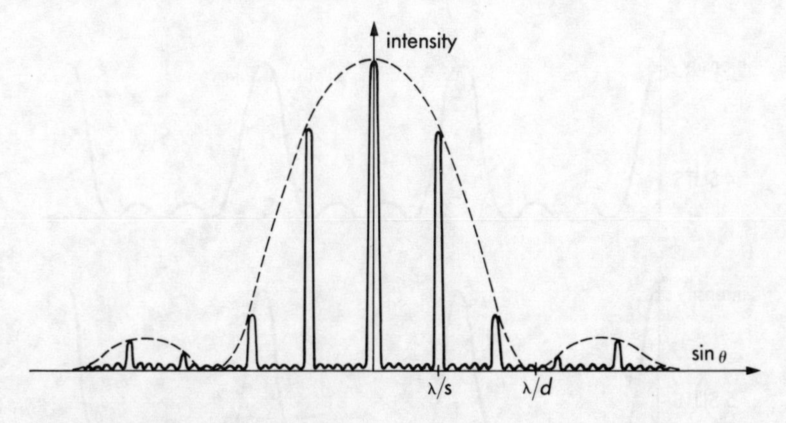

Fig. D.13 Intensity pattern with several slits

number of wavelengths, n, and so these maxima occur at angles θ which are given by the equation

$$\sin\theta = n\lambda/s$$

i.e. their positions are governed by the separations, s, of the slits. The diagram shows clearly the modulation of the overall intensity by the single-slit pattern, the first minimum of which is given by

$$\sin\theta = \lambda/d$$

and is determined by the width d of the slits.

Fig. D.14 shows the effect of adding progressively more slits of the same separation as each other. The effect is progressively to increase the sharpness of the maxima. In this diagram the modulating effect of the slit width has been ignored. A *diffraction grating* consists of many thousands of equally wide and equally spaced parallel slits.

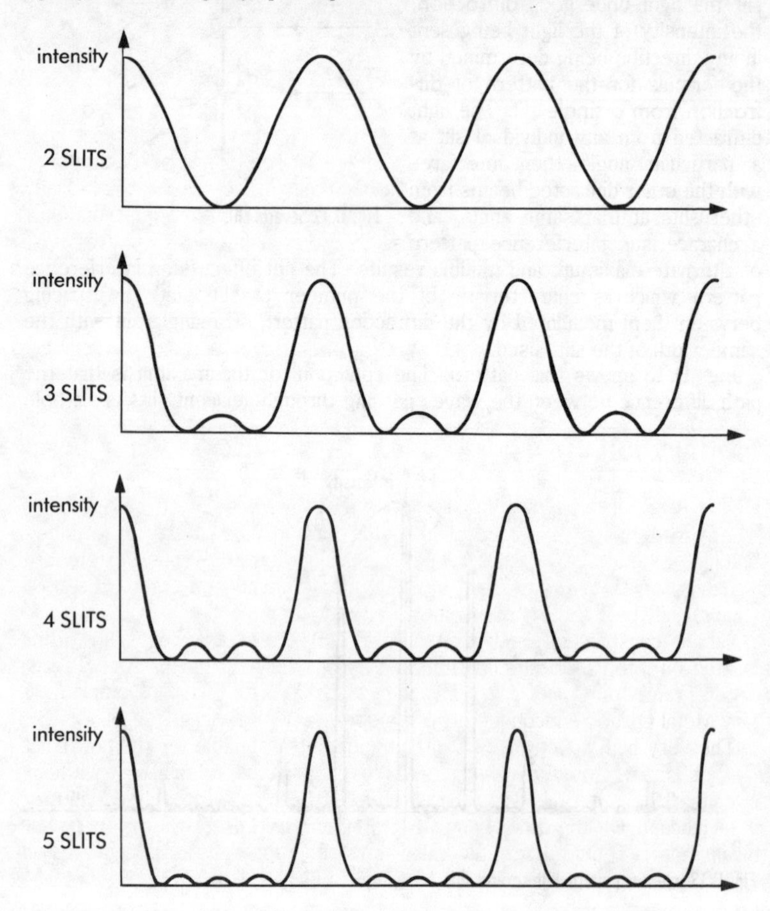

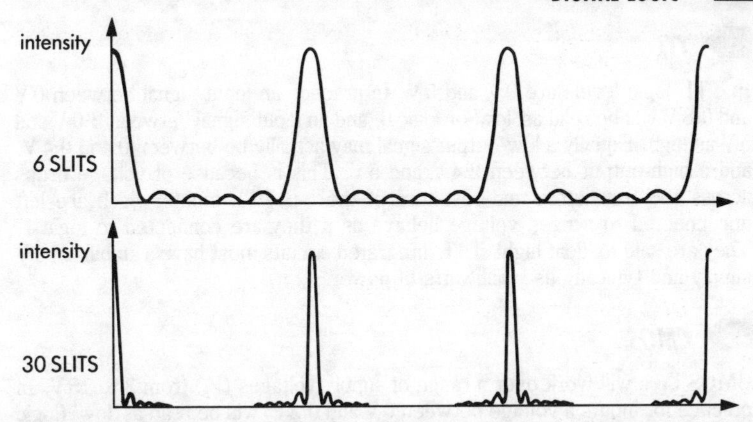

Fig. D.14 How increasing the number of slits in a grating gradually increases the sharpness of the 'images'

DIFFUSION

Diffusion is a term used to describe the spreading of one substance into another. Because of movements at the molecular level a number of atoms or molecules of substance A introduced into another substance B will gradually spread out until they are evenly spread throughout the 'host' environment. The phenomenon takes place most rapidly in gases, more slowly in liquids, and very slowly indeed, if at all, in solids. Even in gases the process takes some time because of the random collisions of the molecules with each other. Measurements of the speed of diffusion, and the differences between the behaviour of gases of different molecular weights at the same temperature, are in agreement with theoretical predictions made by **kinetic theory**.

DIGITAL LOGIC

Digital logic or **combinational logic** is concerned with electronic systems where input voltages are supplied to logic components either at a 'high'-voltage state or a 'low' state. The output voltages of the system are also high or low. For positive logic the high-voltage state is represented algebraically by 1 and the low-voltage state by 0.

Circuit construction is carried out by connecting together **logic gates** located on **integrated circuits** (i.c.s). Typically these might be TTL (Transistor-Transistor Logic, e.g. 7400 series) devices or CMOS (Complementary Metal Oxide Semiconductor, e.g. 4000B series) devices.

The very high speed of TTL circuitry makes it suitable for the construction of large computers which need to contain several million switching circuits. This is because the time taken for data to pass through a computer is significant. On the other hand CMOS circuits are used where low-power dissipation is required, e.g. in calculators, microprocessors and in certain kinds of memory circuits.

TTL

In TTL logic levels are 0 V and 5 V. In practice an input signal between 0 V and 0·8 V will be read as 'low' or logic 0, and an input signal between 2·0 V and 5 V as high. Equally a low-output signal may actually be between 0 and 0·4 V, and a high-output between 2·4 V and 5 V. This is because of voltage drops across the transistors and resistors of the i.c. TTL inputs which are left unconnected to a fixed voltage behave as if they are connected to logic 1. They are said to 'float high'. TTL integrated circuits must have a stabilised 5 V supply and typically use milliwatts of power.

CMOS

CMOS i.c.s will work over a range of supply voltages (V_s) from 3 to 15 V. In practice for inputs a voltage between 0 V and 0·3 V_s will be read as 'low' (logic 0), and a voltage between 0·7 V_s and V_S as high. The output values for the low and high states are more or less attained. CMOS i.c.s typically use microwatts of power. Switching speeds are lower than with TTL.

◀ Sequential logic ▶

DIGITAL METERS

◀ Ammeters and voltmeters ▶

DIMENSIONS

The dimensions of a quantity show how it is related to the seven basic quantities (which are mass, length, time, electric current, temperature, luminous intensity and amount of a substance). All other quantities are derived from one or more of these basic quantities. If an equation is correct the dimensions of the quantities on either side must be identical, a fact which is used in the method of dimensional analysis.

As an example consider speed. Speed is measured in m s^{-1}. The metres and the seconds are the units we use in the SI system. In everyday life we might measure speed in miles per hour and so use the units miles and hours. But both metres and miles are lengths: we say they have the dimensions of length, written [L]. Equally seconds and hours have the units of time, written [T]. So the dimensions of speed are $[L]\,[T]^{-1}$.

Dimensional analysis is the method of solving problems by finding the fundamental dimensions of, say, one side of an equation and equating it to the dimensions on the other side. For example, the potential energy V between a pair of neutral molecules whose centres are a distance r apart may be represented by

$$V = \frac{A}{r^{12}} + Be^{\lambda r^2}$$

Let us find the dimensions of the constants A, B and λ. Both the terms on the right-hand side of the equation must have the dimensions of potential energy. The dimensions of potential energy, $[V]$, are those of force × distance, i.e.

$$[V] = [F] \times [L]$$

where [L] represents the dimension of length and [F] the dimensions of force. The dimensions of force are those of mass × acceleration. So

$$\begin{aligned} [F] &= [M]\,[L]\,[T]^{-2} \\ \text{so } [A/r^{12}] &= [M]\,[L]^2\,[T]^{-2} \\ [A] &= [M]\,[L]^2[T]^{-2}[L]^{12} \\ &= [L]^{14}\,[M]\,[T]^{-2} \end{aligned}$$

$e^{\lambda r^2}$ is a pure number and therefore dimensionless, so the dimensions of B are the same as those of V, i.e.

$$[B] = [M]\,[L]^2\,[T]^{-2}$$

λr^2, the argument of the exponential function must also be dimensionless, so

$$[\lambda] = [L]^{-2}.$$

DIODE

The diode is a two-terminal device which allows current to flow freely in one direction but not in the opposite direction. The first diodes consisted of two metal electrodes in an evacuated glass envelope. Modern diodes are made of a semiconductor material and are thus smaller and cheaper to produce.

A semiconductor diode consists of two interconnected slices of semiconducting material, usually silicon, one of a doped p-type material, i.e. one in which conduction is effectively by positive charges, and one of doped n-type material in which conduction is by electrons. A circuit to show how the characteristics of the diode might be determined is shown in Fig. D.15. Note that in order to measure the characteristics a high-impedance voltmeter has to be used. (If an ordinary low-impedance meter were used the milliameter would record the current passing through the voltmeter when the diode was in a non-conducting mode.) Note also that in order to get full characteristic it is necessary to reverse the polarity of the power supply. The characteristic curve (Fig. D.16) shows clearly that the device is non-Ohmic. The low forward resistance and the high reverse resistance is clearly shown. Note that a forward voltage of at least 0·7 volts is required before the diode will conduct.

Semiconductor diodes are marked with a ring to mark the cathode.

◀ Direct current power supply, Light-emitting diode, Thermionic emission, Transistor, Zenner diode ▶

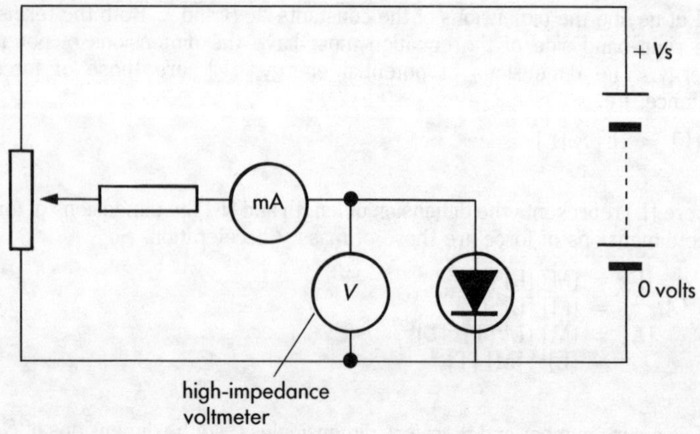

Fig. D.15 Determination of diode characteristics

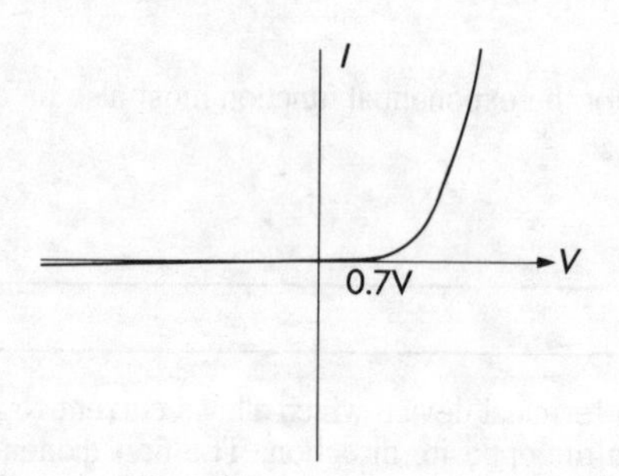

Fig. D.16 Diode characteristics

DIPOLE

As the name implies a dipole consists of two poles. There are two types of dipole: electric ones and magnetic ones.

Those found in electrostatics consist of a positive and negative charge slightly separated from each other. A molecule which is polarised is also an example of a dipole. By a polarised molecule we mean that its net charge is zero but the distribution of charge is such that at one end of the molecule there is an overall positive charge and that at the other end there is an overall negative charge. A magnetic dipole has a common example in the bar magnet with its characteristic north and south poles.

The characteristic features of dipoles is that when placed in a field to which they are sensitive, an electric dipole in an electric field and a magnetic dipole in a magnetic field, they experience a couple causing them to rotate.

◀ Inverse square law fields, Magnetic field configurations ▶

DIRECT CURRENT (d.c.)

Direct current always flows in the same direction round a circuit. The most common way of supplying this is from a battery. The voltage driving the current is usually constant, but many power supplies are not really able to provide this, especially when the current is large, and the current is then direct but not 'smooth'. See **Rectifier.**

◀ Alternating current, Current, Direct current electric motor, Direct current power supply ▶

DIRECT CURRENT ELECTRIC MOTOR

Electric motors supply the motion in a whole host of devices both in the home and engineering; for example, vacuum-cleaners, hair-driers, water-pumps and locomotives. The best way of understanding an electric motor in a school or college is to make one using the parts in the Westminster electromagnetic kit.

To make the motor an insulated shaft is pushed through the wooden block and a number of turns, N, of insulated copper wire wound round it in order to make a flat square coil. The two ends of the wire are bared, looped, and secured underneath a piece of valve rubber tubing. The coil forms the armature of the motor. It is then assembled between the two poles of a magnet (Fig. D.17). In the Westminster kit ceramic magnadur magnets are used to make this U-shaped magnet. The magnadurs have poles on their flat faces. The external power supply is then fed to the coil using two wires which form 'brushes'.

The brushes and loops of bare wire are the key to the operation of the motor. They provide a simple form of the split-ring *commutator* which is used in more sophisticated motors. When current is supplied, a couple is exerted on the coil of an amount $BANI \cos \theta$, where B is the field, A the area of the armature, and θ the angle between the field lines and the plane of the coil (Fig. D.18).

The coil rotates through an angle until the coil faces are facing the poles of the magnet. But its own momentum carries it on and as it goes on turning it should be clear that the connections provided by the split-ring commutator are reversed. This is shown in Fig. D.19, and an end-on view shown in Fig. D.20. When AB reaches the bottom of its rotation the two half rings reverse the positive and negative sides of the circuit. As a result the current in AB now flows from B to A and the force upon it is upwards. Similarly BC moves down, so that the constant rotation is achieved.

More sophisticated motors may have several coils each connected to the contacts of a multi-faced commutator. In addition there is usually an electro-magnet in place of the permanent magnet used in the Westminster model. The magnet windings may be in series with that of the coil, in which case the motor is called a *series-wound motor*, or they may be in parallel, in which case it is called a *shunt-wound motor*.

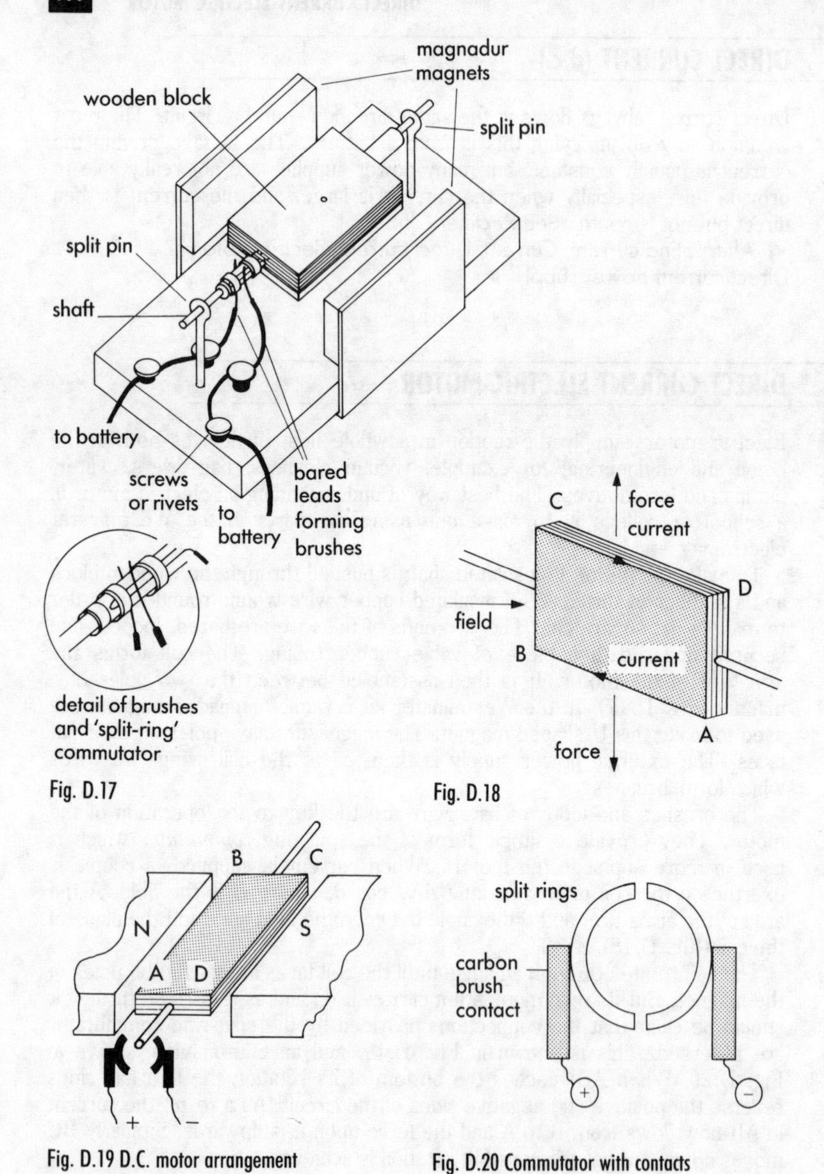

Fig. D.17

Fig. D.18

Fig. D.19 D.C. motor arrangement

Fig. D.20 Commutator with contacts

Steadiness of speed

As the motor speeds up, an increasing back e.m.f. is generated. It settles down at a speed such that the back e.m.f. is slightly less than the applied p.d. For example, a motor on a 100V supply might have a back e.m.f. of 99V. As the load on the motor increases the armature current rises to provide extra torque: this is done by a fall in speed to reduce the back e.m.f.

For a given motor: $E \propto N w$ where E is the back e.m.f., N is the magnetic flux (BA) and w is the speed in radians per second. On a shunt-wound motor N is constant and therefore $E \propto w$. Thus an increase in load is accompanied by a fall in speed, and as long as the motor is not overloaded the speed is steady. On a series-wound motor the field current is the same as the armature current. Any change in E is small. Therefore Nw is constant. N is proportional to the current I, and therefore w is proportional to $1/I$. Therefore if the current has to double to cope with an increased load the speed has to drop to nearly one half of its earlier value. Such a motor is very unstable.

◀ Induction motors ▶

DIRECT CURRENT POWER SUPPLY

Many domestic appliances use electronic circuits which require a low-voltage d.c. power supply. It is therefore necessary to use a step-down **transformer** and to rectify the a.c. supply.

The simplest way to rectify a.c. is to use a single silicon **diode** (Fig. D.21). Current flows only when A is positive with respect to B, as shown. This is called **half-wave rectification.**

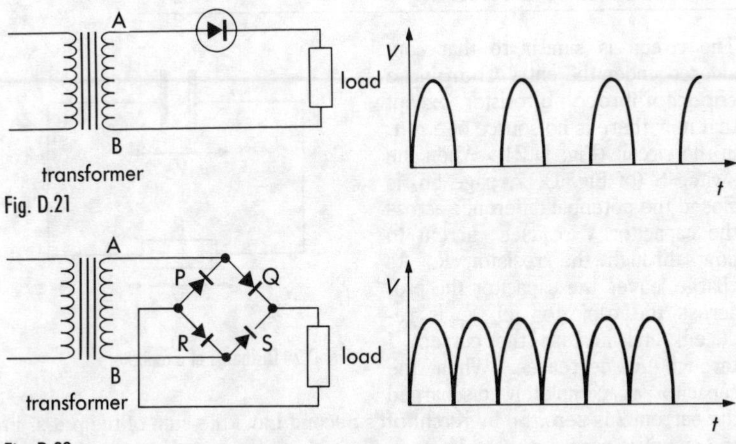

Fig. D.21

Fig. D.22

More commonly a *bridge rectifier* circuit is used (Fig. D.22). If A is positive with respect to B, current flows by the route Q–load–R, and if B is positive with respect to A by the route S–load–P. The wave form now includes every half-cycle and this is called **whole-wave rectification.**

The current is now rectified but is not smoothed. A large **capacitor** across the output terminals of the bridge rectifier helps to keep the voltage 'topped up' when the rectified supply falls to zero (Fig. D.23). The current is then smoothed. Note that the ripple voltage is twice the mains frequency.

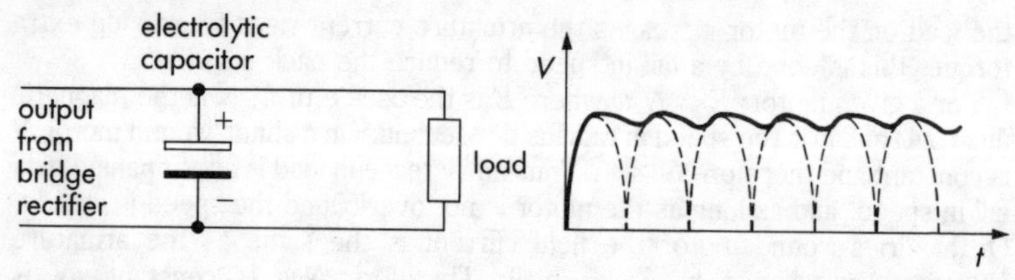

Fig. D.23

These circuits can also be used for converting d.c. moving-coil meters into **alternating current meters.**

◀ Alternating current ▶

DIRECTION RULES

This is a general name given to rules in the theory of electromagnetism for determining the directions of induced electric currents, forces on wires, etc. An example is the **corkscrew rule** (Maxwell's corkscrew rule) and **Fleming's left-hand rule.**

DISCHARGE OF A CAPACITOR

The circuit is similar to that considered under the entry **Charging a capacitor through a resistor**, except that now there is no source of e.m.f. in the circuit (Fig. D.24). When the switch S (of Fig. C.17, page 56) is closed the potential difference across the capacitor V_c causes current to flow through the resistor R. As charge leaves the capacitor the p.d. across the capicator for V_c is reduced, and in turn the current I through R decreases. When the capacitor is completely discharged the current I is zero. So by **Kirchhoff's** Second Law, the sum of the p.d.s. in the circuit is zero, i.e. $V_c + V_R = 0$. This gives $V_R = -V_c$, and writing IR for V_R and Q/C for V_c we have $IR = -Q/C$, giving $I = -Q/RC$.

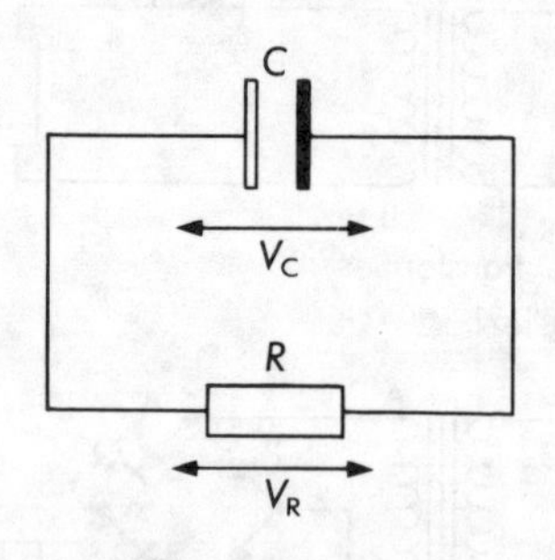

Fig. D.24 Discharge of a capacitor

Note that the minus sign indicates that Q is decreasing. $I = \mathrm{d}Q/\mathrm{d}t$ and so we have

$$\frac{\mathrm{d}Q}{\mathrm{d}t} = -\frac{Q}{RC}$$

the solution of which is

$$Q = Q_0\,\mathrm{e}^{-t/RC}$$

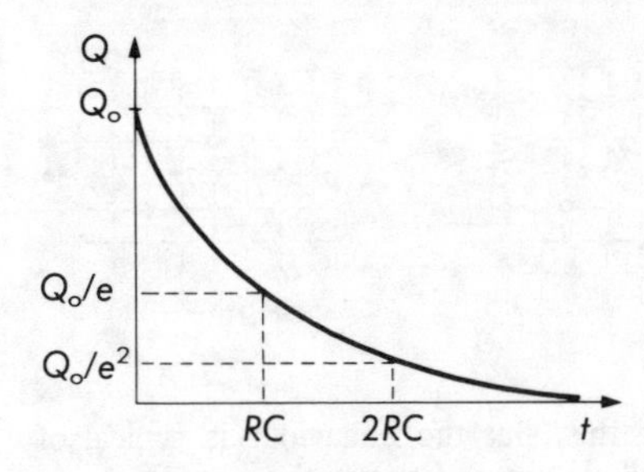

Fig. D.25 Graph of charge against time

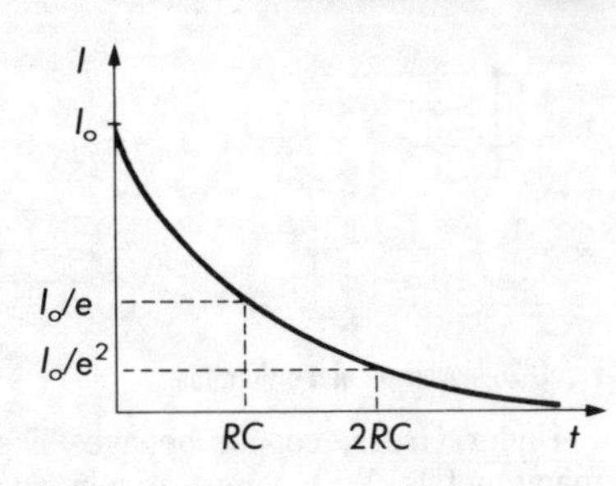

Fig. D.26 Graph of current against time

where Q_0 is the charge on the capacitor at time $t = 0$. The graph of Q against t is a falling exponential graph with **time constant** $\tau = RC$ (Fig. D.25).

The variation of current, I, with time is given by

$$I = I_0 \, e^{-t/RC}$$

The graph of this is shown in Fig. D.26.

Note that the total area under the current curve $= \int I \mathrm{d}t = Q_0$, the initial charge of the capacitor.

◀ Integrating and differentiating circuits ▶

DISLOCATIONS

Dislocations are the sites of missing atomic planes in a crystal structure.

Fig. D.27 shows such a structure with a missing atom, together with the overall picture of the crystal lattice that this absence produces. You should imagine that there are layers and layers of atoms beneath the diagram, so that it is not just one atom which is missing but a whole line of them, and hence a whole plane.

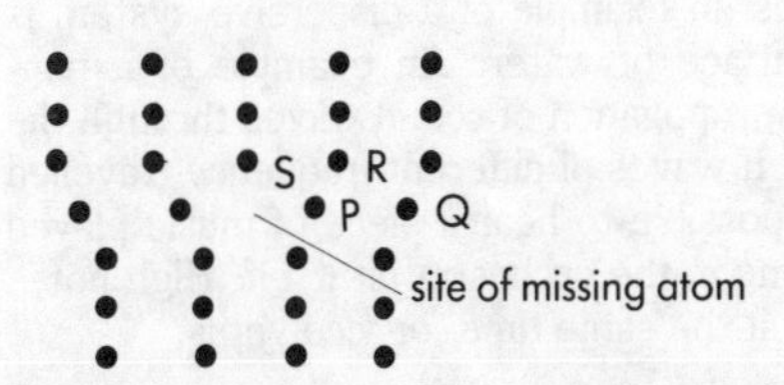

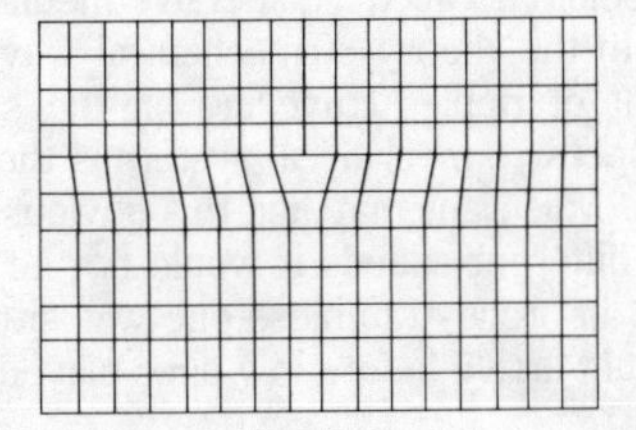

Fig. D.27 Dislocation in a lattice

In the diagram, atom P is a nearest neighbour of atom R. If P moves left into the site of the missing plane it becomes a nearest neighbour of S, and the dislocation moves to the site between P and Q. The whole process can then be repeated with Q. The overall effect is a gradual relative shift of the two layers. This effect is shown in Fig. D.28.

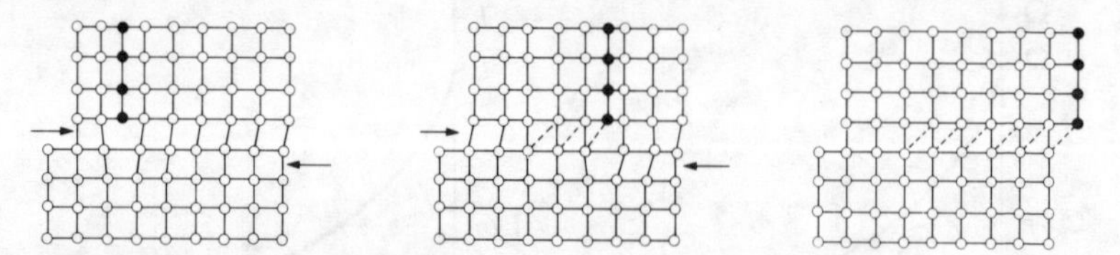

Fig. D.28 Movement of a dislocation

Under stress, copper behaves like this, but the behaviour is typical of many metals. With comparatively small amounts of stress the copper atoms remain in a regular arrangement in the crystal structure, and the stress acts against the strong attractive forces between nearest neighbours. With more stress plasticity occurs, layers of atoms slipping over each other. The mechanism for this process is the movement of 'dislocations'. Little energy is required for each slippage, which is one reason why the process takes place readily.

DISPERSION

When white light passes through a prism the beam is split up into the colours of the spectrum. This effect is known as dispersion. The cause of dispersion is that the *refractive index* of the prism is greater for blue light than for red light. In other words the blue light travels at a lower speed through the glass of the prism than the red light. Hence the red light is deviated by the least amount.

Considering light as a wave process, it is clear that the speed of light waves in the glass block depends upon the wavelength of the light. So the term dispersion has been generalised in wave physics to mean any system in which the speed of propogation depends upon the wavelength. Such a medium is called a dispersive medium.

In the theory of mechanical waves an example of a dispersive system is that of ripples travelling on the surface of water. An example of a non-dispersive mechanical system is the propogation of sound waves through the air. Musicians may find this obvious. If waves of different frequency travelled at different speeds it would not be possible to hear a piece of music played by an orchestra unless one was sitting in the orchestra pit itself. High notes might arrive before low ones played at the same time, or vice versa.

DISPLACEMENT

Displacement is a term used in **kinematics**. It is the distance 'as the crow flies' from some starting point to the finishing point with the direction also specified. Because both magnitude and direction have to be specified it is a **vector**.

As an example consider a shopper in a supermarket going from A to B (Fig. D.29). The distance travelled is 28m but the displacement is 8m east of A.

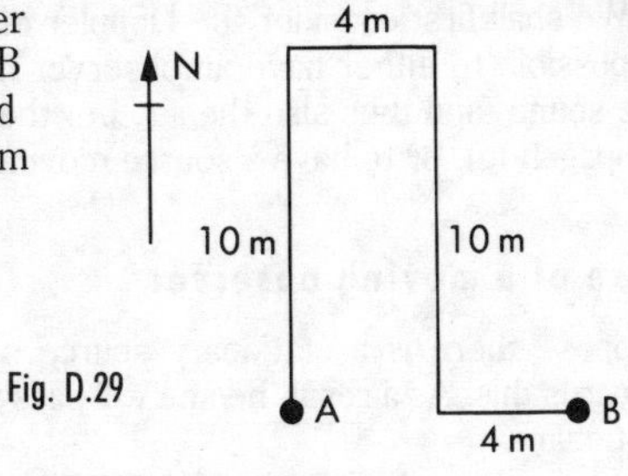

Fig. D.29

DIVERGING LENS

A lens for which rays close to and parallel to the **principal axis** diverge from a point after passing through the lens. The point is called the **focal point** of the lens and the distance from this focal point to the lens is called the focal length. In the 'real is positive' convention for **lens formulae** such a lens is said to have a negative focal length. A diverging lens is always thinner in the middle than at the edges, even though one surface may be convex in profile.

DOMAINS

This term describes regions of magnetisation in a piece of steel or iron.

The reason that steel and iron can be magnetised is that individual atoms of iron behave as atomic magnetic **dipoles**. The dipole behaviour must be caused by a circulation of electric charge within the atom. In an unmagnetised piece of steel or iron it might be thought that the absence of magnetic effects is due to the atomic dipoles being randomly orientated. This is not the case. It turns out that within a piece of steel or iron all the atoms within a region of microscopic dimensions are aligned in the same way. This region is called a domain. In an unmagnetised sample neighbouring domains will have different directions of magnetisation. When a piece of iron or steel is magnetised, the domains individually change their magnetic orientation as an external magnetic field is applied. When a domain changes its magnetic orientation, all the atomic dipoles within it change at once.

DOPPLER EFFECT

The Doppler effect is a well-known phenomenon whereby the observed frequency of a source is less or more than the true frequency as a result of either the source or the observer or both moving. A very common example in sound is the change in the observed frequency of the siren of an ambulance as it approaches and then recedes. The Doppler effect is also important in light, and electromagnetic waves generally, where it is used to measure the speeds of astronomical objects, e.g. distant galaxies, relative to the earth.

We shall first consider the Doppler effect in the theory of sound, where it is possible to either have an observer moving with respect to the source of the sound (and thus also the air, i.e. the medium through which the sound is propagating), or to have a source moving with respect to the air.

Case of a moving observer

Suppose there is a stationary source of sound and an observer is moving towards this. As a result he/she will pass through more complete waves than if stationary.

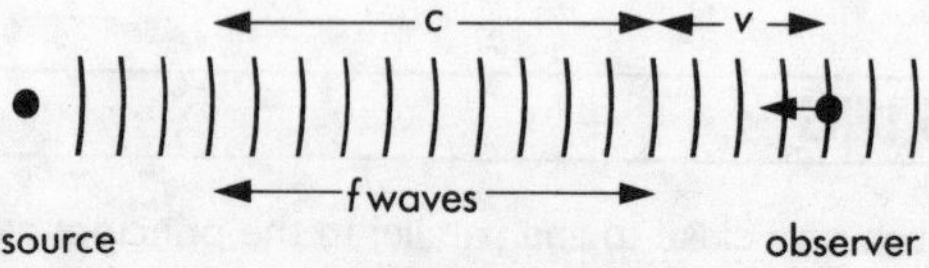

Fig. D.30 Observer moving towards a stationary source

Fig. D. 30 shows all the waves the observer will pass through in one second. If moving at a speed v, he/she will travel a distance v metres to meet the wave which has travelled forward a distance c metres. Here c is the speed of sound. If f waves are emitted in one second, there are f waves in a distance c, so the number of waves in a distance $(c + v)$ is

$$\frac{c+v}{c}.f$$

The apparent frequency heard is f' and we have

$$f' = \frac{c+v}{c}.f$$

If the observer on the other hand is moving away from the source we have

$$f' = \frac{c-v}{c}.f$$

As an example of this phenomenon there is the case of a passenger on a train who hears a sudden fall in the frequency of a level-crossing warning bell as the crossing is passed.

Case of a moving source

If the source approaches the observer at a speed u, it moves a distance u metres in one second, and so the f waves will be contained in a distance $(c - u)$ (Fig. D.31). The wavelength will be equal to this distance divided by the number of waves, i.e. $(c - u)/f$, and so the apparent frequency f' will be given by

$$f' = \frac{cf}{c-u}$$

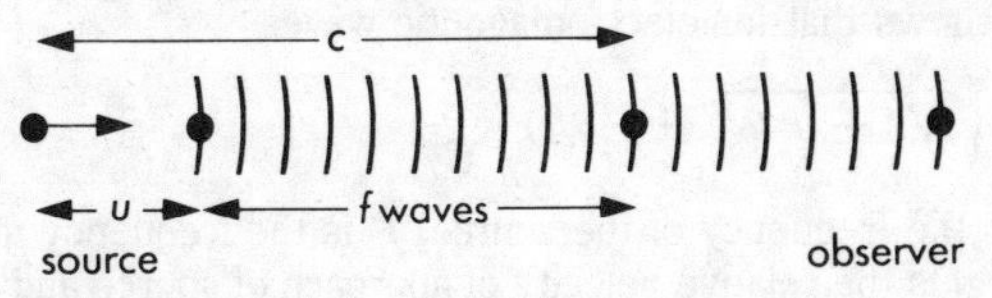

Fig. D.31 Effect of moving the source

If the source is moving away from the observer the apparent frequency will be

$$f' = \frac{cf}{c + u}$$

Case of a moving source and a moving observer

The motion of the source affects the apparent wavelength and the motion of the observer affects the relative speed of the waves as they are received. If both source and observer are moving, we have, using the earlier notation,

$$f' = \frac{(c \pm v)}{(c \mp u)} . f$$

where the upper signs apply to approach and the lower signs to separation.

Another interesting case is the application to the measurement of the speed of a moving object, for example as used by police in radar speed checks. This too is essentially a system in which both source and observer are moving. What happens is that a transmitter sends out a beam of waves towards the moving object, e.g. a car. The frequency of the waves received by the car is different from that transmitted from the source. This is because the observer is moving relative to the source. The waves are then emitted by the object, the car, at this frequency. However, as it is a moving source, the received frequency, say back at the transmitter, is different again. Now the speeds of the moving 'observer' (the car moving through the waves) and the moving 'source' (the car bouncing back the waves) are both the same, w, and so the apparent frequency is given by

$$f' = \frac{c + w}{c - w} . f$$

When this method is used in a radar speed detector system the reflected wave is combined with a wave directly from the transmitter and a beat frequency is measured.

Doppler effect and light

The method used to derive the Doppler effect formulae for sound waves cannot strictly be applied to electromagnetic waves, since these travel through empty space, i.e. without a medium, and so the 'moving observer' and 'moving source' cases cannot be distinguished. The theory of special

relativity shows that for electromagnetic waves

$$f' = f\left(\sqrt{1 - u^2/c^2}/(1 - u/c)\right)$$

where f is the frequency of the source, f' is the frequency measured by the observer, u is the relative velocity of approach of source and observer, and c is the speed of electromagnetic waves in a vacuum, a universal constant independent of any motion of source and of observer. If $u \ll c$ this expression becomes

$$f' = f\left(1 + \frac{u}{c}\right)$$

In many terrestrial and astronomical applications u is so much smaller than c that the approximate formula quoted above can safely be used even when three- or four-figure accuracy is required. It is often easier to measure the wavelength rather than the frequency of an electromagnetic wave. Here the formula

$$\frac{\Delta\lambda}{\lambda_0} = u/c$$

is used, where λ is the wavelength measured by an observer approaching a source at speed u, and λ_0 is the wavelength that would be measured if the source and observer were not in relative motion, and $\Delta\lambda = \lambda_0 - \lambda$.

A source moving away from an observer will result in an apparent decrease in frequency and consequent increase in wavelength known as the *red shift*.

DRIFT VELOCITY

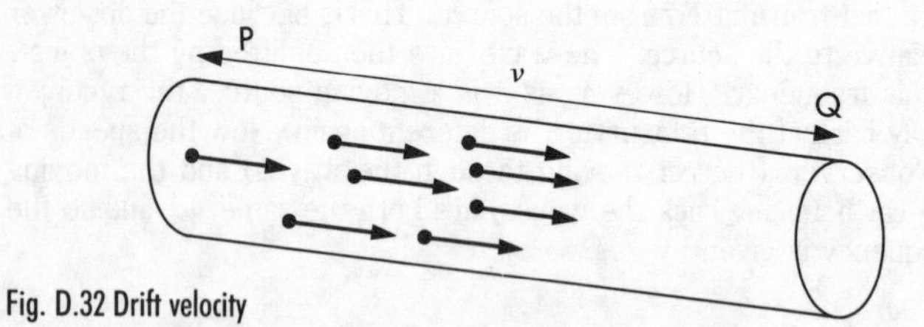

Fig. D.32 Drift velocity

The drift velocity of an electron is its average velocity through a conductor when current flows.

Electric charge cannot be easily stored. So if an electron enters a section of an electrical conductor (Fig. D.32), e.g. at P, a wave of electrical movement takes place throughout the conductor and shortly afterwards a corresponding electron will move out of the section at Q. The time taken for this wave, or domino effect, to take place is what is usually known as the speed of an electric current. This speed is very close to the speed of light. By contrast the drift velocity of the electrons, v, represents the average speed of an electron passing through the conductor. If there are n electrons per unit volume and the cross-sectional area of the conductor is A, the number of electrons in the length v traversed on average in one second is nAv. If each electron carries a charge e, the total charge on these electrons is $nAev$. Thus the current, which is the charge passing through the section Q per second, is $nAev$. For a metal like copper n is typically 10^{29} electrons per metre cubed. An intrinsic semiconductor at room temperature would have a much larger value of n than this. v typically is approximately 0·5 mm s^{-1}.

D-TYPE FLIP-FLOP

This is a standard circuit used in electronics, and is sometimes called a *data latch* (D-latch). It is a modified version of the **bistable**, having only one input, so that the unpredictable state of S = R = 1 cannot occur. Its circuit and its symbol are shown in Fig. D.33. Its uses are similar to those of the more versatile *JK flip-flop*, a device which has two data inputs.

The D in the name of the device stands for data or delay. The term 'delay' derives from the fact that a bit in the data input is held back and does not reach the Q output until CK = 1.

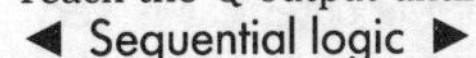
◀ Sequential logic ▶

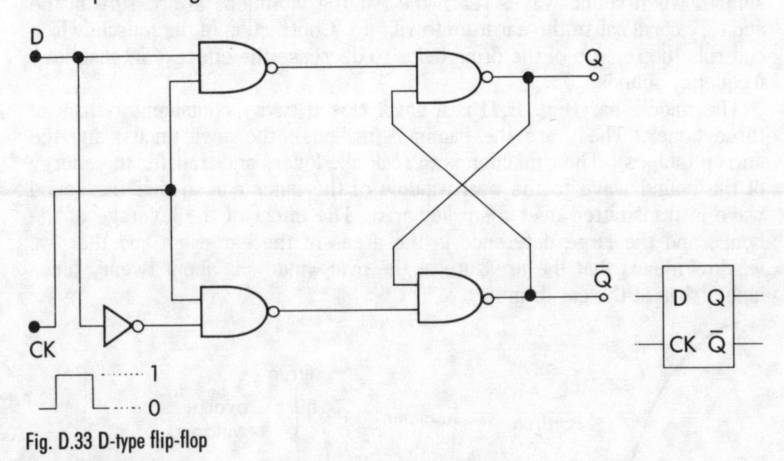

Fig. D.33 D-type flip-flop

DYNAMICS

Dynamics is the name generally given to that branch of mechanics which deals with what happens when the forces acting on a body are *not* in equilibrium and an acceleration of the body results. Note however that all the forces on a body could be in equilibrium with the body moving without acceleration. An example of this is a car travelling at a steady speed.

DYNAMO

◀ Alternator or a.c. generator ▶

EAR

The ear conveniently falls into three main parts, the outer, the middle and the inner ear.

The outer ear consists of the ear flap (pinna) which plays very little part in hearing, and the auditory canal (external auditory meatus), which terminates at the eardrum (tympanic membrane). The physics of the outer ear is very simple: when sound waves reach the ear the vibrations in pressure in the auditory canal cause the eardrum to vibrate. Contraction of the muscle which controls the tension of the drum helps to decrease the effect of intense low-frequency sounds.

The middle ear (Fig. E.1) is a small closed cavity containing a chain of three bones. These are the hammer (malleus), the anvil (incus) and the stirrup (stapes). Their function is to rock like levers and transfer the energy of the sound wave to the oval window of the inner ear so that the sound wave is transmitted over a smaller area. The effect of the leverage of the bones and the large difference in the areas of the ear drum and the oval window means that the pressure at the oval window is about twenty times higher than at the ear drum.

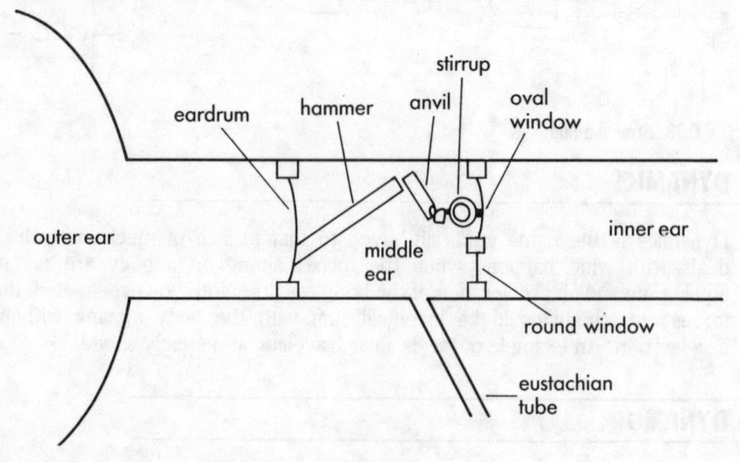

Fig. E.1 Schematic diagram of the outer and middle ear

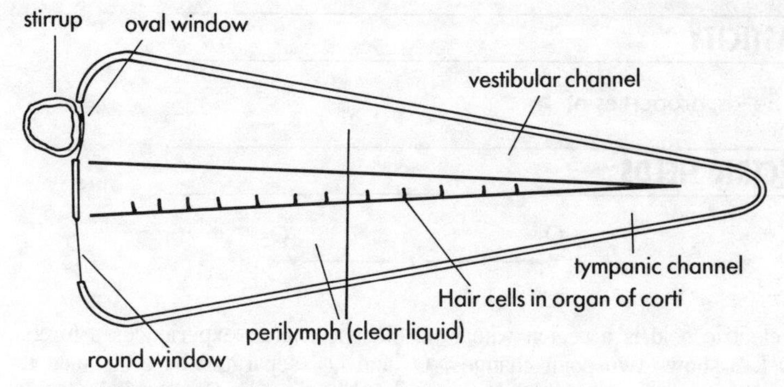

Fig. E.2 Schematic diagram of the inner ear 'unwound' into linear form

The inner ear is a cavity in bone: it has two parts, the semicircular passages and the cochlea. The former is the organ of balance; it has nothing to do with hearing. The latter is a spiral canal which divides into two passages, the vestibular channel and the tympanic channel (Fig. E.2). Both passages are filled with a watery liquid called the perilymph. Sound waves travel into the vestibular channel from the oval window. The physical properties of the cochlea are such that high-frequency waves tend to act at different points from those of low frequency. The former tend to act at the base of the cochlea and the latter at the apex. The receptors for hearing are several rows of hair cells which together with their supporting cells form the organ of Corti. The distribution of nervous activity in this organ thus depends upon the frequency content of the sound and also on the amount of sound energy received.

EDDY CURRENTS

Eddy currents are small circulating whirlpools or eddies of electric current produced in a conductor, usually when the conductor is a sheet or a solid mass of metal, and caused by induced e.m.f. generated by changing magnetic fields. Eddy currents can be advantageous, as in systems which rely on eddy currents for damping, e.g. some **galvanometers** and in **induction motors**. But in other circumstances they can be disadvantageous, as for example in the cores of **transformers**.

EINSTEIN MODEL OF A SOLID

◀ Statistical thermodynamics ▶

ELASTIC COLLISIONS

◀ Energy in collision problems ▶

ELASTICITY

◀ Solids, properties of ▶

ELECTRIC FIELDS

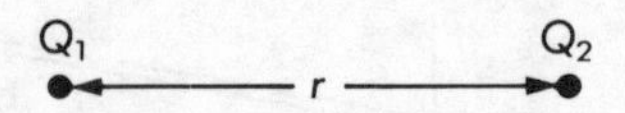

Fig. E.3

An electric field is a region where an electric charge experiences a force. Fig. E.3 shows two point changes, Q_1 and Q_2, separated by a distance r. The charges exert a mutual force on each other given by Coulomb's Law:

$$F = \frac{Q_1 Q_2}{4\pi\epsilon_0 r^2}$$

That is to say the force is proportional to the product of the charges and inversely proportional to the square of the distance between them. The constant is $\left(\frac{1}{4\pi\epsilon_0}\right)$, where ϵ_0 is known as the permittivity of free space having the value $8{\cdot}8 \times 10^{-12}\ \mathrm{C^{-2}\ N\ m^2}$, and

$$\frac{1}{4\pi\epsilon_0} = 9 \times 10^9\ \mathrm{C^2\ N\ m^{-2}}.$$

With electric fields, forces can be attractive or repulsive depending upon the sign of the charges. Coulomb's Law is difficult to test directly in the laboratory. Verification is normally done by indirect methods.

The strength of an electric field in a region surrounding a charged object is defined as the force per unit charge. Thus at a distance r from a point charge Q the field strength, E is given by

$$E = \frac{Q}{4\pi\epsilon_0 r^2}$$

The direction of an electric field is conventionally taken to be that of the direction of the force on a positive test charge.

◀ Inverse square law fields, Radial electric fields, Uniform electric field ▶

ELECTRIC WIND

◀ Action of points ▶

ELECTRICAL CONDUCTIVITY

◀ Conductivities of metals, Conductivity ▶

ELECTRICAL POWER AND THE HEATING EFFECT

When electrical current flows, for example, through a resistor or an electric motor there is conversion of electrical energy into other forms of energy, and we say that a potential difference is generated across the respective components. Often it is important to know the rate at which a component converts energy from one form to another. The power associated with a component is the rate at which it converts energy from one form to another.

From the definition of potential difference, if a current I flows for a time t the charge flowing is an amount It and so the electrical energy converted, W, is given by

$$W = VIt$$

The power, P, of the component will be

$$P = W/t = VI$$

The unit of power is the watt (W), which is a rate of energy conversion of one joule per second. In the formula $P = IV$, P will be in watts, I in amperes and V in volts. Consider a resistance R. If **Ohm's Law** applies, we have the formula

$$V = IR$$

Substitution into $P = IV$ gives two alternative expressions:

$$P = I^2R \quad \text{and} \quad P = \frac{V^2}{R}$$

It should however be noted that these alternative expressions are applicable only to a resistor. For example with an electric motor the formula $P = I \times V$ is true always and this formula will give the total rate of energy conversion by the motor, some of which will be conversion into mechanical energy as a result of the devices connected to the motor and some of which will be heating due to the resistance of the motor. The terms V^2/R and I^2R measure only the latter conversions.

In the electrical power industry it is more convenient to use the **kilowatt** (kW), equal to 1,000 watts, and the **megawatt** (MW), equal to one million watts. It is also more convenient to use the kilowatt-hour rather than the joule. The kilowatt-hour is the quantity of energy converted to other forms of energy by a device of power 1 kilowatt in one hour. Hence $1\text{kWh} = 3{\cdot}6 \times 10^6$ joules.

◄ Maximum power transfer theorem ►

ELECTRICITY AND MAGNETISM FORMULAE

Common formulae used in electricity and magnetism are listed below.

Charge (Q) $Q = It$
Current (I) $I = nAve$
Energy energy $= QV$
Force on charge (F) $F = QE = QV/d$
Ohm's Law $V = IR$
Internal resistance e.m.f. $= I(R + r)$

Resistivity (ρ) $\rho = RA/l$
Temperature variation of resistance $R_\theta = R_0(1 + \alpha\theta)$
Series resistance $R = R_1 + R_2$
Parallel resistance $1/R = 1/R_1 + 1/R_2$
Power (W) $W = VI = I^2R = V^2/R$

Wheatstone bridge $R_1/R_2 = R_3/R_4$
Electric field strength (E) $E = -\mathrm{d}V/\mathrm{d}x$
Force between charges (F)

$$F = \frac{1}{4\pi\epsilon_0}\frac{Q_1Q_2}{d^2}$$

Field due to charge Q (E)
$E = Q/(4\pi\epsilon_0 d^2)$
Potential (V) $V = W/Q_0$
Potential due to charge Q
$V = Q/(4\pi\epsilon_0 d)$
Capacitance (C) $C = Q/V$
Parallel-plate capacitor $C = A\epsilon_0/d$
Parallel capacitors $C = C_1 + C_2$
Series capacitors $1/C = 1/C_1 + 1/C_2$
Energy stored $E = \frac{1}{2}QV = \frac{1}{2}CV^2$
Capacitor discharge $V = V_0 e^{-t/RC}$
Capacitor charge $V = V_0(1 - e^{-t/RC})$
Force on current (F) $F = BIl \sin\theta$
Couple of coil (C) $C = BANI \sin\theta$
Field at centre of coil (B) $B = \mu_0 NI/2r$
Field in solenoid $B = \mu_0 nI$
(n turns m^{-1})
Field at end of long solenoid $B = \mu_0 nI/2$
Field near straight wire $B = \mu_0 I/2\pi r$
Velocity of e.m. waves $c = 1/(\epsilon_0\mu_0)^{\frac{1}{2}}$
Current sensitivity $\theta = BANI/c$
Self-inductance (L) $L = N\phi/I$
Mutual inductance (M)
$M = N_s\phi_s/I_p$
Induced e.m.f. (E) $E = -L\,\mathrm{d}I/\mathrm{d}t$
Induced e.m.f. (E)
$E = -M\,\mathrm{d}I_p/\mathrm{d}t$
Induced e.m.f. in coil $E = BAN\omega \sin\theta$
Induced e.m.f. $E = -N\,\mathrm{d}\phi/\mathrm{d}t$
Ballistic galvanometer $Q \propto \theta$
Transformer $n_p/n_s = V_p/V_s$
$I_p/I_s = n_s/n_p$
Root mean square current (I)
$I = i_0/\sqrt{2}$
Alternating current $i = i_0 \sin(\omega t)$
Capacitative reactance (X_c)
$X_c = 1/(\omega C)$
Inductive reactance (X_L)
$X_L = \omega L$
Impedance (series RCL)
$Z = (R^2 + (X_L - X_c)^2)^{\frac{1}{2}}$
Resonance condition for I
$X_L = X_c$
Current gain of a transistor
$\beta = h_{fe} = I_c/I_b$
Operational amplifier
Open loop gain
$V_{out} = A(V_+ - V_-)$
Inverting amplifier

$$V_{out} = \frac{-R_f}{R_i}V_{in}$$

Non-inverting amplifier

$$V_{out} = \frac{R_f + R_i}{R_i}V_{in}$$

ELECTROCARDIOGRAPH

Electrocardiography is the name used in medical physics for the observation of electric activity in the heart. Electric activity at standard electrode sites on the body is amplified and sent either to an **oscilloscope** or, if a permanent record is required, to a chart recorder.

The electrical activity which is recorded results from the polarisation and depolarisation of cells in the muscles of the heart. Body fluids are capable of electrical conduction and so the potentials appear, much reduced, at the electrode sites on the body's surface.

◀ Action potential ▶

ELECTROENCEPHALOGRAM

Electroencephalography is the name used in medical physics for the measurement of the electrical activity of the brain. The output is sent to an **oscilloscope** or a chart recorder.

A patient is typically asked to perform some operation, such as closing or opening an eye or using a limb. A marked deviation from normal activity can indicate the possibility of brain disorder or damage.

◀ Electrocardiograph ▶

ELECTROMAGNETIC DAMPING

Electromagnetic damping is used in analogue meters, i.e. ammeters, milliammeters and **galvanometers**, to damp away oscillations which would otherwise go on for a long time once a current is passed to move the needle from a previous equilibrium position. Were it not for this damping, on applying current to a meter the needle would overshoot the required position and subsequently oscillate with **simple harmonic motion.**

In most galvanometers there are two ways in which electromagnetic damping may occur:

a) By having the coil mounted on a metal frame, usually aluminium. As the coil moves, eddy currents are set up and hence there is a mechanism by which kinetic energy can be lost from the system. If no damping is required the coil has to be mounted on a wooden frame.
b) When the coil swings in the field of the magnet an e.m.f. is induced in the coil itself equal to $-NAB\mathrm{d}\theta/\mathrm{d}t$. If E is the external e.m.f. and R is the total resistance in the circuit to which the coil is connected, including the galvanometer coil resistance, i, the current flowing, is given by:

$$E - NAB\,\frac{\mathrm{d}\theta}{\mathrm{d}t} = Ri$$

The equation of motion of the coil is therefore

$$I\,\frac{\mathrm{d}^2\theta}{\mathrm{d}t^2} = -k\theta + NABi = -k\theta + \frac{NABE}{R} - \frac{(NAB)^2}{R}\,\frac{\mathrm{d}\theta}{\mathrm{d}t}$$

where I is the moment of inertia of the coil and k the couple per unit angle of twist provided by the spring. This equation is the equation for simple harmonic motion for equilibrium about a value of θ given by the external e.m.f. E, and containing a damping term $-\dfrac{(NAB)^2}{R}\dfrac{\mathrm{d}\theta}{\mathrm{d}t}$. Note that the damping depends upon the total resistance, R, in the circuit. By varying this resistance the damping can be changed to one of the three types of damping in a s.h.m.-type system, i.e., small, critical or large damping.

◀ Ammeters and voltmeters, Ballistic galvanometer ▶

ELECTROMAGNETIC INDUCTION

When a single wire is connected to a very sensitive galvanometer and is

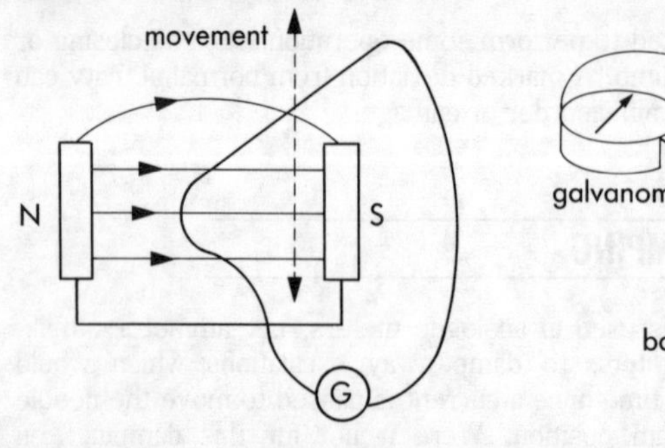

Fig. E.4 Moving a wire in a field induces an e.m.f.

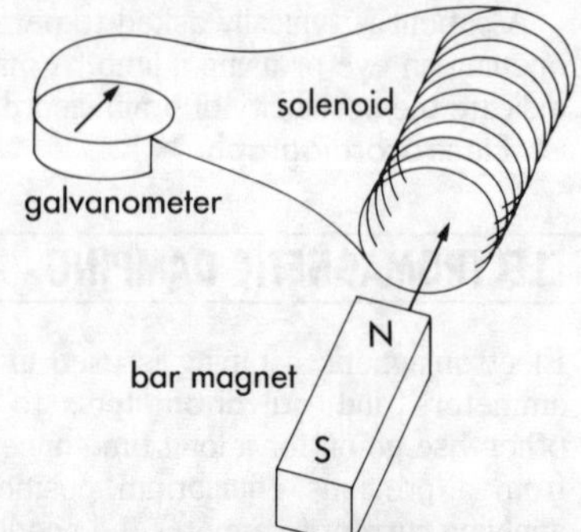

Fig. E.5 Induction with a solenoid

moved across a magnetic field, as shown in Fig. E.4, there is a small movement of the galvanometer indicating the flow of a tiny current. This is an example of electromagnetic induction. The flow occurs only when the wire moves and only if the motion is across the magnetic field. There is no effect when it moves in the same direction as the field. As there is a current flowing, there must be a source of e.m.f. The e.m.f. is induced in the wire and current flows because of the existence of a complete circuit.

The effect is much more pronounced if the wire is in the form of a coil or of a solenoid (Fig. E.5). Again, the e.m.f. is produced only when the magnet moves relative to the coil. Note that it is only the relative motion that is important. Similar effects are produced if the coil moves relative to a fixed magnet. The effect is increased by

a) increasing the number of turns on the coil
b) using a stronger magnet
c) moving the magnet more quickly

A second way of inducing an e.m.f. is by changing the magnitude of the magnetic field (Fig. E.6). This is sometimes called the transformer effect. One way of demonstrating this is to have two coils which are co-axial. One coil, called the primary, is put in series with a battery, a switch and a protective resistor to limit the current flowing. The other coil, called the secondary, is connected to a galvanometer as before. Closing and opening

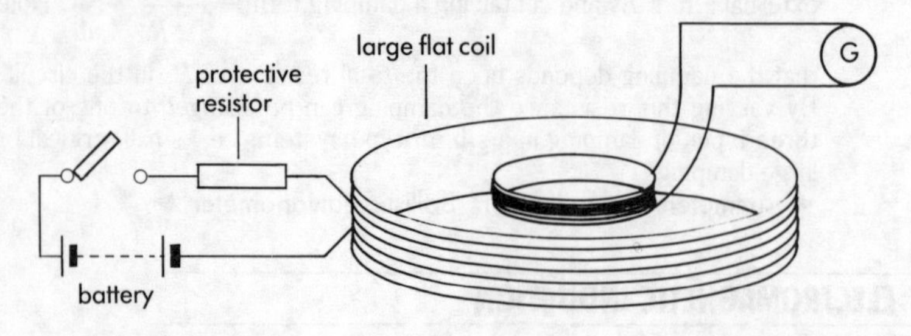

Fig. E.6 The transformer effect

the switch in the primary causes a short-lived e.m.f. and current to be induced in the secondary. If the protective resistor is replaced by a rheostat, the switch closed, and the value of the resistance of the rheostat is quickly changed, electromagnetic induction is also seen. Thus it occurs whenever there is any change in the primary current and so in the magnetic field produced by it.

LAWS OF ELECTROMAGNETIC INDUCTION

It is helpful when studying electromagnetic induction to invoke the concept of magnetic flux, ϕ, measured in webers. The magnetic flux in webers in an area of space A through which there is a field B is the product of the magetic flux density in teslas and the area A.

First law

The first law of induction is the one which describes the size of the induced e.m.f., and is often referred to as the *Faraday Law* or occasionally the Faraday-Neumann Law. The basic idea is best grasped by considering a conductor of length L moving through a magnetic field B at a speed v (Fig. E.7). For convenience let us consider that the velocity vector, the axis of the wire and the B-field are mutually at right angles. Because the free electrons in the conductor are moving charges in the presence of a magnetic field they experience a force Bev which pushes them to one end of the conductor (Fig. E.8). The charges move and set up an electric field. Movement ceases when the forces generated by this electric field are equal and opposite to those generated by the Bev force. (Note that there is a similarity here to the **Hall effect**.) When this happens the condition is: $Ee = Bev$, where E is the field produced. Hence, as $E = V/L$ we have $V = Bvl$.

Now vL is the area A, swept out by the wire per second (see Fig. E.9). $BvL = BA$ which is the flux, ϕ, cut, or swept through, by the wire in 1 second. In other words the induced e.m.f. is equal to $\frac{\mathrm{d}\Phi}{\mathrm{d}t}$ in magnitude.

The e.m.f. described above produces no current, because there is no circuit. In order to produce a current we would have to complete a circuit.

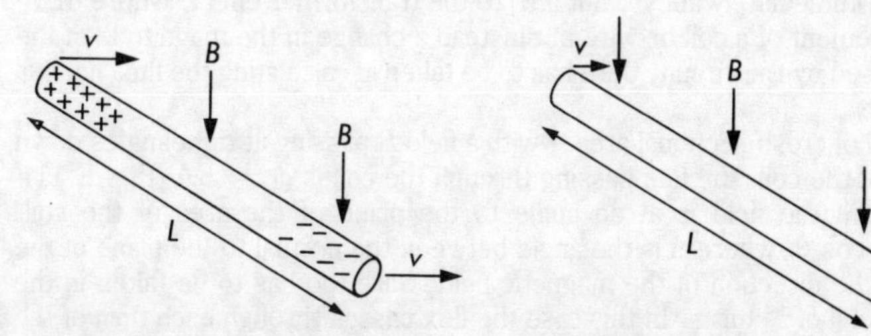

Fig. E.7 Wire length *L* travelling at speed *v* through field *B*

Fig. E.8 Migration of electrons

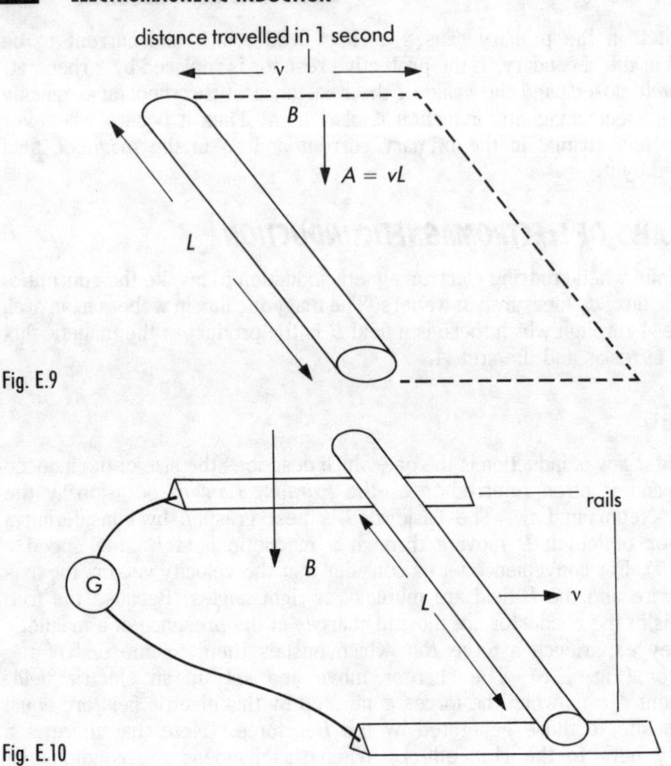

Fig. E.9

Fig. E.10

One way of doing this is shown in Fig. E.10, where the wire is moved along two rails which are connected by a galvanometer at the right-hand end.

In both of these cases we can regard the circuit as a coil of wire through which the flux passing is steadily increasing. The increase in flux linked, i.e. enclosed, by the coil per second, is BvL.

This result – that the e.m.f. is equal to the rate of change of flux linked by the circuit – is a general result which applies to all situations, not just that described immediately above, but also to the transformer effect, where there is no movement of a coil or wire but instead a change in the magnitude of the flux enclosed by the circuit. Care has to be taken in calculating the flux 'linking' the circuit.

In a coil of cross-sectional area A with a field B passing at right angles down the axis of the coil, the flux passing through the coil is $\phi = BA$ (Fig. E.11). However, if the field is at an angle to the plane of the area of the coil, $\phi = BA \cos \theta$, where θ is the angle between the normal to the plane of the area and the direction of the magnetic field. Care too has to be taken in the case of a coil of N turns. In this case the flux passes through each turn of the coil so that the flux linked is NBA. Sometimes the symbol Φ is used to represent $N\phi$, the total flux linked by the circuit.

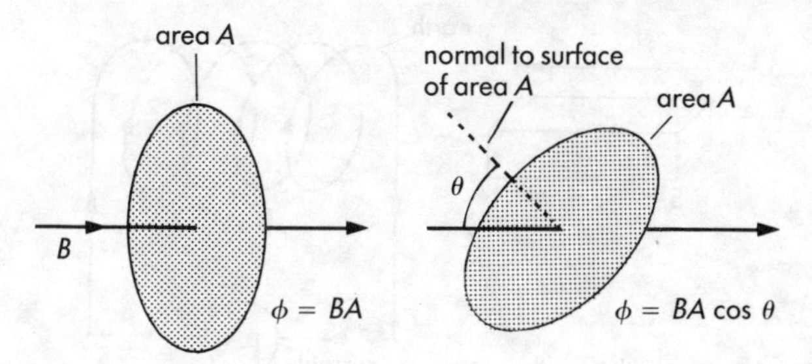

Fig. E.11

Second law

The second law of electromagnetic induction is known as *Lenz's Law* and gives the sign of the induced e.m.f. Lenz's Law states that the induced e.m.f. must be in such a direction as to oppose the change which is causing the induced e.m.f. It should be fairly obvious that the law is a consequence of the law of conservation of energy. Consider Fig. E.10 again. If the e.m.f. produced conventional current in a clockwise sense viewed from above, the effect would be to generate even more magnetic field in a downward sense, by application of Maxwell's **corkscrew rule.** But this increase in magnetic field would further increase the flux linked by the circuit and give rise to an increase in the current flowing, which again in turn would give rise to an even greater magnetic field, and so on. Such a process would clearly contravene the law of conservation of energy and hence the induced e.m.f. must be in such a direction as to oppose the change which is causing the induced e.m.f.

Direction rules

There are two ways of working out the direction of the induced currents which flow in electromagnetic induction. The first is applicable to the situation of moving a wire through a magnetic field. Of course only if the wire forms part of a complete circuit will a current flow. The direction of the current is given by **Fleming's right-hand rule.** This is similar in form to **Fleming's left-hand rule** except that here the right hand is used. The first finger points in the direction of the magnetic field, the thumb points in the direction of the motion of the wire, and then the second finger gives the direction of the induced current.

The second useful rule applies to situations such as that of a bar magnet approaching a coil or solenoid (Fig. E.12). If the north pole of the magnet is pushed towards the coil or solenoid, the current which flows in the coil, opposing the motion or change, is such that the left-hand end of the coil becomes a north pole. In this way the movement of the incoming magnet is opposed.

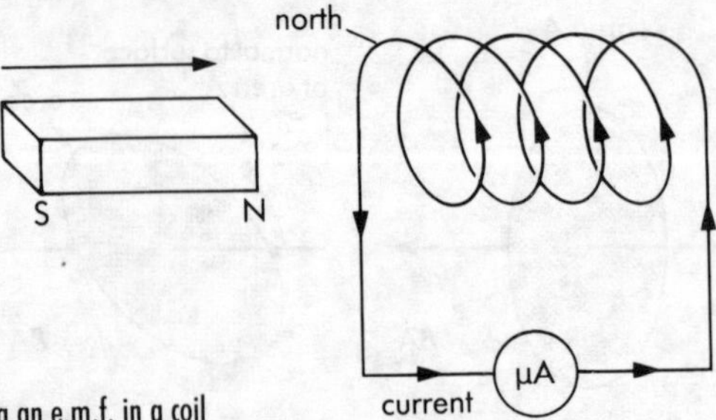

Fig. E.12 Inducing an e.m.f. in a coil

ELECTROMAGNETIC SPECTRUM

This is the name given to a family of waves, including **radio** waves, light, **X-rays**, and **gamma** rays, all of which travel by the same mechanism and at the same speed. The principal difference between these waves is their frequency, f, and therefore, from the theory of **quantum mechanics**, the energy, $E = hf$, carried by an individual wave packet (photon). (Here h is the **Planck constant**.)

The waves are transverse waves consisting of an oscillating electric field E and an oscillating magnetic field B which vibrate mutually at right angles and at right angles to the direction in which the wave is travelling (Fig. E.13).

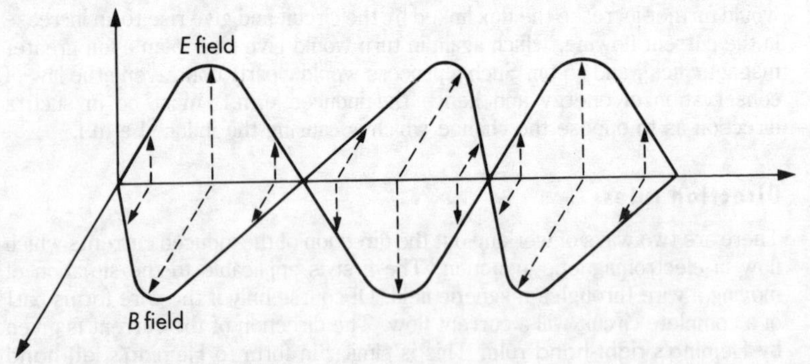

Fig. E.13 Electromagnetic waves

The complete theory of electromagnetic waves was provided by the British scientist Maxwell. Before Maxwell the only waves of the spectrum which were known were light waves, and of these it was known from experiments like **Young's slits** that they were waves, but the form of the oscillation was unknown. Maxwell's proof thus not only provided a complete theory of light waves but also anticipated the discovery of radio waves. He showed that no medium is required for the propagation of electromagnetic waves and that they can travel through a vacuum at a speed c given by

$$c = \frac{1}{\sqrt{\epsilon_0 \mu_0}}$$

where ϵ_0 is the permittivity constant of electrostatics, and μ_0 is the permeability constant of magnetism. The speed given by this theory is in fact the speed of light, $c = 3 \times 10^8 \mathrm{m\,s^{-1}}$. The waves travel through air at a speed which is only slightly less than the speed in a vacuum. The waves exhibit the properties of **reflection, refraction, interference** and **diffraction** and, as they are transverse waves, they can be polarised. In considering these waves either the frequency, f, or the wavelength, λ, can be quoted: they are related by the equation $c = f\lambda$.

The table shows some of the features of the range of the electromagnetic spectrum. The ranges of wavelength and energy are only approximate and there is some overlap. The names given to different parts of the spectrum derive from their methods of production: for example there is some overlap between X-rays and γ-rays. The former are generated in the laboratory by accelerating electrons and causing them to collide with metal objects, whereas the latter are produced by a process of nuclear physics in the nucleus of the atom.

◀ Velocity of electromagnetic waves ▶

Name	*Wavelength in air/m*	*Method of production/origin*	*Method of detection*	*Uses*
γ-ray	$10^{-13} - 10^{-11}$	radioactive decay	Geiger tube	medicine, tracer, cancer treatment
X-ray	$10^{-12} - 10^{-8}$	decelerating electrons	Geiger tube	photography
Ultraviolet	$10^{-8} - 10^{-7}$	electron transitions	photocell	spectroscopy
Visible light	$(4 - 7) \times 10^{-7}$	electron transitions	retina photographic	photography
Infrared	$10^{-7} - 10^{-3}$	hot bodies	thermopile	heating, photography
Micro-waves	$10^{-3} - 10^{2}$	oscillators	diodes	cooking
Radio	$10^{2} - 10^{5}$	oscillators, aerials	tuned circuit	communication

ELECTROMETER

The electrometer is basically a purpose-built instrument for measuring electric charge and so is sometimes called a **coulomb meter**. It can also be used for measuring small electric currents. Electrometers found in school and college laboratories are better for quantitative measurements than the other laboratory instrument for charge measurement, the **gold-leaf**

electroscope. The device is basically a voltmeter with a resistance as high as 10^{12} to 10^{13} Ω. A steady voltage, usually between 0 and 1V, developed across its input goes to an amplifying circuit which draws a minute current ($\approx 10^{-12}$A) and develops at the output a current of the order of milliamps which can be used to drive an ordinary meter. Consequently an electrometer can be replaced by a high-impedance digital *voltmeter*.

In all its applications, the electrometer indicates the voltage across its input. Small charges may be measured by connecting a **capacitor** across the input terminals, as in Fig. E.14. If its capacitance is, say, 10^{-9}F (1 nF), an output indication corresponding to 1V across the input shows that the charge on the capacitor is 10^{-9}C (neglecting the input capacitance of the electrometer). If the capacitance of the object from which the charge came (a charged ball, for example) is small compared with that across the electrometer input, nearly all this charge will have passed to the electrometer capacitor, if the object was touched on to the input terminal. If the resistance across the input is, say 10^{13} Ω, at 1V the charge will leak away, initially at a rate of 10^{-13}A, so that a charge of 10^{-9}C will only be reduced by 1 per cent after 100 s. This will give plenty of time to take a reading.

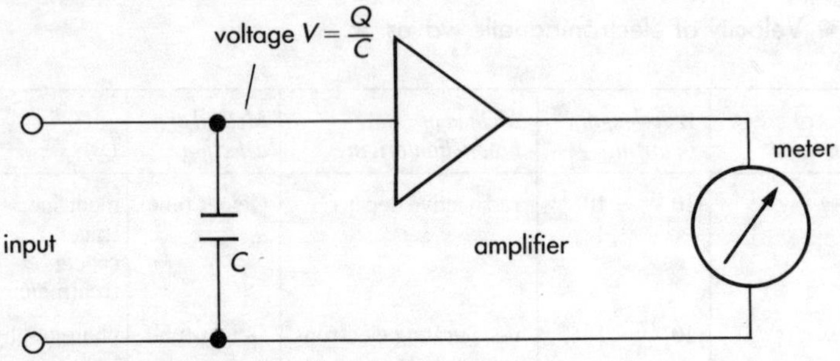

Fig. E.14 Charge measurement with an electrometer

Small currents can be measured by connecting a **resistor** across the input (as in Fig. E.15) through which the current flows. If the resistor has a resistance of, say, 10^{10} Ω, an output indication corresponding to 1V across the input shows that the current in the resistor is 10^{-10}A (neglecting the higher input resistance of the amplifier in parallel with the 10^{10} Ω resistance).

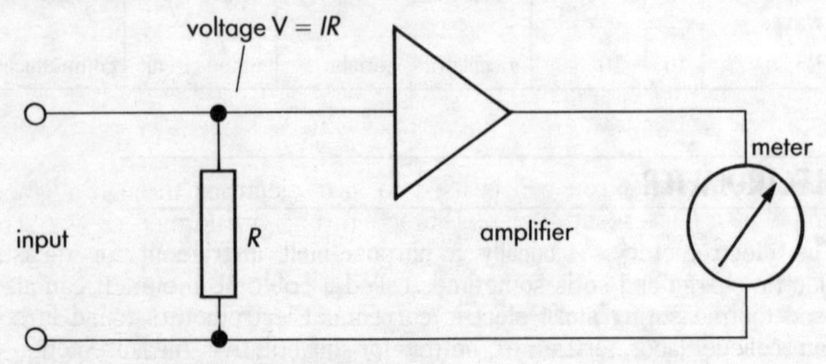

Fig. E.15 Current measurement with an electrometer

The electrometer may be provided with an internal 1V supply for calibration. If not, an external 1V supply can be used. The electrometer is then adjusted, by using the gain or sensitivity control, so that the output meter gives a convenient reading.

ELECTROMOTIVE FORCE (e.m.f.)

The term e.m.f. is applied to cells (batteries), thermocouples, dynamos, coils in changing magnetic fields, etc., i.e. devices in which there is a conversion of energy from non-electrical form to electrical. For example, in a simple dry cell (battery) with zinc and carbon electrodes, energy is converted from chemical form to electrical form. The e.m.f. of the cell is measured in volts and is the electrical potential energy (in joules) gained by one coulomb of electricity passing through the cell when a current flows. Thus one volt is one joule/coulomb.

The energy carried by the electrical charge is merely transferred round the electrical circuit to components, e.g. resistors, where it is converted from electrical forms into non-electrical forms, e.g. heat, light. The term 'potential difference' is used in these energy transfers. Because the energy is merely transferred from one place to another, and because in simple circuits electrical charge cannot be stored, the e.m.f. is equal to the sum of potential differences round the circuit.

◀ Internal resistance ▶

ELECTRON

The particle of electric charge which is found in all neutral atoms.

ELECTRON DIFFRACTION

In most areas of physics the electron can be treated as a particle. But it can also behave as a wave. For example, it does this when it is used instead of light in the electron microscope. Another case is when it is diffracted by the regular arrays of atoms in matter in a manner similar to that of X-rays.

The ability to exhibit the phenomenon of **diffraction** is one of the classic ways in which physicists decide that something is a wave. The experiment which convinced physicists that the electron had wave properties was its diffraction by graphite. Using a special evacuated tube, this experiment can be easily carried out with low-energy electrons in the school or college laboratory. An electron gun is used to 'fire' electrons through a graphite sample at a fluorescent screen. Diffraction rings are formed on the screen (Fig. E.16). Graphite is carbon which forms into two-dimensional crystals. So a graphite target is like a random collection of crystals all at different orientations. The crystals behave like **diffraction gratings** and give rise to the diffraction rings. Increasing the accelerating voltage of the tube reduces the size of the rings. So increasing the energy of the electron must decrease

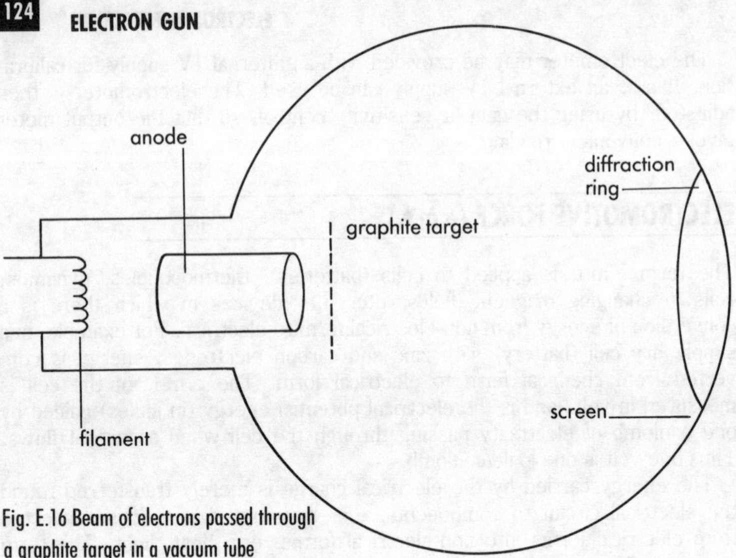

Fig. E.16 Beam of electrons passed through a graphite target in a vacuum tube

the wavelength. The relationship between the energy of the electrons and the wavelength is explained by the de Broglie relation (see **Quantum mechanical model of the atom**).

Electron diffraction is used in nuclear physics in order to obtain a reasonable idea of the size of a nucleus. To obtain electrons of an appropriate very short wavelength, i.e. from 10^{-14} to 10^{-15}m, the electron must be accelerated up to a value between 100 MeV to 1000 MeV. These are very large energies for electrons and are obtainable only from sophisticated facilities in high-energy physics laboratories such as electron linear accelerators. The nucleus size is obtained by applying diffraction theory as used in optics to this case of electron scattering. In the diffraction of light from a spherical object of radius R, the first minimum of the scattered intensity occurs at an angle θ from the direct beam where θ is given by

$$\sin \theta = 0{\cdot}61\ \lambda/R$$

Fig. E.17 shows the angular distribution of electron scattering for $^{12}_{6}C$, in which electrons of energy of 420 MeV are used. From the angle of the first diffraction minimum and using a value for the wavelength of the electron an estimate of the nuclear radius can be found.

◀ **Matter waves, Nuclear sizes, Quantum mechanical model of the atom** ▶

ELECTRON GUN

The electron gun is a piece of circuitry used in a number of evacuated tubes, including a television tube, when high-speed electrons are required.

At the end of the tube is a cathode from which electrons are generated by a process of **thermionic emission.** Using a very high-voltage supply, electrons are accelerated from this cathode up to a cylindrical anode. The

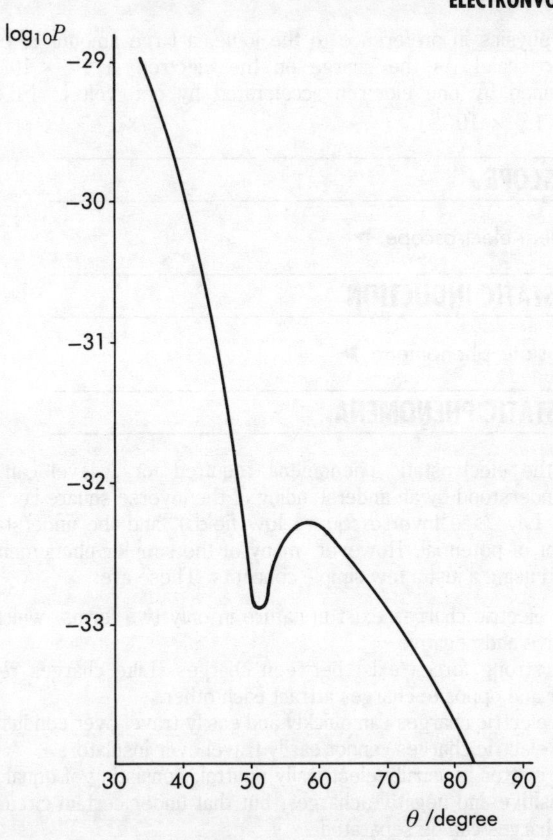

Fig. E.17 Results of electron scattering experiments for $^{12}_{6}C$ in which electrons of energy 420 MeV are used. P is a measure of the number of electrons scattered at angle θ to the incident beam

electric field propels the electrons to the centre of the anode. They shoot through the cylinder of the anode and then carry on at very high speed like bullets.

◀ Cathode ray tube ▶

ELECTRONIC METERS

◀ Ammeters and voltmeters ▶

ELECTRONVOLT

The electronvolt (eV) is defined as the energy gained by one electron accelerated by a p.d. of one volt. It is a convenient unit of energy used in atomic physics in preference to the joule, a large amount of energy on the atomic scale! As the charge on the electron is $1{\cdot}6 \times 10^{-19}$C, the energy gained by one electron accelerated by one volt is $1{\cdot}6 \times 10^{-19}$J. So 1eV = 1.6×10^{-19}J.

ELECTROSCOPE

◀ Gold-leaf electroscope ▶

ELECTROSTATIC INDUCTION

◀ Electrostatic phenomena ▶

ELECTROSTATIC PHENOMENA

Many of the electrostatic phenomena required for A-level can only be properly understood by an understanding of the inverse square law nature of Coulomb's Law (see **Inverse square law fields**), and the understanding of the concept of potential. However, many of the simpler phenomena can be appreciated using a just a few simple concepts. These are:

a) That electric charges exist in nature in only two forms, which we call positive and negative.
b) That strong forces exist between charges. Like charges repel each other and opposite charges attract each other.
c) That electric charges can quickly and easily travel over conductors
d) That electric charges cannot easily travel over insulators.
e) That matter is usually electrically neutral, consisting of equal numbers of positive and negative charges, but that under certain circumstances the charges can be separated.

Separation of charges by friction

If polythene is rubbed with cloth the polythene gains a negative charge and the cloth a positive charge. These charges are equal in magnitude but opposite in sign. If cellulose acetate, perspex or glass are rubbed then they gain a positive charge and the cloth used a negative charge. Since two polythene strips both have a negative charge and an acetate strip a positive charge, the tests shown in Fig. E.18 show repulsion by two polythene strips, and attraction of a polythene strip by an acetate strip.

If a small lightweight uncharged metallised polystyrene ball is placed near a piece of polythene it becomes attracted to the strip (Fig. E.19). This is because, being a conductor, the charges on it can redistribute themselves. The side nearest the polythene strip becomes positively charged, i.e. it has a net positive charge on that side, and the side away from the strip becomes negatively charged. If the attraction is very great the ball may make contact with the polythene and hence become negatively charged. Because both ball and strip have a negative charge it will then be repelled away instantly from the negatively charged strip.

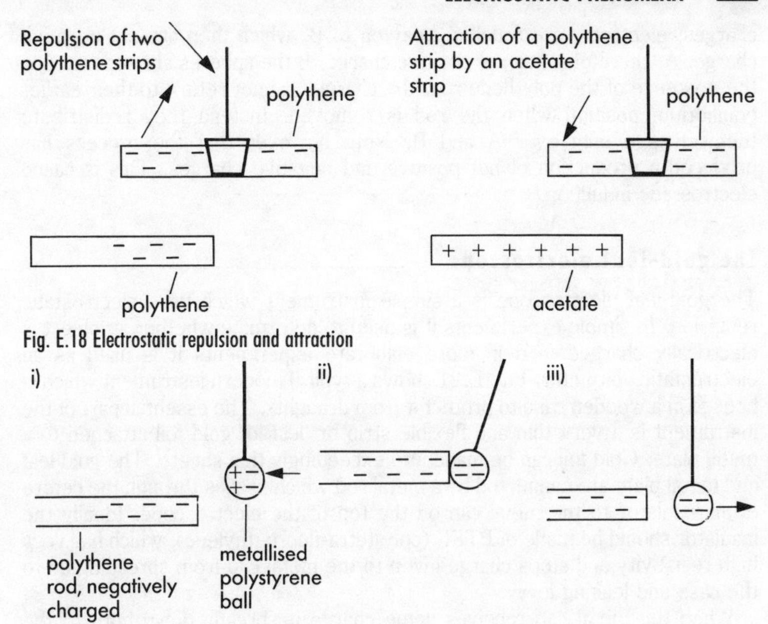

Fig. E.18 Electrostatic repulsion and attraction

Fig. E.19 i) Ball attracted to rod ii) Ball in contact with rod, acquiring negative charge iii) Ball repelled away

Electrostatic induction

The separation of electric charge seen in the above example can be further demonstrated by experiments with two metal spheres, A and B, initially held in contact (Fig. E.20). If a polythene rod is brought near them, negative

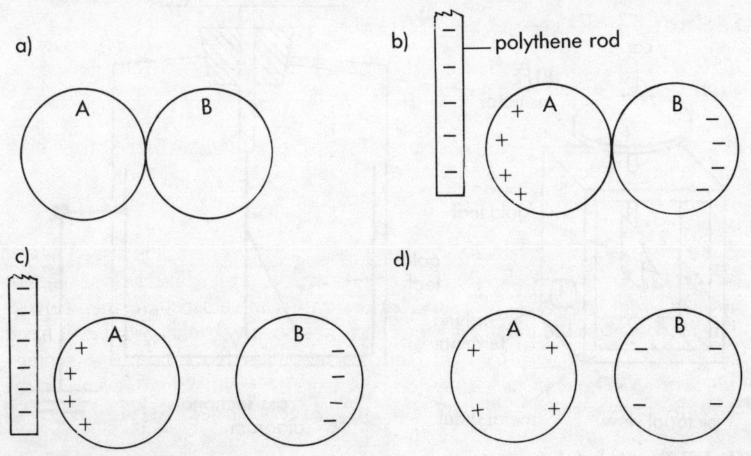

Fig. E.20 Electrostatic induction

charges, electrons, are repelled away on to B, which then has net negative charge. A, therefore, has net positive charge. If the spheres are separated in the presence of the polythene rod, the charges cannot return to their earlier equilibrium position when the rod is removed. Instead they redistribute themselves evenly over A and B. Note however that the process has produced a production of net positive and negative charges. This is called electrostatic induction.

The gold-leaf electroscope

The gold-leaf electroscope is a simple instrument which uses electrostatic repulsion. In simple experiments it is used to determine whether an object is electrically charged, and in more elaborate experiments it is used as an electrostatic voltmeter. Fig. E.21 shows a typical modern instrument which is housed in a wooden case to protect it from draughts. The essential part of the instrument is a very thin and flexible strip or 'leaf' of gold foil attached to a metal plate. Gold foil can be made into exceedingly thin sheets. The gold leaf and metal plate are connected by a metal rod which passes through the centre of an insulator to the metal cap on the top of the electroscope. Ideally the insulator should be made of PTFE (poly-tetra-fluoroethylene), which has very high resistivity and stops charge given to the metal cap from spreading on to the case and leaking away.

When the metal cap receives some charge it spreads down both to the metal plate and to the gold leaf. Since both the plate and leaf receive the same kind of charge they repel each other and the very light leaf rises away from the metal plate. A terminal is provided on the side of the case connected to a strip of metal foil inside the wooden case for connection, usually, to earth. This is important particularly if the device is used as a voltmeter connected up to a high-voltage (tension) supply where, as with all electrical instruments, two connections have to be made.

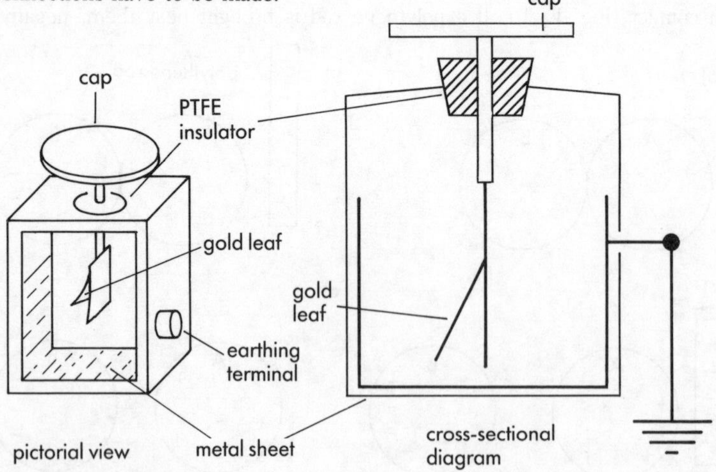

Fig. E.21 The gold-leaf electroscope

Using the electroscope to detect the sign of charge

The electroscope must first be charged. This can be done either by stroking it with a charged rod, so that some charge is collected from the surface of the insulator, or by charging it by induction. For example, to charge it positively by induction a charged polythene strip (negative) is held near the electroscope (Fig. E.22). There is a redistribution of charge on the cap and leaf, with electrons, that is net negative charge, moving down to the bottom of the leaf, and a net positive charge collecting at the top. If the electroscope is earthed in the presence of the strip it becomes temporarily part of a much larger conductor and the redistribution of charge is over that whole conductor, i.e. the cap, leaf and earth. The electrons which were on the leaf now spread themselves over the earth. If the earth connection is broken, there is net positive charge on the metal of the electroscope, which redistributes itself

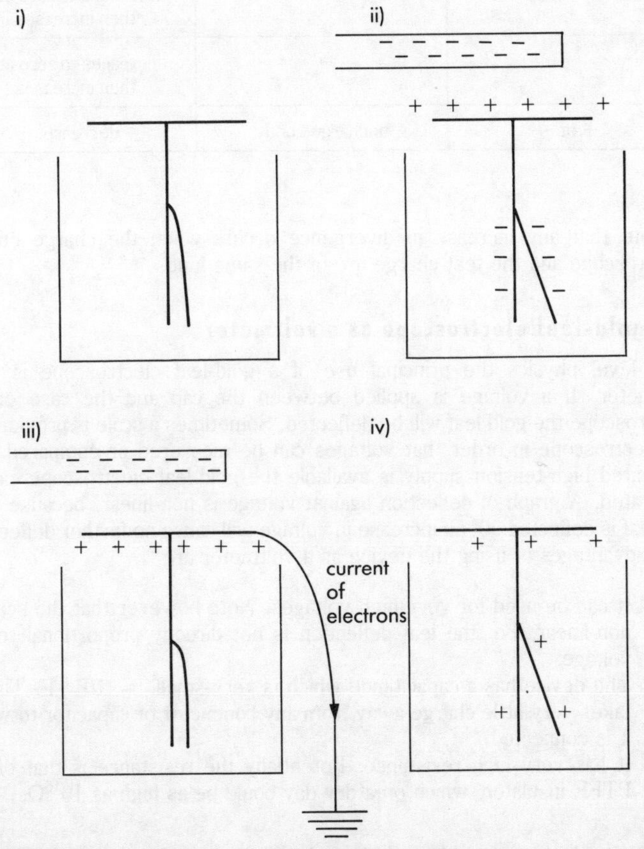

Fig. E.22 Charging an electroscope by induction i) Electroscope initially uncharged (no leaf deflection) ii) Polarisation in the presence of external negatively charged rod iii) Electroscope earthed in presence of negative charge iv) Earth lead disconnected and negatively charged rod removed

over the cap and leaf when the polythene strip is taken away. This will give rise to a deflection of the leaf due to the net positive charge on the electroscope. Note that the electroscope can be earthed simply by touching it. Once charged the electroscope can be used to test the sign of a charge brought up to it. The table shows how to interpret results.

Charge on electroscope	*Charge brought near cap*	*Effect on leaf divergence*
+	+	increases
−	−	increases
+	−	decreases to zero and then increases
−	+	decreases to zero and then increases
+ or −	uncharged body	decreases

Note that any increase in divergence occurs when the charge on the electroscope and the test charge are of the same kind.

The gold-leaf electroscope as a voltmeter

In A-level physics the principal use of a gold-leaf electroscope is as a voltmeter. If a voltage is applied between the cap and thc casc of the electroscope the gold leaf will be deflected. Sometimes a scale is provided on an electroscope in order that voltages can be measured or compared. If a calibrated high-tension supply is available the gold-leaf electroscope can be calibrated. A graph of deflection against voltage is non-linear, because once the leaf is deflected 90° an increase in voltage will cause no further deflection. The advantages of using the device as a voltmeter are

i) It can be used for very high voltages. Note however that the scale is non-linear, i.e. the leaf deflection is not directly proportional to the voltage.
ii) The device has a capacitance which is very small, $\approx 10^{-10}$F. Thus it takes very little charge away from any conductor or capacitor to which it is connected.
iii) It has very high resistance. Potentially the resistance is that of the PTFE insulator, which on a dry day could be as high as $10^{16}\Omega$.

A modern alternative to the gold-leaf electroscope is the electronic coulomb meter (see Unity gain voltage follower).

◀ Electrophorus ▶

ELEMENTARY PARTICLE

Just as until the end of the nineteenth century the atom was thought to be the basic building block of matter, so the elementary particles were until recently thought to be the basic building blocks of matter. The elementary particles come in two types, **leptons** and **hadrons.**

Leptons are particles such as the electron which do not experience the **strong interaction** of nuclear physics. Hadrons are elementary particles which do experience the strong interaction. Leptons are today still believed to be truly fundamental particles, but hadrons are thought to be built from more fundamental entities called **quarks.**

ELEMENTS

The elements and their symbols, atomic numbers and atomic weights are listed below. The atomic weights are based on the exact number 12 for the carbon-12 isotope.

	Sym-bol	At. no.	At. wt
Actinium	Ac	89	—
Aluminium	Al	13	26·9815
Americium	Am	95	—
Antimony	Sb	51	121·75
Argon	Ar	18	39·948
Arsenic	As	33	74·9216
Astatine	At	85	—
Barium	Ba	56	137·34
Berkelium	Bk	97	—
Beryllium	Be	4	9·0122
Bismuth	Bi	83	208·980
Boron	B	5	10·811*
Bromine	Br	35	79·909
Cadmium	Cd	48	112·40
Caesium	Cs	55	132·905
Calcium	Ca	20	40·08
Californium	Cf	98	—
Carbon	C	6	12·01115*
Cerium	Ce	58	140·12
Chlorine	Cl	17	35·453
Chromium	Cr	24	51·996
Cobalt	Co	27	58·9332
Copper	Cu	29	63·54
Curium	Cm	96	—
Dysprosium	Dy	66	162·50
Einsteinium	Es	99	—
Erbium	Er	68	167·26
Europium	Eu	63	151·96
Fermium	Fm	100	—
Fluorine	F	9	18·9984
Francium	Fr	87	—
Mercury	Hg	80	200·59
Molybdenum	Mo	42	95·94
Neodymium	Nd	60	144·24
Neon	Ne	10	20·183
Neptunium	Np	93	—
Nickel	Ni	28	58·71
Niobium	Nb	41	92·906
Nitrogen	N	7	14·0067
Nobelium	No	102	—
Osmium	Os	76	190·2
Oxygen	O	8	15·9994*
Palladium	Pd	46	106·4
Phosphorus	P	15	30·9738
Platinum	Pt	78	195·09
Plutonium	Pu	94	—
Polonium	Po	84	—
Potassium	K	19	39·102
Praseodymium	Pr	59	140.907
Promethium	Pm	61	—
Protactinium	Pa	91	—
Radium	Ra	88	—
Radon	Rn	86	—
Rhenium	Re	75	186·2
Rhodium	Rh	45	102·905
Rubidium	Rb	37	85·47
Ruthenium	Ru	44	101·07
Samarium	Sm	62	150·35
Scandium	Sc	21	44·956
Selenium	Se	34	78·96
Silicon	Si	14	28·086*
Silver	Ag	47	107·870

	Symbol	At. no.	At. wt		Symbol	At. no.	At. wt
Gadolinium	Gd	64	157·25	Sodium	Na	11	22·9898
Gallium	Ga	31	69·72	Strontium	Sr	38	87·62
Germanium	Ge	32	72·59	Sulphur	S	16	32·064*
Gold	Au	79	196·967	Tantalum	Ta	73	180·948
Hafnium	Hf	72	178·49	Technetium	Tc	43	—
Helium	He	2	4·0026	Tellurium	Te	52	127·60
Holmium	Ho	67	164·930	Terbium	Tb	65	158·924
Hydrogen	H	1	1·00797*	Thallium	Tl	81	204·37
Indium	In	49	114·82	Thorium	Th	90	232·038
Iodine	I	53	126·9044	Thulium	Tm	69	168·934
Iridium	Ir	77	192·2	Tin	Sn	50	118·69
Iron	Fe	26	55·847	Titanium	Ti	22	47·90
Krypton	Kr	36	83·80	Tungsten	W	74	183·85
Lanthanum	La	57	138·91	Uranium	U	92	238·03
Lawrencium	Lw	103	—	Vanadium	V	23	50·942
Lead	Pb	82	207·19	Xenon	Xe	54	131·30
Lithium	Li	3	6·939	Ytterbium	Yb	70	173·04
Lutetium	Lu	71	174·97	Yttrium	Y	39	88·905
Magnesium	Mg	12	24·312	Zinc	Zn	30	65·37
Manganese	Mn	25	54·9380	Zirconium	Zr	40	91·22
Mendelevium	Md	101	—				

*These atomic weights are known to be variable because of natural variations in isotopic composition.

ELLIPSE

◀ Kepler's Laws of Motion ▶

E.M.F.

◀ Electromotive force ▶

EMISSION SPECTRUM

An emission spectrum is that of a light source which stands in front of a dark background and emits light across a range of wavelengths. It contrasts with an **absorption spectrum**.

An emission spectrum is typically that given by excited atoms. Laboratory examples are the spectra from neon and sodium lamps. The spectra result from the excitation of atoms. As the atoms revert to more stable states electrons 'fall down' from higher **energy levels** to lower ones. As they do so there is an emission of light according to the Planck equation $E = hf$, where E is the energy change, h is the **Planck constant**, and f is the frequency of the radiation emitted.

EMISSIVITY

Emissivity is a term used in the theory of **thermal radiation**. The emissivity of a surface, e, is a constant of value between 0 and 1 which measures the fraction of radiation emitted from unit area of the surface that the surface emits compared with what it would be if it were a **black body**. So for a surface which emits no radiation, i.e. a perfect silvery surface, in other words a perfect reflector, e is zero, and for a perfect black body, $e = 1$.

ENDOSCOPE

An endoscope is an instrument used in medicine to make observations at points inside the body. Such an instrument is commonly an **optical fibre** device. (The principle of such an instrument is shown in Fig. E.23. The image falls on a certain number of fibres and each one receives light forming part of the image. The fibres transmit this through to the opposite end provided that the arrangement of fibres is the same throughout the bundle. Such a bundle is called a coherent bundle. In an incoherent bundle the fibres are jumbled up and although light can be transmitted by such a system, images cannot.

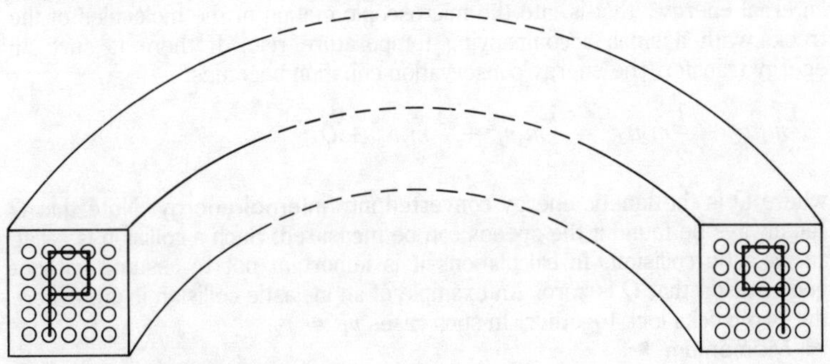

Fig. E.23 Coherent bundle of fibres

ENERGY

Energy is often defined as that which enables a 'job' to be done, a 'job' being the raising of a **weight**, the **acceleration** of a mass, etc. In the complete theory of energy and in **thermodynamics** it is regarded as a conserved quantity, following the pattern of **momentum**, changes in energy being merely changes from one form to another, e.g. from kinetic to potential to radiation etc.

In mechanics it has an intimate connection with the concept of work or work done. Work done, W, is defined as the component of the force in the direction of the distance moved × the distance moved. The units of work are joules, the joule being the work done when a force of 1 newton moves through a distance of 1m:

$$W = F \times s$$

Now work is the amount of energy transferred from one form to another when a force moves through a distance. If energy is likened to money, work is like a cheque measuring the money transferred from one account to another. So the units of energy are also joules.

◀ Conservation Law, Kinetic energy, Potential energy, Power ▶

ENERGY IN COLLISION PROBLEMS

When two objects collide, **momentum** conservation *always* holds, i.e. $m_1u_1 + m_2u_2 = m_1v_1 + m_2v_2$, with the usual symbols (see Fig. M.18, page 248). But the conservation of **energy** in its kinetic form, i.e.

$$\frac{1}{2}m_1{u_1}^2 + \frac{1}{2}m_2{u_2}^2 = \frac{1}{2}m_1{v_1}^2 + \frac{1}{2}m_2{v_2}^2$$

holds only in the case of *elastic collisions*. These are collisions in which there is no transfer of energy from the motion of the trucks (see Fig. M.18) into 'internal energy', that is into the microscopic motion of the molecules of the trucks with a small accompanying temperature rise. If there is such an energy transfer, the energy conservation equation becomes:

$$\frac{1}{2}m_1{u_1}^2 + \frac{1}{2}m_2{u_2}^2 = \frac{1}{2}m_1{v_1}^2 + \frac{1}{2}m_2{v_2}^2 + Q$$

where Q is the kinetic energy converted into **internal energy**. Note that Q can always be found if the speeds can be measured. Such a collision is called an inelastic collision. In calculations it is important not to assume without good reason that Q is zero. An example of an inelastic collision is one where the two trucks lock together. In such cases $v_1 = v_2$.

◀ Momentum ▶

ENERGY LEVELS

This is a term used in atomic physics to describe the possible energy states of an electron in an atom.

In metals some of the electrons are free electrons not bound to any particular atom in the metal. On the other hand the majority of electrons in metals and all the electrons in non-metallic substances are bound to individual atoms. They are held there by the forces of attraction that exist between the positive charge on the nucleus of the atom and their own negative charges. We cannot 'see' the electrons in an atom and so have to construct a model of the way in which they are bound. The first successful model of the atom was the Bohr model of hydrogen, in which the electrons were thought to orbit the nucleus in circular orbits rather like the planets in orbit round the sun. However, in the Bohr model of the atom only certain orbits were allowed and therefore only certain energies were available to the electrons. In the quantum mechanics which replaced the Bohr theory the electrons in an atom are considered to be a kind of standing wave. As a result the mechanism by which the electron exists in an atom is really very different in this model. But the idea of electrons having only discrete amounts of energy remains and this leads to the idea of energy levels.

Fig. E.24 shows the electron energy levels for an imaginary atom. The lowest energy level is that of the ground state. In the imaginary atom it is associated with an energy of −40 eV. This means that an electron, such as that indicated by A, would need an energy of 40 eV in order to be removed from the atom. That is to say it is in a bound state of negative potential energy and has to be given energy to escape from the nucleus. The electron marked in state E is in a higher energy level and needs only 16 eV to leave the atom. The arrow in C is meant to illustrate the *ionisation* of the atom. In this case the electron is moved from the ground state up to the level of zero energy, i.e. becomes free of the atom. The atom left behind then has a net positive charge and is said to be ionised. The energy needed to move the electron is called the ionisation energy. The potential difference needed to give a free electron sufficient energy to enable it to ionise an atom is called the ionisation potential. In this case it would be 40 volts. If electrons were accelerated through an electric field with this potential difference they could subsequently collide with the atom and cause ionisation. With less energy than this they would be unable to do so. The arrow at D shows an electron which is given more energy than the 40 eV. This is enough to move it into the region of the energy level diagram called the continuum. The continuum is the region of the diagram which contains all the possible energies of free electrons, i.e. those which are not bound to the atom. There is a continuous spread of energies available to free electrons and hence the name

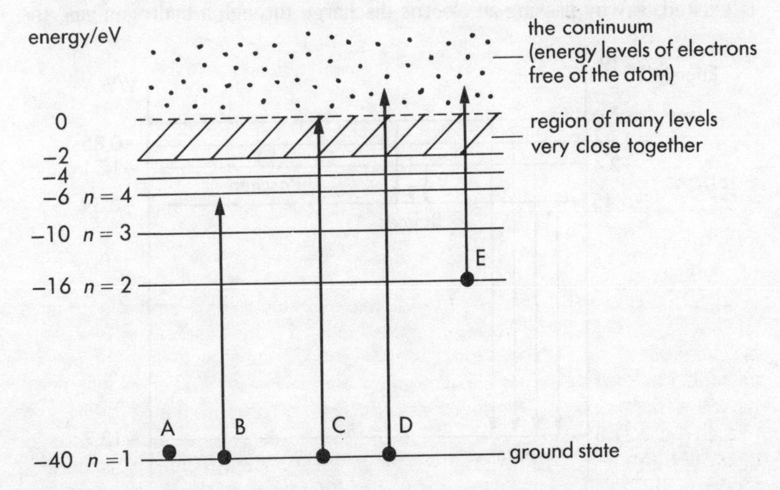

Fig. E.24 Energy levels in an atom

continuum. So if for example 50 eV were available to a colliding electron there would be enough energy available to remove an electron from the ground state and for it to have 10 eV of kinetic energy on escaping from the atom. The electron marked at E shows an ionisation process but from a higher energy level, requiring less energy.

The electron at B is simply raised from the ground state to a higher energy level. This process is called *excitation* and the atom that is left is said to be in an excited state. It is not stable in this state and subsequently it is likely that the atom will reach a higher level of stability by the electron 'falling down' into a lower energy state. The energy levels of the atom form a ladder of levels which are usually numbered. Towards the bottom of the ladder the spaces are usually very wide and these close up until, as the continuum is approached, there is a region of many levels very close together which are difficult to represent on a diagram.

The atom with the simplest set of energy levels is the hydrogen atom. For hydrogen the energy of the levels is given by $13{\cdot}6/n^6$eV. In joules these are $21{\cdot}8 \times 10^{-19}/n^2$ J, where n is the number of the levels.

ENERGY LEVELS IN HYDROGEN

Hydrogen is the simplest atom and has the simplest set of *energy levels*. Theorists have therefore regarded hydrogen as the starting point for theories of the atom.

For hydrogen it was recognised at an early stage that there was a simple formula for the energy levels available to the single electron. The energies are $13{\cdot}6/n^2$ eV (where $n = 1,2,3\ldots$). In joules this is $21{\cdot}8 \times 10^{-19}/n^2$ J. Here n is the number of the energy levels. $n = 1$ corresponds to the lowest possible energy state, called the ground state. If the hydrogen atom is excited, say by passing an electric discharge through a hydrogen gas, the

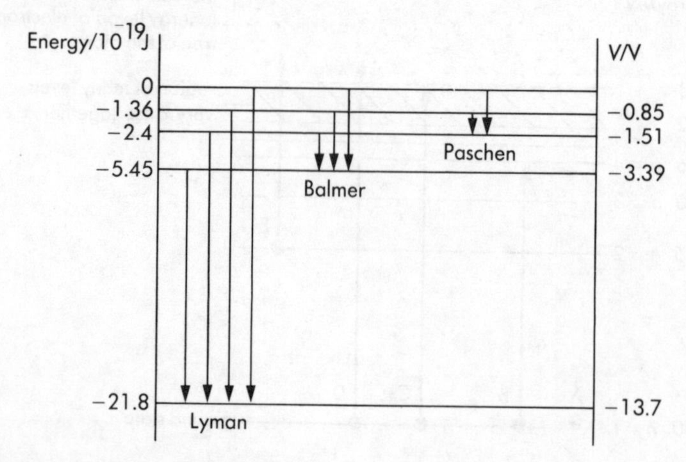

Fig. E.25 Lyman, Balmer and Paschen series

atom is raised from its lowest energy state. This will usually be a state with the electron in the $n = 1$ level. But if the gas is very hot, as it might be in the hydrogen gas of a star, the collisions of kinetic theory in the gas may have raised the electron to the $n = 2$ or $n = 3$ level. Either way, after the electric discharge the atom will revert to a more stable state, with the electron moving from a state with a large value of n to a smaller one. Such transitions are naturally called downward transitions.

Observations of the electromagnetic spectrum of hydrogen reveal several sets of lines, each in a clear sequence or series. The **Lyman series** corresponds to transitions down to level 1 ($n = 2,3,4,\ldots \rightarrow n = 1$). The **Balmer series** consists of transitions down to level 2 ($n = 3,4,5,\ldots \rightarrow n = 2$). The **Paschen series** consists of transitions down to level 3, and the **Pfund series** consists of transitions down to $n = 4$, and so on. The Lyman lines are in the ultraviolet spectrum and the Paschen and Pfund lines in the infrared spectrum. Only the Balmer series has lines in the visible region of the spectrum.

Such a spectrum is a **line spectrum** characteristic of hydrogen.

◀ Pauli exclusion principle, Quantum mechanical model of the atom ▶

ENERGY OF A CHARGED CAPACITOR

Consider the charging of a **capacitor** from first principles. If the capacitor is initially uncharged, we would begin by transferring a little charge, dQ, from one plate to another. Note that the net charge on one plate would be then $-\mathrm{d}Q$ and the net charge on the other plate $+\mathrm{d}Q$. Note also that the net charge on the two plates considered together is still zero. Because there is no p.d. between the plates the energy required to move the charge dQ is very small. However, once the charge has been transferred there is a p.d., V, between the plates and an electric field $E = V/d$. As more and more charge is transferred from one plate to the other the p.d. across the plates increases in proportion. To transfer a small charge dQ when the p.d. is V volts requires $V\mathrm{d}Q$ joules of energy. This is the area of the strip shaded in Fig. E.26. The total energy stored in the capacitor is the area under the graph given by

$$\frac{1}{2}QV = \frac{1}{2}CV^2 = \frac{1}{2}\frac{Q^2}{C}$$

As an example consider a simple **parallel-plate capacitor** made using two sheets of aluminium kitchen foil and having a polythene shopping bag as the dielectric. Assuming a parallel-plate capacitor, we have $C = \dfrac{A\epsilon_r\epsilon_0}{d}$.

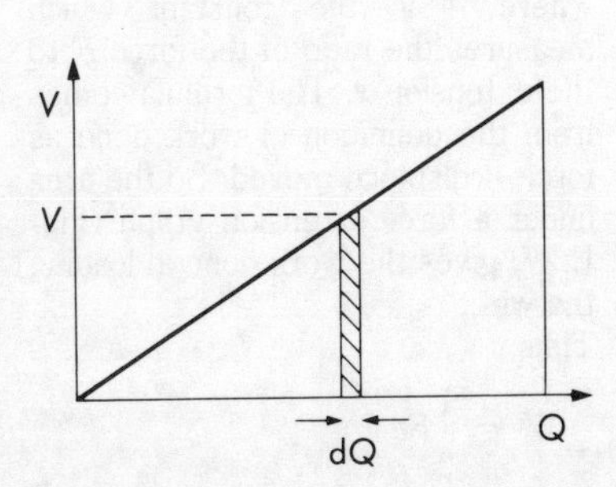

Fig. E.26 Energy stored in a capacitor

With aluminium foil 30cm × 30cm, $A = 0{\cdot}09\mathrm{m}^2$. $\epsilon_0 = 8{\cdot}85 \times 10^{-12}\mathrm{Fm}^{-1}$, and we can take the relative permitivity, ϵ_r, of polythene as 2. Assuming $d = 0{\cdot}5$mm, we get $C = 3{\cdot}18 \times 10^{-9}$F.

$E = \frac{1}{2}CV^2$ so if we were to charge the capacitor to 5000 volts the energy stored would be

$$E = \frac{1}{2} \times 3{\cdot}18 \times 10^{-9} \times (5000)^2$$
$$= 0{\cdot}0398\text{J}$$

Note that such a charged capacitor could give an unpleasant and dangerous shock.

ENERGY SOURCES

Energy sources are classed into two types: renewable and non-renewable.

Renewable energy sources are those which in some ways are replaced by nature. Solar energy and wind power are two examples. In both cases the energy comes from the sun. Tidal energy is strictly not an example of a renewable energy source. This is because the energy of the tides comes from the rotation of the earth and if this energy were tapped the rate of rotation of the earth would diminish. However, the amount of energy 'locked up' in the rotation of the earth is so huge that the reduction in the speed of the earth's rotation would be a very slow process indeed.

Non-renewable energy sources include coal, oil and nuclear power derived from uranium.

ENERGY STORED IN A STRETCHED WIRE

The energy W stored in a stretched wire is given by

$$W = \frac{1}{2}kx^2$$

where k is the constant which measures the ratio of the force F to the extension x. The formula comes from the definition of work done as force × distance moved. So the area under a force/extension graph (Fig. E.27) gives the work done in loading the wire.

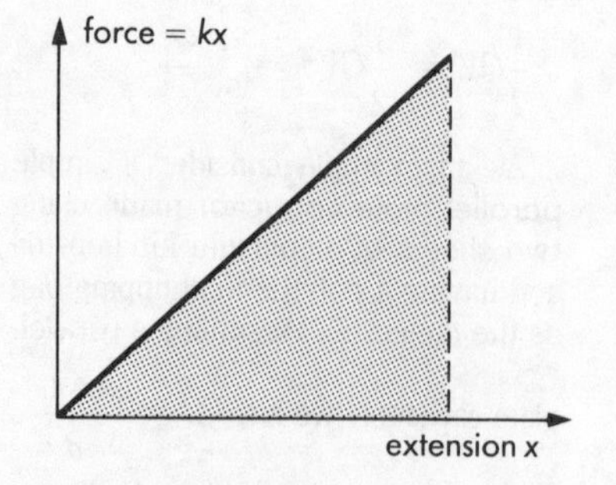

Fig. E.27 Force/extension graph

Thus,

$$W = \frac{1}{2}Fe$$

where e is the extension. If the wire has cross-sectional area A and length l, division by the volume of the wire Al gives the energy per unit volume:

$$\frac{1}{2}\frac{Fe}{Al} = \frac{1}{2} \times \frac{F}{A} \times \frac{e}{l} = \frac{1}{2}(\text{stress}) \times (\text{strain})$$

◀ Hooke's Law ▶

ENGINES

Engines come in various forms. They all burn fuel in order to turn 'heat' into 'work'.

The common types used in transport are internal combustion engines such as the diesel and the petrol engine. In these engines the fuel is burned inside the cylinder. In a petrol engine it is ignited by an electric spark, in a diesel engine the fuel ignites because the temperature induced in the compression cycle of the engine takes the cylinder temperature above the temperature at which the fuel ignites. Steam engines, in which steam is heated externally in a boiler, are still used in some countries for rail transport. Another engine which is not an internal combustion engine is the Stirling engine.

When larger power supplies are needed it becomes more efficient to use turbines. Examples are the large steam turbines used in power stations and gas turbines used in smaller power stations.

To analyse an engine we need to begin with the formula for the work done when a piston is pushed by a gas down a cylinder. The formula for work done is $W = F\Delta x$. If the pressure of the gas in the cylinder of an engine is constant we can write $F = pA$, where A is the cylinder area. Thus $\Delta W = pA\Delta x = p\Delta V$, ΔV being the volume change of the gas. If the pressure changes, then using the notation of the calculus for an infinitesimal change, $\mathrm{d}W = p\mathrm{d}V$.

To study engines, use is made of a so-called indicator diagram, i.e. a graph of p against V for a whole cycle of operation of the piston in the cylinder (Fig. E.28). On such a graph the work done is shown by the hatched are under the curve and equals $\int_{v_1}^{v_2} p\mathrm{d}V$

A whole cycle is shown in Fig. E.29, the net work done being the shaded area.

Now to proceed further it is sometimes necessary to know the relation between the two molar specific heats (defined under **Calorimetry**). C_p, the molar specific heat capacity at constant pressure, is greater than C_v, the molar specific heat capacity at constant volume, because when the volume changes some of the heat is converted into mechanical energy when the gas expands.

It can be shown that $C_p = C_v + R$. In a monatomic gas, **kinetic theory** gives $C_v = 3R/2$ and so $C_p = 5R/2$. $\frac{C_p}{C_v}$ is usually written as γ, the ratio of molar specific heats.

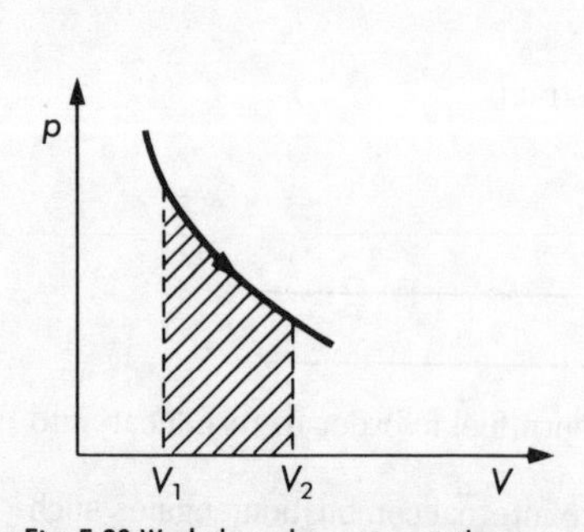

Fig. E.28 Work done shown on an indicator diagram

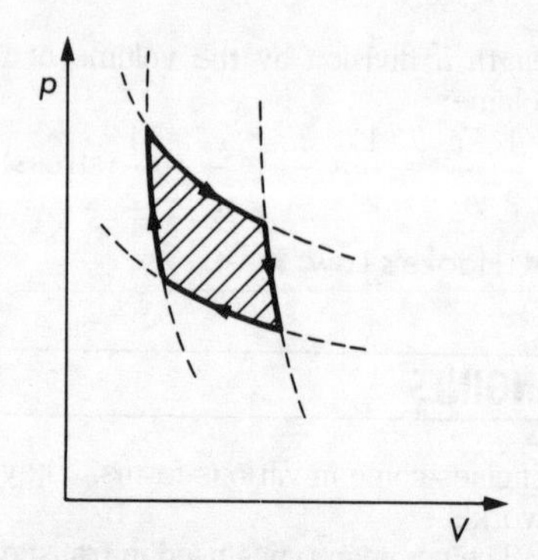

Fig. E.29 Net work done in a cycle

Particular types of *p*, *V* change

Fig. E.30 shows the indicator diagram for an imaginary engine with four different types of p, V change.

A → B represents a heating of the gas at constant volume. Because V does not change no work is done (the area under the curve is zero). So $\Delta Q = \Delta U$, i.e. the gas gains internal energy by taking in heat.

B → C represents an isothermal (constant temperature) expansion during which the gas absorbs more heat. There is no change in U, the **internal energy** of the gas, as there is no change in the temperature. Here work is done by the gas.

C → D represents a rapid further expansion of the gas during which there is insufficient time for heat to leave the gas. As a result the work done by the gas is equal to the loss in internal energy. The curve C → D is described by the formula $pV^{\gamma} = $ constant, where γ is the ratio of molar specific heats.

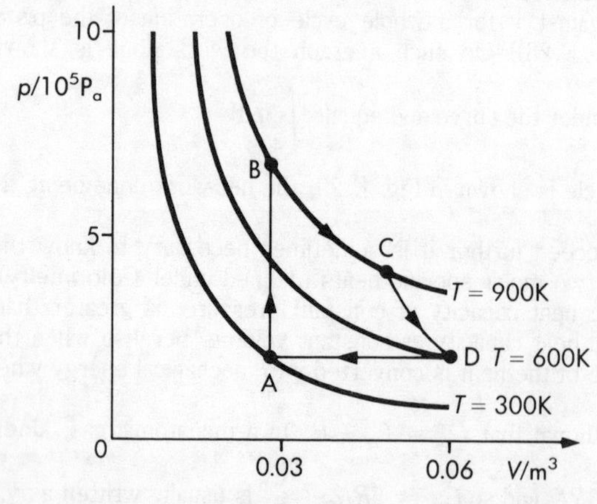

Fig. E.30 Indicator diagram for an engine with four different types of p, V change

Finally D → A represents an isobaric (constant pressure) change. In this change the gas loses heat energy. Some of the heat energy comes from the work done on it to compress it and some from the drop in temperature, and therefore the reduction in internal energy.

Notice that for the cycle taken as a whole $\Delta U = 0$.

Calculations

At A-level, calculations will largely be limited to situations where the changes are isobaric (as in D → A above). For such a change $\Delta U = nC_p(T_2 - T_1)$, where n is the number of moles and $\Delta W = p(V_2 - V_1)$. Note especially this last formula. Because p is constant the area under a pV graph is simply $p(V_2 - V_1)$.

ENGINE EFFICIENCY AND THE SECOND LAW OF THERMODYNAMICS

Applied to engines, this law states that while it is always possible to turn work into heat, it is not possible for an engine working in a cycle to turn heat completely into work.

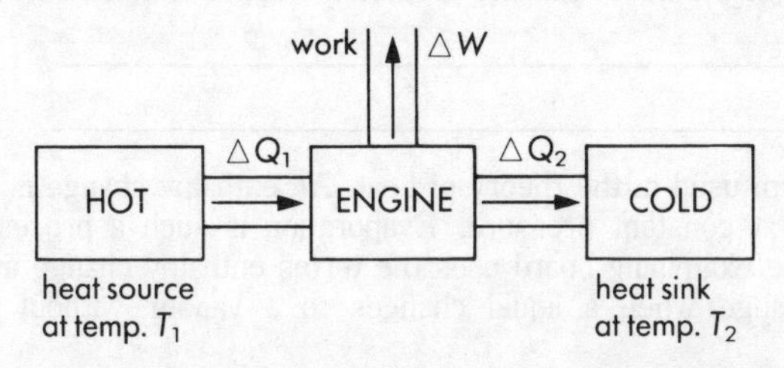

Fig. E.31

For the purpose of the Second Law an engine is idealised as a device in which heat is taken from a heat source at a high temperature T_1, in which some of the heat is converted into work, and out of which the remaining heat is transferred to a heat 'sink' at a low temperature, T_2 (Fig. E.31). For example in a power station, steam turbine water is heated to steam at a high temperature in the boiler. In the turbine the steam does work by expanding and cooling, but it cools only to a certain temperature and is then discarded. As in the earlier hypothetical engine the process is cyclic and $\Delta U = 0$. By the first law

$$\Delta Q_1 - \Delta Q_2 = \Delta W$$

The efficiency of the engine as a converter from heat to work is

$$\frac{\Delta W}{\Delta Q_1} = \frac{\Delta Q_1 - \Delta Q_2}{\Delta Q_1}$$

In order to do calculations using the second law it has been useful to define a property called **entropy**. When an amount of heat ΔQ is supplied into an engine at a temperature T there is an increase in entropy, ΔS, given by

$\Delta S = \Delta Q/T$. (Note that the unit of entropy is JK^{-1}.) The Second Law of Thermodynamics is then usually described by saying that in the cyclic process of an engine

$\Delta S \geqslant 0$

When an engine is working at the upper limit of its theoretical efficiency $\Delta S = 0$, ΔS being taken over the whole cycle

As $\Delta S = \dfrac{\Delta Q_1}{T_1} - \dfrac{\Delta Q_2}{T_2}$ for the whole cycle

ΔQ must be proportional to T, so that

$$\frac{\Delta Q_1}{T_1} = \frac{\Delta Q_2}{T_2}$$

Using this result the formula for efficiency becomes

$$\frac{\Delta W}{\Delta Q_1} = \frac{T_1 - T_2}{T_1}$$

So the higher the temperature of the heat source and the lower the temperature of the heat sink, the greater the upper limit on efficiency.

ENTHALPY

This is a term used in the theory of heat. An enthalpy change is one which takes place at constant pressure. Evaporation is such a process, so, for example, one examining board uses the terms enthalpy change and specific enthalpy change when a liquid changes to a vapour without change in pressure.

◀ Calorimetry ▶

ENTROPY

Entropy is a term used in thermodynamics to measure the degree to which a process in which heat produces work, or vice versa, is reversible. It is defined as $\Delta Q/T$, where ΔQ is the heat transferred into a thermodynamic system and T the temperature at which this transfer takes place. It is only correct to talk about changes of entropy: there is therefore no zero of entropy. Further details of entropy are given in the entries **Laws of thermodynamics** and **Engines**. A treatment of entropy in terms of the microscopic processes of molecules is given in the entry **Statistical thermodynamics**.

EQUATION OF CONTINUITY

This is an equation used in the physics of fluid flow and applied to situations where the fluid cannot be compressed.

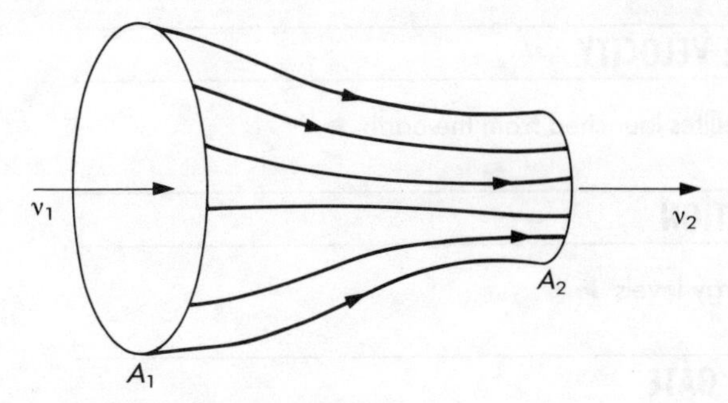

Fig. E.32 Narrowing pipe showing possible streamlines

Fig. E.32 shows a pipe in which the area of cross-section narrows from A_1 to A_2. The fluid has to speed up. The equation of continuity states that

$$v_1A_1 = v_2A_2$$

◀ Bernouilli's principle, Streamline ▶

EQUIPOTENTIALS

◀ Inverse square law fields ▶

EQUITEMPERED SCALE

◀ Diatonic scale ▶

ERRORS

Experimental errors result in a measurement differing from its true value. There are two main types of error, random errors and systematic errors.

A *random error* arises in any measurement, usually when the observer has to estimate the last figure with an instrument which is then at the limit of its sensitivity. Random errors are small for a good experimenter and taking the mean of a number of separate measurements reduces them in all cases. A measurement with a small random error is precise but it may not be accurate. Because of the nature of this type of error some authors prefer to use the word uncertainty.

A *systematic error* may be due to an incorrectly calibrated scale on, for example, a ruler or an electrical meter. Another type of error of this kind occurs when the scale divisions are of the right size but the zero point is displaced. Repeating the observation does not help and the existence of the error may not be suspected until the final result is calculated and checked, say by a different experimental method. If the systematic error is small a measurement is accurate.

◀ Composition of errors ▶

ESCAPE VELOCITY

◀ Satellites launched from the earth ▶

EXCITATION

◀ Energy levels ▶

EXNOR GATE

◀ Logic gates ▶

EXOR GATE

◀ Logic gates ▶

EYE

The human eye uses a **converging lens** system to produce a real image of an object on a curved screen called a retina (Fig. E.33). Light-sensitive cells on this retina called rods and cones receive the light and send electrical impulses along the optic nerve to the brain. This processes the nerve signals to form a view of the outside world.

The amount of light reaching the retina is controlled by the iris. Light entering the eye is converged mainly by the cornea and the watery liquid (aqueous humour) behind it. The lens itself is used to make focusing

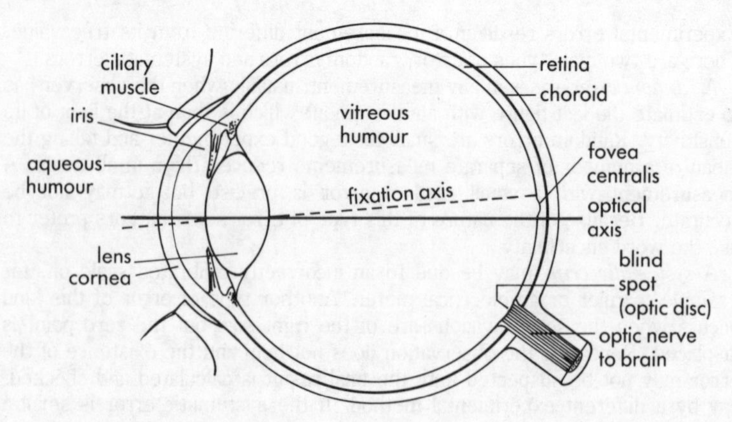

Fig. E.33 Horizontal section of the right human eye

adjustments, a process called **accommodation**. The shape of the lens is adjusted by the action of muscles, the ciliary muscles. When an object is brought close to the eye the lens thickens so that with the reduced focal length the image is kept in focus. People with **defects of vision** may need spectacles or contact lenses to improve their eye sight.

Fig. E.34 is a cross-section through the retina to show the rods and cones and the nerve endings to them. The eye has been considered by some biologists as a perfect example of engineering, but this diagram shows that it is not. This is because the nerve fibres leading to the optic nerve run away from the retina on the side from which light comes. A better biological structure would have the nerves on the far side of the rods and cones. Each rod and cone can be thought of as a photoelectric cell in which light energy is converted to electrical energy.

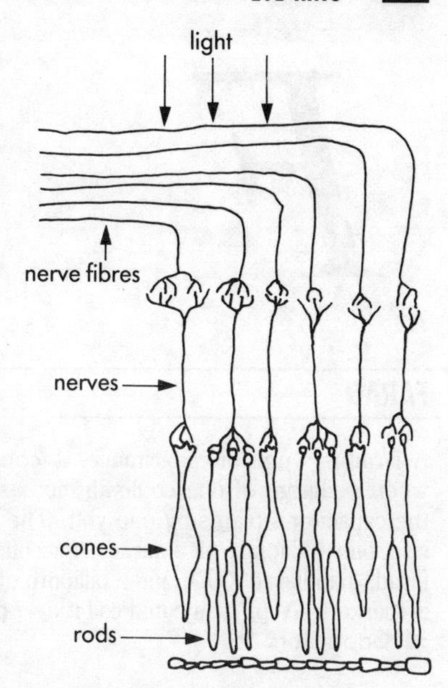

Fig. E.34 Section through the retina

Rods are about 100 times more sensitive than cones except for long wavelengths. Thus, in very low light conditions, vision is almost entirely by rods. Cones on the other hand give distinct vision in colour, as they are sensitive to different wavelengths within the visible spectrum. Thus in very low light conditions, when only the rods are operating, the image produced by the eye is monochromatic, i.e. like that of a black and white television. The way in which the eye sees colour is a three-colour (red, green and blue) system very similar to that used in colour television. Thus if the eye is looking at light of wavelength 500 nm, i.e. yellow light, both the red and green cones are activated and the brain reconstructs this as a vision of yellow.

The ratio of rods to cones is not the same at all points on the retina. The region immediately opposite the lens is almost entirely cones. Whereas further away on the edge of the eye the retina is mainly rods. So for example in poor light conditions objects sometime disappear when looked at directly and can only be seen by moving the eye so that the image is cast upon the outer regions of the retina.

EYE RING

◀ Astronomical telescope ▶

FARAD

A farad is a unit of capacitance. A **capacitor** has a capacitance of one farad when a charge of one coulomb increases the **potential difference** between the capacitor's plates by one volt. The farad is a large unit and is subdivided into one millionth of a farad, 'microfarad' (μF), a thousand millionth of a farad, 'nanofarad' (nF), and a billionth of a farad 'picofarad' (pF). If a capacitor is marked 470 pF you could call it a 47 picofarad or a '47 puff' capacitor.

◀ Capacitors ▶

FARADAY'S ICE-PAIL EXPERIMENTS

Michael Faraday performed two famous experiments in electrostatics, called the ice-pail experiments. Note that these have nothing to do with ice: they are called such simply because Faraday did the experiments using a metal ice-pail.

Faraday's first experiment

A positively charged metal sphere, charged, for example, by induction, is supported by an insulating thread and lowered into a hollow can standing on a **gold-leaf electroscope** (Fig. F.1). Negative charge becomes induced on the inside of the can (a). Because the total net charge of the can is zero the positive charge appears on the outside of the can and on the leaf. The sphere may be moved about inside the can without altering the leaf divergence. If the charged sphere then touches the bottom of the can there is still no movement of the leaf (b). This must mean that the negative charge on the inside of the can is exactly equal and opposite to the charge on the sphere. When the sphere is removed it is found to have no charge.

Faraday's second experiment

In this experiment (Fig. F.2) the can is earthed in the presence of the sphere (b). The sphere is then removed and the divergence of the leaf is exactly the same as it was in the first experiment (c). This shows that the negative induced charge must be equal in magnitude to the positive induced charge. We

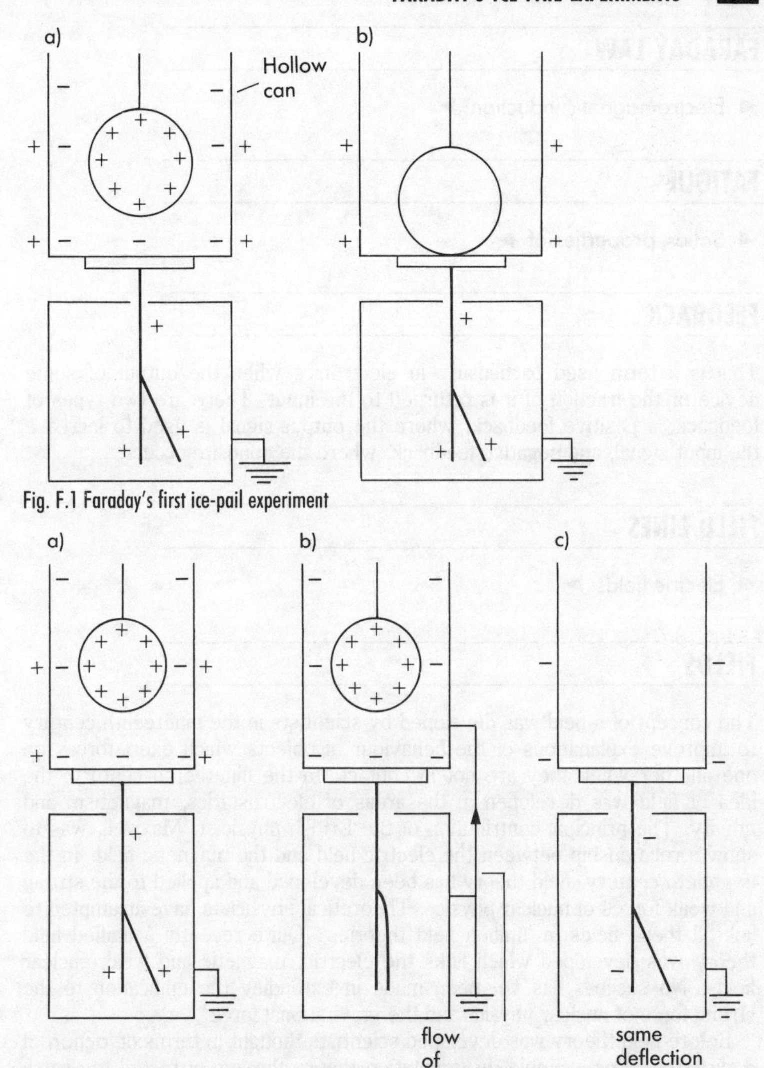

Fig. F.1 Faraday's first ice-pail experiment

Fig. F.2 Faraday's second ice-pail experiment

would expect this, as the total charge on the pail plus the gold-leaf electroscope at the start of the experiment was zero.

The principal consequence of these experiments is the clear experimental indication that at all times the total or net charge inside a hollow conductor is zero. All charge given to a conductor goes to its outside surface. This principle is used in the Van de Graaf generator.

◀ Electrostatic phenomena ▶

FARADAY LAW

◀ Electromagnetic induction ▶

FATIGUE

◀ Solids, properties of ▶

FEEDBACK

This is a term used particularly in electronics when the output of some device or the fraction of it is returned to the input. There are two types of feedback, a positive feedback, where the output signal is used to increase the input signal, and negative feedback, where the opposite occurs.

FIELD LINES

◀ Electric fields ▶

FIELDS

The concept of a field was developed by scientists in the nineteenth century to improve explanations of the behaviour of objects which exert forces on one another when they are not in contact. In the nineteenth century, the idea of field was developed in the areas of electrostatics, magnetism and gravity. The principal contribution of the British physicist, Maxwell, was to show a relationship between the electric field and the magnetic field. In the twentieth century, field theory has been developed and applied to the strong and weak forces of nuclear physics. Theoretical physicists have attempted to link all these fields in 'unified field theories'. Quite recently a unified field theory was developed which links the electric, magnetic and weak nuclear fields. No success has yet been made in extending the unification to the strong force of nuclear physics and the gravitational force.

Before field theory was developed scientists thought in terms of **'action at a distance'**. For example, in gravitation theory the sun attracted the earth according to an inverse square law and somehow managed to exert this external force on the earth from a huge distance. To calculate the force the formula $F = GMm/R^2$ would be used, where M is the mass of the sun, m is the mass of the earth, G is the universal gravitational constant, and R is the distance apart of the two bodies.

In the alternative approach of field theory the whole of the space round a massive object such as the sun is thought to change. A mass placed in the field responds to this change, and this response is what we call the force on the object. In the case of the sun we say that the change in space is the production of a gravitational field strength which has a magnitude $g = \dfrac{GM}{R^2}$ at the earth. The earth then experiences a force mg. Described like this it would seem that the field description is only another way of coding up the formula $F = GMm/R^2$.

This is certainly true of this particular example, and if this were all that there was to fields the concept would be unimportant. The real usefulness of fields is that they have their own properties, and once these are known they give an insight into both the real nature of how the fields work, and assist in calculations.

As an example, consider the electric field which is set up when some electrodes are placed into a conducting fluid. Fig. F.3 shows the kind of arrangement which can be constructed with a tray of copper sulphate solution and some copper electrodes. By using a voltmeter the potentials at all points in the field between the electrodes can be measured (see **Electric fields**). But using a simple property possessed by the electric field these potentials could instead by found by calculation. This is done as follows.

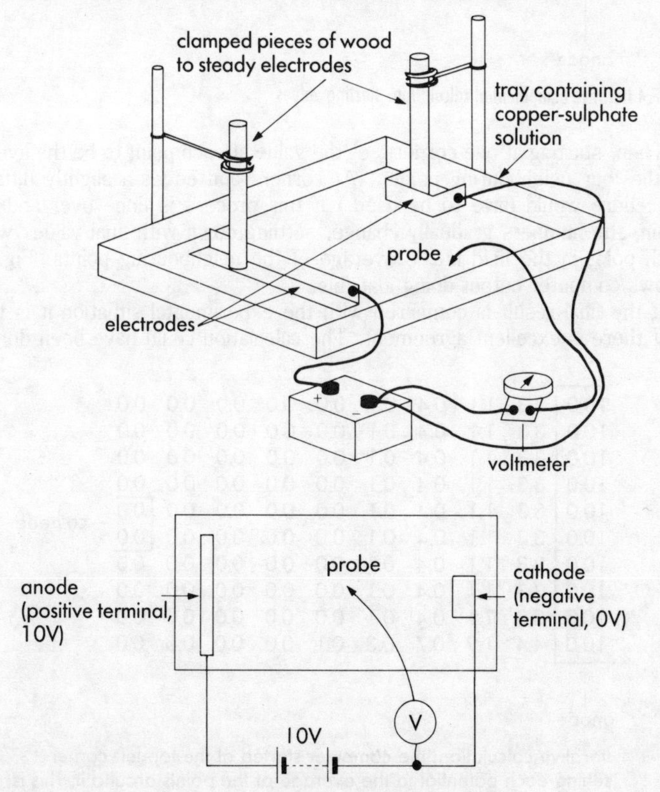

Fig. F.3 Plan view of the tray of electrolyte and electrodes, with circuit diagram

The potentials of the two electrodes are fixed by the battery to which they are connected. In order to calculate the potentials at other points the simple field property to be used is that each point in the field has the average value of the potential at neighbouring points. This is best done on a computer. The space between the electrodes is divided into a grid. Initially zeros can be entered for all points in the grid except those of the electrodes (Fig. F.4).

anode									cathode
10.0	0.0	0.0	0.0	0.0	0.0	0.0	0.0	0.0	0.0
10.0	0.0	0.0	0.0	0.0	0.0	0.0	0.0	0.0	0.0
10.0	0.0	0.0	0.0	0.0	0.0	0.0	0.0	0.0	0.0
10.0	0.0	0.0	0.0	0.0	0.0	0.0	0.0	0.0	0.0
10.0	0.0	0.0	0.0	0.0	0.0	0.0	0.0	0.0	0.0
10.0	0.0	0.0	0.0	0.0	0.0	0.0	0.0	0.0	0.0
10.0	0.0	0.0	0.0	0.0	0.0	0.0	0.0	0.0	0.0
10.0	0.0	0.0	0.0	0.0	0.0	0.0	0.0	0.0	0.0
10.0	0.0	0.0	0.0	0.0	0.0	0.0	0.0	0.0	0.0
10.0	0.0	0.0	0.0	0.0	0.0	0.0	0.0	0.0	0.0

Fig. F.4 Iterative equipotential calculation: starting values

Then, starting at one corner, set the value at each point to be the average of the four neighbouring points. (At corners and edges a slightly different procedure would have to be used.) If this process is done over and over again, the numbers gradually change, settling down with final values where each point in the field is the average of the neighbouring points. Fig. F.5 shows computer output doing just this.

If the final result is compared with the experimental situation it is found that there is excellent agreement. The calculation could have been done by

anode									cathode
10.0	3.3	1.1	0.4	0.1	0.0	0.0	0.0	0.0	0.0
10.0	3.3	1.1	0.4	0.1	0.0	0.0	0.0	0.0	0.0
10.0	3.3	1.1	0.4	0.1	0.0	0.0	0.0	0.0	0.0
10.0	3.3	1.1	0.4	0.1	0.0	0.0	0.0	0.0	0.0
10.0	3.3	1.1	0.4	0.1	0.0	0.0	0.0	0.0	0.0
10.0	3.3	1.1	0.4	0.1	0.0	0.0	0.0	0.0	0.0
10.0	3.3	1.1	0.4	0.1	0.0	0.0	0.0	0.0	0.0
10.0	3.3	1.1	0.4	0.1	0.0	0.0	0.0	0.0	0.0
10.0	3.3	1.1	0.4	0.1	0.0	0.0	0.0	0.0	0.0
10.0	4.4	1.9	0.7	0.3	0.1	0.0	0.0	0.0	0.0

Iterative calculation: the computer started at the top left corner, setting each potential to the average of the points around it. This is the result after just one calculation.

10.0	7.2	4.9	3.2	1.9	1.1	0.6	0.4	0.2	0.2	
10.0	7.2	4.9	3.2	1.9	1.1	0.6	0.4	0.2	0.2	
10.0	7.2	4.9	3.2	1.9	1.1	0.6	0.4	0.2	0.1	
10.0	7.2	4.9	3.2	2.0	1.1	0.6	0.4	0.2	0.1	
10.0	7.2	4.9	3.2	2.0	1.2	0.7	0.4	0.2	0.0	— cathode
10.0	7.3	5.0	3.2	2.0	1.2	0.7	0.4	0.2	0.0	
10.0	7.3	5.0	3.3	2.0	1.2	0.7	0.4	0.2	0.1	
10.0	7.3	5.1	3.4	2.1	1.3	0.7	0.4	0.2	0.2	
10.0	7.4	5.2	3.5	2.3	1.4	0.8	0.5	0.3	0.2	
10.0	7.5	5.4	3.7	2.4	1.5	0.9	0.6	0.4	0.3	

anode

The result after eight calculations. Note the values for the electrodes are fixed.

10.0	9.1	8.3	7.4	6.6	5.8	5.1	4.5	4.0	3.8	
10.0	9.1	8.3	7.4	6.6	5.8	5.0	4.4	3.8	3.5	
10.0	9.1	8.3	7.4	6.6	5.7	4.9	4.1	3.4	3.0	
10.0	9.1	8.2	7.4	6.5	5.6	4.7	3.8	2.8	1.9	
10.0	9.1	8.2	7.4	6.5	5.6	4.6	3.5	2.1	0.0	— cathode
10.0	9.1	8.2	7.4	6.5	5.6	4.6	3.5	2.1	0.0	
10.0	9.1	8.3	7.4	6.5	5.6	4.7	3.8	2.8	1.9	
10.0	9.1	8.3	7.4	6.6	5.7	4.9	4.1	3.4	3.0	
10.0	9.1	8.3	7.4	6.6	5.8	5.1	4.4	3.9	3.5	
10.0	9.1	8.3	7.5	6.6	5.9	5.2	4.5	4.1	3.8	

anode

The result after 100 calculations. The values here settled into results close to those obtained by experiment.

Fig. F.5

considering the charges on each of the two electrodes and using an action at a distance method of analysis. But this would have been a hard calculation. The iterative method explained above employs one of the most important and simplest properties of the electric field and shows that if we wish to know about some part of the field all we need to know about is neighbouring points, not particularly very distant ones.

So, far from being just a model, physicists see fields as having real properties which can be ascribed and measured.

Fields at A-level

Only gravitational, electric and magnetic fields are studied in any detail at A-level. Gravitational fields are produced by masses, electric fields by electric charges and magnetic fields by electric currents travelling in wires or as beams of charged particles.

Terminology

The strength of any of these fields is determined by the amount of the force upon a 'test object' placed in the field. The 'test object' is always 'one unit' of whatever senses the particular field. The gravitational field is tested with a unit mass (1 kg) and an electric field with unit charge (1 C). For a magnetic field the definition is harder: here the unit object is a wire one metre long carrying a current of 1 A. The direction of the field is the direction in which the test object experiences a force. Thus, because like charges repel, the field direction of a positive charge is away from the charge, since here a test object, +1C, would experience a force away from the other charge.

The force exerted by a field upon an object can be found from information on the strength of the field and the nature of the object placed in it. For example, if a mass of 4 kg were placed in a gravitational field of strength 10 N kg^{-1}, the force the mass would experience would be

$$4 \text{ kg} \times 10 \text{ N kg}^{-1} = 40 \text{ N}.$$

There are considerable similarities between gravitational and electric fields. See the entry **Inverse square law fields**, where the similarities are explored.

◀ **Electric fields, Inverse square law fields, Radial electric fields** ▶

FISSION

Fission is the process in nuclear physics whereby a large mass splits (fissions) into two nuclei of smaller mass with a release of energy. It contrasts with **fusion**, a process where nuclei 'fuse', i.e. join together.

The common nuclear disintegration processes are α, β, and γ emission. It is possible for isotopes to emit single neutrons or protons (nucleons), but any process that does this will have a very short half-life and the substances would be so unstable as not to be normally recognised in a chart of the nuclides (known isotopes). On a chart of **neutron number against proton number**, or a chart of proton number against mass number, they would appear a long way from the line of stability. The fission process is a rare fourth type of disintegration.

There are two types of fission. One is spontaneous fission and the other is fission following the absorption of a neutron. In spontaneous fission the nucleus suddenly (spontaneously) breaks into two fragments of roughly equal size. This is normally considered to be a 'forbidden' process in nuclear physics. However, examples are Curium-250 with a half-life of 13000 years and Americium-234 with more typical half-life of 2·6 minutes. Note that both of these isotopes exist only as a result of artificial manufacture.

The other type, neutron-induced fission, occurs with both the long-lived (metastable) uranium isotopes, $^{235}_{92}U$ and $^{238}_{92}U$. A typical process is

$$^{235}_{92}U + n \rightarrow \underset{\text{an excited state}}{^{236}_{92}U^*} \rightarrow \underset{\text{fission fragments}}{X + Y} + n + n$$

Note how there is a possibility here of a chain reaction. The process yields two neutrons which can be used to start fission processes in other uranium atoms. This process is used in both atom bombs and in **nuclear reactors**.

◀ Binding energy ▶

FLEMING'S LEFT-HAND RULE

Fleming's left-hand rule indicates the direction in which a current-carrying conductor experiences a force when it is placed in a magnetic field. If the current and the field are at right angles (Fig. F.6) and if the first finger of the left hand is pointed in the direction of the field and the second finger in the direction of the current, the thumb indicates the direction in which the force of thrust is exerted.

If the field is not at right angles to the current direction, it is necessary to resolve the field into components in the direction of the current and at right angles to that direction. The first finger is then pointed in the direction of the component of the field at right angles to the current and the rule, as described, is applied.

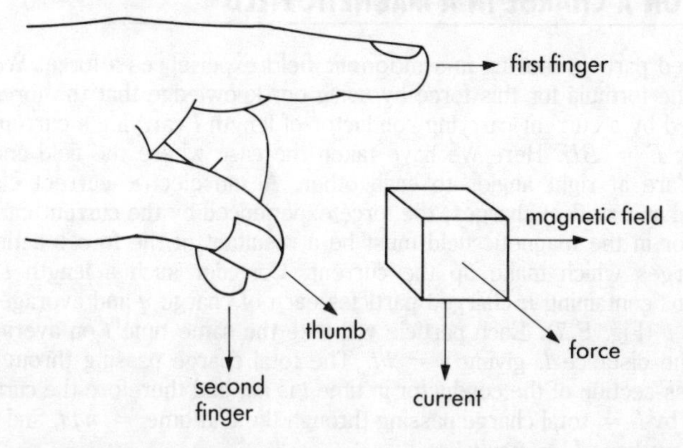

Fig. F.6 Fleming's left-hand rule: Thumb in same direction as Thrust (force); seCond finger in same direction as Current

FLEMING'S RIGHT-HAND RULE

This is similar to **Fleming's left-hand rule** but is used in the case of induction.

◀ Electromagnetic induction ▶

FLUID

A fluid is something which flows. In physics a liquid, a vapour and a gas are all considered as examples of fluids.

◀ Pressure in fluids ▶

FOCAL LENGTH

◀ Focal point ▶

FOCAL POINT

This is a term used in the physics of both mirrors and lenses. Rays close to and parallel with the **principal axis** converge to the focal point. The distance from this point to the centre of the lens or mirror is called the focal length, f. The more powerful a lens or mirror is in terms of its converging power for a beam of parallel rays, the shorter the focal length. The term the power of a lens or mirror is therefore defined as $1/f$. The power of a lens or mirror is measured in dioptres if f is in metres; e.g. a lens of power 10 dioptres has a focal length of 1/10 metres or 0·1m.

FORCE ON A CHARGE IN A MAGNETIC FIELD

A charged particle moving in a **magnetic field** experiences a force. We can derive the formula for this force by using our knowledge that the force experienced by a current-carrying conductor of length l carrying a current I is given by $F = BIl$. Here we have taken the case where the field and the current are at right angles to each other. As an electric current can be regarded as a drift of charges, the force experienced by the current-carrying conductor in the magnetic field must be a resultant of the forces acting on the charges which make up the current. Consider such a length l of a conductor containing n charged particles each of charge q and average drift velocity v (Fig. F.7). Each particle will take the same time t on average to travel the distance l, giving $v = l/t$. The total charge passing through the end cross-section of the conductor in time t is nq, and therefore the current I is given by I = total charge passing through the end/time $= nq/t$, and since $t = l/v$ we have $I = nqv/l$.

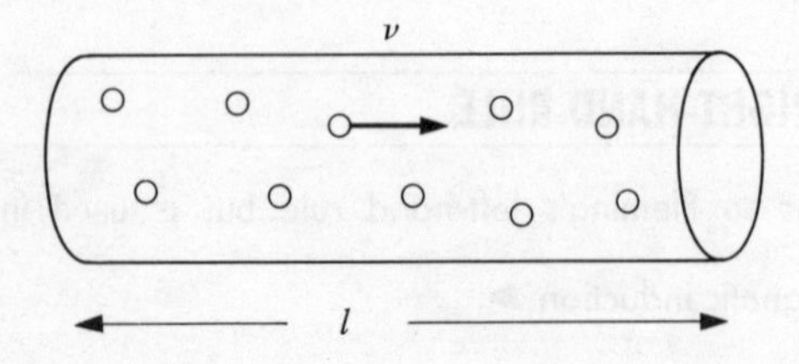

Fig. F.7

But $F = BIl$ and so $F = Bnqv$. This is the force on n particles and therefore the force on one particle is given by $F = Bqv$.

◀ Deflection of charged particles, Deflection tube ▶

FORCED OSCILLATIONS

Forced oscillations are the oscillations that an oscillating system has when it is driven by an external periodic force. An example could be the oscillations of the driving mirror of a car when the engine is vibrating the structure on which the mirror is mounted. A simple system which can be set up in the laboratory is shown in Fig. F.8. Here the oscillating system is a **light-beam galvanometer** suspension. The forced oscillations come from tiny currents generated by a very low-frequency signal generator. The oscilloscope is in the circuit with its time base switched off purely to monitor the forced oscillations and the high resistance is provided so that only a minute current drives the galvanometer. Note that although this arrangement has electrical components it is essentially a mechanical system.

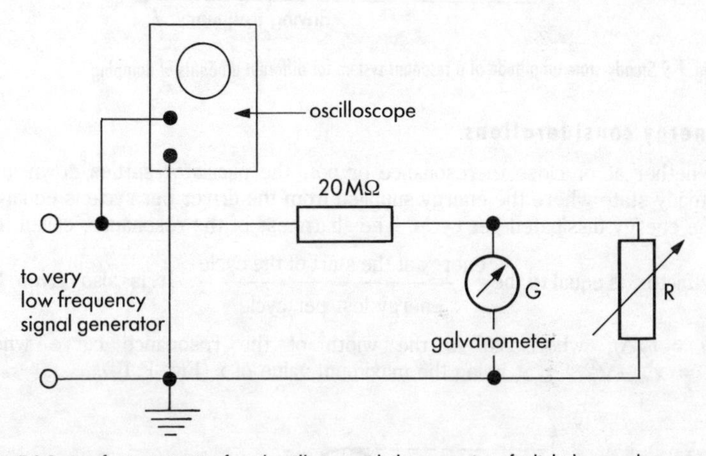

Fig. F.8 System for investigating forced oscillations with the suspension of a light-beam galvanometer. *R* is a resistance box and by changing *R* the damping can be varied

When a periodic force of the kind described acts on an oscillating system so-called transients are first exhibited. Transients are short-lived patterns of oscillation which soon die away. For example, if the forced oscillation is close in frequency to the natural frequency of the oscillator, the transients may consist of a large-amplitude oscillation followed by a small one and then a large one and so on. But eventually the system settles down with oscillations at the frequency of the driving force.

When the driving frequency is at the same frequency as the natural frequency of the oscillator, the amplitude of oscillation is at its greatest. This is called **resonance.** Fig. F.9 shows the steady-state amplitude of a resonant system for different driving frequencies and with different amounts of damping. For a simple harmonic oscillator there will be only one frequency of resonance.

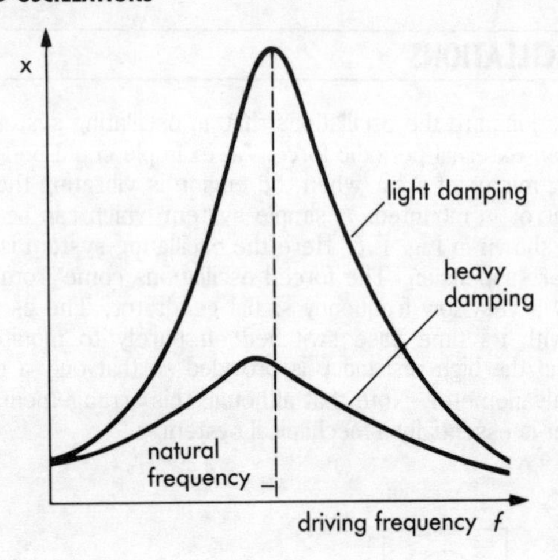

Fig. F.9 Steady-state amplitude of a resonant system for different amounts of damping

Energy considerations

Whether at or close to resonance or not, the oscillator settles down in a steady state where the energy supplied from the driver per cycle is equal to the energy dissipated per cycle. The sharpness of the resonance, called the Q-factor, is equal to the $\frac{\text{energy at the start of the cycle}}{\text{energy lost per cycle}}$. It is also given by $Q = f_0/\Delta f$, where Δf is the width of the resonance curve when $x = x_{max}/\sqrt{2}$, x_{max} being the maximum value of x (Fig. F.10).

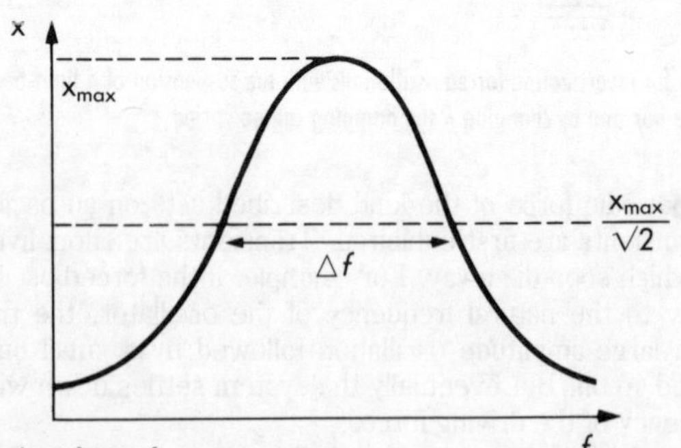

Fig. F.10 Finding the Q-factor of a resonant system

Phase

At resonance an oscillator lags behind the driver by 90°, i.e. it is 90° out of phase with the driver. When the driver is at a much lower frequency than the

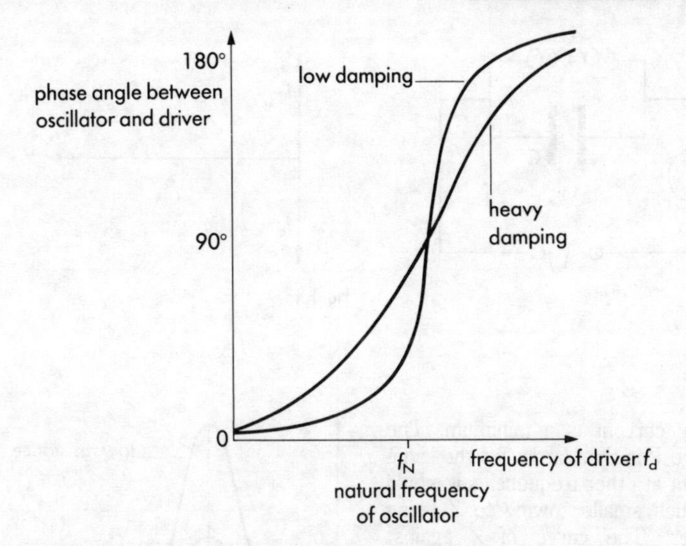

Fig. F.11 Phase relationship between driver and oscillator for different amounts of damping

oscillator's natural frequency ($f_d \ll f_N$) the oscillator is in step with the driver. When the driver frequency is much higher than the natural frequency ($f_d \gg f_N$) the driver and the oscillator are 180° out of phase (Fig. F.11).

Resonance in electricity

Resonance also occurs in electrical circuits when **alternating currents** are used. The simplest example is an LCR series circuit. The expression for the impedance of the circuit is

$$Z = \sqrt{R^2 - \left(\omega L - \frac{1}{\omega C}\right)^2}$$

where $\omega = 2\pi f$ and L, C and R have the usual meanings.

Z takes a minimum value when $V_L = V_C$, where V_C is the voltage across the capacitor and V_L the voltage across the inductor. In this case the current is naturally a maximum. When this happens $\omega L = 1/\omega C$ giving $\omega^2 = 1/LC$, or

$$f = \frac{1}{2\pi} \frac{1}{\sqrt{LC}}$$

Thus if the supply frequency, f, is varied through this value the current will go through a maximum when $f = 1/2\pi\sqrt{LC}$.

Another circuit that gives resonance is an LC parallel circuit (Fig. F.12). The **phasor** diagram is shown in Fig. F.13.

When $1/\omega C = \omega L$ the two currents I_L and I_C have the same magnitude but are in antiphase. This occurs at the frequency $f = 1/2\pi\sqrt{(LC)}$ and the

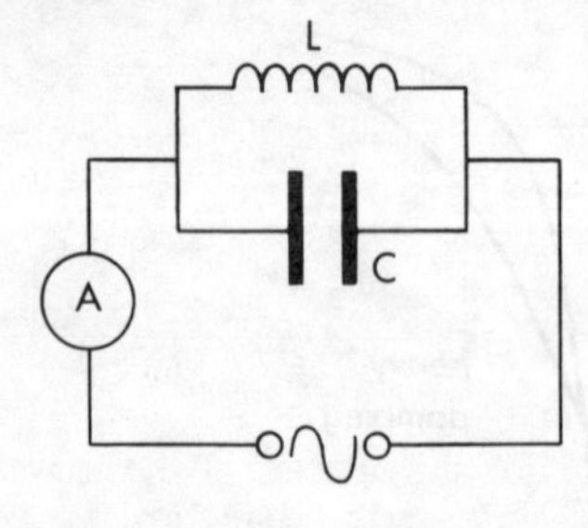

Fig. F.12

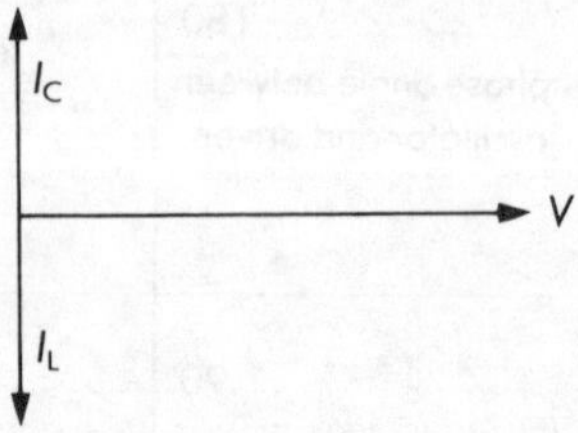

Fig. F.13

supply current is a minimum. The voltage V is then large; for the same current at other frequencies it would be much smaller owing to Z being smaller. The curve of Z against frequency is shown in Fig. F.14. As resistance is introduced into the circuit the curve becomes less sharp.

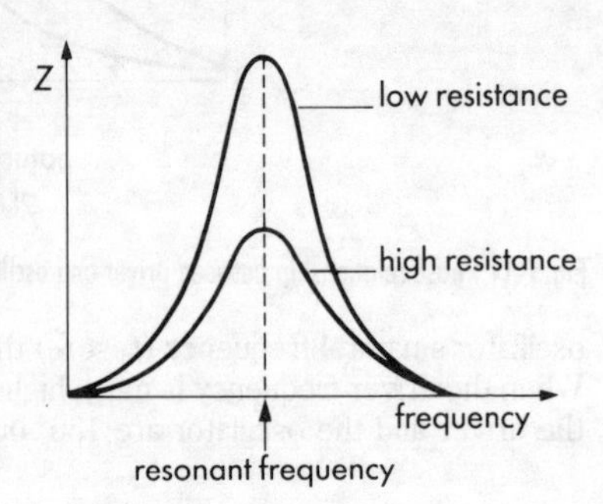

Fig. F.14

FORCES

A force is a push or pull in a particular direction. A force which is not balanced by other forces, and therefore is not in equilibrium, will cause the body on which it acts to accelerate.

The usual types of forces encountered in equilibrium situations (statics) are:

i) Weight (W). This is always considered to act at the centre of mass (centre of gravity).
ii) Normal reaction forces (N). These results from the solidity of an object when another is pushing into it. They act at 'right angles' to the surface. (This is what is meant by the adjective 'normal').
iii) Friction (F). Frictional forces act between surfaces when they move or try to move relative to each other. Friction acts parallel to a surface and is proportional to the weight or normal force.
iv) Tension (T) (or compression).

◀ Moment, Parallelogram of vectors, Resolution of vectors, Solids, Solving problems of several forces acting on a body, Static equilibrium ▶

FOURIER METHODS

Fourier methods are used in the technologies of the recording and communication industries for analysing and constructing waveforms which do not have a sinusoidal profile.

Fourier methods derive from a theorem of the nineteenth-century French mathematician Fourier, who showed that any regular waveform, such as a square wave or a saw-tooth wave, can be regarded as the superposition of a set of sinusoidal waves of frequencies which are all multiples of the basic frequency. In Fourier analysis a complicated wave form is analysed by a piece of instrumentation in order to determine the sine waves which would reproduce it if they were added together. In Fourier synthesis, a technique which can be used in electronic synthesisers, several sine waves of different frequencies are put together, for example in a summing amplifier, in order to construct a more complicated waveform.

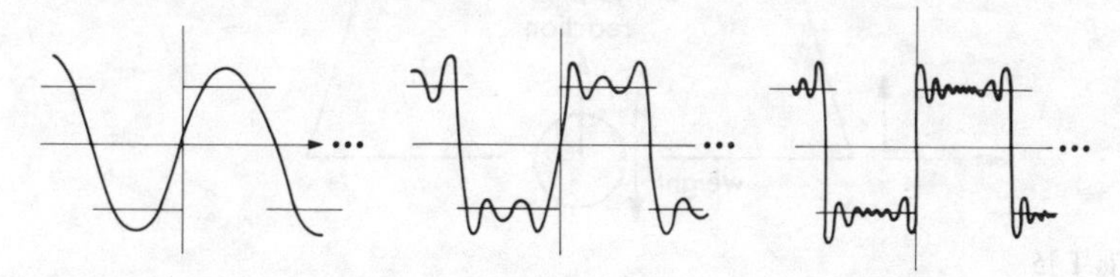

Fig. F.15 Partial sums of the Fourier series for square waves with increasing number of terms

Fig. F.15 shows the effect of putting together a number of sine waves of higher and higher frequencies in order to produce a square wave. Of course the proportions of the different frequencies and the different frequencies themselves must be right. For a square wave as a function of time we have

$$\text{Square wave} = \sin \omega t + \frac{\sin 3\,\omega t}{3} + \frac{\sin 5\,\omega t}{5} + \frac{\sin 7\,\omega t}{7} + \ldots$$

◄ Musical instruments ►

FRAUNHOFER DIFFRACTION

◄ Diffraction ►

FREE-BODY DIAGRAM

This is a term used in mechanics to refer to a diagram of a body which shows the body alone, isolated from its surroundings, and the forces which act on it. Consider a car towing a caravan, for example. The free-body diagrams of both car and caravan are as shown in Fig. F.16.

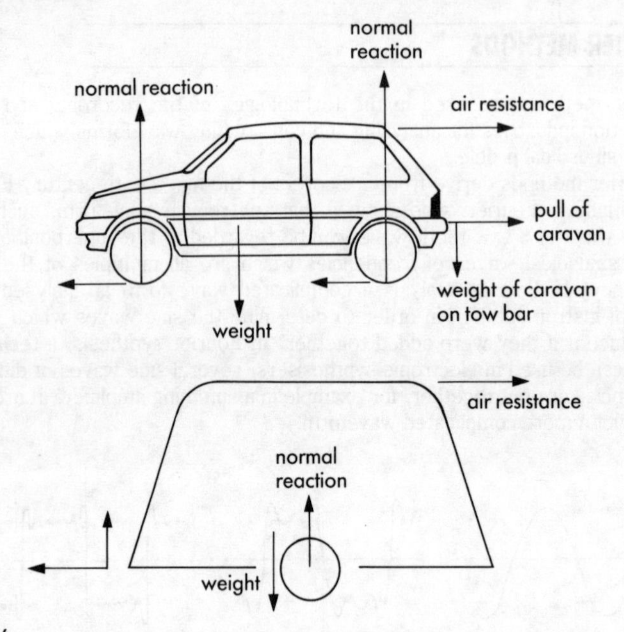

Fig. F.16

Note that by Newton's Third Law the force exerted by the car on the caravan is equal and opposite to that exerted by the caravan on the car.

The usefulness of a free-body diagram is that once it is drawn you can begin to apply the laws of motion or obtain the conditions for equilibrium without the danger of having inappropriate forces applied to the body under consideration.

FREE FALL

This is the state of an object which is accelerating freely under gravity. If you were in free fall you would experience a sensation of weightlessness. This is because we don't actually 'feel' the force of gravity, but instead the normal (reaction) forces which occur as the ground 'prevents' us from falling under gravity.

A man standing on the ground experiences normal (reaction) forces N_1 and N_2 at his feet (Fig. F.17). By Newton's First Law $N_1 + N_2 = W$,

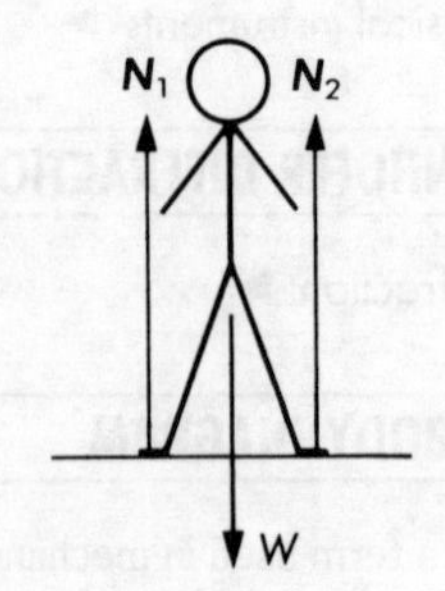

Fig. F.17

as he does not move. If the ground were not there he would accelerate downwards with acceleration *g*. His experience would be the 'weightless' experience of free fall. He would still have weight but would have lost the forces N_1 and N_2 which were what he felt.

Note that skydivers, people who jump from aeroplanes and don't pull their parachute ripcords until they are near the ground, are NOT in a state of free fall. Instead they fall at a steady speed called their **terminal velocity**. The downward force of gravity is balanced by the frictional (viscous) force of the air.

◀ Friction, Newton's Laws of Motion ▶

FREQUENCY

This is a term used in **oscillation**, wave and **alternating current** theory.

In all these cases there is a periodic cycle of events. The frequency *f* is the number of complete cycles per second. In the case of an oscillator it is the number of return journeys from and to an extreme position of the oscillator which occur per second.

The unit of frequency is the hertz. 1 Hz = 1 cycle/s.

$$\text{Frequency} = \frac{1}{\text{Period}}$$

FREQUENCY MEASUREMENT

In the school or college laboratory frequency measurements are generally likely to be made only with sound. The frequency of a sound wave can be measured in a number of different ways.

i) By using a microphone and amplifier and displaying the waveform on an **oscilloscope**. If the oscilloscope is suitably calibrated, the time for one cycle can be noted and thus the number of cycles per second, the frequency, can be measured.

ii) Using a calibrated variable frequency signal generator.

   a) By using the method of *beats*. In this method the output of the variable frequency signal generator is sent to a loudspeaker. The note from the loudspeaker is played simultaneously with the sound to be measured and the frequency adjusted until it is similar in pitch to that of the sound. The observer must then listen for the beats between the two notes. As the frequency of the signal generated is adjusted, there should be an observed change in the beat frequency. As the frequencies approach each other the beat frequency should decrease. Hence it should be easy to establish the frequency at which the two notes are the same. The frequency can then be read from the scale on the signal generator.

b) By the method of *Lissajous' figures*. This again uses an oscilloscope but with the time base turned off. The note to be measured is detected using a microphone and an amplifier. The output is sent to, say, the X plates of the oscilloscope, and simultaneously the output of the signal generator is sent to the Y plates. Steady traces, called Lissajous' figures, are observed when the ratio of the two signals is a simple one. Fig. F.18 shows some examples of what to look for. A suitable steady pattern, e.g. 1:1, 1:2, or 2:3, is observed and the frequency can then be read from the scale.

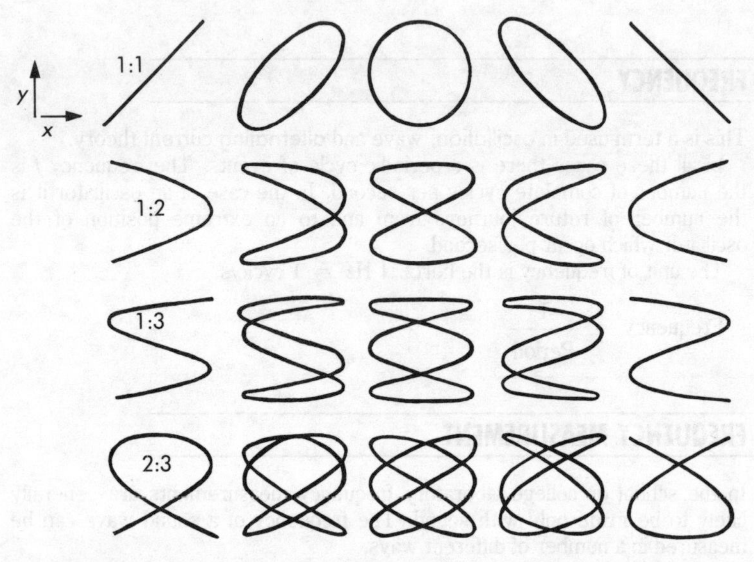

Fig. F.18 Lissajous figures. The ratio of the number of oscillations in *y* to those in *x* is shown

iii) By using a microphone and amplifier and programable data-collection device, e.g. VELA. The data capture device is programmed to measure frequency. It operates by counting the number of electrical oscillations in a particular time interval and gives a direct readout of the frequency.

The frequencies of vibration of objects which vibrate with amplitudes sufficiently large to be seen can be determined using a **stroboscope**.

FREQUENCY MODULATION

This is a term used in telecommunications to describe the way information is transmitted by varying the frequency of a radio wave.

Frequency modulation is an alternative to **amplitude modulation** as a means of using a carrier wave to transmit information such as speed or

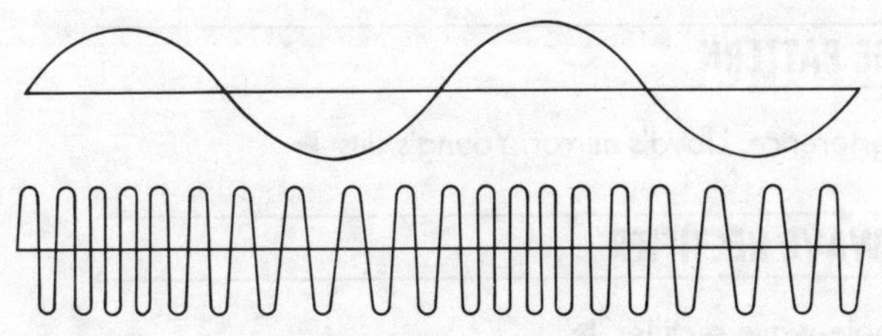

Fig. F,19 The upper curve shows an audio-frequency signal used to modulate a carrier wave

music. Instead of keeping the frequency constant and varying the amplitude, the amplitude is kept constant and the frequency is varied. This is shown in Fig. F.19. The chief advantage of frequency modulation (f.m.) is that under certain conditions reception is less likely to be disturbed by interference or noise. With frequency modulation the transmitting signal radiates at its full power all the time and so it is much more likely to outdo interference than with amplitude modulation, the signal of which falls to quite low levels when the modulating frequency has large amplitude. Another way in which noise is reduced results from the fact that the modulation can be made to move the carrier way frequency up and down a relatively wide range or band. A detailed treatment of this lies outside the scope of this book.

◀ Signal to noise ratio ▶

FRESNEL DIFFRACTION

◀ Diffraction ▶

FRICTION

Friction is the name given to the force which acts between surfaces and causes moving objects to slow down. When a frictional force acts there is usually a conversion of energy into internal energy (heating).

Two types of friction are treated in mechanics. The first is static or limiting friction. For example, if a mass is on a level surface and a sideways force is applied to move it, unless the force exceeds a certain amount the mass will not move. The reason it will not move is because of the action of an opposite sideways frictional force. The maximum force which is available is called the limiting friction and it is proportional to the normal reaction force. Thus we write

$$F = \mu_l N$$

where μ_l is the coefficient of friction. Note that μ_l is dimensionless and takes a maximum value of 1.

The other kind of friction is called dynamical friction and is the friction which is offered when a force is moving an object. Again the force is proportional to the normal reactional force and written $F = \mu_d N$, where μ_d is the coefficient of dynamic friction.

Usually $\mu_l > \mu_d$.

FRINGE PATTERN

◀ Interference, Lloyd's mirror, Young's slits ▶

FULL-WAVE RECTIFIER

◀ Whole-wave rectifier ▶

FUNDAMENTAL CONSTANTS

The table (Fig. F.20) gives the fundamental constants and energy conversion factors of importance in A-level physics.

FUSION

Fusion is the process in nuclear physics whereby two small nuclei or a nucleus and an elementary particle such as an electron 'fuse' (combine) together into a larger nucleus with a release of energy. It contrasts with **fission** a process where heavy nuclei split into smaller fragments.

The process is the source of the energy of the sun. In the sun and other stars the principal way in which energy is produced is by the production of helium from hydrogen. The mass of helium is less than that of the component nucleons and so energy is released.

There are two important nuclear reactions for making helium from hydrogen: one is direct – the proton—proton chain; the other uses carbon as a catalyst and it is called the carbon—nitrogen cycle.

The *proton—proton chain* (p–p chain) proceeds as follows:

$$^{1}H + {}^{1}H \rightarrow {}^{2}H + e^{+} + \nu$$
$$^{2}H + {}^{1}H \rightarrow {}^{3}He + \gamma$$
$$^{3}He + {}^{3}He \rightarrow {}^{4}He + {}^{1}H + {}^{1}H$$

Here e^{+} is a positron, the positively charged electron of β^{+} decay, and ν is an neutrino, a tiny particle of nearly zero mass and no charge. γ is a gamma ray.

In the *carbon–nitrogen cycle reaction* (CN cycle) carbon (symbolised by C) is used as a catalyst and the main-line of the reaction is:

$$^{12}C + {}^{1}H \rightarrow {}^{13}N + \gamma$$
$$^{13}N \rightarrow {}^{13}C + e^{+} + \nu$$
$$^{13}C + {}^{1}H \rightarrow {}^{14}N + \gamma$$
$$^{14}N + {}^{1}H \rightarrow {}^{15}O + \gamma$$
$$^{15}O \rightarrow {}^{15}N + e^{+} + \nu$$
$$^{15}N + {}^{1}H \rightarrow {}^{12}C + {}^{4}He$$

In the final line of the reaction we see that the original carbon-12 atom is returned and the net effect is that four hydrogen nuclei have been turned into a ^{4}He one. The carbon–nitrogen cycle also has side chains; for example

Quantity	*Symbol*	*Value*	*Units*	*Uncertainty, parts in 10^6*
Speed of light in vacuum	c	2·997 924 580(12)	$10^8 m s^{-1}$	0·004
Permeability of vacuum	μ_0	4π exactly	$10^{-7} H m^{-1}$	—
Permittivity of vacuum $1/\mu_0 c^2$	ϵ_0	8·854 187 818(71)	$10^{-12} F m^{-1}$	0·008
Planck constant	h	6·626 176(36)	$10^{-34} J Hz^{-1}$	5·4
Elementary charge	e	1·602 189 2(46)	$10^{-19} C$	2·9
Mass of the electron at rest	m_e	9·109 534(47)	$10^{-31} kg$	5·1
		5·485 802 6(21)	$10^{-4} u$	0·38
		0·511 003 4(14)	MeV	2·8
1 electron volt	eV	1·602 189 2(46)	$10^{-19} J$	2·9
Mass of proton at rest	m_p	1·672 648 5(86)	$10^{-27} kg$	5·1
		1·007 276 470(11)	u	0·011
		938·279 6(27)	MeV	2·8
Ratio of proton mass to electron mass	m_p/m_e	1836·151 52(70)	—	0·38
Mass of neutron at rest	m_n	1·674 954 3(86)	$10^{-27} kg$	5·1
		1·008 665 012(37)	u	0·037
		939·573 1(27)	MeV	2·8
Electron charge to mass ratio	e/m_e	1·758 804 7(49)	$10^{11} C kg^{-1}$	2·8
Atomic mass unit, $10^{-3} kg mol^{-1} N_A{}^{-1}$	u	1·660 565 5(86)	$10^{-27} kg$	5·1
		931·501 6(26)	$10^6 eV$	2·8
MeV to kilogram, $10^6 e/c^2$	MeV	1·782 675 9(51)	$10^{-30} kg$	2·9
Faraday constant of electrolysis $N_A e$	F	9·648 456(27)	$10^4 C mol^{-1}$	2·8
Gravitational constant	G	6·672 0(41)	$10^{-11} N m^2 kg^{-2}$	615
Avogadro constant	N_A	6·022 045(31)	$10^{23} mol^{-1}$	5·1
Boltzmann constant R/N_A	k	1·380 662(44)	$10^{-23} J K^{-1}$	32
Molar gas constant, $p_0 V_m/T_0$	R	8·314 41(26)	$J mol^{-1} K^{-1}$	31
Stefan constant $2\pi^5 k^4/15h^3c^2$	σ	5·670 32(71)	$10^{-8} W m^{-2} K^{-4}$	125

Fig. F.20 Fundamental constants and energy conversion factors

◀ Physical quantities in the SI system ▶

$^{15}N + {}^{1}H$ may go to $^{16}O + \gamma$ and then the reaction proceeds through stages that involve nuclei of oxygen and fluorine to produce eventually a ^{12}C nucleus and a ^{4}He one.

◀ Binding energy ▶

GALILEAN TELESCOPE

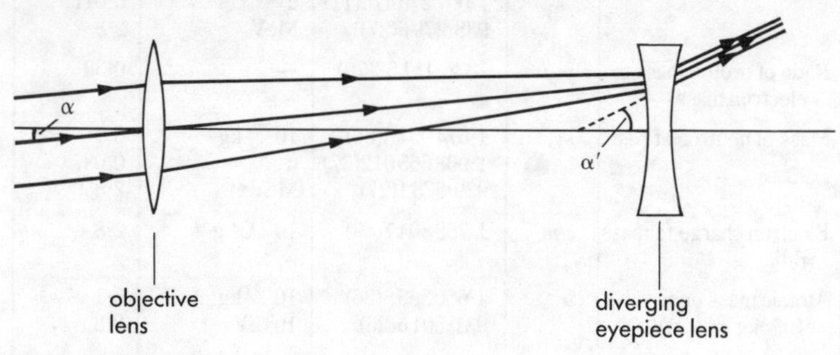

Fig. G.1 Galilean telescope

The Galilean telescope is named after Galileo, its inventor. Fig. G.1 shows a ray diagram of it set in what is called normal adjustment (see **Angular magnification**) with rays emerging from the eyepiece lens in a parallel beam. In the diagram the telescope might be pointed at an object such as the moon with the rays indicated coming from the 'bottom' of the moon and the rays from the 'top' of the moon along the **principal axis**. The function of the telescope is to increase the angular separation between these sets of rays, α, to a value α'. In this way the telescope is like the **astronomical telescope**. The difference between the telescopes is that this uses a diverging eyepiece lens and thus produces an upright image of the object, unlike the inverted image of the astronomical telescope.

◀ Reflecting telescope ▶

GALVANOMETERS

This is a general name given to a meter which measures small electric currents.

◀ Ammeters and voltmeters, Ballistic galvanometer,
Light-beam galvanometer ▶

GAMMA RADIATION

Gamma radiation consists of discrete quanta (photons) of electro-magnetic radiation produced by the emission of energy from the nucleus, usually following **alpha** or **beta** emission. On the basis of the shell model of the nucleus, a nucleon may be considered to move from a shell of high energy to a vacancy in one of lower energy. The energy difference is emitted as a quantum of defined characteristics (line spectrum). Gamma photons are massless and uncharged.

- Ionisation by gamma photons. Gamma photons are the least powerful ionising agents of the three types of radiation, being 1/100th as effective as beta particles. This makes detection by ionisation less efficient than for alpha and beta particles.
- Penetrating power of gamma photons. Gamma photons are more penetrating than alpha or beta particles. Absorption is exponential and complete reduction of intensity to zero is (theoretically) never reached. High-energy gamma photons are more penetrating than those of low energy, and dense materials are better shields than those of low density. The inverse square law is obeyed.
- i) Compton effect. A photon may interact with a free or lightly bound electron, giving the electron kinetic energy. The scattered photon loses energy by increasing its wavelength.

  ii) Photoelectric effect. A photon may interact with a tightly bound (inner K shell) electron and all the photon energy reappears as kinetic energy of the ejected electron. Such photoelectrons have a line spectrum. Relatively weak X-rays are emitted when electrons re-occupy the inner shell vacancy.

  iii) Pair production. High-energy gamma photons passing near a heavy nucleus can disappear as electromagnetic radiation and reappear as a positron–electron pair of high-speed electrons. The photon must have a greater energy than 1·02 MeV as this is needed to produce the rest masses of the two electrons. The presence of positrons is detected by the photons of annihilation radiation.

  All three effects contribute to the absorption of gamma rays.
- Detection of gamma rays: Gamma rays may be detected using:
  i) **An ionisation chamber**
  ii) A photographic plate (low efficiency)
  iii) **A Geiger tube**
  iv) **A scintillation counter**
- Screening. Thick shields of dense materials are necessary. Lead and dense concrete are commonly used.

Typical gamma emitters

^{226}Radium	0·2–2 MeV	half-life 1620y	+ alpha and beta
^{60}Cobalt	1·25 MeV	half-life 5·3y	+ beta
^{198}Gold	0·41 MeV	half-life 2·7d	+ beta
^{137}Caesium	0·66 MeV	half-life 30y	+ beta

Also from **Bremsstrahlung** sources.

GAS LAWS

The three gas laws are Boyle's Law, Charles' Law and the Pressure Law. They describe the relationships between the pressure, volume and temperature of a fixed mass of gas. They provide a good description of both gases and unsaturated vapours. The laws are:

Boyle's Law

For a fixed mass of gas at constant temperature, pressure, p, is inversely proportional to volume, V.

i.e. $p \propto \frac{1}{V}$

or $pV = \text{constant}$

or $p_1V_1 = p_2V_2$

Charles' Law

For a fixed mass of gas at constant pressure the volume increases by $\frac{1}{273}$ of its volume at 0°C for each degree C rise in temperature *or*, as an equivalent statement, the volume is directly proportional to the absolute temperature.

i.e. $\frac{V}{T} = \text{constant}$

or $\frac{V_1}{T_1} = \frac{V_2}{T_2}$

The Pressure Law

For a fixed amount of gas at constant volume the pressure increases by $\frac{1}{273}$ of the pressure at 0°C for each degree C rise in temperature, *or*, as an equivalent statement, the pressure is directly proportional to the absolute temperature.

These three laws are combined in the general gas equation:

$pV = nRT$

where p is in Pa, V in m^3, n is the number of moles of gas present, and R is the molar gas constant. R is 8·31 J mol^{-1} K^{-1}.

◀ Gases, liquids, vapours and plasmas, Ideal gas, Saturated vapour ▶

GASES, LIQUIDS, VAPOURS AND PLASMAS

The gaseous state of matter is the state in which the molecules are no longer in close contact with each other but move separately throughout the space available to them. By contrast with a liquid and a **solid** it is a very disordered state which can be easily studied only because of the statistical effect of very large numbers of particles.

Strictly speaking the term gas should be used only when above the substance's **critical temperature.** This is the temperature above which the gas cannot be liquefied by compression alone. The term **vapour** is used below this temperature. Below the critical temperature liquefaction can occur by simply compressing the gas. When a closed vessel contains a vapour in equilibrium with its liquid the vapour is called a **saturated vapour,** otherwise it is **unsaturated.**

At very high temperatures the collisions between molecules become so energetic that ionisation (see **Energy levels**) takes place. The gas is then called a *plasma*. Taking the universe as a whole the plasma is the most common state, as it is the state of the atmospheres of stars.

◀ Gas laws, Ideal gas, Kinetic theory of gases ▶

GEIGER TUBE

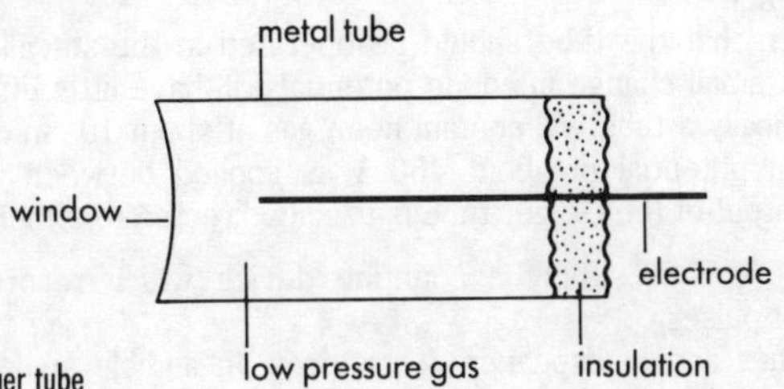

Fig. G.2 Geiger tube

The Geiger tube is one of the simplest ways of easily measuring radioactivity. It is sometimes called the Geiger-Müller tube, or just a G-M tube for short (Fig. G.2).

The mode of operation is similar in some ways to that of the **ionisation chamber** in that an electric field is used to accelerate ion pairs produced by the incoming particles. However, whereas the ionisation chamber contains air at atmospheric pressure, the Geiger tube contains a gas at low pressure so that the accelerated electrons are able to acquire sufficient kinetic energy in between collisions to be able to cause further ionisation. This effect increases the number of electrons arriving at the central electrode. This is because an electron which has been accelerated collides energetically enough with a gas atom to produce further electrons, which in turn are themselves accelerated to collide with further gas atoms, producing further electrons and so on. This avalanche of charge is sufficient to be detected by a pulse-counting circuit. About 10^8 ions are produced in a few microseconds. To

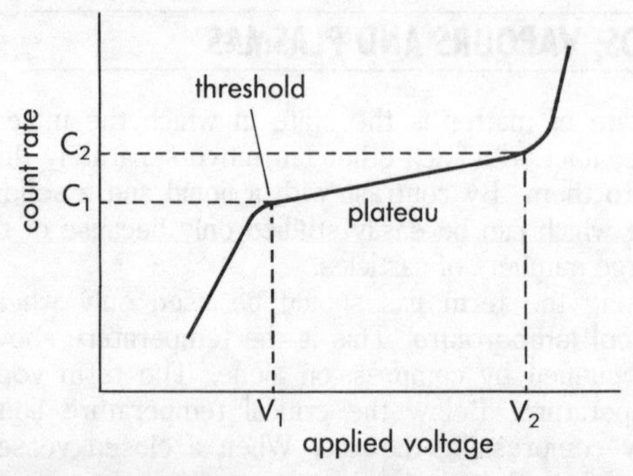

Fig. G.3 Characteristic of a Geiger tube

prevent continuous ionisation of this kind a little bromine gas is added to the tube, acting as a 'quenching agent' and absorbing the kinetic energy of the positive ions. As a result of the avalanche and quenching process there is a dead time in which the tube cannot detect particles. A typical tube can detect separate particles as long as they arrive more than 200 microseconds apart, and thus there is a maximum count rate of about 5000 counts per second. If a Geiger tube is exposed to a moderate level of radiation and a graph is plotted of count rate against anode voltage, a result such as that shown in Fig. G.3 is obtained.

It can be seen that the tube should be operated in the so-called plateau region, where a small change in anode potential will have little effect on the count rate. Typically a tube will contain neon gas at about 10 cm of mercury pressure, and a potential of about 450 V is applied between anode and cathode. The output of the Geiger tube is usually directed to either:

i) A scaler. This is simply a counting device which records a total number of pulses.
ii) An amplifier and loudspeaker. This gives an audible signal for each pulse received.
iii) A rate meter. This is a device which actually records the count rate in pulses per second.

The Geiger-Müller tube is suitable for detecting **betas** and **gammas** but for **alphas** the tube needs a specially thin window in order to allow in the alphas which would otherwise be completely stopped within the window.

GENERAL GAS EQUATION

◀ Gas Laws ▶

GLASS

◀ Solids ▶

GOLD-LEAF ELECTROSCOPE

This is a simple instrument used for detecting electric charge and working on the principle of the electrostatic repulsion of two like charges. Further details are given in the entry **Electrostatic phenomena**.

GRAPHS AND TABLES

In physics the following convention is recommended for the labelling of graphs and the heading of columns.

A symbol for a quantity, e.g. L for inductance, represents the product of a magnitude and a unit. Thus $L = 2\text{H}$ means $L = 2 \times 1\text{H}$. Hence $2 = L$ divided by 1H and $2 = L/\text{H}$ or $2 = L\text{H}^{-1}$.

A graph is a mathematical device dealing with pure numbers only. When 2 is plotted for inductance in the case above, it refers to a value of L/H and this is the label which should appear on the relevant axis.

When $p = 2 \times 10^5\text{Pa}$, $2 = p/10^5\text{Pa}$ and when $V = 4 \times 10^{-4}\text{m}^3$, $4 = 10^4 V/\text{m}^3$. The graph in Fig. G.4 could therefore be relabelled as shown in Fig. G.5. This is a preferred style, as it avoids repeating the powers of ten each time.

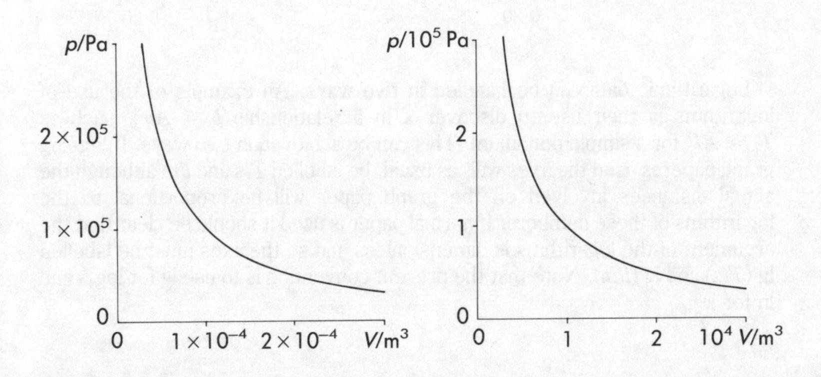

Fig. G.4 Labelling of p versus V (Boyle's Law, where pV = constant)

Fig. G.5

When a quantity is raised to a power in order to give a straight-line graph, the unit involved must also be raised to that power (Fig. G.6).

The use of this convention gives the correct units for gradients of graphs. Consider the case of acceleration, which is the slope of a v, t graph (Fig. G.7). If $x = t/\text{s}$ and $y = v/\text{m s}^{-1}$,

$$\frac{\text{d}y}{\text{d}x} = \frac{\text{d}(v/\text{m s}^{-1})}{\text{d}(t/\text{s})} = \frac{\text{d}v}{\text{d}t}/\text{m s}^{-2} = a/\text{m s}^{-2}.$$

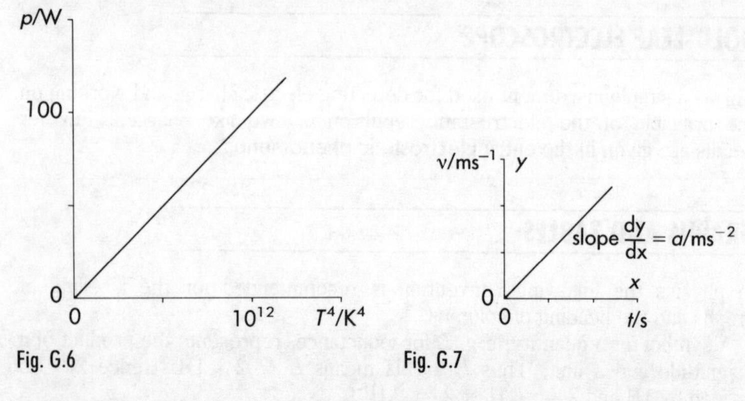

Fig. G.6

Fig. G.7

The same convention applies when heading columns of readings. If the column is headed by the quantity divided by its unit, only numerical magnitudes need be entered in the column. Two ways of recording the same results are shown:

V/kV	λ/nm
3	0·28
4	0·20

$V \times 10^{-3}$/V	$\lambda \times 10^9$/m
3	0·28
4	0·20

Logarithmic data can be handled in two ways. An example of the use of logarithms is their use to discover x in a relationship $p = Aq^x$, such as $T = Al^x$ for a simple pendulum. This can be achieved in two ways. If log–log graph paper is used the axes will, as usual, be labelled T/s and l/m although the actual distances involved on the graph paper will be proportional to the logarithms of these numbers. If normal paper is used it should be clear that the argument of the logarithms is dimensionless and so the axes must be labelled lg (T/s) and lg (l/m). Note that the present convention is to use lg for $\log_{10}$ and ln for $\log_e$.

GRAVITATIONAL FIELD OF THE EARTH

First consider the gravitational effect of a thin spherical shell of mass. Because of the inverse square law of gravity the gravitational field external to the shell is exactly the same as if all the mass were concentrated at its centre. Within the shell the field is zero. This behaviour is exactly the same as that of the electric field generated by a spherical shell of charge. (For an indication of the reasons for this, see **Radial electric fields**.) The proof of this result can be found in some textbooks. It was first done by Newton and the difficulties of doing it held up his publication of the Universal Law of Gravity for several years.

Applying the result to the huge mass of the earth, we can regard the earth as a kind of onion made up of a set of concentric shells. For an object on the surface of the earth or above the surface of the earth, the earth behaves as if all its mass were concentrated at a point at its centre. Hence the force that the earth exerts on such a mass m is given by

$$F = \frac{GMm}{r^2}$$

where M is the mass of the earth and r is the distance from its centre. The mass m is said to be in the gravitational field of the earth and the strength of the field is found by substituting unit mass, i.e. one kg, for m. Hence the field strength g is given by

$$g = GM/r^2$$

at the surface of the earth $r = R_E = 6{\cdot}4 \times 10^6$ m, and we get

$$g = GM/{R_E}^2$$

Alternatively, and usefully, this can be written as $g{R_E}^2 = GM$.

The value of the field strength g decreases as you move away from the earth, obeying an inverse square law, e.g. at a distance R_E above the surface, i.e. $2R_E$ from the centre, $g = 9{\cdot}8/4 = 2{\cdot}5\,\mathrm{N\,kg^{-1}}$ (Fig. G.8).

The force exerted by the earth on a mass m is mg, which is called the weight of the mass. From Newton's Second Law of Motion the acceleration of an object is equal to the force acting on unit mass, 1 kg, and hence the acceleration of any mass falling freely at the earth's surface is $g = 9{\cdot}8\,\mathrm{m\,s^{-2}}$.

If the value of G can be measured in a laboratory experiment, we can substitute in the equation $g{R_E}^2 = GM$ in order to obtain a value for the mass of the earth M. This is why experiments to determine the value of the gravitational constant, G, are sometimes called experiments to weigh the earth.

Field inside the earth

Continuing to consider the earth as an onion-like object made up of a set of concentric shells, it is possible to determine the field at a point P within it, distance r from the centre (Fig. G.9).

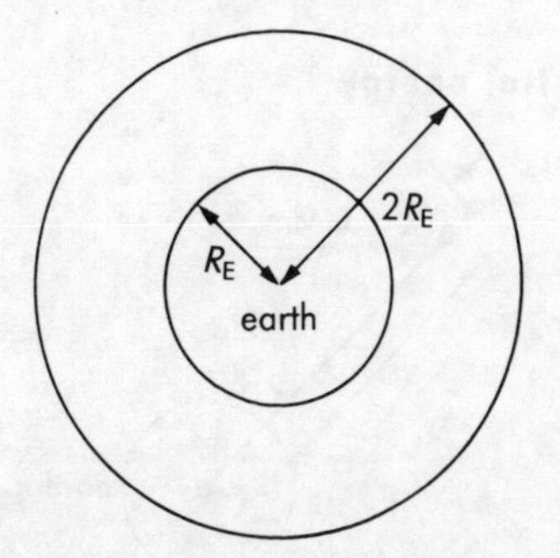

Fig. G.8 Gravitational field of the earth

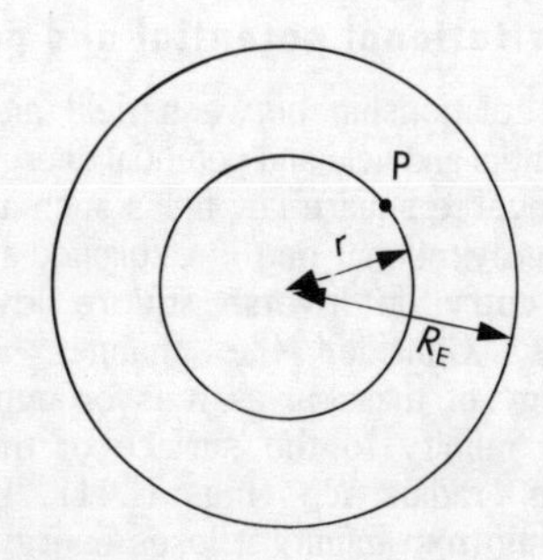

Fig. G.9

Because the field inside a shell of mass is zero we only have to consider the effect of masses on shells beneath us, i.e. on shells of radius less than r. For each of these the earth behaves as if all the mass were concentrated at the centre. If therefore we consider the earth to be of uniform density, ρ, then at a distance r from the centre, the mass of the earth beneath us is given by $\frac{4}{3}\pi r^3\rho$. The field is thus

$$g = G.\frac{4}{3}\pi r^3\rho.\frac{1}{r^2} = \frac{4G}{3}\pi\rho r$$

i.e. the field decreases uniformly with r, below the earth's surface.

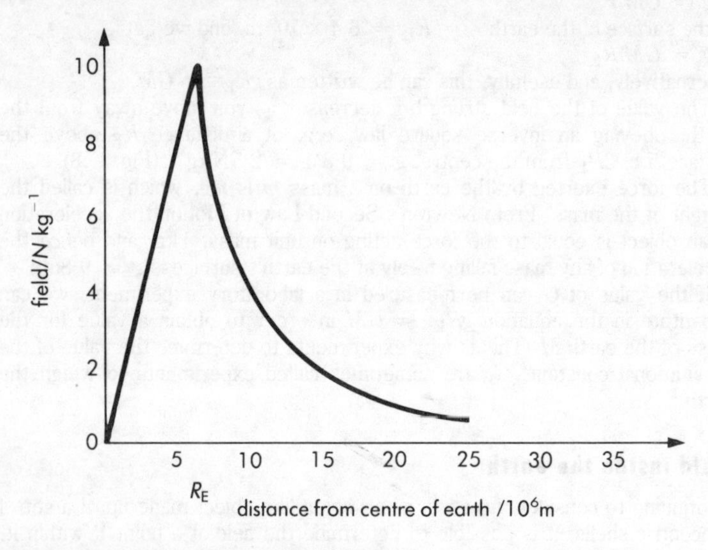

Fig. G.10 Variation of the gravitational field of the earth

Gravitational potential and potential energy

The relationship between field and potential and field and potential energy for inverse square law fields such as the gravitational one is explained in the entry on **Inverse square law fields**. Consider the changes in energy of mass m as it is brought from infinity to the surface of the earth, radius R_E (Fig. G.11). In coming from infinity it loses energy, i.e. the gravitational potential energy

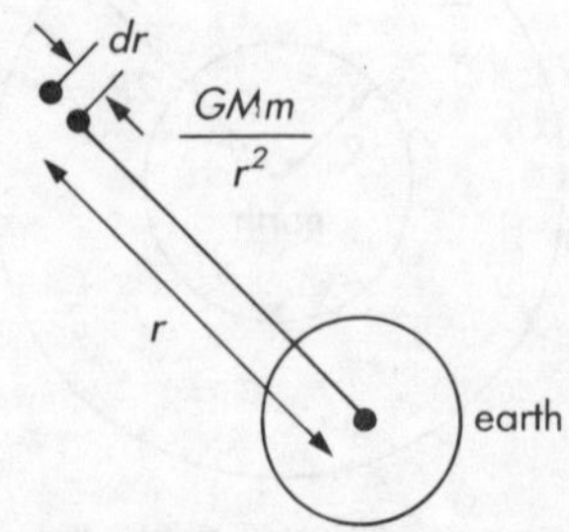

Fig. G.11 Work done in moving mass m

decreases. The loss in energy is found by the work done by the gravitational field in moving the mass a small distance dr over which the force might be considered to be constant according to the equation

$$dW = \frac{GMm}{r^2}dr$$

The total work done is found by adding all these small amounts of work.

The decrease in gravitational potential energy equals

$$\int_{R_E}^{\infty} \frac{GMm\,dr}{r^2} = \left[\frac{GMm}{r}\right]_{R_E}^{\infty} = -\frac{GMm}{R_E}$$

Taking the potential energy as zero at infinity, the potential energy at the surface of the earth is $-GMm/R_E$.

The potential at the surface of the earth is the potential energy per unit mass and hence this is given by $-GM/R_E$. Note that the potential obeys an inverse law, i.e. a $1/r$ law. Here again there is a similarity with the electrostatic case.

◀ Satellites launched from the earth ▶

GRAVITATIONAL FIELDS

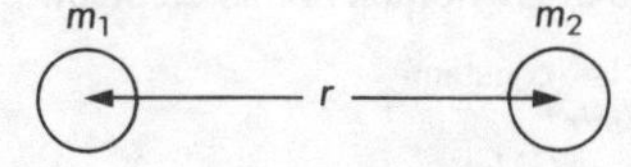

Fig. G.12 Two 'point' masses

A gravitational field is an area where a mass experiences a force. Any two masses m_1 and m_2 attract each other with a force F (Fig. G.12). This is given by Newton's Law of Gravitation according to the equation:

$$F = G\frac{m_1 m_2}{r^2}$$

r being the distance between the two masses. G is the universal constant of gravitation having a value $6{\cdot}7 \times 10^{-11}\,\mathrm{Nm^2kg^{-2}}$. The very small value of G implies that gravitational effects are minuscule in laboratory situations. However, when the whole mass of the earth is taken into account, the effect is appreciable. Going further in scale, when stars and galaxies are considered, gravitational forces are by far the most dominant in determining the structure of the universe.

The similarity between Newton's Law of Gravitation and Coulomb's Law for electric charges should be noted. The two basic formulae are:

$$F = G\frac{m_1 m_2}{r^2} \quad \text{and} \quad F = \left(\frac{1}{4\pi\epsilon_0}\right)\frac{Q_1 Q_2}{r^2}$$

Note that in the electrostatic case the constant $\left(\frac{1}{4\pi\epsilon_0}\right)$ replaces the gravitational constant G. Because of the inverse square law nature of both fields there are a number of similarities between them. For example, just as the electric field inside a sphere of charge is zero so the gravitational field inside a thin spherical shell of mass is also zero.

But there are some important differences. The obvious one is that whereas gravitational forces are always attractive, in the electrostatic case forces may be positive or negative depending on the signs of charges. Another important difference is that the charges responsible for electric fields are often placed on conductors where they can move round under the action of the fields produced. Thus if a large charge is brought up towards a sphere carrying another charge, the distribution of charge on the sphere will be changed. Masses cannot move round so easily and so this effect is smaller in the gravitational case. Nevertheless there is a gravitational effect similar to the electric redistribution of charge described above. This is the tidal effect, when the position of the oceans is slightly distorted by the gravitational attraction of the sun and the moon.

GRAVITATIONAL FORMULAE

Common formulae used in gravitation are listed below.

Kepler's third law $T^2/r^3 = \text{constant}$
Newton's law $F = GMm/r^2$
Potential energy $\text{p.e.} = -GMm/r$
Kinetic energy $\text{k.e.} = +GMm/2r$
Total energy $E = -GMm/2r$
Potential $V = -GM/r$
g and G $g = GM/R^2$
Escape velocity $v = (2Rg)^{\frac{1}{2}}$

GRAY

◀ Radioactivity: units of measurement ▶

HADRON

An **elementary particle** that can experience the **strong interaction** of nuclear physics.

◄ Quarks ►

HALF-ADDER

This is used for electronic arithmetic and performs addition of binary arithmetic. It has to deal with four cases:

	sum (EXOR)	carry (AND)
0 + 0 =	0	0
0 + 1 =	1	0
1 + 0 =	1	0
1 + 1 =	0	1

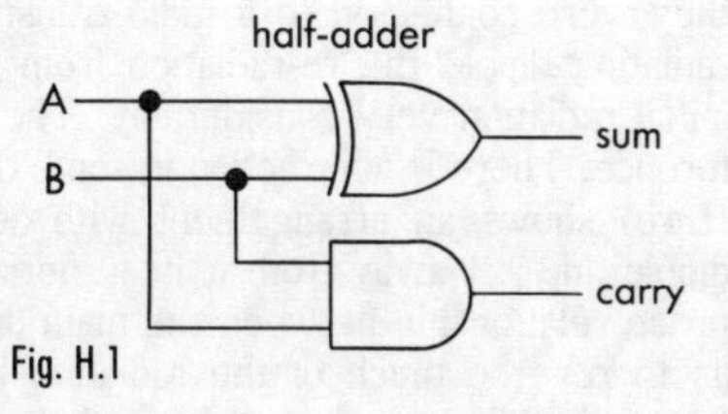

Fig. H.1

In the last case the 0 is called the 'sum' and the 1 is the 'carry', i.e. it is carried over to the next column on the right.

As with all logic circuits there are several combinations of **logic gates** which would perform the required operation. The simplest is that shown using an EXOR and an AND gate (Fig. H.1).

HALF-LIFE

◄ Radioactive decay law, Radioactivity ►

HALF-WAVE DIPOLE AERIAL

The half-wave dipole aerial is used as both a transmitter and a receiver of radio signals.

It consists of two metal rods connected to the feed circuit with each rod of length λ/4, where λ is the wavelength of the radio wave (Fig. H.2). The aerial has an inductance L and a capacitance C. For example, the capacitor arises from the existence of the two conductors separated by an air gap. All conductors have an inductance L: at ordinary frequencies this effect is insignificant, but at the very high frequencies of radio transmission this is not the case. The overall effect is that the dipole behaves as a series LC circuit with a resonant frequency which depends upon L and C and hence on the length of the device. It turns out that this occurs when the overall length of the system is λ/2.

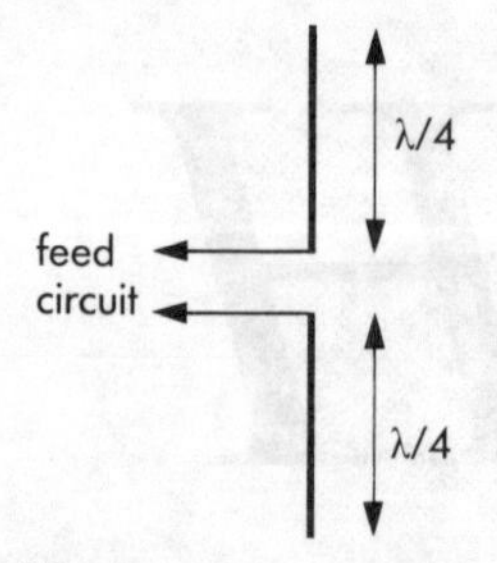

Fig. H.2 Dipole aerial

Radio engineers draw so-called 'polar' diagrams to represent the radiation from an aerial. Fig. H.3 shows the polar diagrams of radiation from a simple half-wavelength dipole. With an end-on view the radiation emitted is the same in all directions, but from a sideways view it is clear that more radiation is transmitted at right angles to the aerial and none in directions along its length.

Any metal rod is a tuned circuit which will have maximum currents going in it by waves twice its own length. These currents radiate waves just as if they were connected to a radio transmitter. If such a rod is placed near a radiating dipole the re-radiation from it is powerful enough to modify the initial radiation very considerably. The phenomenon is an example of interference. There is subtraction in some directions and additions in others. Fig. H.4b) shows an arrangement with aerials of this kind. Behind the main dipole and λ/4 away from it is an aerial of this kind called a reflector. The phase relationship between the main dipole and the additional dipole is such as to reverse much of the radiation beyond the main dipole, so that the former is called a reflector. This phase effect depends upon distance and can be varied by changing the spacing between the two dipoles. With a shorter dipole and a spacing of 0·1λ the effect is opposite reflection and so such a rod

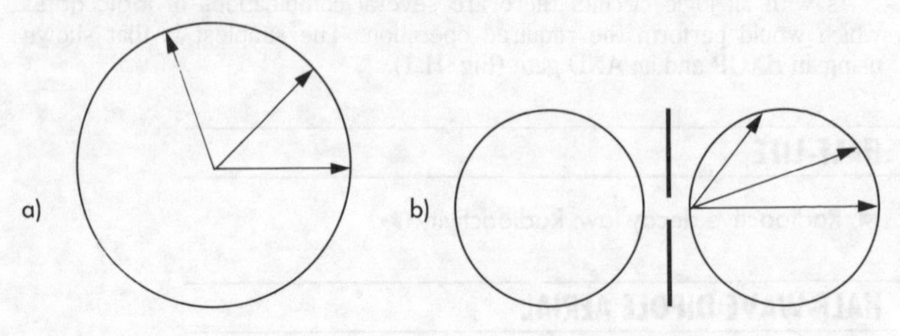

Fig. H.3 'Polar' diagram of radiation from a simple half-wavelength dipole. a) is an 'end-on' view and b) is a 'side-view'

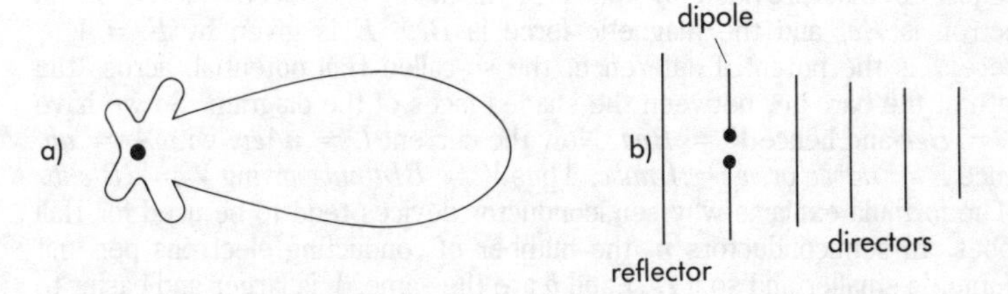

Fig. H.4 Polar diagram of an aerial system consisting of dipole, one reflector and four directors

is called a director. Fig. H.4a) shows the polar diagram of a dipole with reflector and directors. This arrangement is sometimes called a **Yagi aerial**. As explained such aerials can be used for transmission or reception. In reception the reflector described above is not so much used to strengthen the incoming signal as to cut out the interference from the opposite direction.

HALF-WAVE RECTIFIER

◀ Direct current power supplies ▶

HALL EFFECT

The simplest laboratory way to obtain a **magnetic flux density measurement** is to use a Hall probe, which generates a small voltage which depends upon the magnetic field to be measured. The device relies on the Hall effect, i.e. the phenomenon by which a small voltage is developed across a current-carrying conductor when it is placed in a magnetic field.

Fig. H.5 shows a metal bar of rectangular cross-section through which a steady current, I passes. A uniform magnetic field of flux density B acts normally to the upper face of the bar. The electric current consists of electrons moving to the left. Because the electrons are moving through a magnetic field at right angles to their velocities, they experience a force towards the back edge of the bar (by the application of **Fleming's left-hand rule**). The electrons are therefore pushed towards the back, leaving a net positive charge on the front edge. As a result of the redistribution of charge an electric field E is set up. Equilibrium is obtained once the magnetic force

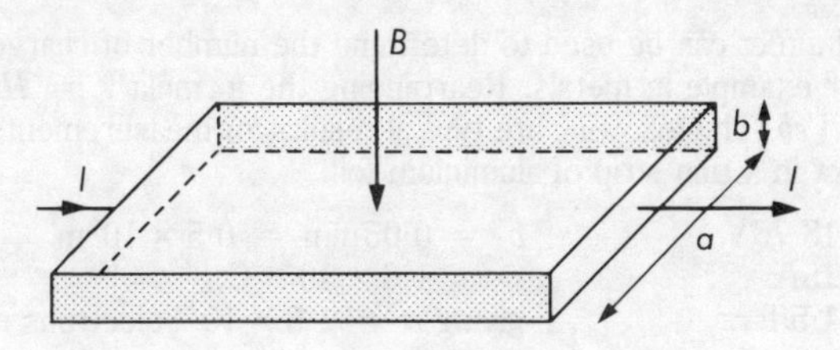

Fig. H.5

is equal to that provided by this electric field. The electric force on an electron is Ee, and the magnetic force is Bev. E is given by $E = V/a$, where V is the potential difference, the so-called Hall potential, across the width of the bar, i.e. between the shaded faces of the diagram. So we have $Ee = Bev$ and hence $V = Bva$. Now the current $I = nAev$, with $A = ab$. Hence $I = nabev$ or, $v = I/nabe$. Thus $V = BIa/nabe$ giving $V = IB/enb$.

The formula explains why semiconductor devices tend to be used for Hall probes. In semiconductors n, the number of conducting electrons per unit volume, is smaller and so if I, B and b are the same, V is larger and easier to measure.

A typical miniaturised integrated circuit Hall probe already contains a small amplifier. Typically, the device has an output voltage of about 2·5 volts even when there is no magnetic field. A field in one direction will cause an increase in this voltage, and a field in the other direction a decrease. Such a device is usually connected up to an **operational amplifier**, as shown in Fig. H.6. By making adjustments with the potentiometer the amplifier can be adjusted so that at zero field the output is zero. The device needs to be calibrated using the standard magnetic field, i.e. the field at the centre of a solenoid of a known number of turns per metre and electric current.

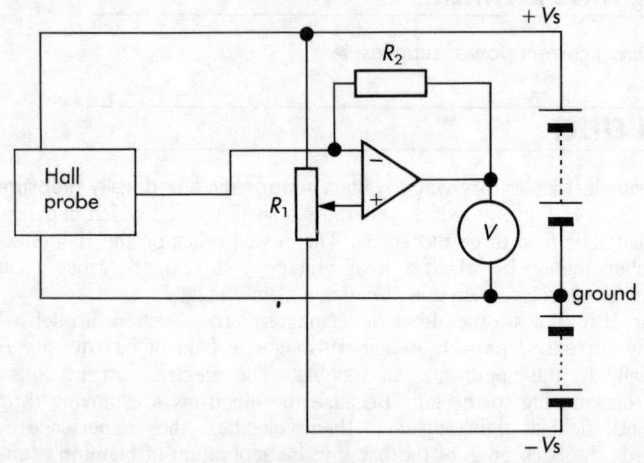

Fig. H.6 Hall probe connected to an operational amplifier. R_1 can be adjusted so that V reads zero in a zero field. The gain of the op. amp. is controlled by R_2.

Number of charged carriers per atom

The Hall effect can be used to determine the number of charge carriers per atom, for example in metals. Rearranging the formula $V = IB/enb$, we get $n = IB/Veb$. The following are typical results for measurements made on the Hall effect in a thin strip of aluminium foil:

$V = 18{\cdot}75\text{V}$. $\quad b = 0{\cdot}05\text{mm} = 0{\cdot}5 \times 10^4\text{m}$.
$I = 15\text{A}$ $\quad e = 1{\cdot}6 \times 10^{-19}\text{C}$.
$B = 1{\cdot}5\text{T}$ $\quad$ giving $n = 1{\cdot}5 \times 10^{29}$ electrons m^{-3}.

A calculation using the Avogadro constant ($6{\cdot}0 \times 10^{23}$ atoms mol^{-1}), the density of aluminium ($2700 kg m^{-3}$) and its relative atomic mass (27) gives $6{\cdot}0 \times 10^{28}$ atoms m^{-3}. The number of conduction electrons per atom must therefore be $1{\cdot}5 \times 10^{29}/6{\cdot}0 \times 10^{28} = 2{\cdot}5$, in other words a value between 2 and 3. This value is similar to that confirmed by chemical evidence where aluminium is considered to be trivalent, having three electrons per atom which can be given up in chemical reactions.

HARMONIC

◀ Overtone ▶

HEAT

In everyday usage 'heat' is a quality which gives something 'hotness'. In physics its meaning is more precise and slightly different. Heat is energy which is in transfer from one body to another by conduction, (see **Conductivities of metals**), **convection** or **radiation**.

It should not be confused with internal energy or temperature (see **thermodynamics** and **temperature**).

HEAT AND THERMODYNAMICS: FORMULAE

Common formulae used in thermometry, heat and thermodynamics are listed below:

Heat supplied	ΔQ
Heat capacity (C)	$\Delta Q = C \Delta Q$
Specific heat capacity (c)	$\Delta Q = mc\Delta\theta$
Specific latent heat	$\Delta Q = ml$
Electrical heating	$\Delta Q = VIt$
Scale of temperature	$\frac{t}{100} = \frac{X_t - X_0}{X_{100} - X_0}$
Isothermal change	$PV = \text{constant}$
Adiabatic change	$PV^{\gamma} = \text{constant}$
Ideal gas equation	$PV = nRT$
Charles's law	$V/T = \text{constant}$
Conduction of heat	$dQ/dt = -kA(\theta_1 - \theta_2)/x$
Stefan's law	$E = \sigma A(T^4 - T_0^{\,4})$
Wien's law	$\lambda_{max}T = \text{constant}$
Principal specific heats of gas	$c_p - c_v = R; \quad c_p/c_v = \gamma$
First law of thermodynamics	$\Delta Q = \Delta U + \Delta W = \Delta U + P\Delta V$
Work done in isothermal change	$W = nRT \ln(V_2/V_1)$
Kinetic theory equation	$PV = \frac{1}{3}mnc^2$
Root mean square velocity	$<c^2> = (c_1^{\,2} + c_2^{\,2} + c_3^{\,2} + \ldots c_N^{\,2})/N$

Average energy of a monatomic molecule $= \frac{3}{2}kT$

Entropy (S) $\Delta S = \frac{\Delta Q}{T}$

Boltzmann factor (f) $f = e^{-\epsilon/kT}$

Latent heat of vaporisation (L) $L = \frac{1}{2}N_A n\epsilon$

HELICOPTER

The way in which a helicopter supports itself above the ground provides a useful example of Newton's Second Law of Motion in a situation of continuous flow.

Suppose a helicopter is stationary in the air (Fig. H.7). It supports itself by collecting air with its rotor blades and forcing this air downwards with a speed v. As a result the air acquires a certain **momentum** downwards. The rate of change of momentum of the air is equal to the force which needs to be applied by Newton's Second Law. This is of course the force acting on

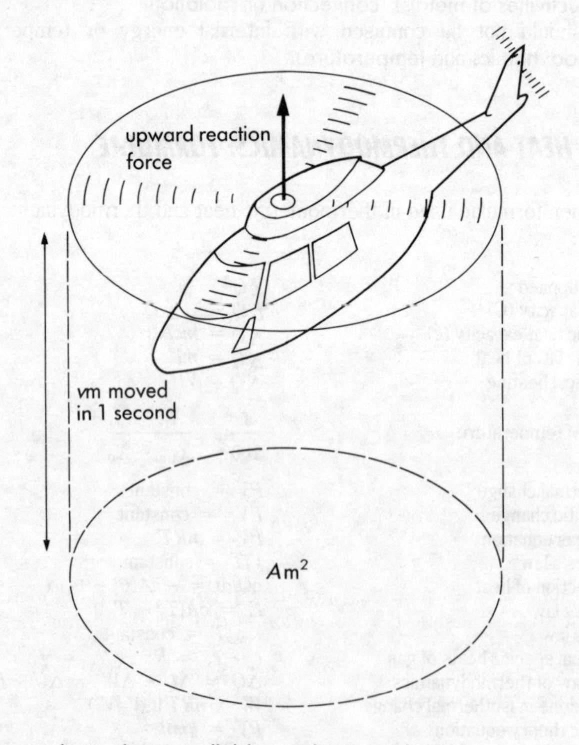

Fig. H.7 A helicopter showing the air propelled downwards in 1 second

the air. The helicopter experiences a reaction force in the opposite direction by Newton's Third Law. Because it is a reaction force this is upwards.

The mathematics of the situation is as follows: let us suppose that the area of cross-section swept out by the rotor arms is A. In one second the volume of air $= Av$ is swept out, where v, is the velocity imparted to the air. The mass of this air is $A\rho v$. And the momentum imparted to it, the mass $\times$ velocity, is $A\rho v^2$. This momentum is imparted in 1 second and so the rate of change of momentum is $A\rho v^2$. By Newton's Second Law this is the force.

This kind of analysis can be applied to other continuous flow problems. For example it can be used to find the force of reaction on a fireman who is holding a hose which is ejecting water at speed.

◀ Newton's Laws of Motion ▶

HELMHOLTZ COILS

◀ Deflection tube, Magnetic field configurations ▶

HERTZSPRUNG-RUSSELL DIAGRAM

This is a scatter graph used in astronomy for analysing a collection of stars. On the *y*-axis is plotted the brightness of the stars and on the *x*-axis a measure of the temperature. Such graphs have been very useful in understanding the nature of stars.

If stars were like electric light bulbs, we might expect to have all sorts of combinations:

e.g.	Hot and bright	(like 1000 W tungsten bulbs)
	Hot and dim	(like 3 V torch bulbs)
	Cold and bright	(like a 150 W fluorescent tube)
	Cold and dim	(like a 15 W fluorescent tube)

That is to say there is no 'correlation' between brightness of electric light bulbs and temperature. Now it turns out that when Hertzsprung-Russell (HR) diagrams are drawn to analyse stellar data the stars are quite different, as there are quite definite correlations between brightness and temperature.

A typical HR diagram for stars in our galaxy is shown in Fig. H.8. On the *y*-axis is plotted absolute magnitude as a measure of the intrinsic brightness of the stars on the plot, with the brightest stars at the top. Sometimes luminosity is plotted instead, although usually on a logarithmic scale. On the *x*-axis is plotted spectral type, although a temperature scale has been added as well. Sometimes the colour index $(B - V)$ is used instead, but always the colder stars are drawn on the right and the hotter ones on the left.

Most stars, including the sun, lie on a track across the diagram called the main sequence. They will stay in one position, a position which is largely determined by their mass, until their reserves of hydrogen are exhausted. The other two groups marked on the diagram are giants and supergiants, stars in a later stage of evolution, and white dwarfs, which are small hot stars also in a later stage of evolution.

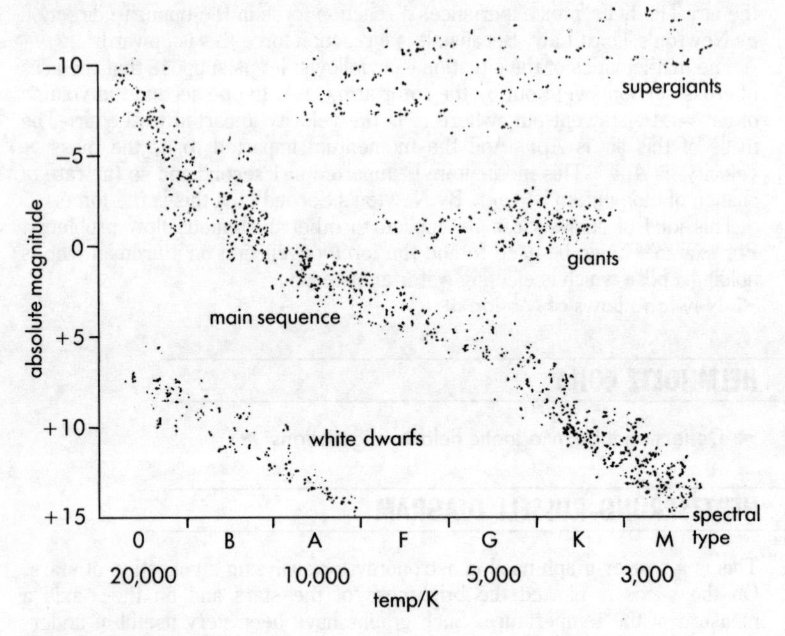

Fig. H.8 Hertzsprung-Russell diagram

HOOKE'S LAW

Hooke's Law states that the extension of a spring or wire is proportional to the load applied to it during elastic deformation. It is probably the most important law for the engineer. It is the law which describes the way most substances respond to the action of a force provided the force is not too great.

Writing x for extension (change in length) and F for force we get $F = kx$, where k is the constant of proportionality. Note that k has the units of newtons per metre. It is the force that is obtained with unit extension.

Hooke's Law is rather like **Ohm's Law** in electricity. It is precisely obeyed in many cases and approximately in many more, hence its usefulness.

HOOKE'S LAW AND SIMPLE HARMONIC MOTION

The simplest example of **simple harmonic motion** is that of a trolley tethered between two springs. The motion is simple harmonic because the restoring force is proportional to the displacement from equilibrium. This is a consequence of **Hooke's Law** applied to each of the two springs, as is explained below.

In an account of the s.h.m. of the trolley we can write $F = -kx$, where F is the restoring force and x is the displacement from equilibrium. k is then simply the constant which relates the displacement to the net force. The force, of course, arises from the separate extensions of both springs. In equilibrium the trolley is as shown in Fig. H.9.

If both springs are the same, each exerts a force of amount $k_H e$, where k_H is the constant which relates force to extension in Hooke's Law, i.e. force $= k_H \times$ extension, and e is the extension. One spring pulls to the left and the other to the right. Forces are vectors and so as usual we need to set up a sign convention. If we take forces to the right as positive and those to the left as negative, the net force to the right is $k_H e - k_H e = 0$.

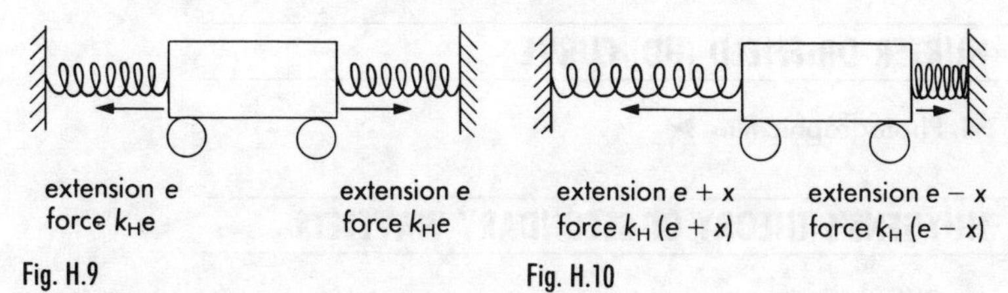

Fig. H.9

Fig. H.10

When the trolley is displaced to the right by an amount x (Fig. H.10), the left-hand spring exerts a greater force, and one to the left (i.e. a negative one), and the right-hand one a smaller one to the right. If e is the original extension, the force of the left-hand spring is $-k_H(e + x)$, and the force of the right-hand spring is $k_H(e - x)$. The net force is therefore $-k_H(e + x) + k_H(e - x) = 2k_H x$. This shows that k, the constant used to describe the resultant behaviour of the two springs, is equal to $2k_H$.

HUBBLE'S LAW

This is an empirical law in astronomy which describes the recession of galaxies and the expansion of the universe.

From observations of the **Doppler** shifts of the spectra of distant galaxies it is possible to measure their relative motion with respect to the earth. In 1929 the American astronomer Edwin Hubble was able to show that the galaxies seem to be receding with velocities which are proportional to their distances from us, i.e. $v \propto D$. Hubble's law is therefore written as

$$v = Hd$$

where v is the recessional velocity, usually expressed in $\mathrm{km\,s^{-1}}$, d is the distance of the galaxy usually expressed in megaparsecs (Mpc), and H is the Hubble constant expressed in $\mathrm{km\,s^{-1}\,Mpc^{-1}}$.

H is currently accepted to be about $50\,\mathrm{km\,s^{-1}\,Mpc^{-1}}$.

Age and size of the universe

In theoretical studies Hubble's constant is related to the 'age' and 'radius' of the universe, in a manner which depends on the choice of a 'cosmological model'. For a simple-minded estimate of the 'radius' of the universe, r is found from the formula $v = Hr$ when the velocity of light c is substituted for v. To convert this radius from megaparsecs into light-years, we multiply by $3{\cdot}3 \times 10^6$.

In most cosmological models, the 'age' of the universe is of the order of $1/H$, but cannot exceed it. First, divide H by 10^{12} to convert it from units of kilometres per second per megaparsec to units of kilometres per year per kilometre. Then the reciprocal of this transformed value is a rough estimate of the 'age' of the universe in years. Thus, taking the currently accepted value of H, we would get the 'age' of the universe to be 2×10^{10} years.

HURTER-DRIFFIELD (HD) CURVE

◀ Photographic film ▶

HUYGENS'S THEORY OF SECONDARY WAVELETS

◀ Diffraction ▶

HYDROGEN

◀ Energy levels in hydrogen ▶

HYDROMETER

This is an instrument used for measuring the relative density of a liquid. A commercial version of the device is shown in Fig. H.11. The device relies on Archimedes' principle (see **Upthrust**). It will float lower in a liquid of low density than in one of a higher density, and the level of the liquid is read on a scale, allowing a direct reading of the relative density.

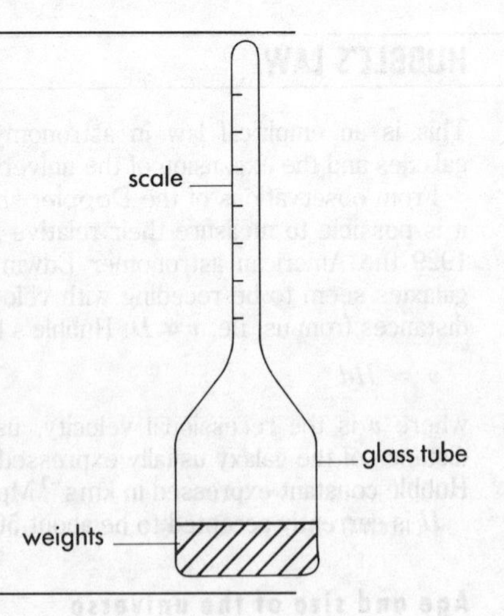

Fig. H.11 Commercial hydrometer

HYSTERESIS

◀ Solids, properties of ▶

IDEAL GAS

An 'ideal gas' is one which exactly obeys the general gas equation:

$$pV = nRT$$

Real gases at low pressures are excellent approximations to the ideal gas. As a result they all behave in similar ways, and have properties which can be very simply described mathematically by the above equation.

◀ Gas laws, Kinetic theory of gases, Van der Waals' equation ▶

IMPEDANCE

Impedance is a term used in **alternating current** theory. The greater the impedance the less the current that will flow when a given voltage is applied. Technically speaking it is used when a circuit with a number of components is being considered, i.e. one which may not be just a pure inductor or a pure capacitance, and where the phase angle between current and voltage may not be exactly 90° (π/2 radians). Impedance is analogous to resistance in d.c. theory, and is the ratio of peak voltage V_o divided by peak current I_o (or r.m.s. voltage divided by r.m.s. current), i.e.

$$\text{Impedance, } Z = V_o/I_o = V_{\text{r.m.s.}}/I_{\text{r.m.s.}}$$

Its units are ohms.

◀ Reactance ▶

IMPULSE

This is a term in mechanics which is defined as the force that acts on a body, usually for a short time, multiplied by its time of action. For example, when you catch a cricket ball you have to apply a big force for a time lasting tens of milliseconds. The product of force × time is the same however you catch the ball and is equal to its momentum change. It is usually written as I, so when a force acts for a short time Δt we get $I = \bar{F}\Delta t = \Delta p$, where $\bar{F}$ is the average force acting over the time interval Δt, and Δp is the momentum change it produces.

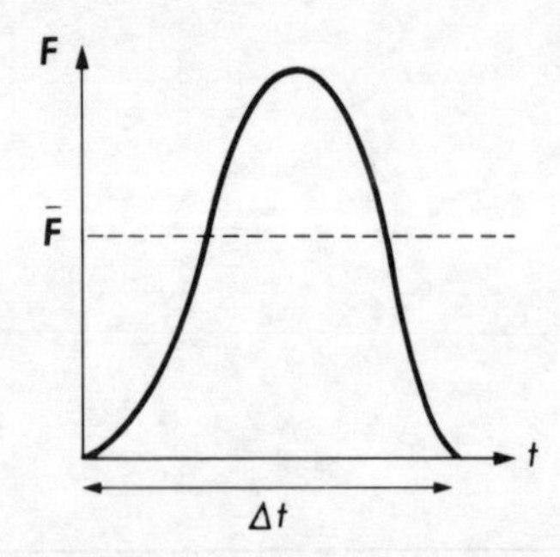

Fig. I.1 Force-time graph

Consider a golfing example: when a golf club strikes a golf ball the manner in which the force on the ball varies with time is shown by the F, t graph in Fig. I.1. The impulse I = the area under the graph, and the average force $\bar{F}$ acting is such that

$$\bar{F}\Delta t = \text{area under the graph}$$
$$\bar{F} = \text{change in momentum of the golf ball}$$

Notice again that the same change in momentum can result from either a large force acting for a very short time or a much smaller force acting for a much longer time (Fig. I.2).

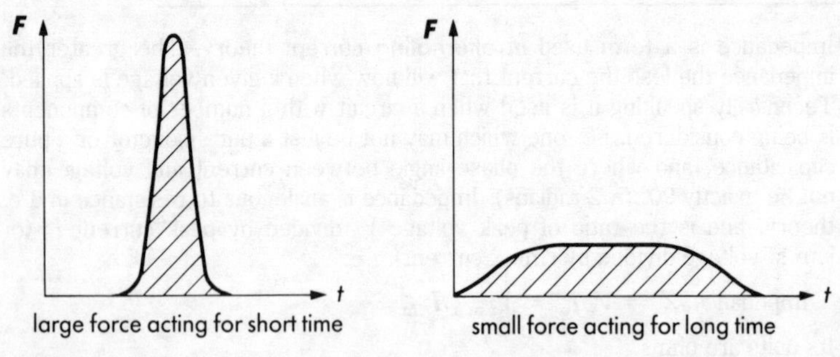

Fig. I.2

INDUCTANCE

◄ Mutual inductance, Self inductance ►

INDUCTION MOTORS

This is a class of electric motor in which there are no brushes, split rings, commutators, etc. They all work on the principle of inducing **eddy currents** in a conductor.

To understand the principle of all induction motors, consider an aluminium disc spinning freely between the poles of a permanent magnet. The disc quickly comes to rest because of eddy currents induced by the movement of the disc conductor in the magnetic field (energy is converted from kinetic energy to electrical energy, and then (as a result of the electric current flowing in the disc) because of heat. The effect depends upon the relative motion of the field and the conductor.

Fig. I.3 shows a different arrangement which has the same relative motion, but with the magnetic field moving. Here there is an aluminium glider on an air track (to reduce friction). If the magnet is moved along the air track with the glider between its poles, it is found that the glider will tend to follow the magnetic field. Note that in both cases nature acts to reduce the relative motions of the conductor and field. The second experiment suggests how a linear induction motor can be made.

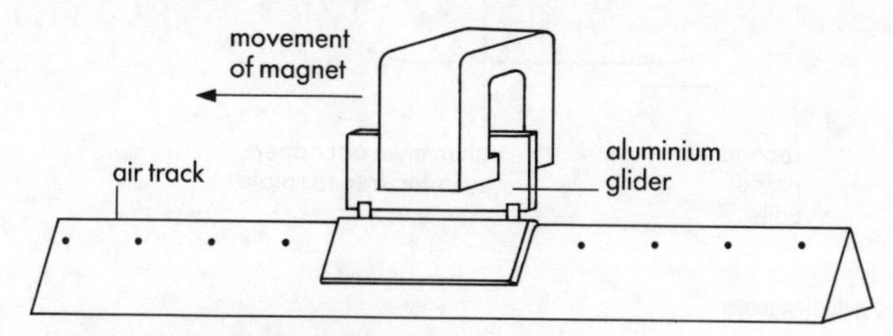

Fig. I.3 Aluminium glider on an air track

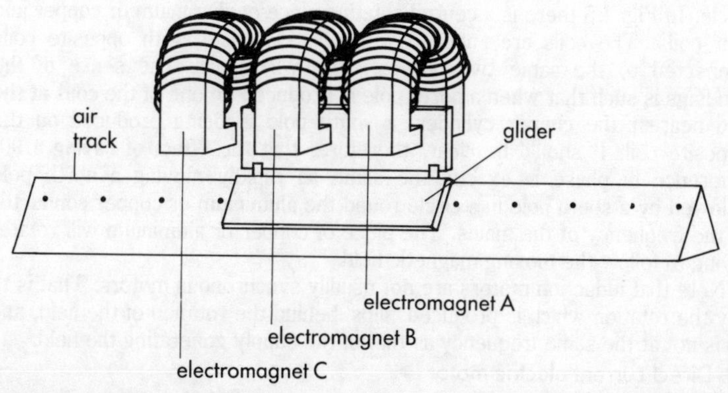

Fig. I.4 Simple linear induction motor

In Fig. I.4 a series of electromagnets are used. If a pulse of electric current is sent first to magnet A, a little later to magnet B, and a little later still to magnet C, the effect, as far as the glider is concerned, is exactly the same as moving the permanent magnet along the track in the second experiment. If a series of consecutive pulses is fed to the array of coils the glider will move forward.

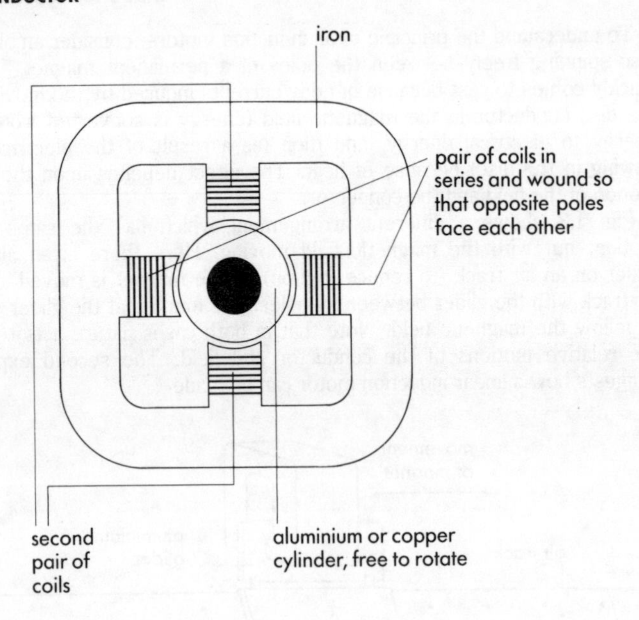

Fig. I.5 Induction motor

A rotational induction motor can be made by having a series of coils in a circle. In Fig. I.5 there is a central rotating piece of aluminium or copper and four coils. The coils are supplied with a.c. electricity with opposite coils connected to the same two phases, 90° (π/2) apart. The sense of the windings is such that when a north pole is produced on one of the coils at the end nearest the copper cylinder, a south pole is being produced on the opposite coil. It should be clear, therefore, that the effect of having a 90° difference in phase is exactly the same as rapidly moving a north pole followed by a south pole in a circle round the aluminium or copper conductor at the frequency of the mains. The piece of copper or aluminium will rotate, trying to follow the moving magnetic field.

Note that induction motors are not usually synchronous motors. That is to say the rotation which is produced 'slips' behind the rotation of the field, and so is not at the same frequency as that of the supply generating the field.

◀ Direct current electric motor ▶

INDUCTOR

This is a component in an electric circuit in which a magnetic field is generated when a current flows. It is said to have inductance. Sometimes it is known as a choke.

◀ Alternating currents, Mutual inductance, Self inductance ▶

INSULATORS

◀ Conductors and insulators ▶

INTEGRATED CIRCUITS (i.c's)

An integrated circuit consists of many interconnected microscopic electronic components (sometimes hundreds of thousands) such as **diodes, transistors, resistors** and **capacitors.**

One of the main reasons why electronics has changed so very rapidly in the past twenty years has been the creation and continued development of integrated circuits (i.c's). Manufacturers can now make complete circuits of diodes, transistors, resistors and capacitors on 0.5 mm thick slices of silicon. The area of a silicon 'chip' is about 5 mm^2 and the most popular packaging for it is the dual-in-line (DIL) shown in Fig. I.6.

Integrated circuits can be roughly classified into two categories: linear i.c's which deal with continuously variable, or analogue, signals; and digital i.c's which deal with voltage pulses representing binary stages (i.e. 'high' or 'low' voltage levels).

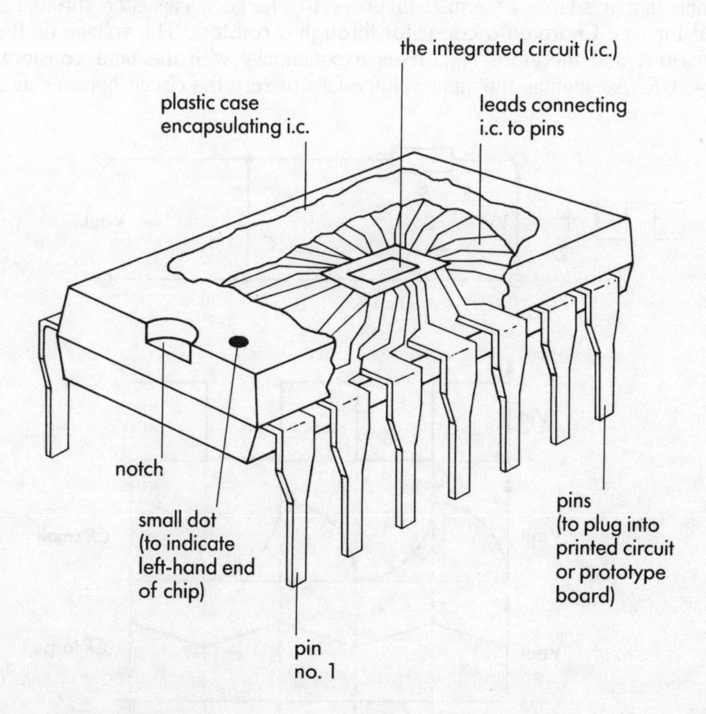

Fig. I.6 Dual-in-line (DIL) silicon chip

Apart from being amazingly cost-effective (i.e. cheap), integrated circuits have the further advantages of being smaller and more reliable than their equivalent circuits made from discrete components. The principal limitation that they have is the maximum power that they are able to handle.

INTEGRATING AND DIFFERENTIATING (RC AND CR) CIRCUITS

In both these circuits the output signal has a different waveform (but not frequency) from the input signal. The integrator circuit sums the input signal over a period of time, while the differentiator circuit gives an output proportional to the rate of change of the input signal.

Consider the circuit shown in Fig. I.7. This might be part of a larger electronic circuit in which the output signal from part of the circuit is received on the left-hand side, passes through the circuit and is, in turn, sent out to other components in the larger circuit on the right-hand side. In the diagram we consider a square wave signal forming the input voltage on the left-hand side, V_{in}. Supposing the capacitor is initially uncharged, the condition when the square wave jumps to its maximum value is precisely that of connecting a source of e.m.f. in order to charge a capacitor through a resistor (see **Charging a capacitor through a resistor**). The voltage on the capacitor, and therefore V_{out}, rises exponentially with the **time constant**, $\tau = CR$. As soon as the input voltage falls to zero the circuit behaves as if

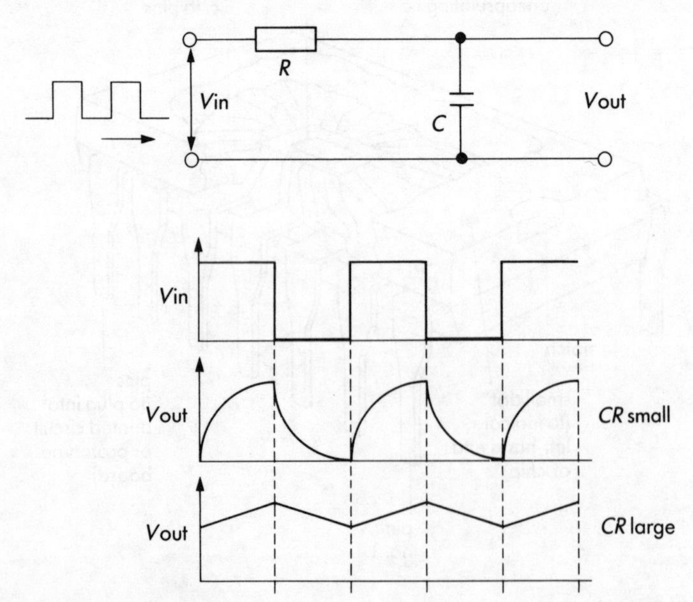

Fig. I.7 Circuit acting as an integrator

the left-hand side of R were connected to the ground rail, i.e. a circuit in which a capacitor is discharging through a resistor (see **Discharge of a capacitor**). Now the voltage on the capacitor, and therefore V_{out}, diminishes exponentially to zero with the same time constant. The overall effect, with a small value of $\tau = CR$, is shown in the middle graph of Fig. I.7. When the time constant is fairly large, V_{out} does not change very much, and essentially the voltage changes at the input are smoothed out.

This kind of circuit is called an integrator because it sums the input signal over a period of time. Circuits used for smoothing in power supplies are essentially of this kind. The analysis has used a square wave signal but the effect of integration is the same whatever the profile of the input signal.

CR COUPLING

In Fig. I.8 the positions of the resistor and capacitor have been changed. When the square wave voltage suddenly rises from 0 volts to its maximum, the output voltage, V_{out}, also rises immediately. This is because the capacitor cannot charge instantly. The p.d. across it is initially zero and so the output voltage is the same as the input voltage. The capacitor then starts to charge

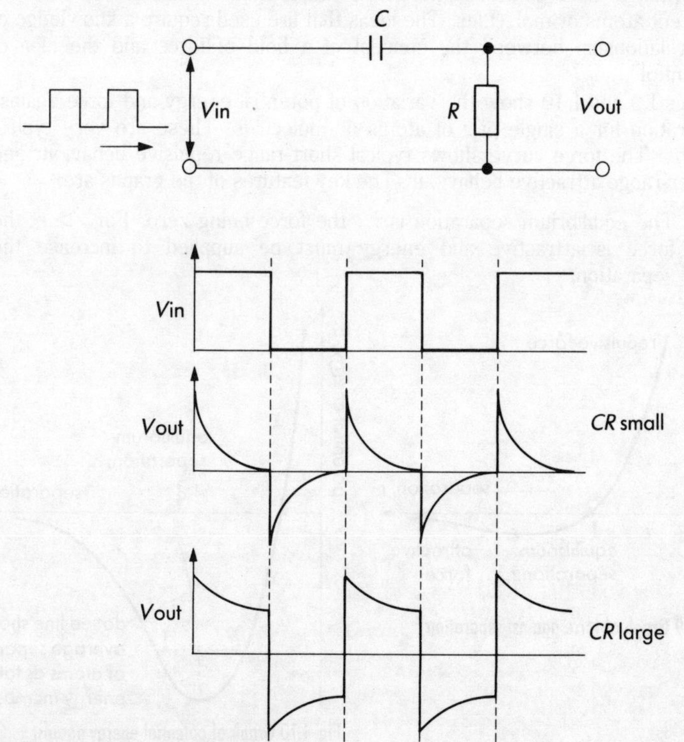

Fig. I.8 Circuit acting as a differentiator

through the resistor. The p.d. across the capacitor, therefore, rises and so V_{out} falls. The time constant for this process is given by $\tau = RC$. When τ is comparatively small and the capacitor charges quickly, V_{out} falls rapidly. When the input voltage falls to zero the charged capacitor starts to discharge. The overall waveform is that shown in the middle graph. Such a circuit is called a differentiator. It gives an output only when the input is changing and the faster the rate of change the larger the output signal. The bottom diagram shows the effect of having a comparatively large value of $\tau = CR$.

INTENSIFYING SCREEN

◀ Radiography ▶

INTERATOMIC FORCES

The properties of materials are to a very large extent determined by the kinds of force between adjacent atoms or molecules. For this reason it is important to have some insights into a simple model of the forces between adjacent atoms or molecules. The ideas that are used require a knowledge of the relationship between the concept of a **field** of force and the idea of **potential**.

Figs I.9 and I.10 show the variation of potential energy and force against separation for a single pair of atoms or molecules. These are very typical graphs. The force curve shows typical short-range repulsive behaviour and longer-range attractive behaviour. The key features of the graphs are:

a) The equilibrium separation is r_o, the force being zero. For $r > r_o$ the force is attractive and energy must be supplied to increase the separation.

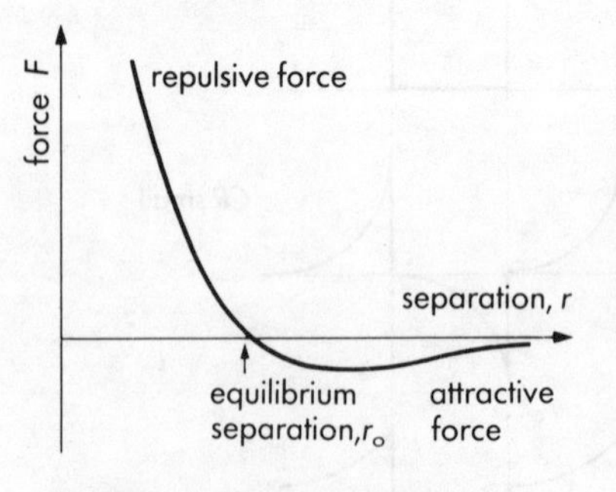

Fig. I.9 Graph of force against separation

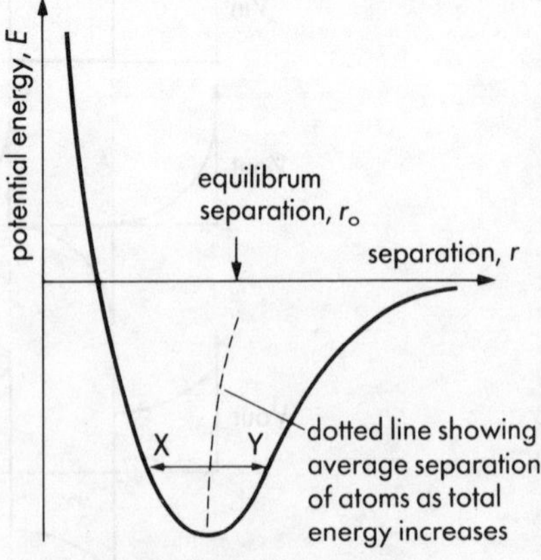

Fig. I.10 Graph of potential energy against separation

b) For $r < r_0$ the force is repulsive and energy has to be supplied to decrease the separation.

c) So at $r = r_0$ the potential energy is a minimum corresponding to zero force. In general $F = -\frac{dE}{dr}$, i.e. the force is the slope of the potential energy graph.

d) Energy is needed to completely separate the atoms.

e) When atoms are oscillating as they do in a solid, the potential energy varies with separation, as shown by the curve between X and Y. As the temperature increases the atoms have more energy and the amplitude of the oscillations is greater. The average separation is shown by the dotted line, which shows that solids expand on heating.

INTERFERENCE

This is the phenomenon in the physics of waves whereby when two waves, say of the same **frequency, amplitude** and **wavelength**, arrive at the same place, the result may be either no waves at all, a wave of double amplitude or something in between. The phenomenon is an example of the **superposition principle:** that is to say the displacements of the two waves add algebraically to produce a resultant displacement.

An example in the physics of water waves occurs in the Dyfi estuary in mid-Wales as the tide is coming in (Fig. I.11 a). The northern side of the estuary is a rocky shore which remains in the same place whatever the height of the water. But the southern side is a gradually sloping sandy beach, the waterline of which depends on the height of the water. A sailor out in the middle estuary might suddenly find that the sea has gone calm. But in fact what has happened is that he is at a point where two trains of waves are simultaneously reaching him out of phase (Fig. I.11 b). After a few minutes the path travelled by the wave 'bouncing' off the southern shoreline will

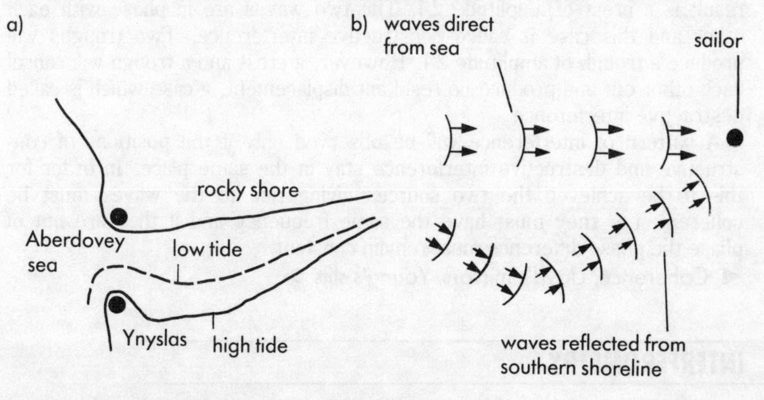

Fig. I.11 a) The Dyfi (Dovey) estuary b) Interference of two waves

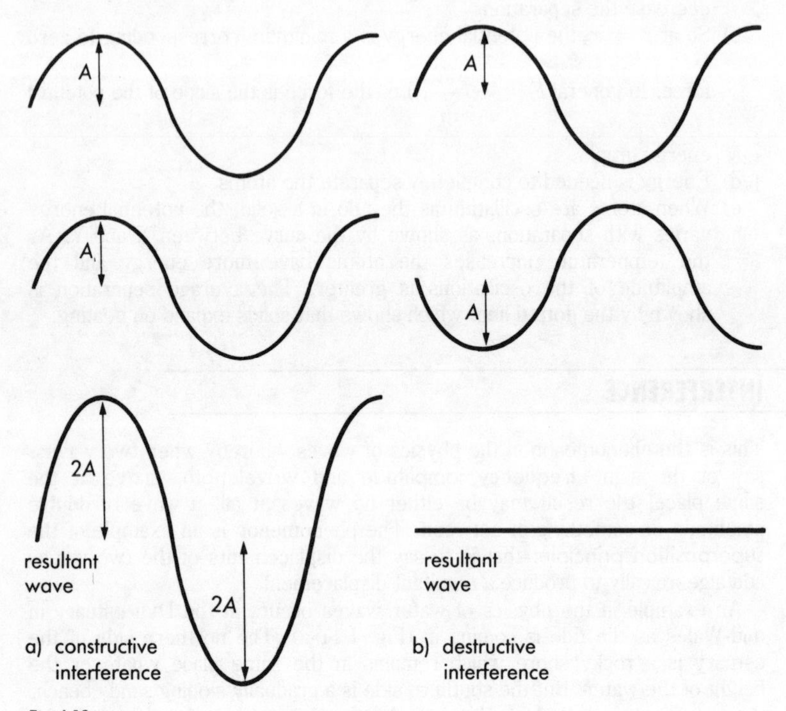

Fig. I.12

change to bring it in phase with the other wave, and a rough sea will be reported.

In Fig. I.12 a wave crest of amplitude of A meets a similar crest and the result is a crest of amplitude $2A$. The two waves are in phase with each other and this case is called constructive interference. Two troughs will produce a trough of amplitude $2A$. However, a crest and a trough will cancel each other out and produce no resultant displacement, a case which is called destructive interference.

A pattern of interference will be observed only if the positions of constructive and destructive interference stay in the same place. In order for this to be achieved the two sources giving rise to the waves must be coherent: i.e. they must have the same frequency and if they are out of phase the phase difference must remain constant.

◀ Coherence, Lloyd's mirrors, Young's slits ▶

INTERFEROMETRY

◀ Radio telescope ▶

INTERNAL ENERGY

This is a special piece of terminology used in thermodynamics. It is what most people in everyday life call 'heat', for example if they were to say 'I got burned by the heating element of the stove because it had a lot of heat in it.' Here they think of heat as what is possessed by a hot body. While we can talk about a body at high temperature as being hot, we should talk about it having a great deal of internal energy.

Note that at the atomic and molecular level this energy is the kinetic and vibrational energy of the component atoms and molecules. Note also that for an **ideal gas** the internal energy depends only on the **temperature** of the gas.

◀ Heat, Thermodynamics ▶

INTERNAL RESISTANCE

This is the resistance of a cell, battery or electronic power supply. When current is delivered to an external circuit, current also flows through the cell or power supply itself. Because it has resistance a potential difference develops across the cell or power supply, thus reducing the potential difference available to the external circuit to less than the e.m.f.

If a cell (battery) had no internal resistance, it would be able to drive very large amounts of current through small load resistances, and would not get hot. Everyday experience with batteries and cells shows that this is not the case. With the notable exception of lead-acid cells used in motor-car batteries, real cells have an appreciable internal resistance, r. Thus if the cell has an e.m.f. E volts, then when a coulomb of charge passes through the cell it gains electrical energy, E joules. However, because of the internal resistance some of this energy is converted to heat inside the cell. The net effect is that the equation $E = V + Ir$ holds, where V is the p.d. around the circuit, and Ir is the p.d. developed across the internal resistance.

The p.d., V, would be what was measured by a voltmeter placed across the terminals of the cells (Fig. I.13). V will always be less than E. As a simple example consider the case when the external resistance R of the circuit is equal to the internal resistance r. In this case it is clear that as the total p.d. in the circuit is equal to E, the p.d. across R is equal to the p.d. across r, and so a voltmeter connected to the cell would read half the e.m.f.

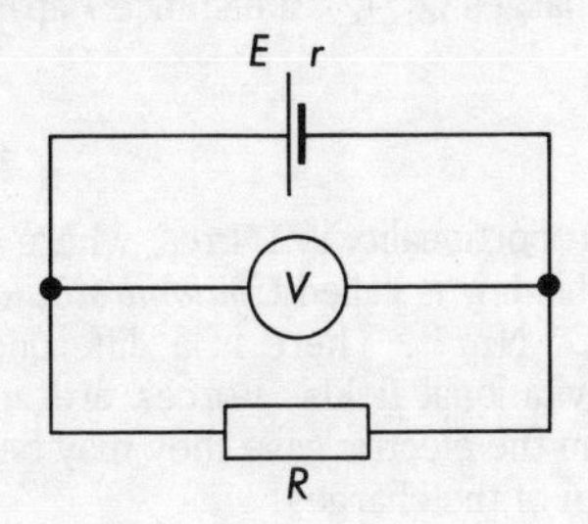

Fig. I.13

E. Note that as the current I decreases the p.d. across the supply will increase and reach a maximum value E when the current falls to zero. The supply is then said to be on open circuit and the p.d. across the supply equals the e.m.f.

Note that a potentiometer circuit measures the e.m.f., E, because this is a *null method* and no current flows in the measurement.

◀ Electromotive force, Potential difference, Potentiometer ▶

INTERNATIONAL SYSTEM OF UNITS (SI)

◀ Physical quantities in the SI system ▶

INVASIVE TECHNIQUES

◀ Ultrasonics ▶

INVERSE SQUARE LAW FIELDS

Both electric fields and gravitational fields are examples of inverse square law fields. If a point object exerts an inverse square law field, the force exerted acts either attractively or repulsively along radial lines centred on the point. If the distance of a test object sensing the force from the point is doubled, the force experienced reduces to a quarter of its initial value. At three times as far away the force is 1/9th, etc. A point mass m_1 attracting another mass m_2 behaves in this way. The force is given by the formula

$$F = G\frac{m_1 m_2}{r^2}$$

where F is the force in newtons, m_1 and m_2 are the masses measured in kg, and r is the distance between them measured in m. G is the universal constant of gravitation whose value is $6.7 \times 10^{-11}\,\mathrm{N\,m^2\,kg^{-2}}$. The formula is a description of what is called Newton's Universal Law of Gravitation. The term 'universal' is used to imply that the law is obeyed by all masses in the universe.

In the case of electric charges a similar law of force obtains. The force between two electric charges Q_1, Q_2, a distance r apart, is given by

$$F = \left(\frac{1}{4\pi\epsilon_0}\right)\frac{Q_1 Q_2}{r^2}$$

Here the constant of proportionality is $1/4\pi\epsilon_0$, where ϵ_0 is the permittivity of free space constant. This law is called *Coulomb's Law.* Note that $1/4\pi\epsilon_0$ has the value of $9 \times 10^9\ \mathrm{C^2\,N\,m^{-2}}$. There is a difference, however, between electric fields and gravitational fields. Forces are always attractive in the gravitational case, but in the electric case they may be attractive or repulsive depending upon the sign of the charges.

Potential and potential energy in inverse square law fields

It is a familiar experience that a mass placed in a gravitational field can acquire energy. A mass placed at the bottom of a cliff has to be given energy in order to raise it to the top of the cliff, but once there the energy is merely stored and if released from the top of the cliff this **potential energy**, as it is called, can be converted back into kinetic energy. The same is true of electric charges, except that here things are slightly more complicated because of the existence of attractions and repulsions. For example, if one charge is brought close to another charge work has to be done on that charge to bring it close to the second charge because of the attractive nature of the force between them. If the charge is released it will spring away, having acquired kinetic energy from the potential energy initially stored. In both of these cases the energy is stored in the field. The amount of energy stored depends upon the position of the object in the field as well as upon the strength of the field and the nature of the object involved.

In the examples chosen it is only possible so far to talk about changes in potential energy. But in inverse square law fields physicists have found it useful to have a reference position where the potential energy is defined to be zero. In both the electrostatic and gravitational cases the reference position is chosen to be some infinite distance from the position of the masses or the charges. However, there are cases where it is more convenient to use a different reference position. For example, in considering a simple gravitational energy problem on the earth, the zero is often taken as the energy at the surface of the earth.

Physicists also use the term *potential.* The potential at a point in a field is the potential energy that a 'test object' would have at that point. In a gravitational field such a test object is a unit mass, say 1 kg. In an electrostatic field the test object is unit charge, i.e. 1 C. Once we know the potential at a point we can find the potential energy of a particular mass or charge by simply multiplying the potential by the amount of the mass or charge, e.g. for a gravitational field, p.e. $= Vm$; for an electrostatic field, p.e. $= Vq$, where V is the potential, m is the mass and q is the charge. There is an important general relationship between the field intensity, which we can denote by E and the potential, V.

Fig. I.14 shows a force field E at a distance r from a source of the field. Assume that the field is an attractive one (the simplest kind of course might be the gravitational field attracting a mass). If a 'test object' is brought up from a distance, $r + \mathrm{d}r$ to r, then work done $= -E\,\mathrm{d}r$; E being the force acting on the unit test object, and the work done being negative, i.e. because of the attractive nature of the field, energy is lost as the test object gets closer. The total work done is the result of adding the work

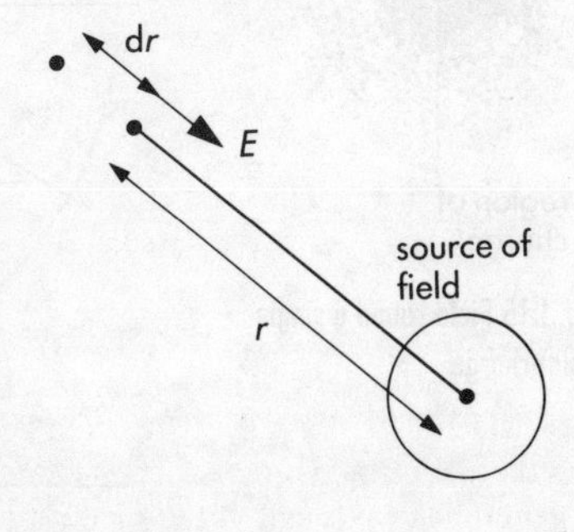

Fig. I.14 Source of field

done for each small distance dr in bringing the test object from infinity, and by definition this is the potential at a distance r. Hence we can write

$$V = -\int E\,\mathrm{d}r$$

An alternative way of considering this relationship is to write it in the differential form, i.e.

$$E = -\frac{\mathrm{d}V}{\mathrm{d}r}$$

(For examples of the use of this equation, see **Gravitational field** and **Electric field**.)

At A-level there is no expectation that you will be able to manipulate the calculus and differentials, but you should be able to use the second equation to interpret the graphs which appear in questions. Some examples of this are given in the relevant entries.

Representing fields in graphs and diagrams

There are several ways of representing the field in an electrostatic or a gravitational system. For example the field round a single point charge can be represented as shown in Fig. I.15, where depth shading has been used to illustrate the strength of the field. Alternatively different colours could be used in the same way that colours are used in geography for representing different heights above sea level. Both of these methods are difficult and so generally two easier methods are employed.

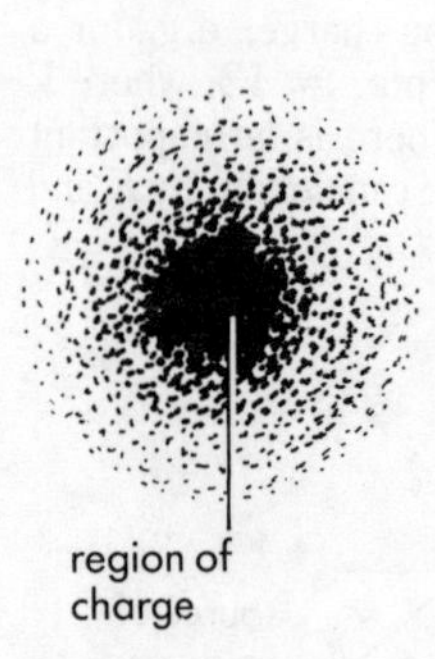

Fig. I.15 Field round a single point charge

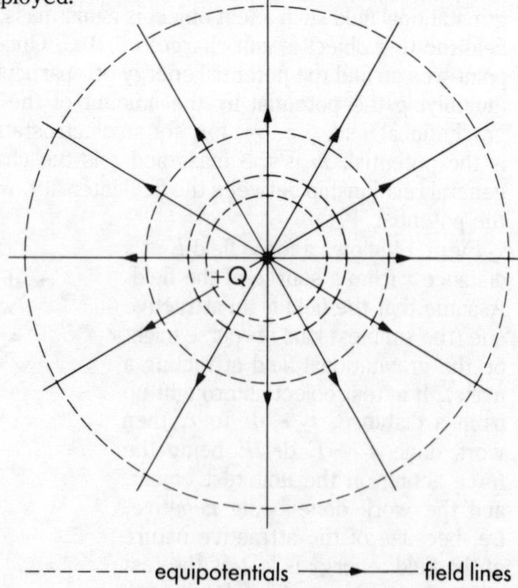

Fig. I.16 Electric field and potential surrounding a point charge

Fig. I.16 shows the method of field line representation. In this method the field is represented by drawing lines to represent the direction in space. By definition the arrows show the direction in which the suitable test object would experience force. Here, with a positive charge and with the test object for an electrostatic case being unit positive charge, i.e. 1 C, the field lines point away from the single positive charge at the centre. The strength of the field is roughly indicated by the distance between these field lines. Note that at any given radius from the central charge the lines are at the same distance apart, showing that the field strength is constant for all points at this radius. A second way of representing the field is also shown on the diagram. The variation of potential in a field can be represented by drawing lines joining points which are at the same potential. These are known as *equipotentials* or lines of equipotential, and are similar to contour lines on geographical maps joining points of equal height. The equipotentials are always at right angles to the field lines; this makes it easy to draw an equipotential diagram if the field shape is known, and vice versa. If a test object is moved along an equipotential line, no work is done and it is for this reason that the lines must be perpendicular to the field lines. As with contours on maps, it is conventional to draw the lines with equal spacings of potential.

Graphs can also be used to indicate features of a field. The entry on measuring equipotentials shows how an experiment may be conducted to determine the equipotentials in the field between a metal plate and a small square conductor. Fig. I.17 shows the result if a graph is plotted of potential as a function of distance from the metal plate and the square conductor is replaced by a pointed one. In this case the metal plate is taken as a zero of potential and the pointed conductor has been set at a potential difference 10 V below this (Fig. I.18). Here x is the distance from the plate. The graph of field against distance, x, is found by using the equation

$$E = -\frac{dV}{dx}$$

The result is in Fig. I.19. Note that the field graph is equal to the negative of the slope of the potential graph at every point. The significance of the varying

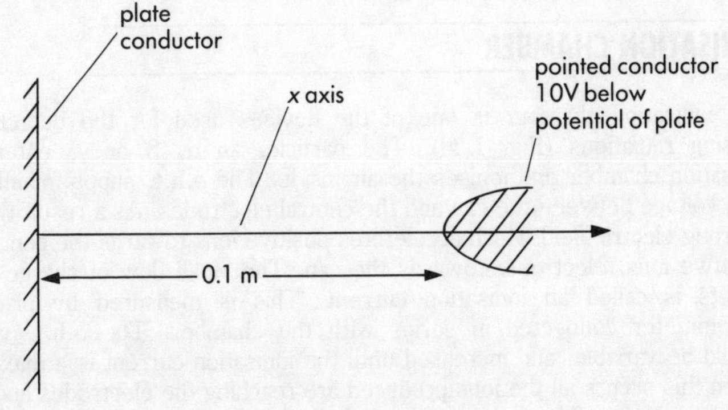

Fig. I.17

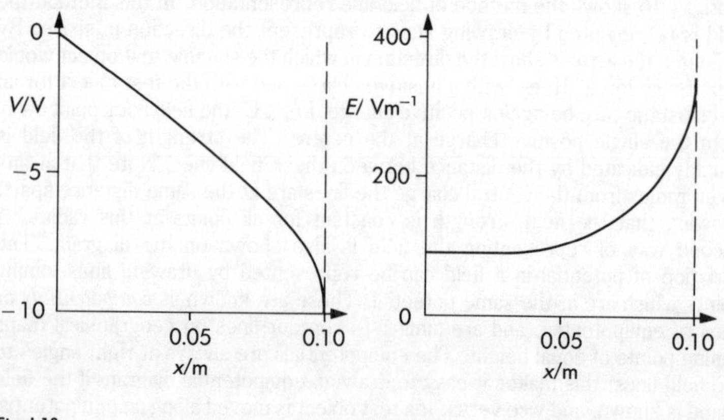

Fig. I.18

Fig. I.19

slope of the field graph is that the strength of the field increases as the point conductor is approached. This is an example of the well-known phenomenon in electrostatics called **action of points**. The area under the graph between any two points measures the potential difference between them.

◀ Uniform electric field ▶

IONIC BONDING

◀ Solids ▶

IONISATION

◀ Energy levels, Nuclear model of the atom ▶

IONISATION CHAMBER

The ionisation chamber is one of the devices used for the detection of ionising radiations (Fig. I.20). The particle, an α, β or γ, enters the ionisation chamber and ionises the air inside. The e.h.t. supply maintains a high voltage between the can and the central electrodes. As a result there is a strong electric field which accelerates positive ions towards the centre and negative ions, electrons, towards the can. The small flow of charge which results is called an ionisation current. This is measured by placing a picoammeter connected in series with the chamber. The e.h.t. voltage should be variable, and increased until the ionisation current is a maximum. When this occurs all the ions produced are reaching the electrodes and none are recombining. Thus we have

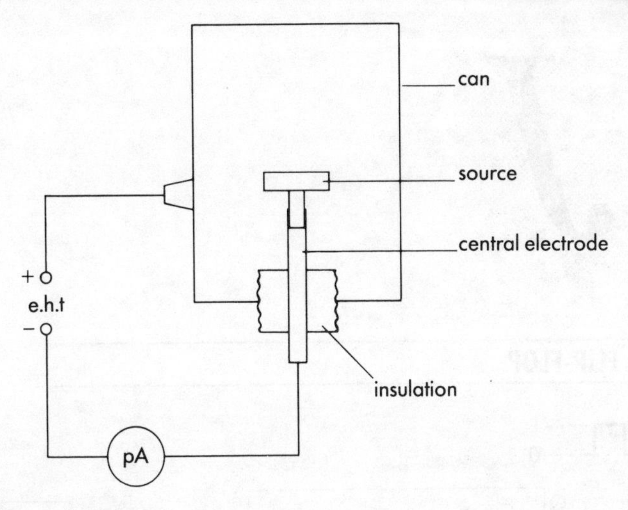

Fig. I.20 Ionisation chamber

$$I = ne$$

where I is the current, that is the charge produced per second, n is the number of ion pairs produced per second, and e is the charge on each ion, the electronic charge 1.6×10^{-19} C. By measuring I the number of ion pairs produced per second by the source can be calculated. The ionisation chamber is a good method of detecting alphas as they produce a large number of ions in a short distance. Betas and gammas generally do not produce a large enough ionisation current to be easily detected by this method.

◀ Alpha radiation, Geiger tube ▶

IONOSPHERE

◀ Radio transmission ▶

ISOTOPE

The chemical properties of an atom are determined by the number of protons in the nucleus. This is because the number of protons in turn determines the number of electrons in the surrounding **shells** or groups of electrons. For a given element and therefore a given number of protons there can be several values of the **neutron number**. These different types of nuclei with different neutron numbers but the same **proton number** are called isotopes of the element. Unstable isotopes which exhibit radioactive decay are called radioisotopes.

JK FLIP-FLOP

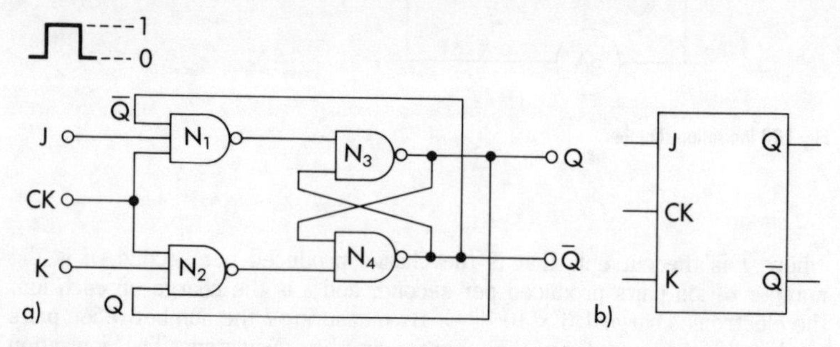

Fig. J.1

This is a standard circuit used in electronics. Unlike the **bistable** the data inputs J and K are both allowed to be high simultaneously and this makes it more useful. And unlike the **astable** circuit it has a third input called a clock (CK) into which is fed a pulse from a clock circuit, i.e. a square-wave pulsing circuit like that produced by the astable or like that produced by a **relaxation oscillator**, the pulse going from logic 0 to 1 and then back to 0 again.

In a typical JK flip-flop, e.g. a 7474 dual-type positive-edge JK flip-flop, Q will take on the value of the J input at the time when the clock is rising from logic 0 to 1 (positive-edge triggering). It will do this provided J = 0 and K = 1, or J = 1 and K = 0. If the two data inputs J and K are both at logic 0, Q will not change. If the two data inputs are at logic 1, Q 'toggles' between 0 and 1 each time the clock rises from logic 0 to logic 1.

The circuit and the truth table are shown in Fig. J.1 and Table J.1. Note that N_1 and N_2 are three input NAND gates. These have an output of 1 unless all three inputs are 1.

You should note that there are other types of flip-flop which follow negative-edge triggering, i.e. there is a change of state as the clock falls from 1 to 0.

Note that Q = 1 occurs only once every two pulses, i.e. the output has half the frequency of the input. The flip-flop is therefore a frequency divider

Inputs		Outputs before clock pulse		Outputs after clock pulse		
J	K	Q	$\overline{Q}$	Q	$\overline{Q}$	
0	0	1	0	1	0	No change in
0	0	0	1	0	1	outputs
1	0	1	0	1	0	Stays at or sets to
1	0	0	1	1	0	$Q = 1$ and $\overline{Q} = 0$
0	1	1	0	0	1	Stays at or resets to
0	1	0	1	0	1	$Q = 0$ and $\overline{Q} = 1$
1	1	1	0	0	1	Toggles
1	1	0	1	1	0	

Table J.1

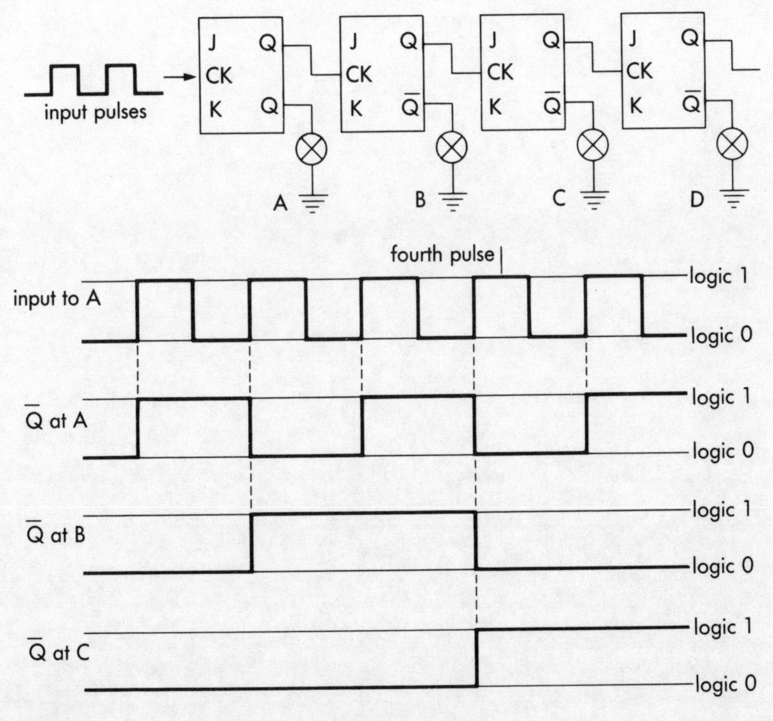

Fig. J.2

circuit and could be used in an electronic organ for dividing the frequency of a master oscillator in order to produce a note one octave lower. It also forms the basic component of a binary counter. Fig. J.2 shows several flip-flops connected together. Suppose all the JK inputs are connected to logic state 1 and the flip-flops are all initially set to Q = 1. The graphs show what happens when a train of pulses is sent to the CK of A. For example after the fourth input pulse, and before the fifth, Q at C is 1 and all other outputs are 0. The outputs in order DCBA are therefore 0100, which is the number 4 in binary.

◀ D-type flip-flop, Sequential logic, Positive feedback and electrical oscillations ▶

JOULE

◀ Energy ▶

KILOWATT

◀ Electrical power and the heating effect ▶

KINEMATICS

This is an old-fashioned word which simply means the science of motion. It is used in situations where motion is being measured but where the causes of the motion are not being explored. If the causes of motion were being explored we would call the subject **dynamics**.

KINETIC ENERGY

This is a term used in mechanics to refer to the **energy** a body has by virtue of its velocity v:

$$T = \frac{1}{2}mv^2$$

where m is the mass of the body and T is the kinetic energy.

◀ Potential energy ▶

KINETIC THEORY OF GASES

The kinetic theory of gases is a model used to explain the properties of gases. It is a remarkably successful model in which the properties of the gas derive from collisions between particles which are moving at very high speeds (comparable with bullet speeds) in empty space. Prior to the development of this theory in the eighteenth century, it was assumed that a gas, like the air, was full of invisible particles in contact with each other, and which could be curled up on compression. The particles might be like the feathers in a down-filled pillow.

In constructing a kinetic theory model the main assumptions made are:

i) The gas is largely empty space in which a very large number of molecules are moving about in random directions at high speed, colliding with each other and the walls of the container. The average distance between collisions is called the mean free path.
ii) The intermolecular forces are negligible except during collisions.
iii) The volume occupied by the molecules is negligible compared with the volume of the gas.
iv) There is no loss of energy in the collision process, i.e. the collisions are 'elastic'.

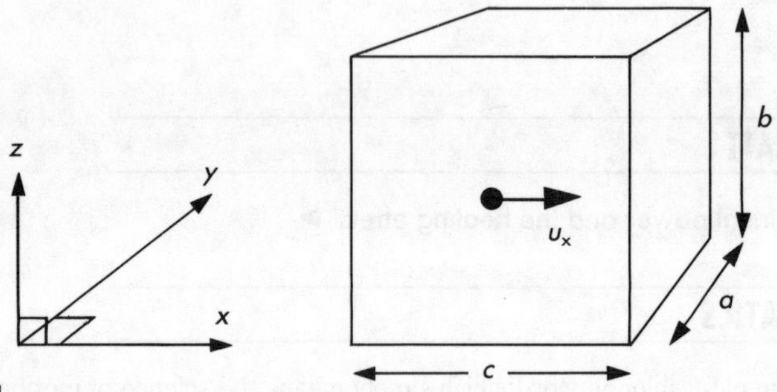

Fig. K.1

In a very simplified treatment of the theory the gas particles can be treated as spheres moving in a rectangular box with the statistics treated by dividing them into three groups, one third travelling in each of the three dimensions of space. Consider such a box of sides, *a, b* and *c* (Fig. K.1). Assume that one third of the molecules are approaching the right-hand face of area *ab* with a speed which is on average u_x. Each time one of these molecules collides with the face its change of velocity is $u_x - (-u_x) = 2u_x$. Consequently its change of momentum is $2mu_x$, where *m* is its mass. The molecule has to travel a distance $2c$ before it hits the face again. So the number of times it does so per second is $u_x/2c$. The amount of momentum 'exchanged' at the face per second is therefore $2mu_x(u_x/2c) = mu_x/c$. But by Newton's Second Law the force is equal to the rate of change of momentum. Hence we have: $F = mu_x^2/c$.

The pressure on the face is F/area, which is F/ab. This gives $p = mu_x/abc = mu_x/V$, where p is the pressure and V the volume of the box.

Finally, as only one third of the molecules travel in this direction, the total pressure on the face of the box is given by $p = \frac{1}{3}\frac{mN}{V}u_x^2$, where N is the number of molecules.

A more elaborate treatment provides a better handling of the statistics. The form of the formula which is derived is nevertheless the same:

$$p = \frac{1}{3}\frac{mN\langle c^2\rangle}{V} \quad \text{or } p = \frac{1}{3}\rho\langle c^2\rangle$$

Here $\sqrt{<c^2>}$ is called the root mean square (r.m.s.) speed of the gas molecules. That is to say it is the square root of the mean value of the (molecular speeds), i.e.

$$\text{r.m.s. speed} = \sqrt{<c^2>} = \sqrt{\frac{c_1^{\,2} + c_2^{\,2} + \ldots + c_N^{\,2}}{N}}$$

where c_1, c_2, ... c_N are the individual molecular speeds.

When 1 mole is considered, the formula $p = \frac{1}{3} mN <c^2>$ becomes

$$pV = \frac{1}{3} N_A m <c^2>$$

Here N_A is the Avogadro constant, 6.02×10^{23} particles mol^{-1}

Meaning of temperature and heat capacity

The result of the kinetic theory can be used to give a meaning to the macroscopic quantities of temperature and heat capacity.

Rearranging the expression for pV:

$$pV = \frac{2}{3} N_A \left(\frac{1}{2} m <c^2>\right)$$

$\frac{1}{2} m <c^2>$ is the mean kinetic energy of a gas molecule, and this is also equal to its mean total energy as it has no potential energy.

The experimental result embodied in the general gas equation is $pV = RT$ for one mole. Combining these two equations gives:

$$RT = \frac{2}{3}\left(N_A \times \frac{1}{2} m <c^2>\right)$$

$$= \frac{2}{3}(\text{total energy of 1 mole of the gas})$$

and hence a meaning to temperature, T, and heat capacity.

Rearranging:

$$\text{Total energy of 1 mole of the gas} = \frac{3}{2} RT.$$

Thus the energy required to raise the temperature of 1 mole of the gas by $1\text{K} = \frac{3}{2} R$, i.e. its molar heat capacity at constant volume, c_V (for a monatomic gas).

Also dividing $RT = \frac{2}{3}\left(N_A \times \frac{1}{2} m <c^2>\right)$ by N_A gives

$$\frac{RT}{N_A} = kT = \frac{2}{3} \text{(mean energy of a molecule)}$$

where $k = R/N_A$ is the *Boltzmann constant* ($= 1.38 \times 10^{-23}$ J K^{-1})

$$\text{Thus } \frac{1}{2} m <c^2> = \frac{3}{2} kT$$

showing that the temperature T is proportional to the mean kinetic energy of a gas molecule.

Distribution of molecular speeds in a gas

The theory so far, and the use of the root mean square speed $\sqrt{<c^2>}$, is only approximate. A more accurate treatment results in Fig. K.2, which shows the general way in which the molecular velocities are distributed and the effect of an increase in temperature.

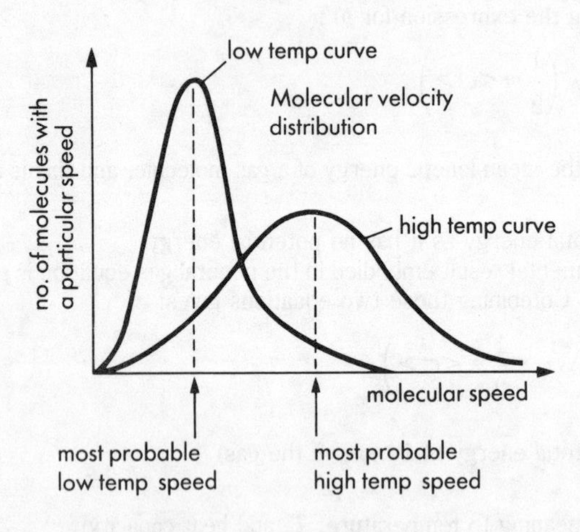

Fig. K.2 Molecular velocity distribution

The following features are of importance:

i) The molecular speeds range from zero to infinity.
ii) The speed for which the curve is a maximum is the most probable speed, i.e. the most likely speed found in an experimental measurement.

Experimental evidence for the kinetic theory of gases is provided by the phenomena of **diffusion** and **Brownian motion**.

KIRCHHOFF'S LAWS

Kirchhoff's First Law

This states that the algebraic sum of the currents at a junction in a circuit is zero. Essentially this is a conservation law which says the amount of current entering a junction is equal to the amount of current leaving it. Regarding currents as positive if they enter the junction and negative if they leave it, the law applies in the form stated in Fig. K.3, with I_3 negative.

Kirchhoff's Second Law

In a closed loop in a circuit the algebraic sum of the e.m.f.s is equal to the algebraic sum of the p.d's (i.e. the products of current times resistance). Essentially this too is a conservation law, in this case that of the conservation of energy. It states that if we were to consider the energy changes to an imaginary coulomb of charge passing round a closed loop, the electrical energy gained from any e.m.f's is the same as that lost through passing through resistors, etc., where there are p.d's.

As an example consider the slide-wire **potentiometer** circuit shown in Fig. K.4, and consider the loop PQRS. Start at P and go round the loop in a clockwise direction. Care has to be taken with signs. The e.m.f's are added together, remembering that going from the negative to the positive terminals is considered positive, and going the other way negative. The p.d's are also added together, remembering that passing through a resistor in the direction of current gives a positive p.d., and going the other way a negative one. Thus we see that the only e.m.f. is E and we note that as no current flows through the galvanometer the only p.d. is that along the slide wire, iR_{PQ}.

Hence $-E + iR_{PQ} = 0$

giving $E = iR_{PQ}$

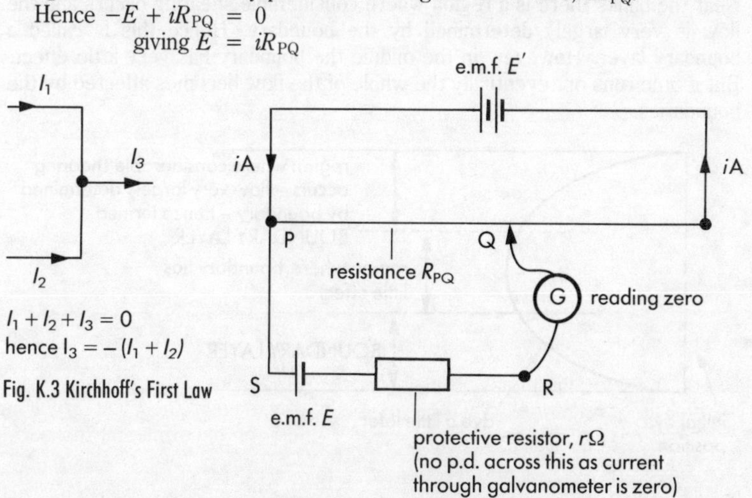

Fig. K.3 Kirchhoff's First Law

Fig. K.4 Kirchhoff's Second Law and the slide-wire potentiometer

LAMINAR FLOW

This is a term used in the physics of fluids to describe how a **fluid** flows past an object and in particular in a channel between two containing 'banks'. It applies to situations where the flow is determined by the friction or the viscosity of the fluid, but where the flow is not so fast that turbulence occurs.

Consider the flow of a fluid along a channel. The flow is fastest in the middle and reduces to zero at the boundaries of the channel (the banks). This is because a fluid finds even a polished surface very rough on the molecular scale and is dragged to a standstill at the surface.

Each layer of the liquid 'shears' past its neighbouring layer, again as a result of friction between layers.

Suppose fluid is introduced into such a channel and a dye is spread across the channel. A little later the dye will adopt the shape shown in Fig. L.1. Near the banks there is a region where considerable shearing occurs and the flow is very largely determined by the boundary. Hence this is called a boundary layer. However, in the middle the boundary has very little effect. But if time runs on, eventually the whole of the flow becomes affected by the boundaries.

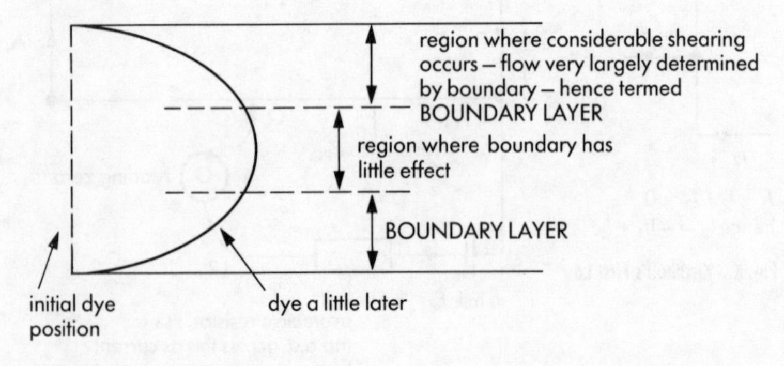

Fig. L.1 Boundary layers in fluid flow

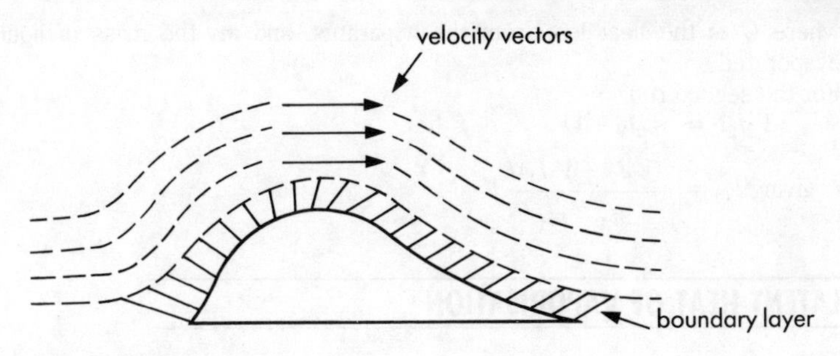

Fig. L.2 Small boundary layer of an aerofoil

However, in circumstances when 'new' fluid meets a boundary of finite size there is insufficient time for the whole flow to be affected. The boundary layer remains very thin. An example of this would be air flowing over an aircraft wing (aerofoil), shown in Fig. L.2.

◄ Bernouilli's principle, Equation of continuity ►

LATENT HEAT DETERMINATION

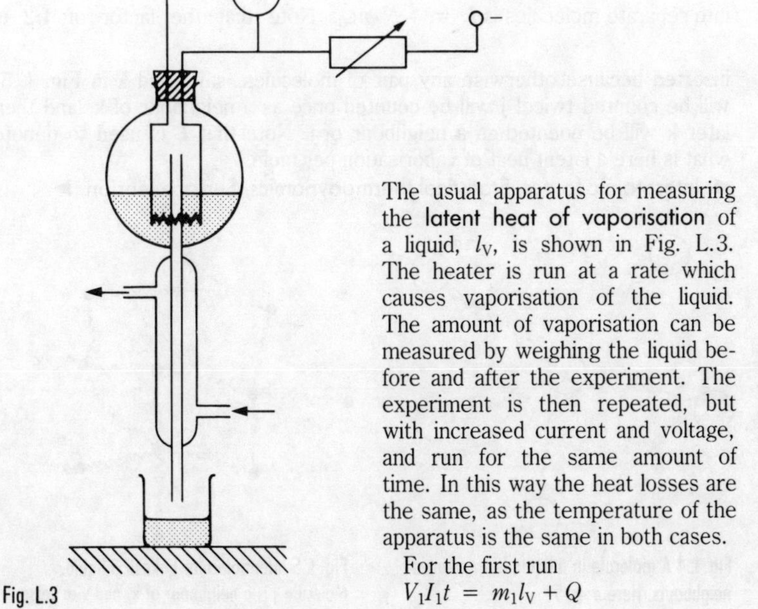

Fig. L.3

The usual apparatus for measuring the **latent heat of vaporisation** of a liquid, l_V, is shown in Fig. L.3. The heater is run at a rate which causes vaporisation of the liquid. The amount of vaporisation can be measured by weighing the liquid before and after the experiment. The experiment is then repeated, but with increased current and voltage, and run for the same amount of time. In this way the heat losses are the same, as the temperature of the apparatus is the same in both cases.

For the first run

$$V_1 I_1 t = m_1 l_V + Q$$

where Q is the heat lost from the apparatus, and m_1 the mass of liquid evaporated.
For the second run

$$V_2I_2t = m_2l_V + Q$$

$$\text{giving } l_V = \frac{(V_2I_2 - V_1I_1)t}{m_2 - m_1}$$

LATENT HEAT OF VAPORISATION

The latent heat of vaporisation is the quantity of thermal energy required to change unit mass of a substance from liquid to vapour without change of temperature. It is a quantity which can easily be found by experiment (see **Latent heat determination**). Knowledge of it tells us a good deal about the energy stored in the intermolecular forces and the average number of nearest-neighbour molecules in the liquid.

Inside a liquid molecules continually break and re-form bonds with their neighbours. The latent heat of vaporisation is the energy needed to break all the bonds. Suppose ϵ_0 is the energy needed to separate molecule X from one of its nearest neighbours (Fig. L.4). ϵ_0 is obviously the energy per pair of molecules and is sometimes called the **binding energy** of a molecular pair. If there are n nearest neighbours per molecule the energy needed to separate all the bonds between X and its neighbours is $n\epsilon_0$. In one **mole** of liquid there are N_A molecules. So the energy required to separate the liquid into separate molecules is $L = \frac{1}{2}N_A n\epsilon_0$. Note that the factor of 1/2 is inserted because otherwise any pair of molecules, say j and k in Fig. L.5, will be counted twice! j will be counted once as a neighbour of k, and then later k will be counted as a neighbour of j. Note that L is used to denote what is here a latent heat of vaporisation per mole.

◀ Interatomic forces, Statistical thermodynamics, Surface tension ▶

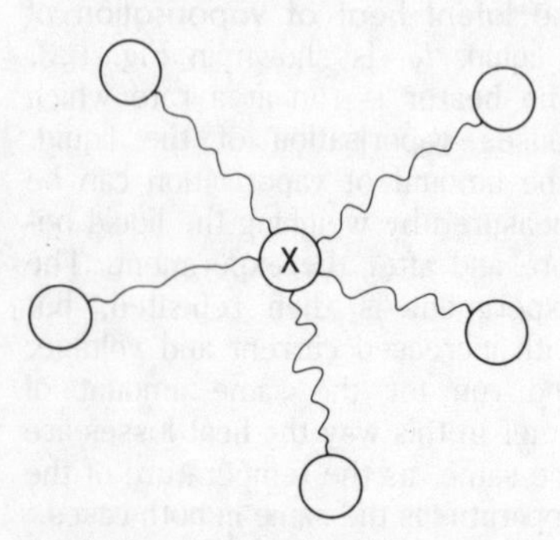

Fig. L.4 A molecule in a liquid has n nearest neighbours. Here $n = 5$

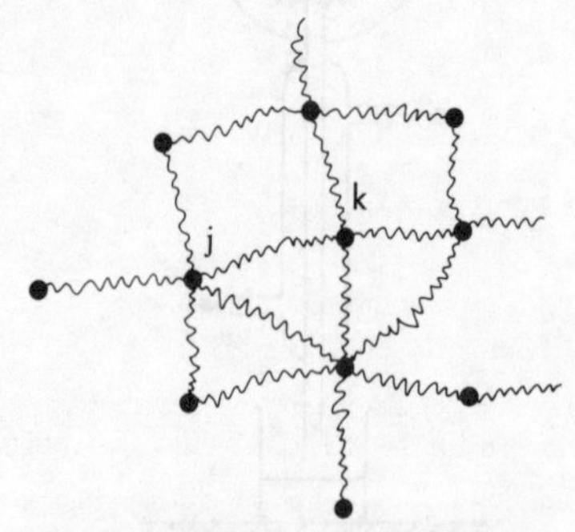

Fig. L.5 Intermolecular links in a liquid. Molecule j is a neighbour of k, and vice versa

LATTICE

◀ Solids ▶

LAWS OF THERMODYNAMICS

There are two important laws of thermodynamics, the First Law and the Second Law.

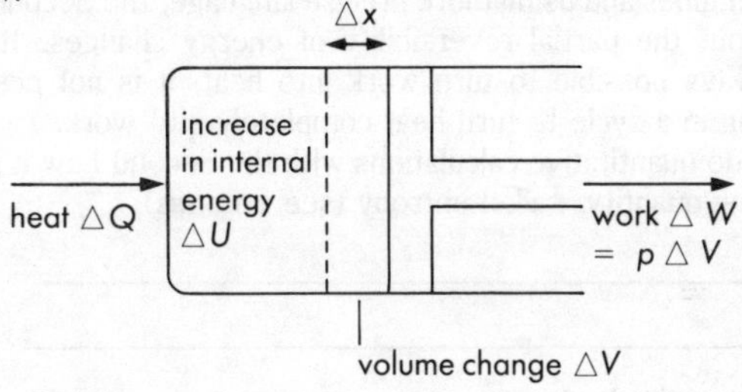

Fig. L.6

First Law of Thermodynamics

The First Law is really a statement of the principle of the conservation of **energy** and states that the work done by an engine is equal to the heat which is lost. Formally it states that when an amount of heat ΔQ is applied to, say, a gas (but equally to any thermodynamic system) the effect is to increase the **internal energy** of the gas by an amount ΔU and generate external work of an amount ΔW, so that $\Delta Q = \Delta U + \Delta W$

The sign convention adopted here is that:

ΔQ is positive if heat is supplied to the gas and negative if heat is transferred from it.

ΔW is positive if the gas expands to do external work and negative if it is compressed, i.e. if work is done on it.

In an adiabatic change no heat enters or leaves the system, i.e. $\Delta Q = 0$, and so $-\Delta U = \Delta W$, i.e. any external work is performed at the expense of the internal energy.

Note that there are some variations among authors and examining boards in this sign convention.

In A-level study the First Law is often applied to gas engines, meaning petrol, diesel and steam engines and sometimes steam turbines. These are usually considered by examination of their indicator diagrams, that is graphs of pressure against volume for a whole cycle of operation.

Second Law of Thermodynamics

The Second Law is essentially concerned with the common experience that although energy can be turned from one form into another, in a series of energy changes it tends to become 'degraded' into less useful forms. For example when a car runs along the road the energy conversion cycle is:

Chemical energy → heat → kinetic energy

The kinetic energy is that of the engine. If the car is moving at a steady speed all the energy is used to overcome the friction of the air, the road surface etc. These frictional processes simply increase the temperature of the surroundings. So all we really do is burn the petrol to increase the temperature of the surroundings (as well as getting from A to B!). There is no loss of energy, but clearly the energy in the raised temperature of the surroundings is not very useful.

Applied to engines and using more precise language, the Second Law states something about the partial reversibility of energy changes. It states that while it is always possible to turn work into heat, it is not possible for an engine working in a cycle to turn heat completely into work.

In order to do quantitative calculations with the Second Law it is necessary to invent a new quantity, called entropy (see **Engines**).

LED

◀ Light-emitting diode ▶

LENS FORMULAE

For both lenses and mirrors the position of an image can be found using the equation

$$\frac{1}{u} + \frac{1}{v} = \frac{1}{f}$$

where u is the distance from the object to the lens or mirror, v the distance of the image from the lens to the mirror and f the focal length of the lens of mirror. A sign convention must be used with this formula.

An example of a sign convention is the 'real is positive' convention. In this convention distances which are associated with real objects or images are treated as positive and distances associated with virtual images or objects are treated as negative. **Concave mirrors** have positive focal lengths, because they focus parallel rays through a real image at the focal point, whereas **convex mirrors** have negative focal lengths, rays parallel to the axis diverging as if coming from a point behind the mirror. Similarly **converging lenses** have a positive focal length and **diverging lenses** a negative focal length.

If as a result of a calculation an image distance v comes out to be negative it implies that there is a virtual image. As an example, consider an object 10 cm in front of a lens of focal length 20 cm. We have $u = 10$ cm, v is an unknown, $f = 20$ cm. Using the formula

$$\frac{1}{u} + \frac{1}{v} = \frac{1}{f}$$

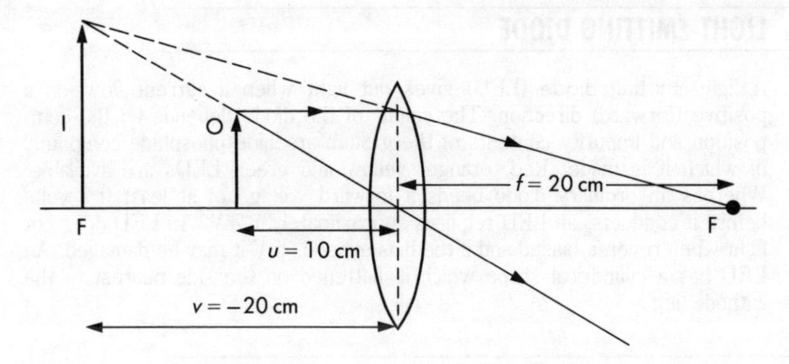

Fig. L.7

we obtain $v = -20$ cm. Hence there is a virtual image distant 20 cm from the lens. The ray diagram from this situation is shown in Fig. L.7.

The other formula used in lens and mirror calculations is the formula for linear magnification:

Linear magnification = image size/object size = v/u

Applying it to the example we have just considered, if the object was 1 cm high, the image is 2 cm high.

LENZ'S LAW

◀ Electromagnetic induction ▶

LEPTON

An **elementary particle** such as the electron which does not experience the **strong interaction** of nuclear physics.

LIGHT-BEAM GALVANOMETER

This is an instrument commonly found in school and college laboratories for measuring small electric currents.

It consists of a very delicate moving-coil suspension which is connected not to a needle as in an ordinary voltmeter or ammeter but to a mirror. Light from a small source shines upon the mirror and the reflected beam is cast upon a scale. As the coil moves so does the light beam.

Such a galvanometer can also be used for charge measurements.

◀ Ballistic galvanometer ▶

LIGHT-EMITTING DIODE

A light-emitting **diode** (LED) gives out light when a current flows in a positive (forward) direction. The colour of the diode depends on the composition and impurity contents of the gallium arsenide phosphide compound of which it is made. Red, orange, yellow and green LEDs are available. Whereas an ordinary diode needs a forward voltage of at least 0.7 volts before it conducts, an LED requires approximately 1.7 V. An LED does not light when reverse biased and if the bias exceeds 5 V it may be damaged. An LED has a cylindrical shape which is flattened on the side nearest to the cathode 'leg'.

LIGHTNING CONDUCTOR

◀ Action of points ▶

LINE SPECTRUM

The optical spectrum of a gas which is at a high temperature, as in a star, or excited by an electric discharge is an example of a line spectrum. It consists of a discrete number of spectral lines. Such a spectrum may be an **absorption spectrum** or an **emission spectrum**.

It contrasts with a **band spectrum** and a **continuous spectrum**.

LINES OF FORCE

◀ Fields ▶

LIQUID-DROP MODEL

The liquid-drop model is used in nuclear physics to explain some of the properties of the **nucleus**, including its **binding energy**. The model owes its origin to the idea that the attractive potentials between two molecules in molecular physics are similar to the attractive potentials of the strong interaction which holds protons together in the nucleus against the repulsive electrostatic force.

A good example of a drop of liquid is a drop of mercury. Large drops can be formed which are held together by attractive molecular forces. The binding energy of a liquid drop can be written as a number of terms:

Binding energy = latent heat − surface energy − charged state energy + other terms

The latent heat depends upon the number of molecules in the liquid drop. The surface energy depends upon the surface area. Most liquid drops are likely to be uncharged, but if there is a net electrical charge upon a drop this, too, will contribute to the energy.

Applying this idea to nuclear physics, the nucleus is treated as a charged nuclear drop. The binding energy can be written as

$$\text{Binding energy} = aA - bA^{2/3} - C\left(\frac{Z^2}{A^{1/3}}\right) - \text{d}\frac{(N-Z)^2}{A}$$

where A is the nucleon number, Z the proton number and N the number of neutrons.

The first term aA would be the only term in expression for the binding energy if there were only 'nearest-neighbour' interactions between the nucleon. It is analogous therefore to the latent heat term in a liquid drop.

The radius of the nuclear drop is proportional to $A^{\frac{1}{3}}$ and the surface area is proportional to $A^{\frac{2}{3}}$. Hence the term $bA^{\frac{2}{3}}$ is a measure of the surface energy of the nuclear drop.

Electrostatic theory shows that the energy needed to assemble a charge Ze into a radius R is $3Z^2e^2/5(4\pi\epsilon_0)R$. Here the radius R is proportional to $A^{\frac{1}{3}}$. Hence the third term represents the electrostatic energy stored by the collection of protons.

The final term $\text{d}\dfrac{(N-Z)^2}{A}$ is a symmetry term. If this were not present in the expression for the binding energy, the electrostatic term would mean that a nucleus consisting only of neutrons would be the most stable. This would not be correct. Consequently this term is an empirical nuclear interaction term. Note that it is zero when $N = Z$ and its effect is to give a model with high stability for a number of neutrons equal to the number of protons.

Binding energy calculated in this way has been compared with empirical values for binding energy and there is reasonable agreement for many nuclides between the model and reality. For the best agreement the following values of the coefficients need to be used:

a = 15.568 MeV b = 17.226 MeV
c = 0.698 MeV d = 23.279 MeV

The model offers a number of insights into the behaviour of nuclei. For example, if the Coulomb force vanished, the third term in the expression would disappear. This would suggest that the binding energy per nucleon increased with A. But although this is true for light nuclei it is not the case for heavy ones. That heavy nuclei are different shows the importance of the electrostatic energy in the energy balance of heavy nuclei. Secondly, the formula allows us to consider whether nuclear transformations from one nucleus to another, for example alpha decay, would be allowed on energy grounds. Only if energy is released is a decay energetically possible. Thirdly, the analogy with the liquid drop shows that there may be energy states in which the drop is not spherically symmetrical and that just as a drop of mercury, for example, can have vibrational states of energy, i.e. be able to wobble, so might a nucleus. The existence of excited nuclear states and the process of nuclear fission is thought to be explained by nuclear wobbling.

LIQUIDS

◀ Gases, liquids, vapours and plasmas ▶

LISSAJOUS FIGURES

◀ Frequency measurement ▶

LLOYD'S MIRROR

This is an alternative method to **Young's slits** for producing a fringe pattern from two coherent sources.

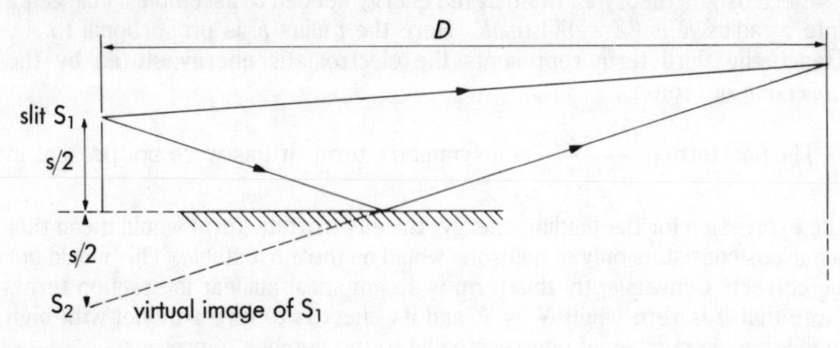

Fig. L.8 Producing fringes using a mirror

One wave goes directly to the screen (Fig. L.8) and interferes with the other wave which is reflected off the surface of the mirror. The virtual image of S in the plane mirror behaves as the second source S. The theory then is similar to Young's fringes, a fringe pattern being observed in the plane shown on the right of the diagram.

There is however an important difference: the centre of the fringe pattern is a dark band, i.e. a point of destructive interference. This is because there is a sudden phase change of π when the wave reflects from the mirror, this being equivalent to a path difference of half a wavelength. This change of phase occurs in optics whenever there is reflection from a medium of higher refractive index. Here the mirror has a higher refractive index than the air and hence this phase change occurs.

◀ Coherence ▶

LOGIC GATES

Logic gates are used in electronics in **digital logic**, or, as it is more properly called, *combinational logic*. The output voltage is either 'high' or 'low' and depends upon the state of the input voltage or voltages. In the case of the simplest logic gate, the NOT gate, there is only one input, but in the other gates encountered at A-level there are usually two inputs. Usually there are two or more inputs. The common gates are detailed below.

i) NOT gate or inverter. This is the simplest, with one input and one output. Its circuit symbols in British and American form are shown in Fig. L.9 and its input-output characteristics are summarised in the **truth table** (Table L.1).

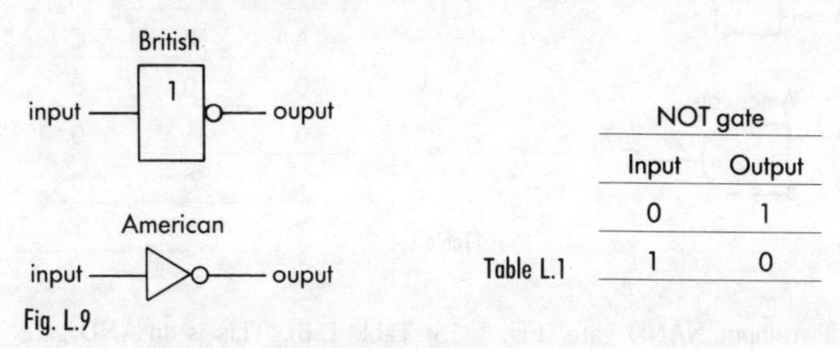

Fig. L.9

Table L.1

NOT gate	
Input	Output
0	1
1	0

ii) Two-input OR gate (Fig. L.10; Table L.2).

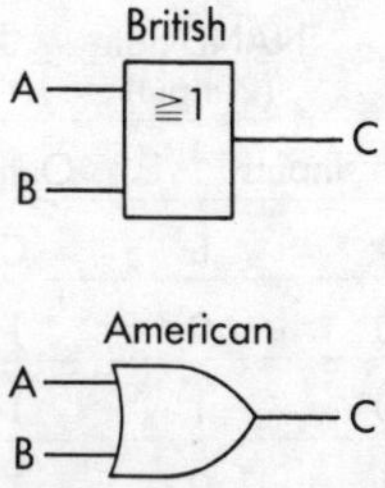

Fig. L.10

Table L.2

OR gate (2-input)		
Inputs		Output
A	B	C
0	0	0
0	1	1
1	0	1
1	1	1

iii) Two-input NOR gate (Fig. L.11; Table L.3). This is an OR gate followed by a NOT gate. (To get its truth table it is easiest to remember the truth table of an OR gate and then to invert the output column of 0s and 1s, or alternatively you can say, 'the output is high if neither A NOR B is high'.)

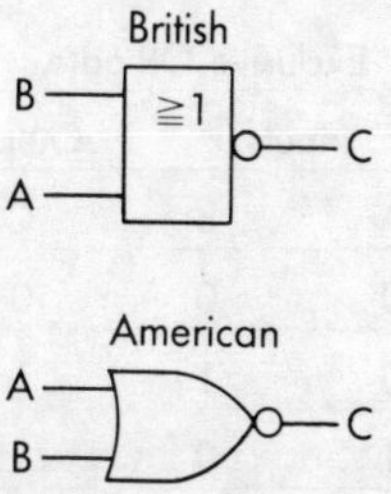

Fig. L.11

Table L.3

NOR gate (2-input)		
Inputs		Output
A	B	C
0	0	1
0	1	0
1	0	0
1	1	0

iv) Two-input AND gate (Fig. L.12; Table L.4). The output is high if and only if both inputs are high. (The output is high if A AND B are high.)

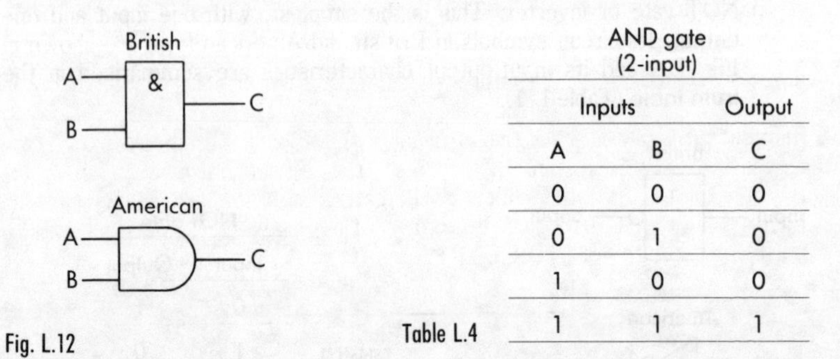

Fig. L.12

Table L.4

AND gate (2-input)		
Inputs		Output
A	B	C
0	0	0
0	1	0
1	0	0
1	1	1

v) Two-input NAND gate (Fig. L.13; Table L.5). This is an AND gate followed by a NOT gate. Again get the truth table by writing the AND truth table and inverting it.

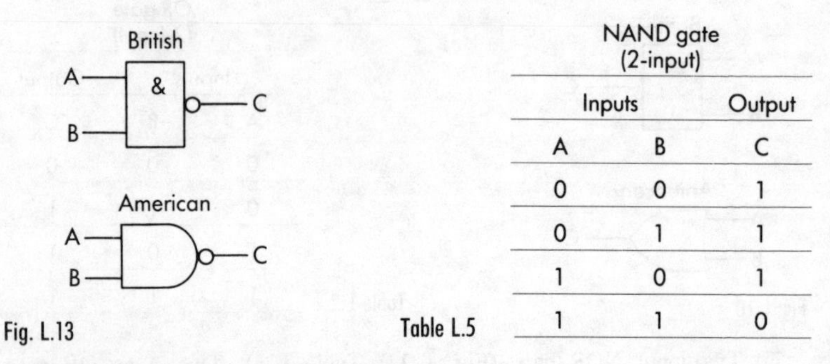

Fig. L.13

Table L.5

NAND gate (2-input)		
Inputs		Output
A	B	C
0	0	1
0	1	1
1	0	1
1	1	0

Two other gates sometimes used are:

vi) Two-input Exclusive-OR (EXOR) gate (Fig. L.14; Table L.6). The output is high if one or other of the inputs is high but not if both are high. This is sometimes called a *difference gate* because the output is high when the inputs are different.

British

= 1

American

Fig. L.14

Table L.6

Exclusive-OR gate		
Inputs		Output
A	B	C
0	0	0
0	1	1
1	0	1
1	1	0

vii) Two-input Exclusive-NOR (EXNOR) gate. This is simply the previous gate followed by a NOT gate. It is sometimes called a *parity gate.* The output is high only when both inputs are high or low.

The term gate refers to the use in **sequential logic** when a train of pulses is applied to a gate. As an example, consider a train of pulses applied to one input of an OR gate. If the voltage applied to the other gate is low, a moment's consideration of the truth table shows that the output is the same as the input. We can think of the pulse train passing through the gate. On the other hand, if the other input of the gate is high, the output of the gate is high irrespective of the current voltage of the pulse train. In this case the pulse train fails to get through the gate.

LONG-SIGHTEDNESS

◀ Defects of vision ▶

LONGITUDINAL WAVES

These are waves in which the local displacements of the medium in which the wave travels are in the same direction as the wave.

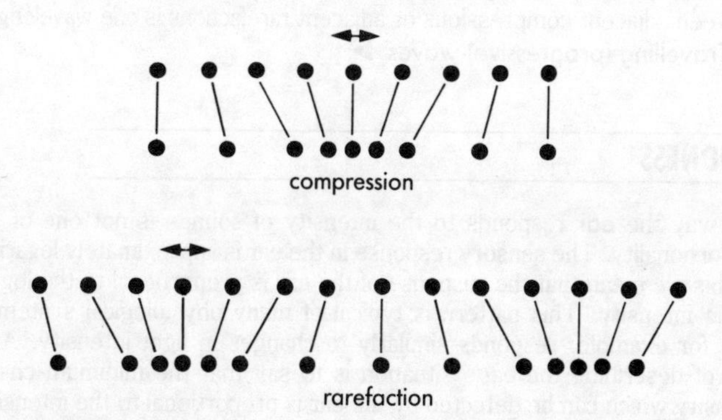

Fig. L.15 Longitudinal waves

The upper part of Fig. L.15 shows, schematically, the equilibrium positions of a set of air molecules. Underneath are the positions of the same molecules when a sound wave, a longitudinal wave, is propagating through the medium. Note that there are positions of compressions and rarefactions. The lines joining the blobs help to show how the molecules have moved from their equilibrium positions.

Graphs of displacement against distance or displacement against time can be plotted for longitudinal waves (Figs. L.16 and L.17). In interpreting these graphs it should be remembered that the actual displacements are along the direction of travel. In the case of such a sound wave travelling in the air, the

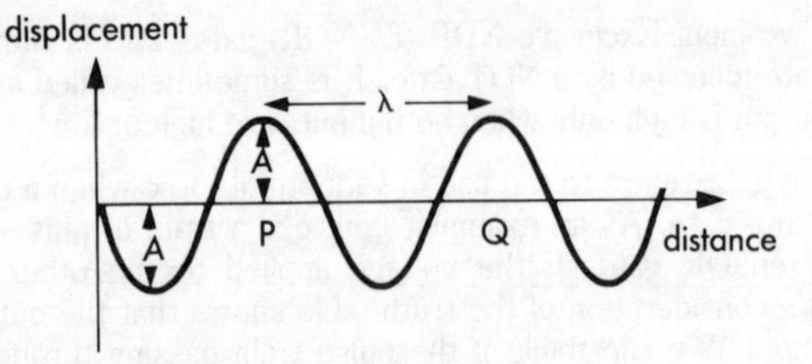

Fig. L.16

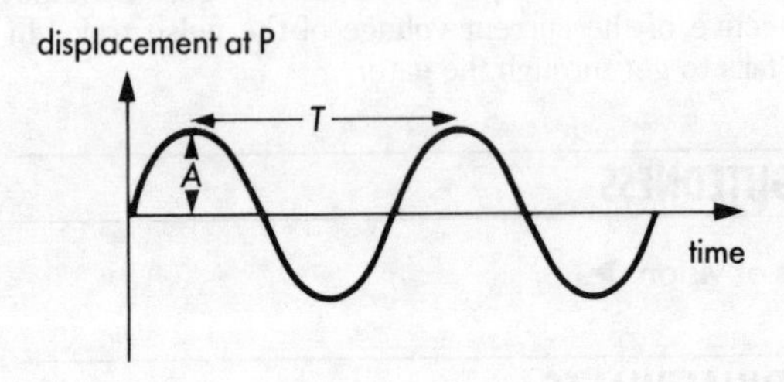

Fig. L.17

compressional regions have the air molecules more densely packed than usual and therefore the pressure is greater than atmospheric pressure. In the regions where the molecules are less densely packed, regions called rarefactions, the pressure is lower than atmospheric pressure. The distance between adjacent compressions or adjacent rarefactions is one wavelength, λ.

◀ Travelling (progressive) waves ▶

LOUDNESS

The way the **ear** responds to the intensity of sounds is not one of simple proportionality. The sensory response in the ear is approximately logarithmic. By this we mean that the response of the ear is proportional to the logarithm of the intensity. This pattern is typical of many physiological systems: the **eye**, for example, responds similarly to changes in light intensity. Another way of describing the ear's situation is to say that the minimum change in intensity which can be detected by the ear is proportional to the intensity it is already hearing. So as a sound gets louder and louder, bigger and bigger changes in intensity are necessary for the ear to note the change. It is in this way that the ear can sense a range of sound intensities.

The relative intensities of two sounds is measured in bels. Hence relative intensity in bels $= \lg(I_1/I_2)$. So when $I_1 = 10\ I_2$, the relative intensity is 1 bel.

A decibel is 1 bel/10. Consequently an increase of 1 decibel represents an increase in intensity of about 26 per cent. As so far defined, this represents merely a ratio of intensity. To create a loudness scale we need a standard level of intensity, and this is defined as a sound intensity level of 10^{-12} W m^{-2}, which is about the smallest sound that the ear can hear. Once this is done it is possible to create a loudness table. An example is shown in Table L.7.

Description of sound	Relative intensity level/ dB	Sound intensity/ $W m^{-2}$
Threshold of hearing	0	10^{-12}
Whispering	20	10^{-10}
Soft music	40	10^{-8}
Conversation	60	10^{-6}
Busy traffic	70	10^{-5}
Pneumatic drill at 8m	90	10^{-3}
Jet plane overhead	100	10^{-2}
Thunder overhead	110	10^{-1}
Threshold of pain	120	1

Table L.7

The ear is not uniformly sensitive over the entire hearing range, and has an upper limit of about 15 kHz, which diminishes with age.

LOUDSPEAKER

The loudspeaker is capable of converting **alternating currents** into sound waves.

Most loudspeakers have a permanent magnet of a special shape, a kind of all-round horseshoe (Fig. L. 18). A small coil lies loose in the magnet's gap and is attached to the loudspeaker's paper cone, which gives out the sound which is heard. A **catapult field** in the coil pushes or pulls the cone backwards and forwards. A radio or a record player drives a rapidly changing current which is amplified and sent through the coil. That current follows the vibration of musical speech; the electromagnetic force follows the currents changes and so the air in front of the loud speaker cone follows the motions of the cone, thus producing a sound wave which is a replica of that originally transmitted or recorded.

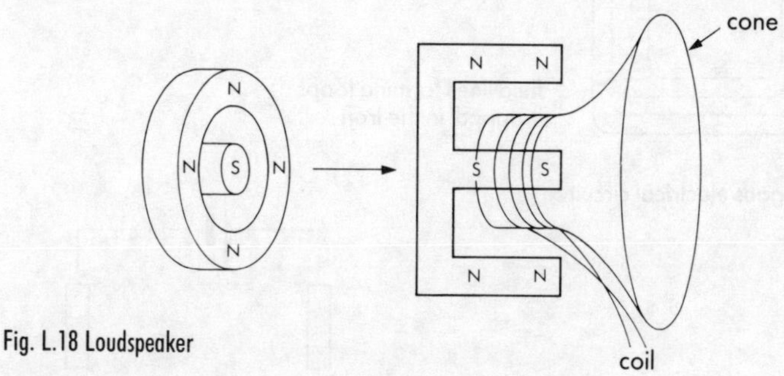

Fig. L.18 Loudspeaker

LYMAN SERIES

◀ Energy levels in hydrogen ▶

MAGNETIC CIRCUITS

As explained in the entry **Magnetic field configurations**, one of the most important properties of a magnetic field is that field lines are continuous loops. In many situations, particularly in problems in engineering, it is useful to consider the looping of a bundle of magnetic field lines and to follow this round in a circuit. The approach is to seek an analogy with current flowing in an electric circuit.

Consider for example an iron ring of cross-sectional area A, round which at one point is a coil of N turns (Fig. M.1). If a current I flows in the coil, a

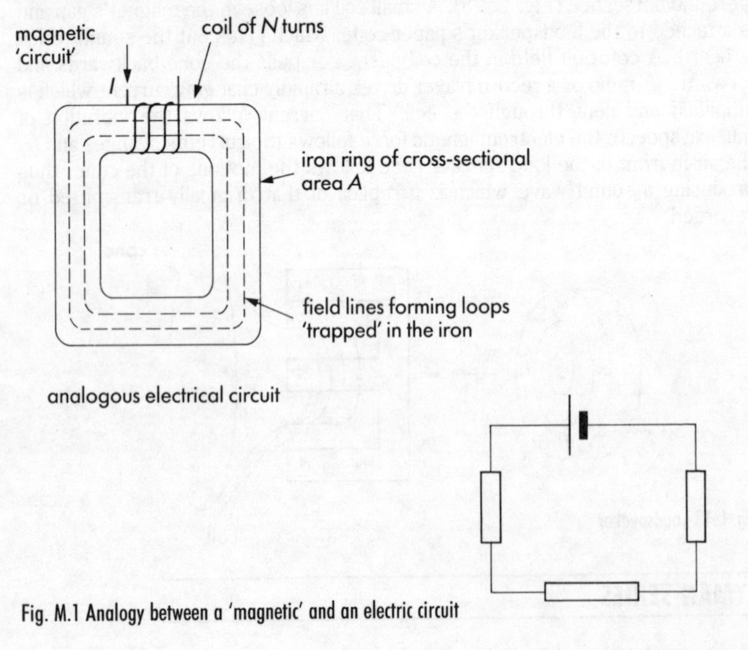

Fig. M.1 Analogy between a 'magnetic' and an electric circuit

magnetic field is set up, and because of the high magnetic **permeability** the field lines generated by the coil are all trapped inside the ring. We have the following parallels between this magnetic circuit and an electrical circuit to which this is analogous:

a) Magnetic flux, ϕ (webers). The magnetic flux is 'driven round' the magnetic 'circuit'. The flux is analogous to electric current, I (amperes), which is driven round an electrical circuit.
b) Current-turns (amperes). It is the current turns of a coil that drive the flux round the current circuit. If N is the number of turns in the coil and I the current in the coil the current turns is NI, which is sometimes called the magnetomotive force or m.m.f. This is analogous to the e.m.f. E is an electrical circuit which drives the electric current round that circuit.
c) Reluctance (henries). The reluctance R_m in a magnetic circuit is analogous to resistance in an electric circuit. Whereas increased resistance causes a reduction in the amount of electric current that can be created for a given value of e.m.f., so increased reluctance causes a reduction in the amount of flux that can be created for a given value of current turns or m.m.f.

The point about analogies in physics is that corresponding quantities must obey the same mathematics. So an approach which can be adopted is to use an understanding of something familiar in electrical circuit theory and to apply it to the more unfamiliar situation of a magnetic circuit. For example, in an electric circuit we can write **Ohm's Law** in the form $I = E/R$. Hence in a magnetic circuit we can write $\phi = NI/R_m$.

In an electric circuit the resistance is proportional to the length of a piece of wire (L) and inversely proportional to the area of cross-section (A), with ρ, the resistivity, being the constant of proportionality. Hence we have $R = \rho L/A$. And in a magnetic circuit we can write by analogy $R_m = (1/\mu_r\mu_o)L/A$ where μ_r is the relative permeability of the material, and μ_o is the permeability of free space.

In electrical circuits $1/\rho$ is known as the electrical conductivity of material and from the above equation it can be seen to be analogous to $\mu_r\mu_o$. $\mu_r\mu_o$ is hence regarded as the 'magnetic conductivity' of material.

As an example consider the magnetic circuit of a magnetising coil in a tape-recorder. The magnet is made of a material with a high relative permeability. For example, if the magnet is made of iron the relative permeability, μ_r, is about 1000. This means that it is about one thousand times better at conducting magnetic flux than the air, for which the relative permeability is about 1. Let us suppose that the relative permeability of the magnetic tape is rather smaller than 1000, and let us take a value of about 200. Suppose the magnetic circuit is as shown in Fig. M.2. The magnetic field is trapped in the iron, a good conductor' of magnetism, and at the gap between the poles it runs preferentially through the magnetic material of the tape, also a relatively good 'conductor', rather than through the air, which is a poor 'conductor' of magnetic flux. If l_{mag} is the length of the field lines in the magnet, the reluctance of the magnet is given by

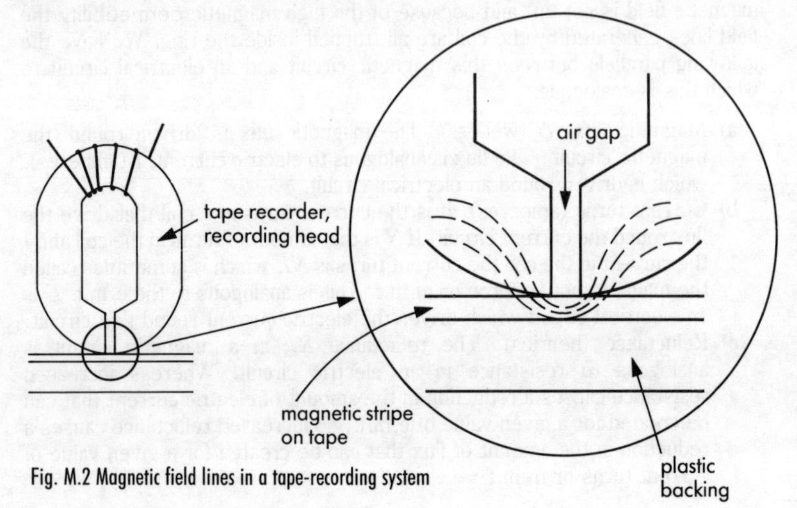

Fig. M.2 Magnetic field lines in a tape-recording system

$$R_{mag} = \left(\frac{1}{1000\,\mu_0}\right) l_{mag}/A_{mag}$$

where A_{mag} is the cross-sectional area of the iron and $\mu_r = 1000$ is the relative permeability of the material of the magnet.

The reluctance of the tape is given by a similar formula:

$$R_t = \left(\frac{1}{200\,\mu_0}\right) l_t/A_t$$

where l_t is the length of field lines in the tape, A_t the cross-sectional area of the tape, and $\mu_r = 200 =$ the relative permeability of the tape.

Hence the total reluctance of the magnetic circuit is given by

$$R_m = \left(\frac{1}{1000\,\mu_0}\right)\frac{l_{mag}}{A_{mag}} + \left(\frac{1}{200\,\mu_0}\right)\frac{l_t}{A_t}$$

and we have

$$\phi = NI/R_m$$

from which ϕ can be found. Hence we can find the strength of the B-field in the tape. This is $B = \phi/A_t$.

This is illustrative of the kind of calculation which can be carried out.

MAGNETIC FIELD CONFIGURATIONS

The shapes of the magnetic fields for some simple arrangements of current-carrying conductors are shown in Fig. M.3.

In the case of the single straight wire the direction of the whirlpools of the magnetic field is given by the right-hand grip rule (Maxwell's **corkscrew rule**).

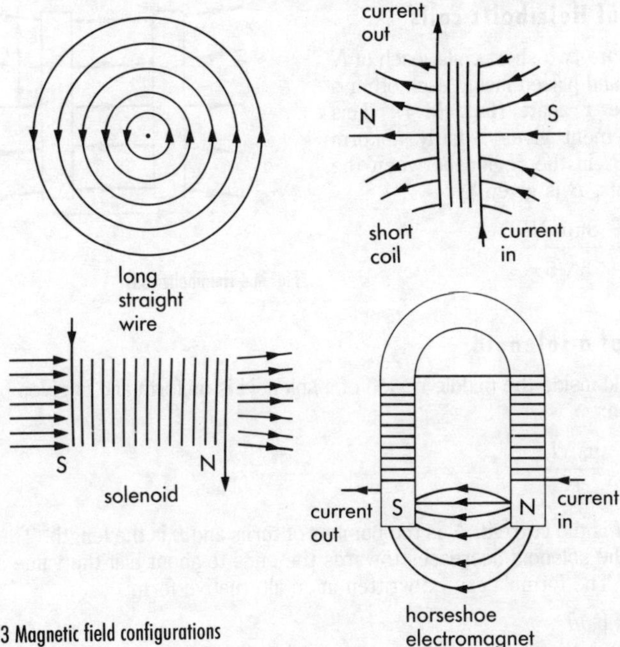

Fig. M.3 Magnetic field configurations

In the cases of the other fields the direction of the field depends upon two factors:

a) the direction of the current flowing
b) the direction in which the wire is coiled

(See **Direction rules.**)

The intensities of fields associated with a straight wire, the short coil, Helmholtz coils and the solenoid are described by the following formulae:

Field of the long straight wire

The strength B of the field at a distance from a wire carrying a current I is given by:

$$B = \frac{\mu_0 I}{2\pi r}$$

Field of a short coil

The field at the centre of a coil of N turns of wire carrying a current I and of radius r is given by:

$$B = \frac{\mu_0 NI}{2r}$$

Field of Helmholtz coils

These are two short coils, each of N turns, and placed facing each other a distance r apart (Fig. M.4). This arrangement gives a fairly uniform field, B, in the region between the two coils. B is given by:

$$B = \frac{8\pi\mu_0 NI}{5\sqrt{5}\,r}$$

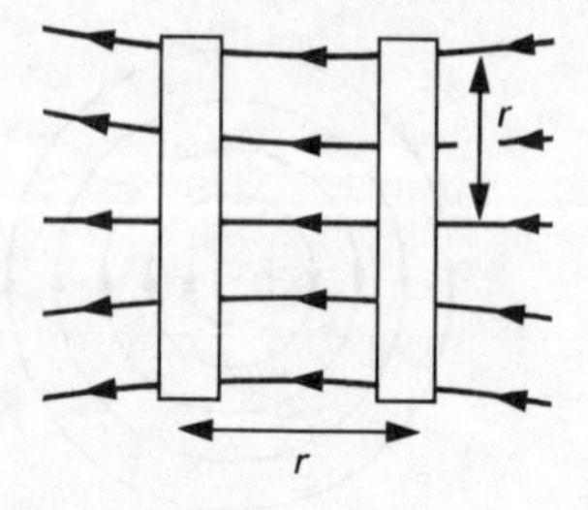

Fig. M.4 Helmholtz coils

Field of a solenoid

The field inside the middle region of a solenoid is uniform and is given by the equation:

$$B = \frac{\mu_0 NI}{L}$$

where I is the current, N is the number of turns and L is the length. The field inside the solenoid decreases towards the ends to about half the value in the middle. The formula can be written in an alternative form:

$$B = \mu_o nI$$

where n is the number of turns per unit length.

Field due to a bar magnet

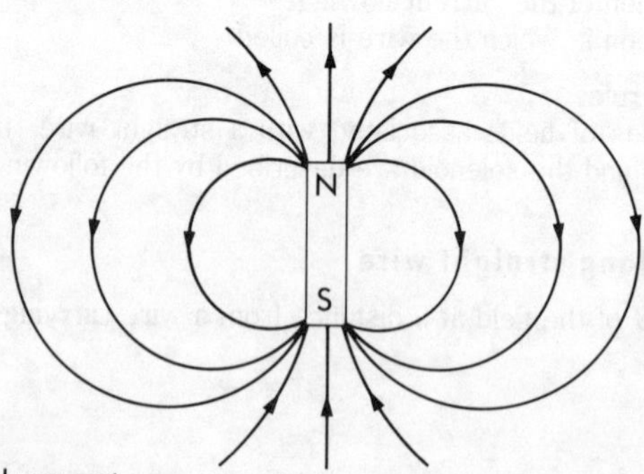

Fig. M.5 Field of a bar magnet

Fig. M.5 shows the magnetic field of a bar magnet. The lines of force appear to originate at certain regions in the magnet called the poles. Experiments show that magnetic poles are of two kinds and that like poles repel each other, that unlike poles attract each other and that poles seem to occur in pairs. Attempts have been made from time to time to identify an isolated magnetic pole, i.e. a monopole, but without success. A freely suspended magnet sets in a north/south line, indicating that the earth itself behaves like a large permanent magnet. The so-called north (N) pole of a magnet is one which points towards the earth's geographical North Pole, and the south pole (S) points towards the geographical South Pole. Strictly speaking the poles should be called the north- and south-seeking poles, because clearly, if opposite poles attract, the type of magnetic pole near the earth's geographical North Pole is a south-seeking magnetic pole.

Fig. M.6 shows a diagram of the magnetic field of the earth. Note that the arrows on the field lines point towards the north, i.e. they show the direction in which a north-seeking pole would point.

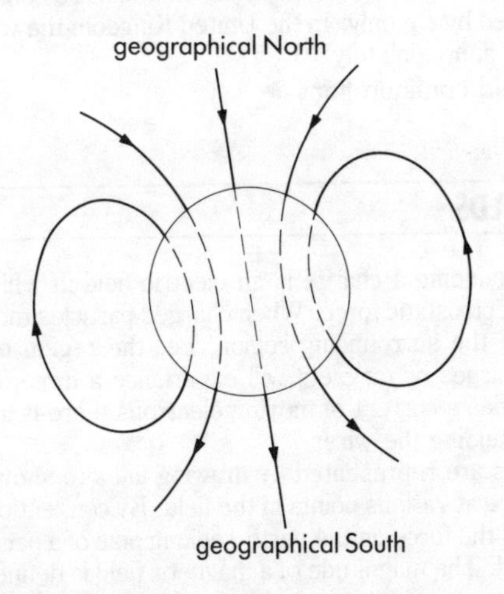

Fig. M.6 Earth's magnetic field (schematic)

MAGNETIC FIELD OF THE EARTH

The magnitude and direction of the magnetic field of the earth varies from place to place on the earth's surface. It also seems to be changing gradually with time, so that the magnetic north pole which is in a different position from the geographical North Pole is shifting year by year. The amount of shift is often stated on maps.

In the United Kingdom the earth's magnetic field is inclined downwards at an angle of about 70° to the horizontal. This angle is called the angle of dip, θ. Naturally, at the magnetic poles $\theta = 90°$. At the magnetic equator the field is parallel to the earth's surface, with $\theta = 0°$. It is convenient to resolve the earth's magnetic field V into horizontal and vertical components, B_H and B_V. From Fig. M.7 we have

$$\frac{B_V}{B_H} = \tan\theta$$

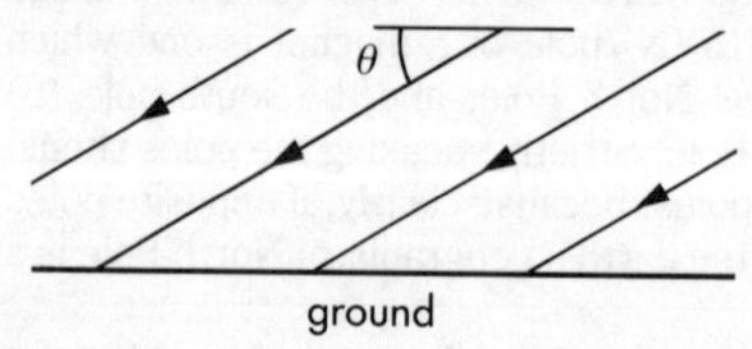

Fig. M.7

Compass needles and other devices whose motions are confined to horizontal planes are affected by B_H only. In the United Kingdom the value of the earth's magnetic field is approximately 10^{-4} T.

◀ Magnetic field configurations ▶

MAGNETIC FIELDS

The region surrounding a charge is an electric field in which other charges experience an electrostatic force. When charged particles move, they create a magnetic field in the surrounding region, i.e. the region of space in which other moving charges or magnets will experience a force. So, for example, when a wire carries a current of moving electrons there is a magnetic field in the region surrounding the wires.

Magnetic fields are represented by drawing lines to show the direction of the magnetic force at various points in the field. By convention the direction of the field is that of the force on the north-seeking pole of a bar magnet placed at a point in the field. The magnitude of a magnetic field is defined in terms of the force it will exert on a current-carrying conductor placed in the field.

So for example the field due to a single straight wire carrying an electric current is as shown in Fig. M.3 on p. 229. The field lines make a set of concentric cylinders centred on the wires. In such a field the strength, B, of the field at a distance r from the wire carrying a current I is given by

$$B = \frac{\mu_0 I}{2\pi r}$$

where B is measured in teslas (T) (see **Magnetic flux**), and μ_o is a constant called the permeability of free space. In the field line representation this $1/r$ field dependence should be represented by drawing the lines further apart where the field is weaker. (See **Fields.**)

Magnetic fields have quite different properties from the gravitational and electrostatic fields considered in the entry **Inverse square law fields.** Both electric and gravitational fields can be considered as gradients of corresponding potential functions. Both of these are studied at A-level and, in the electrostatic case particularly, it is common to map fields by plotting out the potential functions, i.e. plotting out a set of equipotentials. The magnetic field vector B can also be regarded as the gradient of a magnetic potential. However, here the similarity with inverse square law field ends, because it turns out that the potential function required in the magnetic case has to be itself a **vector**, unlike the potential functions of electrostatics and gravity which are **scalars**. Part of the reason for this is because of another difference between magnetic fields and those of gravity and electrostatics. This is that magnetic field lines have no beginnings and no ends (unlike, say, electric fields which begin and end on electric charges). It is for this reason that at A-level the concept of magnetic potential is not studied.

Strength of a magnetic field

In the past magnetic fields were measured in terms of the forces experienced by poles, for example the poles of a bar magnet, placed inside a magnetic field. But recognising that magnets and magnetic fields are the creation of electric currents, contemporary physics measures magnetic fields in terms of the forces experienced by current-carrying conductors placed within them. The vector quantity, B, representing the strength of the field is called the magnetic flux density, or simply the B-field. When a wire of length L, carrying a current I, is placed inside such a field the force F experienced is given by $F = B I L \sin\theta$, where θ is the angle between the direction of the electric current and the direction of the magnetic field. When the field and the current are at right angles the formula simplifies to $F = BIL$ and this provides a definition of the field, i.e. $B = F/IL$.

Here with F in newtons, I in amperes, and L in metres, the field B is measured in N A^{-1} m^{-1} or teslas (T). Note that the direction of the force is perpendicular to both the field direction and the current direction. This relationship is described by **Fleming's left-hand rule.**

Forces between current-carrying conductors

Consider two current-carrying conductors, parallel to each other, and placed side by side. Fig. M.8 shows a cross-section in a plane normal to the current

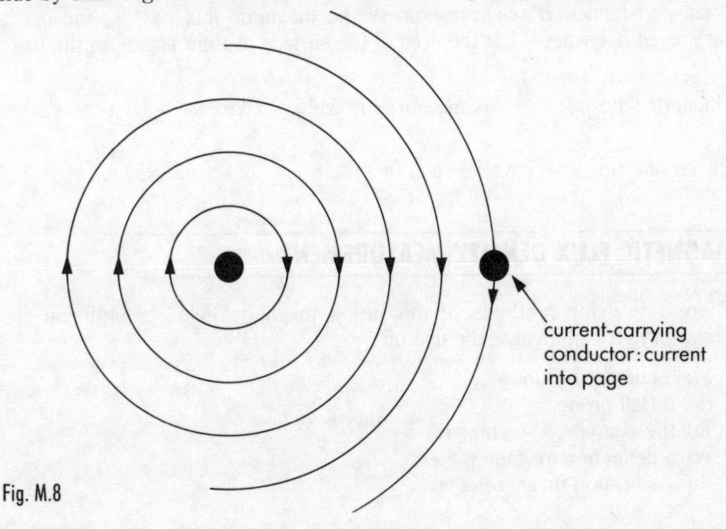

Fig. M.8

flowing in both conductors. We shall take it that both currents are in the same direction, and into the page. The circular field lines which have been drawn are those of the left-hand conductor. It should be clearly seen that the field at the right-hand conductor is at right angles to the direction of its current flow and thus by Fleming's left-hand rule there is a force acting on the right-hand wire pushing it towards the left-hand wire. This analysis is what is done if you consider the right-hand current in the field of that produced by the left-hand current. But equally you can consider everything the other way round, with the left-hand current in the field of the right-hand current. This kind of analysis shows that when the currents are in the same direction the two wires experience a force of attraction to each other, and if the currents are in the opposite direction a force of repulsion occurs.

You may find this kind of analysis unhelpful. Quite another way of thinking about it is to think in terms of the energy of the overall magnetic field between the two wires. The entry **Catapult field** considers this approach further.

Whichever analysis is used this forms the basis of the definition of the ampere. The ampere is defined as that constant current which, flowing in two infinitely long, straight parallel conductors of negligible cross-section, placed in a vacuum one metre apart, produces a force between them of 2×10^{-7} newton per metre length. The value of 2×10^{-7} N m^{-1} is not a measurement but a definition. From it follows the value of μ_o, the **permeability of free space.**

◀ Force on a charge in a magnetic field ▶

MAGNETIC FLUX

In A-level physics the force on a current in a magnetic field forms the basis of the definition of the magnetic flux density B. Sometimes this is simply referred to as the B-field. The units of B are teslas.

Having defined B we can express the magnetic flux passing through a surface as BA where A is the area of the surface at right angles to the field.

Magnetic flux, $\phi = \dfrac{B}{A}$, is measured in webers (Wb).

Hence one tesla = 1 weber m^{-2}.

MAGNETIC FLUX DENSITY MEASUREMENT

There are many methods of measuring magnetic field strengths in the laboratory. It can involve the use of:

i) a **current balance**
ii) a Hall probe
iii) the search-coil technique
iv) a deflection magnetometer
v) a vibration magnetometer

The first three methods should certainly be understood for A-level. In the current balance the force on a current carrying a conductor in the magnetic field is balanced by a weight. By measuring, the weight B can be found. The method is suitable only for steady magnetic field, but does not require a calibration with a known field.

The Hall probe relies on the **Hall effect**. Usually a semiconductor device is used which develops a small voltage proportional to the field. The device usually needs calibration with a known field in order to obtain absolute values. The Hall probe method is suitable for both steady and varying magnetic fields, and very small devices can be produced enabling fine details of a field to be explored.

There are two search-coil methods. To investigate a steady magnetic field a search coil has to be rotated through 180° in order that there is a change of flux through the coil. The search coil is connected to a **ballistic galvanometer**. The field can be found from the 'throw' of the galvanometer. To measure an alternating magnetic field it is simply necessary to place the search coil in the field and the changing magnetic flux gives rise an alternating e.m.f. which can be detected, say, with an **oscilloscope**. Provided the parameters of the coil are known, both methods enable absolute values of a field to be obtained without the need to calibrate with a known field.

The magnetometer, used in either the *deflection* or the *vibrational* mode, is an older device for measuring a field. Bearing a similarity to a compass needle, it consists of an aluminium needle pivoted at its centre, to which is attached a very short and powerful bar magnet (Fig. M.9). To measure a field by the deflection method the field must be applied at right angles to a known magnetic field, e.g. that of the earth, B_E. Because of the vectorial nature of magnetic fields, when both fields are present the bar magnet will be deflected along the line of the resultant magnetic field. If B is the field to be measured, it can be found by measuring the deflection once it is applied, and using the formula $B/B_E = \tan\theta$.

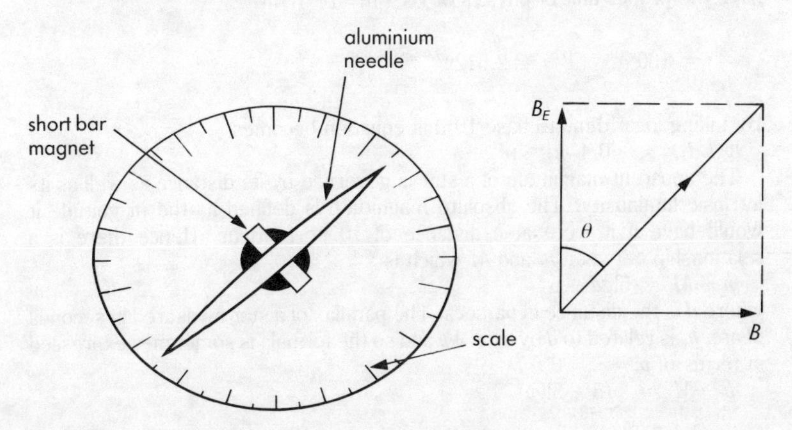

Fig. M.9 Older type of magnetometer

As the method compares the magnetic field with the earth's field, the latter needs to be known in order for an absolute value of the field to be obtained. In the vibrational method the needle is deflected in the magnetic field and then released. The period of oscillation is measured and the magnetic field is proportional to the period squared. Again, the device needs to be calibrated by finding the period for a known magnetic field.

MAGNITUDE SCALE

The magnitude scale is used in astronomy to indicate the brightness of stars. Astronomers use two magnitudes, the apparent magnitude and the absolute magnitude.

The magnitude scale can best be explained by an analogy with photography. Film manufacturers traditionally used two scales for indicating the response of a film. In the USA the ASA scale was used. A general-purpose film might have a rating of 100, a film of twice the sensitivity 200 and one of four times the sensitivity 400. On the continental (DIN) scale these same ratings would be 31, 34 and 37 respectively. So the ASA scale is an arithmetic scale and the DIN scale a logarithmic one. That is to say, equal changes in number on the DIN scale correspond to the same multiplying factor for the actual speed.

In astronomy the magnitude scale is like the DIN scale. The faintest visible stars have an *apparent magnitude* (i.e. a magnitude as viewed from the earth) of 6. Stars of magnitude 5, viewed from the earth, are 2.512 times brighter. Stars of magnitude 4 are $(2.512)^2$ times brighter and so on. The 2.512 factor is chosen so that stars of magnitude 1 are 100 times brighter, as viewed from the earth, as stars of magnitude 6. This definition gives rise to the following relationships between the apparent luminosities, l_1 and l_2, of two stars and their apparent magnitudes, m_1 and m_2. We say 'apparent' because the effect of distance is being ignored for the moment and note that luminosities would have the proper unit of physics of J s^{-1} m^{-2} or W m^{-2}.

$$\frac{l_2}{l_1} = 100^{-(m_2-m_1)/5} = 2.512^{(m_1-m_2)}$$

By taking logarithms to base 10 this equation becomes

$$\lg(l_2/l_1) = -0.4(m_2 - m_1)$$

The apparent magnitude of a star is governed by its distance as well as its intrinsic luminosity. The absolute magnitude is defined as the magnitude it would have if it were at a distance of 10 pc from us. Hence there is a relationship between m and M which is

$$m - M = 5\lg d - 5$$

where d is the distance in parsecs. The parallax of a star measured in seconds of arc, p, is related to d by $d = 1/p$ and so the formula is sometimes expressed in terms of p:

$$m - M = -(5 + 5\lg p)$$

MALTESE CROSS APPARATUS

The Maltese cross apparatus is an evacuated glass tube containing a metal electrode in the shape of a Maltese cross, and an **electron gun**. It is found in school and college laboratories and is used to demonstrate some of the properties of the electron.

On the front of the tube is a fluorescent screen, and in front of the screen is a metal cross, usually cut into the traditional shape called the Maltese cross. Behind this is an electron gun, consisting of a cathode and a cylindrical anode. Electrons are produced from the cathode by **thermionic emission** and accelerated by the potential difference supplied by an extra high tension unit (e.h.t.) through the anode and on towards the screen. When electrons strike the screen the fluorescing material glows brightly, but there is a dark 'shadow' caused by the Maltese cross. If the e.h.t. supply to the anode is switched off, an optical shadow caused by the Maltese cross standing in the light coming from the glowing cathode filament is all that is seen. But as this shadow coincides almost exactly with the electronic shadow previously seen, it provides evidence that in the absence of a deflecting field, electrons travel in straight lines, just like light.

MANOMETER

This is an instrument used to measure gas pressure (Fig. M.10). Essentially it is U-tube filled with a suitable liquid of density ρ. Since the gas pressure is greater than atmospheric pressure the liquid is forced upwards. Then gas pressure p $= h\rho g + p_A$, where p_A is the atmospheric pressure.

In a **barometer** the same principle is used.

◀ Pressure in fluids ▶

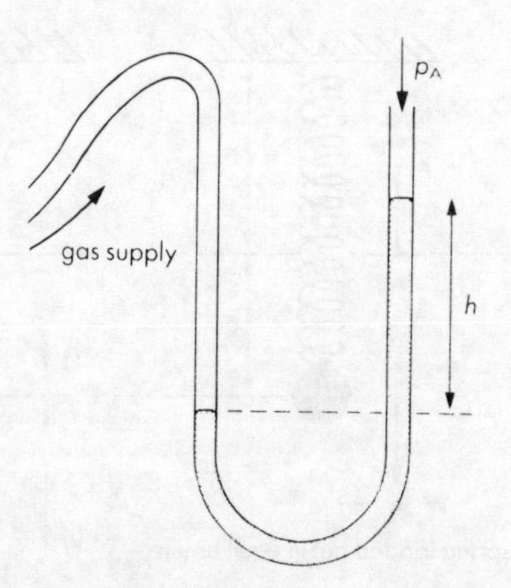

Fig. M.10 Manometer used to measure gas pressure

MASS

Mass is a key concept in Newtonian mechanics. The mass of a body is a measure of its reluctance to change its motion when a force acts, and so is sometimes called its inertia.

Consider a body accelerated by a constant force. If the mass is increased the acceleration, that is the rate at which velocity changes, gets less.

The more mass a body has the more weight it has. Imagine a body falling under gravity. $a = g$ and $F = W$, its weight, so $F = ma$ gives $W = mg$. For a second body $W' = m'g'$. Dividing these two results we get $W'/W = m'/m$, showing that the weight of a body is proportional to its mass.

MASS DEFECT

◀ Binding energy ▶

MASS-SPRING OSCILLATOR

The simple oscillating system produced by having a mass hanging from a spring is an example of a simple harmonic oscillator and hence the motion is an example of **simple harmonic motion.**

In analysing this system we need to note that there are two forces acting in the direction of motion, spring forces where the force is proportional to the extension, and gravity.

The first diagram in Fig. M.11 shows the spring of length l, unloaded. The second shows the spring loaded but in its equilibrium (rest) position, the

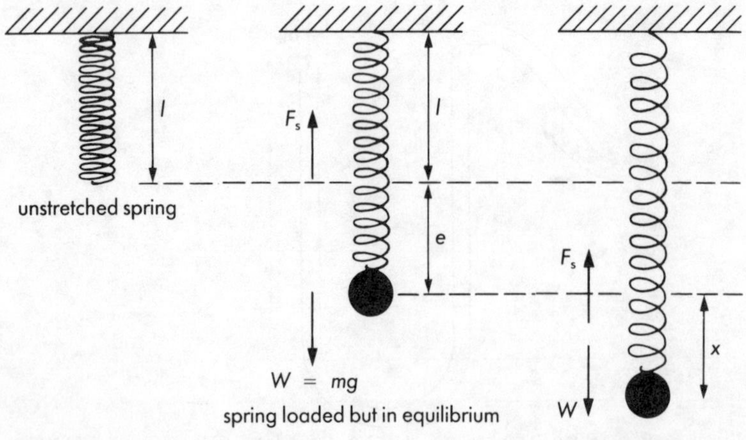

Fig. M.11 Mass hanging from a spring

spring extended by a distance e. The third is a 'snapshot' at a point in the cycle of oscillation with a displacement, x, from the rest position of the second diagram.

Applying **Hooke's Law** to the second diagram we obtain

$F_S = ke$

where F_S is the force exerted by the spring. Because of equilibrium $F_S =$ the weight of the mass m, giving

$ke = mg$

or $k = mg/e$

In the third diagram F_S, acting upwards, is given by

$F_S = k(e+x)$

As elsewhere with up-and-down motion we need to establish a sign convention. Let us regard x as positive when increasing in a downward direction from the equilibrium position.

The net force F in the direction of increasing x is then

$$F = mg - k(e+x)$$
$$= mg - ke - kx$$
$$= -kx$$

Note that it is this result which 'proves' that the motion is s.h.m. We have a restoring force proportional to the displacement.

$F = ma$

so $ma = -kx$

$$a = -\frac{kx}{m}$$

or $a = -w^2x$ where $w^2 = k/m$

so $x = x_0 \cos wt$

$T = 2\pi/w$ and hence $T = 2\pi\sqrt{m/k}$

MATERIALS: FORMULAE

Common formulae used in the study of materials are listed below.

Elasticity

Stress stress $= F/A$

Strain strain $= e/l$

Young modulus (E) $E = Fl/eA$

p.e. stored p.e. $= \frac{1}{2}Fe^2$

$$= \frac{1}{2}\frac{EAe^2}{l}$$

Energy per unit volume

energy $= \frac{1}{2}$ stress × strain

Coefficient of friction (μ) $F = \mu R$

Viscosity

Stokes' law $F = 6\pi\eta rv$

Surface tension (γ) $\gamma = \frac{1}{4}\eta A\epsilon$

Linear expansivity (α) $l_\theta = l_0(1 + \alpha\theta)$

MATTER WAVES

In 1924 the French physicist de Broglie suggested that particles may also sometimes act as waves. He suggested that a particle travelling with momentum mv has a wavelength λ given by

$$mv = h/\lambda$$

where h is the Planck constant. Note that the greater the momentum the smaller the wavelength. The energy of a particle with momentum p is $\frac{1}{2}mv^2 = p^2/2m$. Hence the relationship between energy and frequency is

$$\text{energy} = h^2/2m\lambda^2$$

The first evidence for the wave-particle duality came from experiments on electron diffraction by graphite. But the idea was soon extended by the theorists who were developing a wave-mechanical model of the atom in which the electron is treated as a standing wave trapped in the atom.

◀ Quantum mechanical model of the atom ▶

MAXIMUM POWER TRANSFER THEOREM

Consider a power supply or cell which has an e.m.f. E and an internal resistance r connected to an external load, of resistance R (Fig. M.12). Then $E = IR + Ir$ and $EI = I^2R + I^2r$.

Note that power is dissipated not only in the load resistance but also in the internal one. If the load resistor R is very small compared with the internal resistance, little power will be dissipated in it and instead there will be a great deal of heating in the internal resistance. Equally if the load resistance is very large indeed, hardly any power will be dissipated in it because of the very small amount of current that flows. It can be shown that a supply will deliver a maximum power to an external load resistor when the resistor R is equal to the internal resistance r (Fig. M.13). This is called the maximum power theorem.

This theorem is important in hi-fi where, for example, the output impedance of an amplifier should be matched to that of a loudspeaker.

◀ Electrical power and the heating effect ▶

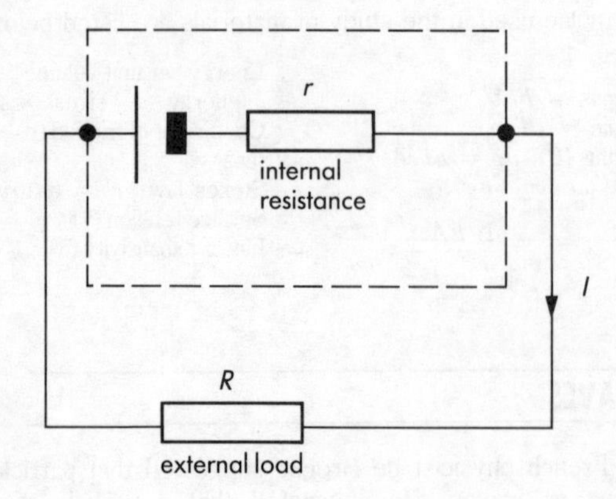

Fig. M.12

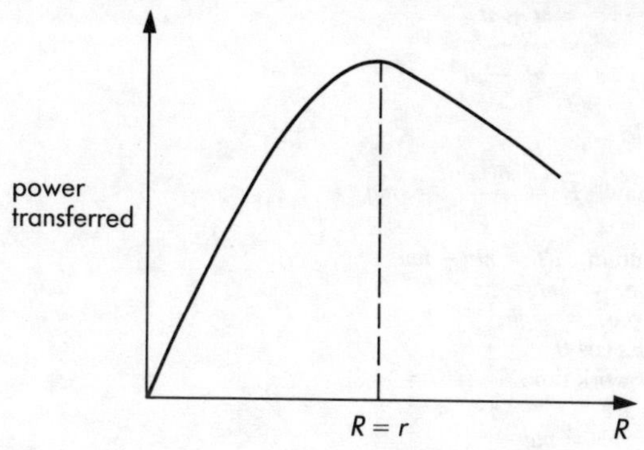

Fig. M.13

MEAN FREE PATH

This is a term used in the **kinetic theory of gases.** It is the average distance that a moving molecule travels between collisions. For air at room temperature and pressure it is only about 10 molecular diameters.

MECHANICS

Mechanics is that part of physics concerned with the action of forces on a system of particles. It has been described as a well-developed yet changing subject, constantly being reconstructed to explain the extremes of nature from the composition of the nucleus to the structures of stars and galaxies. Arguably it is the core subject of physics. This is because all other branches of physics incorporate some mechanics, and the kind of modelling and mathematical manipulation used in mechanics is regarded as the pattern or paradigm for the whole subject. Put in another way, the kinds of process skills acquired from a study of mechanics are then applied everywhere else in physics.

The most basic idea used in mechanics is that of **force.** Particles may be able to move freely, as in a gas or a liquid, or they may be bound together in a rigid body. When the forces are not in equilibrium there is accelerated motion and the subject is called **dynamics.** On the other hand if the forces are in equilibrium then no motion ensues and the subject is called statics.

◀ Static equilibrium ▶

MECHANICS : FORMULAE

Common formulae used in mechanics are listed below:

Equations of motion $s = \dfrac{u + v}{2} t$

$$v = u + at$$
$$v^2 = u^2 + 2as$$
$$s = ut + \tfrac{1}{2}at^2$$

Momentum (p) $p = mv$
Impulse (I) $I = Ft$

Newton's Second Law $F = \dfrac{d(mv)}{dt} = ma$

Impulse and momentum $Ft = mv - mu$
Kinetic energy k.e. $= \tfrac{1}{2}mv^2$
Potential energy p.e. $= mgh$
Work work $= Fs \cos \theta$
Power power $=$ work/time
power $= Fv$
Weight $F = mg$
Pressure pressure $=$ force/area
Pressure in a liquid pressure $= h\rho g$
Density (ρ) $\rho = m/V$
Projectiles
Range range $= u^2 \sin 2\theta / g$
Maximum height $h = u^2 \sin^2 \theta / 2g$
Time of flight $t = 2u \sin \theta / g$
Motion in a circle
Angular velocity (ω) $\omega = \theta / t$
Linear and angular velocity $v = r\omega$
Time of rotation period $T = 2\pi/\omega$
Centripetal force $F = mv^2/r = m\omega^2 r$
Rotational dynamics
Moment of inertia (I) $I = \Sigma mr^2$
Angular momentum (M) $M = I\omega$
Rotational k.e. k.e. $= \tfrac{1}{2}I\omega^2$
Couple (C) $C = I\alpha$
Work done $W = C\theta$

MEGAWATT

◀ Electrical power and the heating effect ▶

MELDE'S APPARATUS

◀ Standing waves ▶

METALLIC BONDING

◀ Solids ▶

MICROMETER SCREW GAUGE

This is used for measuring the sizes of items less than 25 mm long to an accuracy of 0.01 mm.

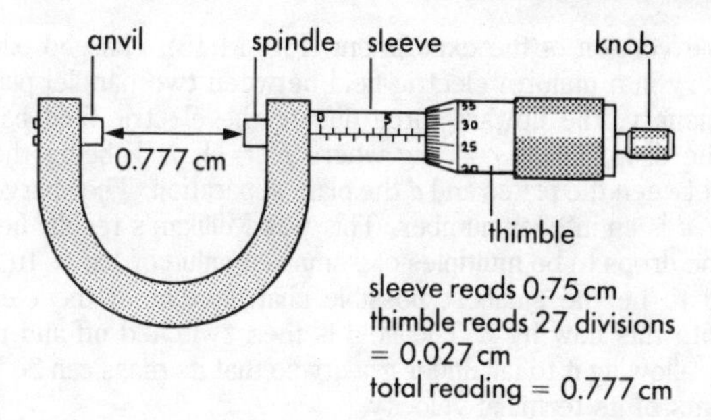

Fig. M.14

The chief features of the instrument are shown in Fig. M.14. When the knob is turned the spindle moves forward 0.5 mm or 0.05 cm for each complete turn. Before use, the faces of the anvil and spindle should be wiped clean in case there are any particles of dirt which would cause errors. The spindle should be closed up against the anvil by turning the knob. There is usually a clutch mechanism so that the instrument cannot be over-tightened. The instrument should be checked to see whether it has a zero error, i.e. to see whether it indicates zero when the jaws are closed together. This should be noted and, if necessary, a + or − correction applied to the final reading. The item to be measured is then placed between the anvil and spindle and the clutch mechanism is again used to set the micrometer. The sleeve has a scale of 0.5 mm, each of which represents one complete turn of the screw, with fractions of a turn being indicated on the thimble. Each division on the thimble, therefore, represents 0.01 cm. The diagram gives an example of how to take a reading, assuming there is no zero error.

MILLIKAN'S EXPERIMENT

Millikan's experiment to determine the charge on the electron is one of the classic experiments of physics. It not only determines the charge on the electron but clearly shows that electric charge comes in discrete amounts and is therefore an important example of the **quantum** (lumpy) structure of matter.

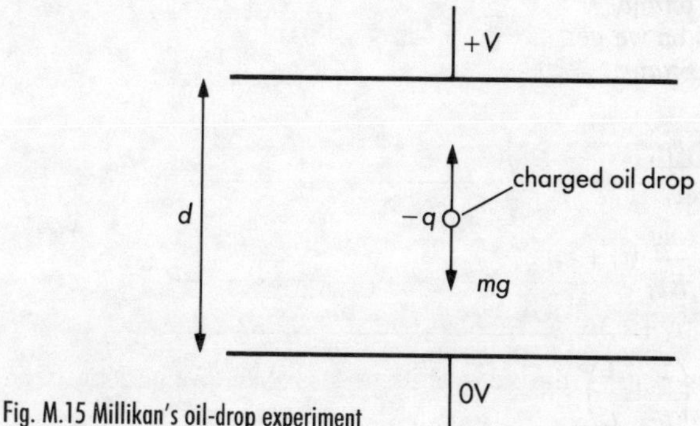

Fig. M.15 Millikan's oil-drop experiment

In a simple version of the experiment (Fig. M.15), charged oil drops are held stationary in a uniform electric field between two parallel plates. If the drop is stationary, the upward force due to the electric field balances the weight of the drop, i.e. $Eq = mg$ where $E = V/d$, V being the potential difference between the plates and d the plate separation. The charge q is equal to ne where n is an integer number. This was Millikan's result: he found the charge on the drops to be multiples of a smallest value of 1.6×10^{-19} C which he assumed to be the smallest possible charge, that of the electron. We always denote this now by e. The field is then switched off and the drop is 'weighed' by allowing it to fall under gravity so that its mass can be found from measurements of its terminal velocity.

Millikan initially observed individual drops of water. These were fed in by an 'atomiser' through a hole in the top of the upper plate. The whole apparatus was held in a constant temperature enclosure, the space between the plates being illuminated so that the drops were seen like little stars. These were observed by using a microscope and observing their movement against a scale in the eyepiece. Hence the terminal velocities of the particles could be found. Later on Millikan used oil drops rather than water. This is because the oil that he chose had a lower vapour pressure and was therefore less likely to evaporate and change in size than water.

The detail of the method Millikan himself adopted is explained below. In his method he did not just keep charges stationary but also observed them moving under an electric field. When the drops enter the space between the plates they already have some charge on them as a result of charging by friction. When the field between the plates is switched on the charges will rise with a **terminal velocity** v_r, and t_r, the time to pass between two marks on a microscope slide, would be noted. The field would then be switched off and the time to fall at a new terminal velocity v_f between the same marks, t_f, would also be noted.

Let us suppose that mg is the apparent weight of a drop (allowing for the buoyancy of the air). The law which governs motion under terminal velocity conditions is called **Stokes' Law** which states that the frictional retarding force due to the viscosity of the air is $6\pi a\eta v$. Here a is the radius of the oil drop and η a constant called the coefficient of viscosity. So for motion under gravity, when the weight of the drop is balanced by the frictional force we get

$$mg = 6\pi a\eta v_f$$

And with the field on we get

$$Eq - mg = 6\pi a\eta v_r$$

Hence

$$\frac{Eq - mg}{mg} = \frac{v_r}{v_f}$$

Therefore $$q = \frac{mg}{Ev_f}(v_f + v_r)$$

i.e. $$q \propto (v_f + v_r)$$

or $$q \propto \left(\frac{1}{t_f} + \frac{1}{t_r}\right)$$

Millikan found that $(1/t_f + 1/t_r)$ was always an integral number of a constant quantity. Now let us suppose that the charge changes. Millikan was able to change the charge by directing in a beam of X-rays. As X-rays are an ionising radiation they caused the charge on the drop to change suddenly. If the charge changes to q' then

$$Eq' - mg = 6\pi a\eta v_r'$$

Hence $$q' = \frac{mg}{Ev_f}(v_f + v_r')$$

and hence $q - q'$, the change in charge is given by

$$\frac{mg}{Ev_f}(v_r' - v_r)$$

It is this difference in charge which is always a constant multiple of the electronic charge. In order to find e it is necessary to substitute for the mass of the drop, as these will vary from drop to drop. Allowing for the buoyancy of the air we have

$$mg = \frac{4}{3}\pi a^3 (\rho - \rho_{air})\, g = 6\pi a\eta v_f$$

where ρ is the density of the oil and ρ_{air} the density of air.

Hence $a^2 = 9\eta v_f/2g(\rho - \rho_{air})$

giving $$mg = \frac{4}{3}\pi\left(\frac{9\eta v_f}{2g(\rho - \rho_{air})}\right)^{\frac{3}{2}}(\rho - \rho_{air})g$$

As all the variables are now known mg can be calculated.

It should be obvious from the detail given here that this experiment depends upon accurate determinations of a great number of physical quantities. Many years after Millikan's work it was discovered that there was an error in one of the measurements of viscosity, and as a result the accepted value of the electron charge had to be recalculated.

◀ Poiseuille's formula ▶

MIRROR FORMULAE

◀ Lens formulae ▶

MODERATOR

◀ Nuclear reactor ▶

MODERN PHYSICS: FORMULAE

Common formulae used in modern physics are listed below.

Electrostatic force on electron $F = eE$
Electromagnetic force on electron $F = Bev$
Crossed fields $eE = Bev$
Energy gain $E = eV$
Kinetic energy $eV = \frac{1}{2}mv^2$
Circular orbit $Bev = mv^2/r$
Quantum energy (E) $E = hv$
Relativistic mass-energy relation $E = mc^2$
de Broglie equation $\lambda = h/mv$
Einstein's p.e. equation $\frac{1}{2}mv^2 = hf - \phi$
Radioactive decay $N = N_0e^{-\lambda t}$
Half-life (T) $T = 0{\cdot}693/\lambda$
Serial relation $\lambda_1N_1 = \lambda_2N_2$

MOLE

A mole of a substance is defined as the amount of the substance containing as many molecules as there are carbon atoms in 12 grams of carbon-12. The concept of the mole is used so that we can compare like with like when we compare one substance with another, and where a difference in the number of particles makes a difference. That is to say when we compare two moles of different substances we are comparing the same number of particles.

MOMENT

This is the name given in the mechanics of rigid bodies to the turning effect of a force about an axis, when the force is not acting through that axis. For example if a stick is used to lever up a stone we say that the force applied at the right-hand end of the stick has a moment of $F \times x$ about an axis through the left-hand end of the stick (Fig. M.16). Note that the moment is always the

Fig. M.16 Applying a moment to lift a stone

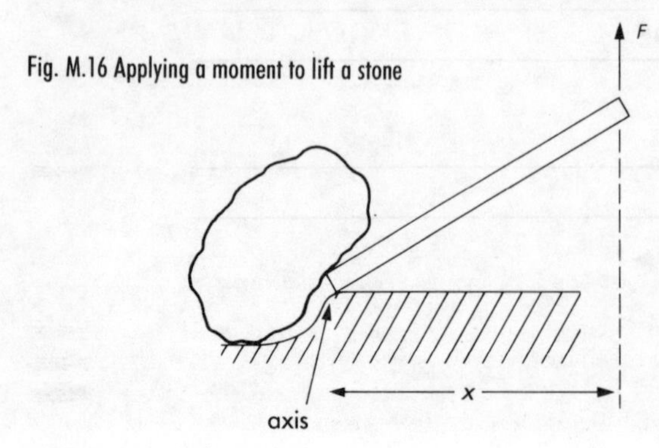

force multiplied by the perpendicular distance from the axis.

In the SI system the units are newton metres. Note that they are not joules, as the force is perpendicular to the distance and no work is done.

◀ Forces, Torque ▶

MOMENT OF INERTIA

This is a term used in the rotational mechanics of rigid bodies. It is analogous to the concept of **mass** in straight line motion. Whereas mass is thought of in Newtonian mechanics as the reluctance of a body to accelerate in response to a force, so moment of inertia is a measure of the reluctance of a body to accelerate angularly under the action of a **torque**.

The moment of inertia of a body is always referred to a particular axis in a body, and a body will have different values of the moment of inertia for different axes. For example a metal bar of circular cross-section has a small moment of inertia about an axis along its length and through the centre of a circle of cross-section, but a much larger moment of inertia about an axis through its middle half-way from each end.

The moment of inertia is defined to be

$$I = \sum_{i=1}^{N} m_i r_i^2$$

where m_i is the element of mass at the point P distance r_i from the axis O. The summation has to be taken over all the elements of mass in the body. The units are kg m^2.

The moment of inertia of a body depends upon the distribution of matter within it. For example it is possible to construct three cylinders each of the same mass but with a different distribution of mass inside (Fig. M.17). If the axis of rotation is the central axis of the cylinders then a) has the largest value of moment of inertia, because all the mass is away from the axis (In Σmr^2 all the values of r are large). By contrast c) has the lowest values of r.

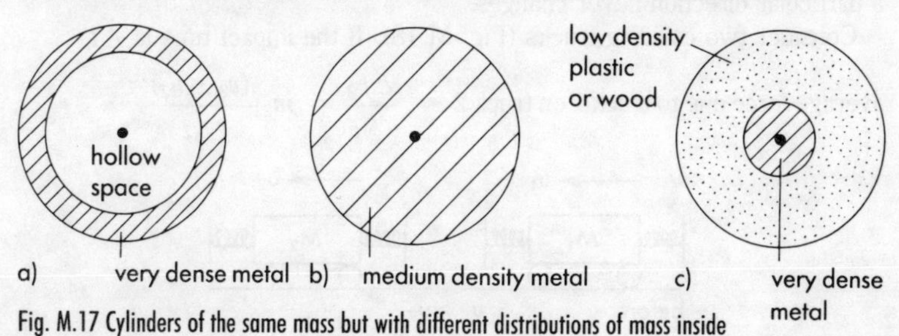

Fig. M.17 Cylinders of the same mass but with different distributions of mass inside

Values of moments of inertia for particular shapes

The moment of inertia of a rigid body is sometimes written as Mk^2, where k is a constant sometimes called the 'radius of gyration'. In the table below values of k, called k_1, k_2 and k_3, are given for rotation about the three possible ('principal') axes through the body's centre of mass.

Body	k_1^2	k_2^2	k_3^2
Rectangular block: length a, width b, thickness c	about length $\frac{1}{12}(b^2 + c^2)$	about width $\frac{1}{12}(c^2 + a^2)$	about thickness $\frac{1}{12}(a^2 + b^2)$
Solid cylinder: length l, diameter d	about length $\frac{1}{8}d^2$	about any diameter $k_2^2 = k_3^2 = \frac{1}{12}l^2 + \frac{1}{16}d^2$	
Hollow cylinder: length l, outside diameter D, inside diameter d	about length $\frac{1}{8}(D^2 + d^2)$	about any diameter $k_2^2 = k_3^2 = \frac{1}{12}l^2 + \frac{1}{16}(D^2 + d^2)$	
Solid sphere: diameter d	$k_1^2 = k_2^2 = k_3^2 = \frac{1}{10}d^2$		
Hollow sphere: outside diameter D, inside diameter d	$k_1^2 = k_2^2 = k_3^2 = \frac{1}{10} \cdot \frac{D^5 - d^5}{D^3 - d^3}$		

◀ Rigid body rotation ▶

MOMENTUM

Momentum, p, is a useful concept used in dynamics. It is defined as mass × velocity, i.e. $p = m \times v$.

One of the reasons for its usefulness is that it is one of nature's conserved quantities. That is to say, in the absence of an external force the momentum in a particular direction never changes.

Consider two colliding trucks (Fig. M.18). If the impact time is Δt,

$$\text{average force due to truck 1 on truck 2} = \frac{\Delta p_2}{\Delta t} = m_2 \frac{(v_2 - u_2)}{\Delta t}$$

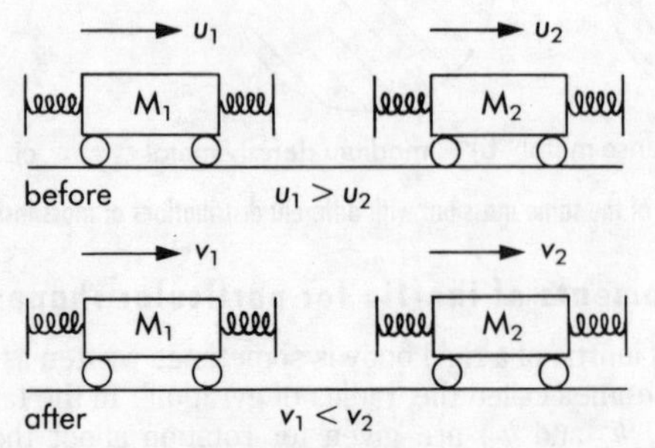

Fig. M.18 Momentum conservation with colliding trucks

average force due to truck 2 on truck 1 $= \dfrac{\Delta p_1}{\Delta t} = m_1 \dfrac{(v_1 - u_1)}{\Delta t}$

By Newton's Third Law these forces are equal but opposite:

so $\Delta p_1 = -\Delta p_2$

giving $m_1u_1 + m_2u_2 = m_1v_1 + m_2v_2$

i.e. the total momentum remains unchanged.

Note that the principle applies only if the two trucks interact only with each other, i.e. providing no external force component acts along the direction of motion. This is called the principle of the conservation of linear momentum and it applies to all collisions, elastic and inelastic.

A mass is a **scalar** and velocity a **vector**, momentum is a vector with units of kg m s^{-1} or, from Newton's Second Law, Ns. Because it is a vector, it follows that if a collision is two-dimensional, for example a collision between two moving billiard balls or between two atomic particles, the momentum in any particular direction is conserved.

So, treating the momentum as a vector, it is best first to resolve into components at right angles (Fig. M.19). The components in these two directions are then conserved in the absence of an external force.

Thus we have

$$m_1u_{1x} + m_2u_{2x} = m_1v_{1x} + m_2v_{2x}$$

and $$m_1u_{1y} + m_2u_{2y} = m_1v_{1y} + m_2v_{2y}$$

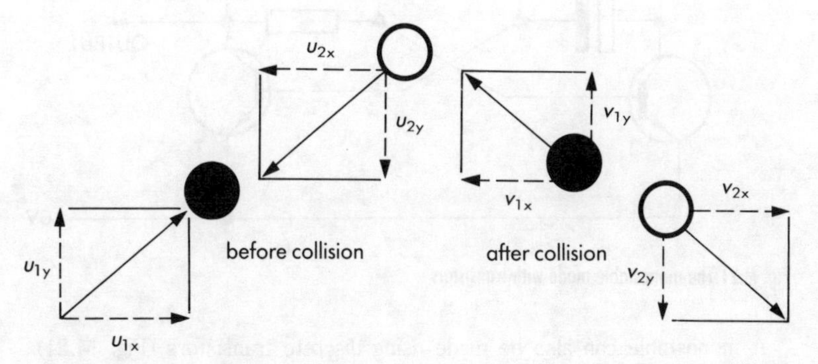

Fig. M.19 Collisions in two dimensions

MONOSTABLE

This is a standard circuit used in electronics. Unlike the **bistable** circuit, which has two stable states, and the **astable** which flips constantly from state to state, the monostable has only one stable state, but one from which it can be momentarily displaced. The circuit in Fig. M.20 shows a monostable circuit made from **logic gates**. It is triggered by making the trigger input momentarily low. Once this is done a single pulse is fed out whose length depends upon the values of R and C.

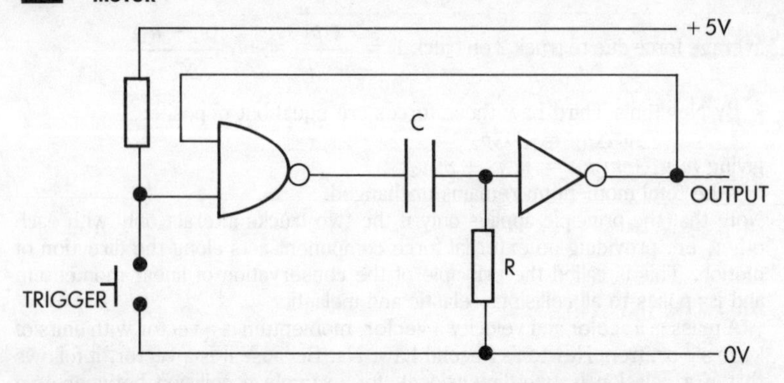

Fig. M.20 The monostable

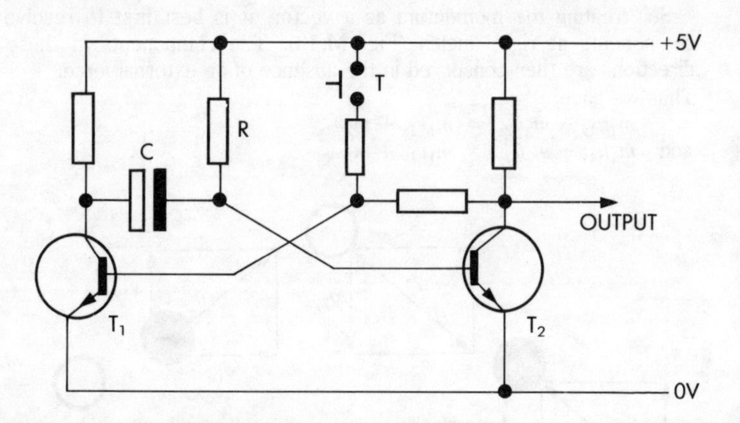

Fig. M.21 The monostable made with transistors

A monostable can also be made using discrete transistors (Fig. M.21). Normally transistor T_2 will be saturated with the output at 0 V. When a brief positive pulse is applied to the trigger, input T, by momentarily connecting T to the positive rail, the output will go high for approximately 0.7 RC seconds.

MOTOR

◀ Direct current electric motor, Induction motor ▶

MOVING-COIL GALVANOMETER

◀ Ammeters and voltmeters ▶

MULTIPLIER

◀ Ammeters and voltmeters ▶

MULTIVIBRATOR

◀ Astable ▶

MUSICAL INSTRUMENTS

There are five principal types of musical instrument: stringed, wind, reed, percussion and electronic.

Stringed instruments

The violin, cello, double bass, guitar etc. are examples of stringed instruments. The sounds are produced by the production of **standing waves** on a stretched string whose vibrations are transmitted to the wooden structure of the instrument and the volume of air inside it. Thus the string produces forced **oscillations** in the wood and the volume of air. The vibrations of the string itself are stationary waves which can be initiated by striking or plucking, and in the case of instruments in the violin family by bowing. If the fundamental frequency of the string is f, the string can also sustain higher frequencies of value $2f$, $3f$, $4f$, etc. When a note is played, some of these higher frequencies or overtones may be present, depending upon how the string was struck, plucked or bowed. Thus the overtones consist of odd and even harmonics.

Wind instruments

Examples of wind instruments are the trumpet, trombone, flute, organ and clarinet. The simplest instrument to understand is the organ. In an organ pipe the sound is produced by the production of stationary waves in an air column. If a column is open at both ends, frequencies f, $2f$, $3f$, can be sustained. A closed (stopped) column will have frequencies f, $3f$, $5f$, etc. When an organ pipe is sounded these higher frequencies may be present as overtones, the strength of the overtones depending upon the pressure of air used to make the note. Closed and open pipes will have a different timbre because of the difference in the pattern of overtone.

To initiate the standing waves air is blown into an end of the pipe where it meets a sharp edge. Provided it is blown fiercely enough the flow of air will produce turbulence, and eddies will be shed from different sides of the edge in a way which will produce force vibrations in the pipe. It will take a finite time for a standing wave to be set up and during this period the pipe is said to emit transients, i.e. waves whose amplitude and frequency are varying with time. Eventually however a stationary and steady wave is set up.

The behaviour of other types of wind instrument is more complicated. For example in a trumpet the lips are an important part of the method of the generation of the note, whereas in a clarinet the note is initiated by vibrations of a wooden reed. Similarly in the case of an organ pipe the pitch of a note is changed simply by altering the length of the air column. This is what is done by an organ tuner when an instrument is tuned. But in the case of the trumpet, recorder or clarinet, the pitch is changed by the use of holes and valves.

Reed instruments

Examples of reed instruments are the harmonica, the reed organ and the harmonium. But note also that the clarinet uses a reed in order to initiate a standing wave in an air column. A reed is simply a thin piece of metal or wood which is clamped at one end. To the musical ear reed instruments produce somewhat discordant sounds. This is because in the case of reed instruments the overtones are not harmonics of the fundamental frequency, f. For a reed clamped at one end the first overtone is at $6.26f$ and the second at $17.54f$. A good ear may detect that such overtones are 'out of tune' with the fundamental note.

Percussion instruments

Examples of percussion instruments are drums, tambourines, cymbals, etc. This family of instrument shares a similarity with the reed instrument described above, in that the overtones are not exact multiples of the fundamental note. The simplest percussion instrument to understand is the drum. The standing wave pattern which is produced is a two-dimensional one. Typical modes of vibration are as shown in Fig. M.22. Antinodes are marked with the + and − signs, corresponding to vibrations which are in antiphase. The straight or circular lines correspond to nodal positions. The rim of the drum is of course a node just like the ends of a string on a stringed instrument. As can be seen from the diagram the vibrations of a drum are much more complicated than those of a string, with many more alternatives, depending upon how the instrument is struck by the player. For example striking the

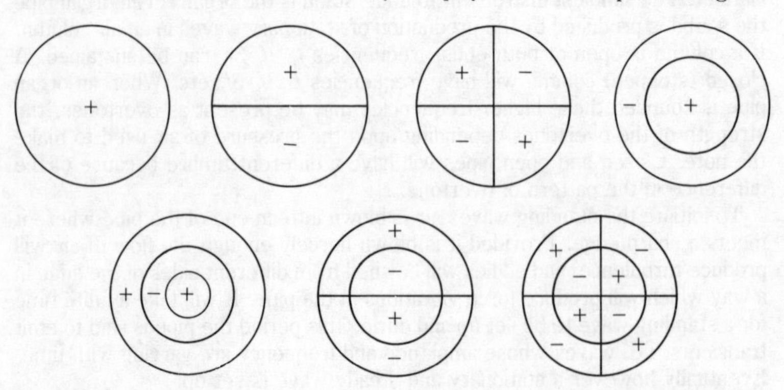

Fig. M.22 Standing wave patterns on a drum

drum in the centre necessitates an antinode at this point and none of the vibrations which have a nodal region at the centre could be started in this way. A cymbal differs from a drum in that the rim of the instrument can be an antinode. Note that because of the varied possibility of overtones, none of which are harmonics, the sound of an instrument may be more 'noise' than 'note'. Hence it may be difficult for a hearer to recognise the pitch. With percussion instruments the pitch may be determined by such factors as where the instrument is struck, how sharply it is struck, the tension of the stretched membrane (in the case of drums and tambourines), the thickness, shape and elasticity and the temperature.

Electronic instruments

Electronic instruments produce sounds by adding together sinusoidal, square, or saw-tooth waves produced by electronic circuits. Instruments may attempt to reproduce the sounds made by any of the preceding types of instruments using Fourier synthesis or other methods to produce waveforms which are indistinguishable from the authentic sounds. But they may also be used to produce entirely new sounds for which there is no 'traditional' equivalent.

◀ Fourier methods, Turbulent flow ▶

MUTUAL INDUCTANCE

Whereas the term **self-inductance** is used to describe the back e.m.f. produced in a coil due to the changing magnetic field caused by the current through itself, mutual inductance is used in the description of the e.m.f. produced in one coil caused by a changing current in another coil. The second coil of course has to produce a magnetic field which is linked by the first coil. That is to say the magnetic field of the second coil threads it way through the first coil. If the current in the first coil is changing at a rage $\mathrm{d}I/\mathrm{d}t$, the e.m.f. in the second coil is equal to $-M\,\mathrm{d}I/\mathrm{d}t$, where M is the mutual inductance and is measured in henries. The negative results from the fact that, according to the laws of induction, the e.m.f. results from a current flow which attempts to oppose the changes in the magnetic field.

An example of two coils which are linked in this way is the **transformer**.

◀ Electromagnetic induction ▶

NAND GATE

◀ Logic gates ▶

NANO AMMETER

◀ Unity gain voltage follower ▶

NEGATIVE FEEDBACK

This is the term used in electronics where the output of an electronic amplifying system is returned to one of the input connections in such a way that the magnitude of the output voltage is reduced from what it would otherwise be. This is usually done so that the behaviour of the system is strictly controlled by the value of resistors and remains constant irrespective of any volatility in the behaviour of the amplifier itself.
◀ Operational amplifier ▶

NEUTRINO

Neutrino is an Italian word meaning 'small' and 'neutral', given by the Italian physicist Fermi to the very small massless neutral particles produced in **beta**-decay processes. Strictly speaking beta-decay (e^- emission) produces antineutrinos and β^+ (e^+ emission) neutrinos.

NEUTRON

A particle of net zero charge found in all nuclei except hydrogen.
◀ Nucleus ▶

NEUTRON NUMBER

This is the number of **neutrons** in a **nucleus**. For light nuclei the number of neutrons is approximately the same as the number of protons, but for heavier nuclei the number of neutrons exceeds the number of protons. Neutron number is denoted by N.

NEWTON'S RINGS

◀ Thin-film interference ▶

NEWTON'S LAWS OF MOTION

These laws are the basic working rules for the physicist and engineer when dealing with problems in mechanics where matter is on the everyday scale. Only with the case of very massive objects or with very small objects do alternative laws have to be sought. The usual textbook definitions are direct translations from Latin, and obscure the physics, particularly the translation of the Third Law. The three laws are:

i) The basic kind of motion is uniform motion in a straight line and a body has this motion unless a resultant **force** acts on it.
ii) If a resultant force acts the **momentum** of the body changes and its rate of change of momentum is equal to the resultant force and in the direction of that force.
iii) Forces between bodies act in pairs, i.e. when one exerts a force (attractive or repulsive) on a second body, the second exerts an equal and opposite force on the first (e.g. the earth attracts me, but I attract the earth with an equal and opposite force).

Using the definition of momentum and in the notation of the calculus the Second Law is written

$$F = \frac{d(mv)}{dt}$$

Normally the mass is constant and so

$$F = \frac{m\,dv}{dt}$$

or $F = ma$

which is the usual form of Newton's Second Law encountered in GCSE science.

NODES

◀ Standing waves ▶

NOR GATE

◀ Logic gates ▶

NORMAL ADJUSTMENT

◀ Angular magnification ▶

NOT GATE

◀ Logic gates ▶

NUCLEAR MODEL OF THE ATOM

The atom is composed of a small massive **nucleus** surrounded by a number of electrons moving in rapid motion and arranged in discrete energy groupings as described by the theory of **quantum mechanics**. In quantum mechanics the electrons are regarded as stationary waves trapped in the region of space forming the atom. The atom has a diameter of about 10^{-10} metres. The nucleus is much smaller than this, having a diameter of about 10^{-14} metres. The transition of electrons from one energy state to another in the atom is associated with the emission or the absorption of photons of electromagnetic radiation.

In a neutral atom there are as many electrons as there are protons in the nucleus and the atom has a net charge of zero. *Ionisation* is the process whereby an atom somehow either loses or gains an electron to become a positive or negative ion.

There are 6.0×10^{23} atoms in a gram atomic weight of a substance. Thus the smallest visible pencil dot on a piece of paper carries a number of carbon atoms greater than the population of the world.

◀ Energy levels ▶

NUCLEAR REACTOR

A nuclear reactor is part of a nuclear power station. In the reactor energy is extracted from the nuclear fuel. Nuclear **fission** is used to generate heat which in turn heats water to steam in order to drive turbines driving generators producing electricity.

The common type of nuclear reactor employs the fission of $^{235}_{92}U$, the rarer of the two isotopes of uranium. The problem is that for the useful running of the process the neutrons must be absorbed by $^{235}_{92}U$. However what is used as a fuel is ordinary uranium metal which contains a mixture of $^{238}_{92}U$ and $^{235}_{92}U$, and neutrons can be absorbed by both isotopes. The following table gives probabilities for the absorption of neutrons.

	$^{235}_{92}U$	$^{238}_{92}U$
fast neutrons	low	low
very slow (thermal) neutrons	very high	almost zero

The fission fragments are produced together with the high-speed neutrons of the reaction and a *moderator* is used to slow down the neutrons. This is a substance with which the neutrons can collide without absorption but with energy loss. Graphite (carbon) is commonly used. There are many collisions and at the end of the process the neutrons are in thermal equilibrium with the other atoms of carbon, i.e. they have only thermal energy $\approx \frac{3}{2}kT$. The thermal neutrons are then almost only captured by $^{235}_{92}U$.

A reactor built in this way would be in danger of running out of control. The equation of the production of the fission products is

$$^{235}_{92}U + n \rightarrow \text{fission products} + x \text{ neutrons}$$

x is usually two or three, with an average value of about 2.45. So clearly a chain reaction would set in unless an effort was made to keep only one neutron in the reactor from each fission event. This is done by control rods with substances which absorb neutrons very easily, e.g. cadmium or boron. The geometry of the inside of a reactor is therefore as shown in Fig. N.1.

The control rods can be raised and lowered to alter the rate of the effective production of neutrons. However, clearly it might not be possible to withdraw the cadmium rods sufficiently fast to avoid the onset of an uncontrolled reaction if the number of neutrons available per fission became greater than 1. The time for a neutron to become thermalised is approximately 1 ms. However, nature has been kind to nuclear physicists by providing substances called delayed neutron emitters.

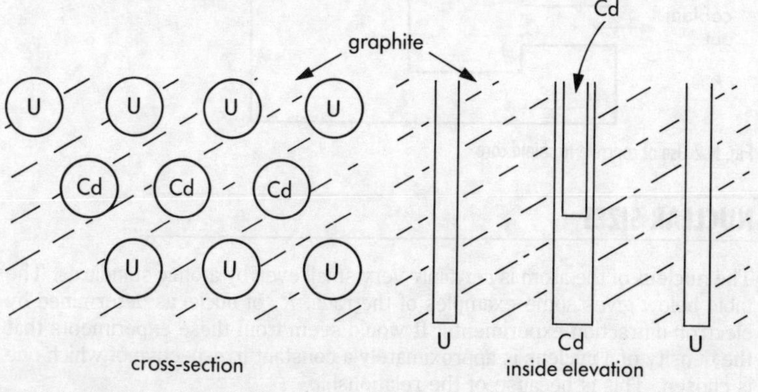

Fig. N.1 Geometry of the inside of a reactor

Delayed neutron emission

A common fission fragment is $^{87}_{35}\text{Br}$. This decays by β^- emission with a half-life of 56 s, i.e.

$$^{87}_{35}\text{Br} \rightarrow\, ^{87}_{36}\text{Kr} + e^-$$

However there are two branches in this decay

$$^{87}_{35}\text{Br} \begin{cases} \xrightarrow{\text{low energy } \beta^-} \, ^{87}_{36}\text{Kr}^* \text{ (excited state)} \\ \xrightarrow{\text{high energy } \beta^-} \, ^{87}_{36}\text{Kr} \text{ (ground state)} \end{cases}$$

Now $^{87}_{36}\text{Kr}^*$ can decay to the ground state by γ emission or by

$$^{87}_{36}\text{Kr}^* \rightarrow\, ^{86}_{36}\text{Kr} + n$$

and the half-life for the second process is essentially zero. It is this neutron which is therefore produced, on average, approximately 56 s after the production of $^{87}_{35}\text{Br}$. Enough neutrons are produced by this route to make the time for adjusting the level of the control rods manageable.

General arrangement of the nuclear reactor

The ultimate product of the fission process is heat, which is extracted as shown in Fig. N.2. Concrete is used to absorb the dangerous flux of neutrons which would be harmful to operators. More typically a gas coolant is used followed by a heat exchanger (Fig. N.3).

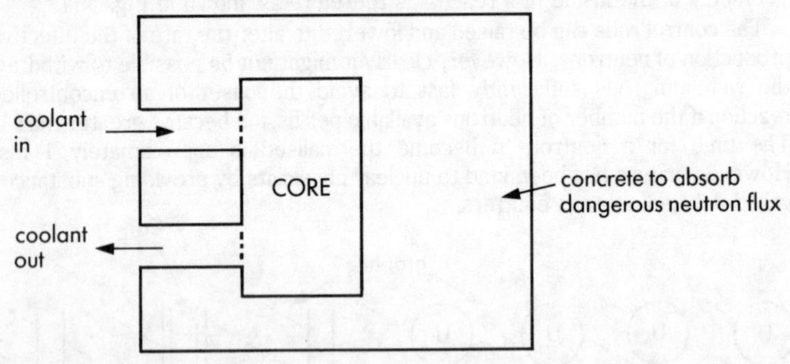

Fig. N.2 Use of concrete to shield core

NUCLEAR SIZES

The nucleus of the atom is certainly very small even by atomic standards. The table below gives some examples of the radii, R, of nuclei as determined by electron diffraction experiments. It would seem from these experiments that the density of a nucleus is approximately a constant irrespective of which one is chosen. This is because of the relationship

$$R \propto A^{\frac{1}{3}}$$

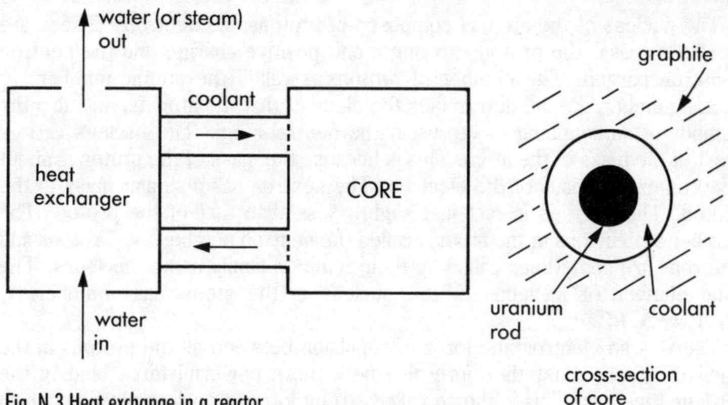

Fig. N.3 Heat exchange in a reactor

which holds very well for a wide range of nuclei, where A is the **nucleon number** (i.e. the total number of neutrons and protons). The density of a nucleus is approximately given by 1×10^{17} kg m^{-3}. The constancy of the density means that the constituent **nucleons** tend to keep more or less the same average distance of separation. This forms the basis of the so-called **liquid-drop model** of the nucleus on account of this analogy between the nucleus and a drop of liquid.

Element	A	$R/10^{-15}$m
silicon	28	3·70
vanadium	51	4·50
cobalt	59	4·82
strontium	88	5·34
indium	115	5·80
antimony	122	5·97
bismuth	209	7·13

NUCLEON NUMBER

A nucleon is the generic name given to protons and neutrons, which in the **quark** theory of high-energy particle physics are regarded as two species of the same elementary quantity. The number of nucleons in a **nucleus** is equal to the number of protons plus the number of neutrons. It is denoted by A.

NUCLEUS

The nucleus is the positively charged 'core' of an atom comprising almost all its mass but only 10^{-12} of its volume.

The nucleus of the atom is composed of protons and neutrons. These are similar in mass, the proton carrying a unit positive charge, and the neutron being uncharged. The number of protons is called the atomic number, or proton number, Z, and determines the element that the atom is, and also the number of surrounding electrons in the neutral atom. The nucleus carries most of the mass of the atom. This is because the mass of the proton is about 1840 times the mass of the electron. The neutron has a similar mass to the proton. The mass is in fact just slightly less than that of the proton. The number of neutrons in the atom is called the neutron number, N. Protons and neutrons are sometimes called by their common family name, nucleons. The total number of nucleons in the nucleus is the atom mass number A. So $A = N+Z$.

There is an electrostatic force of repulsion between all the protons in the nucleus. There must therefore also be a more powerful force binding the nucleus together. This is the so-called strong force of nuclear physics, which is an attractive force existing between all nucleons. It has a very short range and only affects the nearest neighbouring nucleons. By contrast the electrostatic force, which follows an inverse square law, extends across the whole nucleus and beyond. The overall equilibrium of the nucleus is determined by the action of these two forces. If the nucleus has a small number of protons, about the same number of neutrons is sufficient for the nucleus to exist in a stable configuration. So for light nuclei the ratio $N/Z = 1.0$. This ratio increases to approximately 1.5 for heavy nuclei.

Fig. N.4 shows a plot of nucleon number against proton number. If the number of neutrons varies too much from the equilibrium number, the nucleus is unstable and disintegrates in an attempt to become more stable. The elements on the proton-rich side of the dotted line tend to emit β^+ particles and those on the neutron-rich side β^-. Very large nuclei tend to become more stable by sometimes emitting two protons and two neutrons together in an α-particle. It is thought that in these large nuclei the α-particle is already in existence as a grouping in the nucleus before the disintegration.

◀ Alpha radiation, Beta radiation, Gamma radiation, Nuclear model of the atom ▶

NUCLIDE

This is a general name used to refer to all the types of nuclei which can exist. Note that the term **isotope** tends to be used when physicists are referring to all the properties of an isotope, i.e. not only the nuclear properties but those of the electron shells as well. However, when the term nuclide is used, the attention is focused on the nuclear properties and the nucleus alone.

NULL METHOD

This is a term used in experimental physics to describe experiments where adjustments are made until there is a zero reading on a detecting instrument.

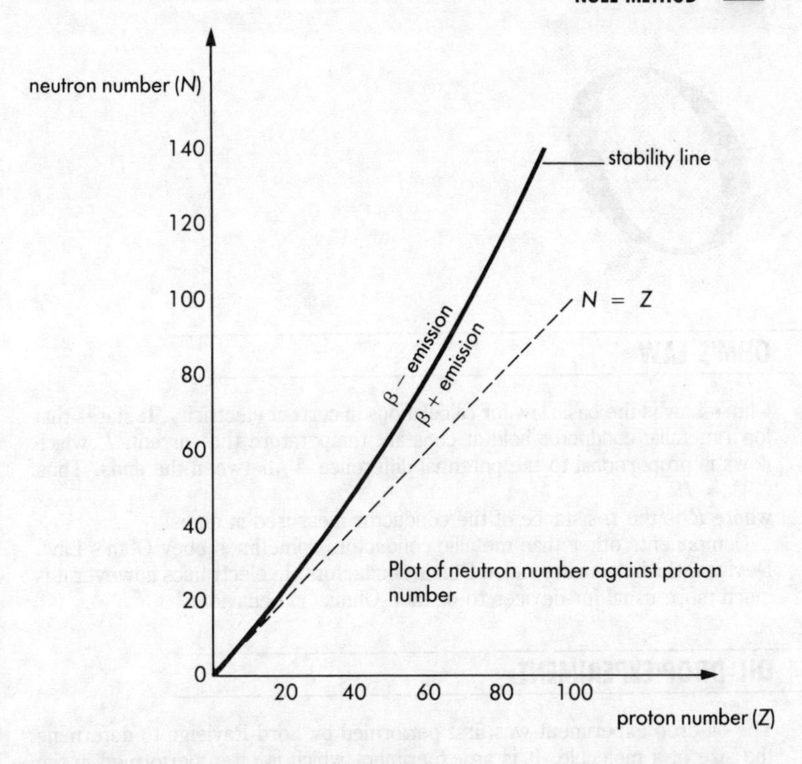

Fig. N.4 Plot of neutron number against proton number

A simple example of an experiment of this kind is the slide-wire **potentiometer**, where the position of contact along the wire is adjusted until there is a zero reading on the galvanometer. A different kind of null method experiment is that of Michelson for the determination of the speed of light. In Michelson's experiment the speed of the rotating mirror is adjusted until the light is reflected back into the observing telescope. No measurements of the deflection of the light itself are made but instead the speed of the mirror is noted.

◀ Velocity of electromagnetic waves ▶

OHM'S LAW

Ohm's Law is the basic law for calculations in current electricity. It states that for a metallic conductor held at constant temperature the current, I, which flows is proportional to the potential difference, V, between the ends. Thus

$$V = IR$$

where R is the resistance of the conductor measured in ohms.

Components other than metallic conductors sometimes obey Ohm's Law. Devices which do so are called Ohmic conductors. In electronics however it is much more usual for devices to be 'non-Ohmic' in behaviour.

OIL-DROP EXPERIMENT

The oil-drop experiment was first performed by Lord Rayleigh to determine the size of a molecule. It is an experiment which is often performed in the school or college laboratory in elementary physics.

The experiment is very simple. It consists of measuring the size of a small drop of oil in order to determine its volume. The drop is then transferred to a sheet of water contained in a clean tray and on the surface of which has been scattered lycopodium powder. The oil film spreads out over a comparatively large area. The assumption is made that when it has finished spreading out it has become as thin as it can be, i.e. is 1 molecular layer thick. In spreading out the oil pushes the lycopodium powder away and so the area of expanse of the oil is easily identified. If A is the area of the expanse of oil and d the thickness of the oil film, then Ad is equal to the original volume of the oil drop. Hence d, the diameter of a molecule, can be found: $d \approx 10^{-9}$ m.

The experiment not only gives a rough idea of the diameter of a molecule but also provides a convincing demonstration of the atomicity of matter.

OPERATIONAL AMPLIFIER

The operational amplifier (op. amp.) is a silicon (**integrated circuit**) chip with a number of terminals, including those for its power supply and for input and output signals. It is an analogue circuit. Most commonly the type 741 chip is used and this has the following properties:

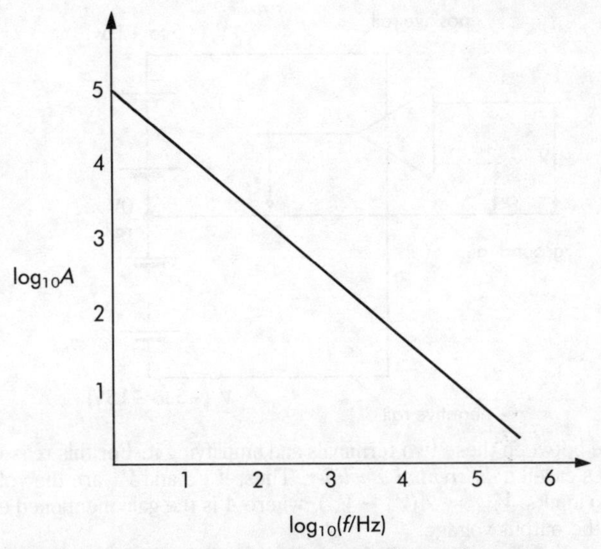

Fig. O.1 Open loop gain of an operational amplifier i.c. as a function of frequency

a) A very high voltage gain, A, which is typically $\approx 10^5$ for d.c. work. With a.c. signals A diminishes with frequency (see Fig. O.1).
b) Very high input resistance, typically $10^{11}\ \Omega$. This means it draws insignificant amounts of current from a source of input, and can therefore be used to amplify signals from very feeble sources, e.g. a thermocouple.
c) Low output resistance (typically $100\ \Omega$). In normal circuit work this would be considered a sizeable resistance, but by the standards of electronics it is very small, and means that the op. amp. is not itself likely to be what limits the power supplied to an output circuit.

The circuit symbol is shown in Fig. O.2.

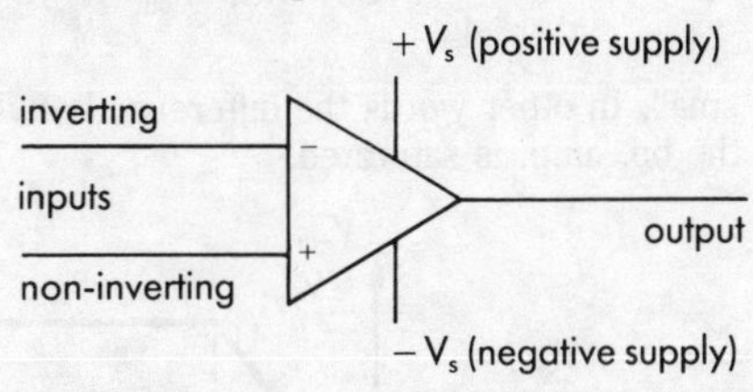

Fig. O.2

Unlike logic ic's, the op. amp. is usually used with three voltage rails (Fig. O.3). These are two rails with voltages between ± 5 V and ± 15 V above and below the third, which is a 'zero' reference voltage or 'ground rail'. On circuit diagrams the connections to the first two rails which power the i.c. are usually omitted for clarity.

The operational amplifier has two inputs, the so-called '+' or 'non-inverting input' and the '−' or 'inverting input'. The device works by sensing the voltage

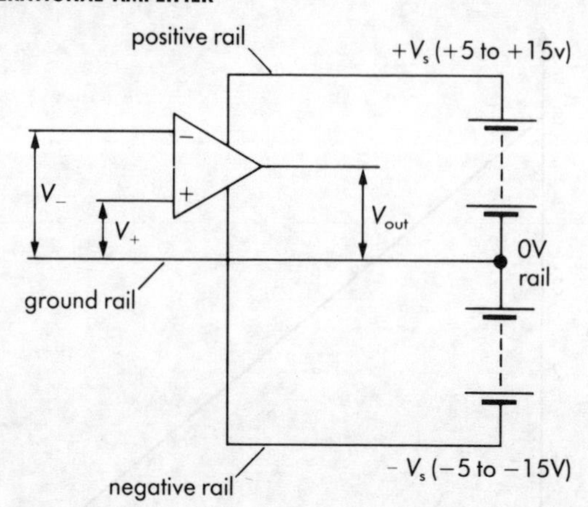

Fig. 0.3

difference between these two terminals and amplifying it. For this reason it is sometimes called a *differential amplifier*. Thus, if V_+ and V_- are the voltages at the two inputs, $V_{out} = A(V_+ - V_-)$, where A is the gain mentioned earlier and V_{out} the output voltage.

The inverting input is so called because if V_+ is held constant an increase ΔV in V_- makes V_{out} fall by an amount $A\Delta V$. Similarly V_+ is called the non-inverting input because if V_- is held constant and V_+ increases by ΔV the output increases by $A\Delta V$.

Because the output cannot rise above $+V_s$ or fall below $-V_s$ the i.c. is only linear for a certain narrow range of input voltages. Here 'linear' means that the output is proportional to the input giving rise to a straight-line or linear output/input graph.

Because $V_{out} = A(V_+ - V_-)$, and A is so large, as soon as $(V_+ - V_-)$ exceeds about 60 μV the device 'saturates' at a maximum output voltage, usually slightly less than V_s (Fig. 0.4).

Note also that $V_+ - V_- = \dfrac{V_{out}}{A}$. So with $V_{out} \approx 10\,\text{V}$ and A large, $V_+ - V_-$ is very small. In other words the difference between V_+ and V_- is negligible unless the op. amp. is saturated.

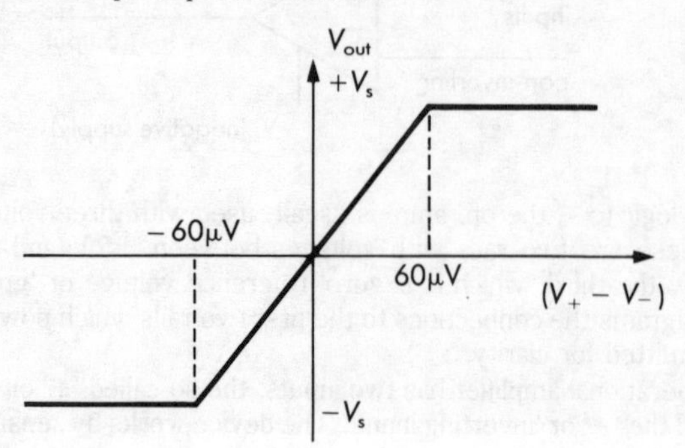

Fig. 0.4

Use of negative feedback to control the gain

To control the gain, external resistors have to be added to the i.c. Consider the circuit shown in Fig. O.5. With the non-inverting terminal connected to the 0 V rail the amplifier action is determined solely by the inverting terminal. Note that in this and in Fig. O.6 power supply rails have not been drawn. Secondly, experiment shows that unless the input voltage V_{in} is relatively large the output voltage V_{out} does not reach one of the power rail voltages $+V_s$, but is proportional to minus the input voltage $(-V_{in})$. Thirdly, such a circuit is an example of **negative feedback**. This is because as V_{in} drives the input in one direction the current through the feedback resistance generates a potential in the opposite sense, thus reducing the effect of V_{in}.

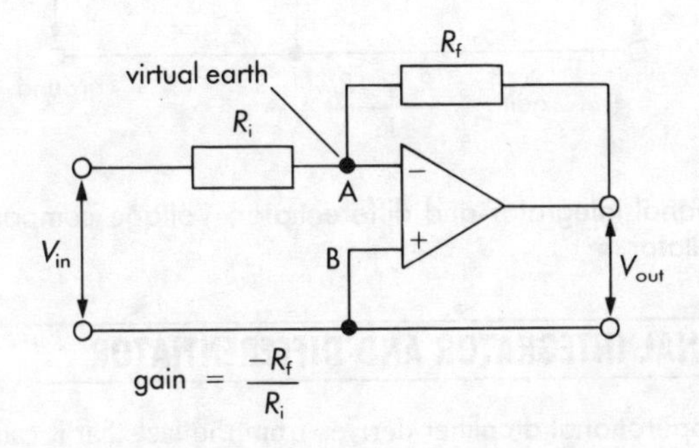

Fig. 0.5

Let the voltage at A with respect to ground be V_A. Then $V_{out} = AV_A$. But because $A \approx 10^5$, V_A must be almost zero. In other words V_+ and V_- are almost at the same potential. Indeed in general negative feedback causes the difference between the two inputs $(V_+ - V_-)$ to always be less than the 60 μV of Fig. O.4. In this particular case, because V_A is almost zero, it is sometimes called a *virtual earth.*

Because of the enormous input resistance of the op. amp. almost none of the current through R_i passes through the op. amp. and so the current i in R_f equals that in R_i.

Applying Ohm's Law to R_i and R_f and assuming $V_A = 0$ we obtain

$$\frac{V_{in}}{V_{out}} = \frac{-iR_i}{iR_f} = \frac{-R_i}{R_f}$$

and so the gain $= -R_f/R_i$. The minus sign indicates that the output inverts the input.

An alternative circuit generates a non-inverting amplifier. Here the gain is

$$\frac{R_f + R_i}{R_i} = 1 + R_f/R_i$$ (See Fig. O.6 overleaf).

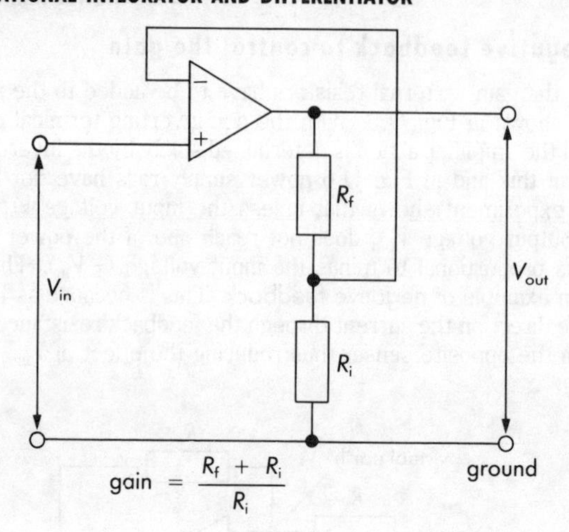

Fig. 0.6

◀ Operational integrator and differentiator, Voltage comparator, Wien bridge oscillator ▶

OPERATIONAL INTEGRATOR AND DIFFERENTIATOR

The name **operational amplifier** derives from the fact that it can be used to perform mathematical operations. For example, if the feedback resistor of the usual amplifier circuit is replaced by a capacitor, the circuit performs the mathematical operation of integration with respect to time. An analogy is a petrol pump which records the total amount of fuel delivered, integrating the flow rate during fuelling. Here of course charge replaces fuel.

In Fig. 0.7, because of the large gain A, A is a virtual earth. If $+q$ is the charge on C at some instant, then as current i in R_i is the rate of change of charge we have

$$\frac{V_{in}}{R_i} = i = \frac{-dq}{dt}$$

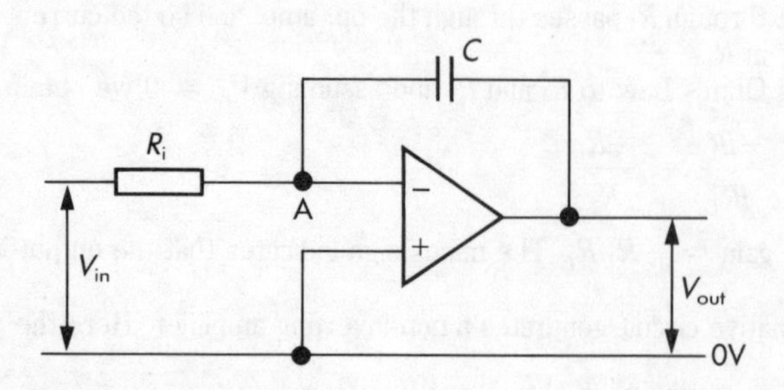

Fig. 0.7 Operational integrator

Now $q = CV_{out}$ giving

$$\frac{-dq}{dt} = C\frac{dV_{out}}{dt}, \text{ and so}$$

$$-C\frac{dV_{out}}{dt} = \frac{V_{in}}{R_i}$$

Integrating with respect to time,

$$V_{out} = \frac{-1}{R_iC}\int V_{in}dt$$

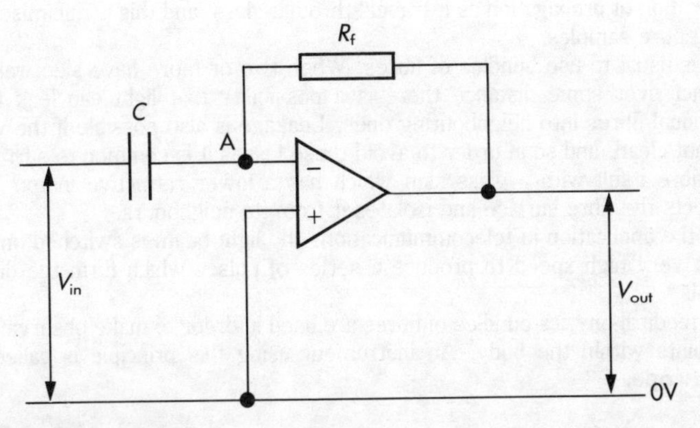

Fig. O.8 Operational differentiator

If R and C are interchanged a differentiator is produced (Fig. O.8). A is again a virtual earth so that

$$i = \frac{-V_{out}}{R_f}$$

and as i is the rate of change of charge,

$$i = C\frac{dV_{in}}{dt}$$

This gives

$$\frac{-V_{out}}{R_f} = C\frac{dV_{in}}{dt}, \text{ or } V_{out} = -R_fC\frac{dV_{in}}{dt}$$

In other words the faster the rate of change of the input, the higher the output voltage. With an a.c. input, therefore, the higher the input frequency the greater the amplitude of the output. However, this is only true initially. As the frequency increases, so the gain A diminishes and the above analysis becomes no longer valid.

OPTICAL FIBRES

Optical fibres are very fine strands of pure glass down which light beams are sent. This is a modern technology used in the communications industry for the transmission of digitally coded data and in medical physics for examining inside the body.

The light stays within the fibre, however it is bent or curled up, because of **total internal reflection.** It reflects backwards and forwards from the walls of the fibre to emerge at the far end. Because the reflection is total internal reflection, i.e. reflection without energy loss, the light is not attenuated (reduced in intensity) by this process, even if there is a very large number of reflections down the fibre. The only attenuation results from the ordinary absorption of propagation as it travels through glass, and this is minimised by using pure samples.

It is usual to use bundles of fibres. When two or more have side walls in contact over some distance there is a possibility that light can leak from individual fibres into neighbouring ones. Leakage is also possible if the walls are not clean, and so in order to avoid these losses it is common to surround the fibre itself with a glass skin which has a lower refractive index. This protects the fibre surface and isolates it from its neighbours.

In the application in telecommunications the light beam is switched on and off at very high speed to produce a series of pulses which form the digital signals.

In medical physics bundles of fibres are used in order to make observations at points within the body. An instrument using this principle is called an **endoscope.**

OPTICAL PATH LENGTH

Optical path length is a useful concept in physical optics; it is defined as the distance a light wave would travel if it were travelling through a vacuum for the same time as it travels in the medium. Optical path length $= nd$, where n is the **refractive index** of the medium and d is the distance in the medium. As the speed of light in all material media is less than the speed of light in a vacuum, n is always greater than 1 and the optical path is always greater than d.

OPTICS: FORMULAE

Common formulae used in optics are listed below.

Refractive index (n) $n = (\sin i)/(\sin r)$

Related to wave velocities $n = c_v/c_m$

Serial relation for n $n_1 \sin\theta_1 = n_2 \sin\theta_2$

Critical angle $n = 1/\sin c$

Lens and mirror formulae $\frac{1}{u} + \frac{1}{v} = \frac{1}{f}$

$m = v/u$

Telescope magnification (m) $= f_o/f_e$

OR GATE

◀ Logic gates ▶

OSCILLATION

This is the name given to a repeated cycle of motion about an equilibrium position, for example that of the end of a tuning fork oscillating about an equilibrium (rest) position. Note however that the idea extends to electrical oscillations where a p.d., charge or current varies cyclically about an equilibrium value.

OSCILLATIONS AND WAVES: FORMULAE

Common formulae used in oscillations and waves are listed below.

Simple harmonic motion
- Acceleration $a = -\omega^2 x$
- Displacement $x = x_0 \cos \omega t$
- Velocity $v = \omega x_0 \sin \omega t$
- Acceleration $a = -\omega^2 x_0 \cos \omega t$
- Velocity $v = \omega \sqrt{x_0{}^2 - x^2}$
- Kinetic energy $\frac{1}{2}m\omega^2(x_o{}^2 - x^2)$
- Potential energy $p.e. = \frac{1}{2}m\omega^2 x^2$
- Total energy $E = \frac{1}{2}m\omega^2 x_0{}^2$

Simple harmonic motion examples:
- Pendulum $T = 2\pi(l/g)^{\frac{1}{2}}$

Spring/mass system

$$T = 2\pi(m/k)^{\frac{1}{2}}$$

Travelling wave

$$y = a \sin(kx - \omega t)$$

$$= a \sin 2\pi\left(\frac{x}{\lambda} - \frac{t}{\tau}\right)$$

$$= a \sin \frac{2\pi}{\lambda}(x - ct)$$

Distance between nodes of standing wave $= \lambda/2$

Frequency of stretched string (f)

$$f = \frac{1}{2l}\sqrt{T/\mu}$$

Intensity of a wave (I) $I \propto a^2$

Beat frequency $f = f_1 - f_2$

Doppler effect

Moving source

$$f' = cf/(c + u)$$

Moving observer

$$f' = \frac{c - v}{c}.f$$

With light

$$f = f_0\left(\frac{\sqrt{1 - v^2/c^2}}{1 - v/c}\right)$$

$$\approx f_0\left(1 + \frac{v}{c}\right)$$

$$\frac{\Delta\lambda}{\lambda_0} = \frac{v}{c}$$

Constructive interference
path difference $= m\lambda$

Destructive interference
path difference $= (2m + 1)\lambda/2$

Young's slits fringe spacing $= \lambda D/s$

Diffraction grating (max) $d \sin\theta = n\lambda$

Brewster's law (polarisation) $\tan p = n$

Resolving power (ϕ) $\phi = 1{\cdot}22\lambda/a$

Single slit minimum
(first) $d \sin\theta = \lambda$

Optical path length nd

OSCILLOSCOPE

The oscilloscope is arguably the physicist's most versatile piece of laboratory instrumentation. It can be used for a wide range of electrical measurements and as a timer. Most oscilloscopes are of the **cathode ray** type, generating a trace on a fluorescent screen by the action of a beam of electrons and in a way similar to that of a TV tube.

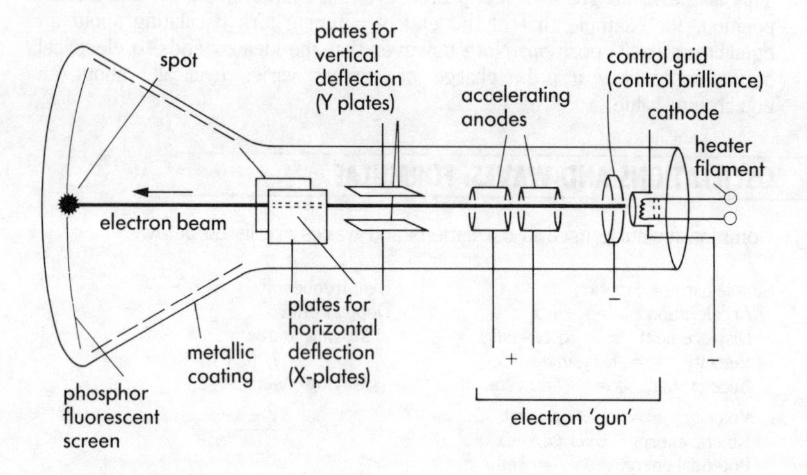

Fig. O.9 Cathode ray oscilloscope

Fig. O.9 shows a typical arrangement. The heated cathode emits a cloud of electrons which are drawn along the **electron gun** by the action of the positive potential difference between the cathode and the accelerating anode. Immediately in front of the cathode is a brilliance grid which, by having a negative voltage (with respect to the cathode) applied to it, controls the flow of electrons, and hence the picture brightness. The potential on the focusing anode is made variable so that this electrode may be used as a focusing control.

Between the accelerating anode and the coated screen are two pairs of plates, slightly inclined to each other within the pair, but with each pair placed perpendicular to each other. These control the position of the spot on the screen: one set, the X-plates, control the spot in a horizontal direction, and the other set, the Y-plates, control the spot in a vertical direction.

The electron beam passes between these deflection plates, and the effect of a potential difference on either pair of plates on the electron beam reaching the screen is shown in Fig. O.10.

If the above type of constant potential difference is applied to either set of deflection plates, the spot will remain stationary on the screen, its displacement from the screen centre depending upon the magnitude of the deflecting potential applied.

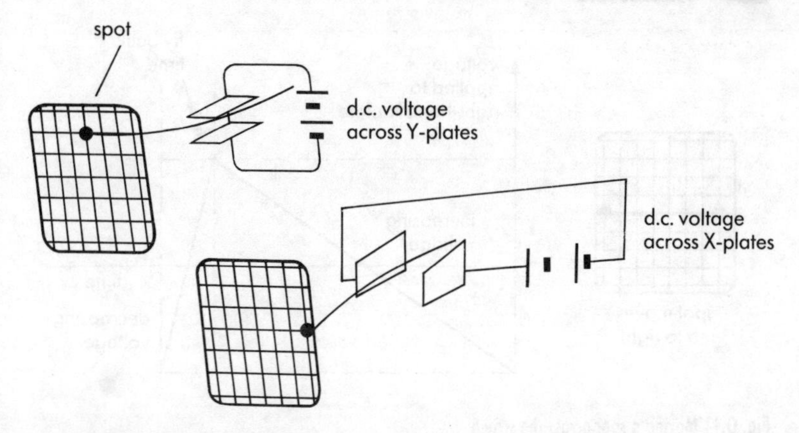

Fig. O.10 Deflection by d.c. voltages

Notice, however, that on switching on the oscilloscope, the spot does not remain in one position but sweeps across the screen, and the speed with which it does so can be varied by means of the control marked Variable Time/cm, which has a coarse and a fine adjustment. This control is called the time base of the oscilloscope.

The time base

Consider a potential difference applied to the X-plates which is not a constant, but which increases from zero to some maximum value at a constant rate. This p.d. will cause the spot to move across the screen from the centre to the right (or vice-versa, depending on the polarity of the plates).

If, when the spot has reached the right-hand side of the screen, the deflecting potential is quickly reduced to its initial zero value, the screen spot will rapidly return to its undeflected position in the centre of the screen. If this constantly increasing potential is again applied, the whole deflection procedure will be repeated.

If the frequency of this alternating voltage is increased to some value above 20 Hz the motion of the spot across the screen will appear as a stationary line owing to the persistence of light on the screen coating.

Since the undeflection position of the spot on the screen is at the centre of the screen, a negative voltage is applied first to the right-hand plate, and this is then slowly reduced to zero potential, and then up to a maximum positive potential as shown in Fig. O.11.

This type of alternating potential which is applied to the X-plates on the oscilloscope is called a sawtooth waveform. In such a waveform, the potential increases constantly with time up to a maximum, and then rapidly returns to its initial value (negative value), at which instant the cycle of voltage values is repeated.

If such a sawtooth waveform potential is applied to the X-plates of the oscilloscope it produces a linear time sweep of the spot across the screen,

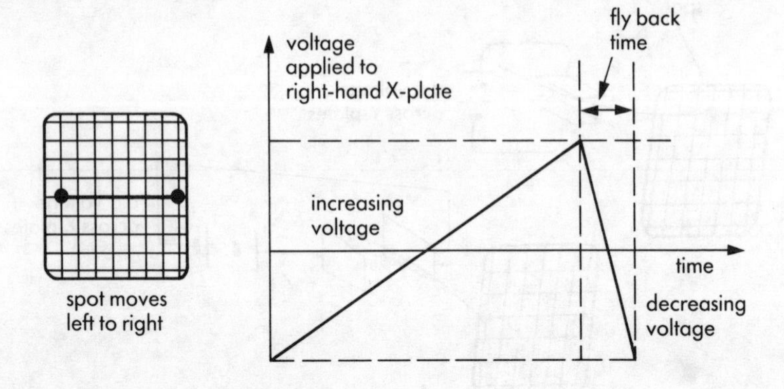

Fig. O.11 Moving a spot across the screen

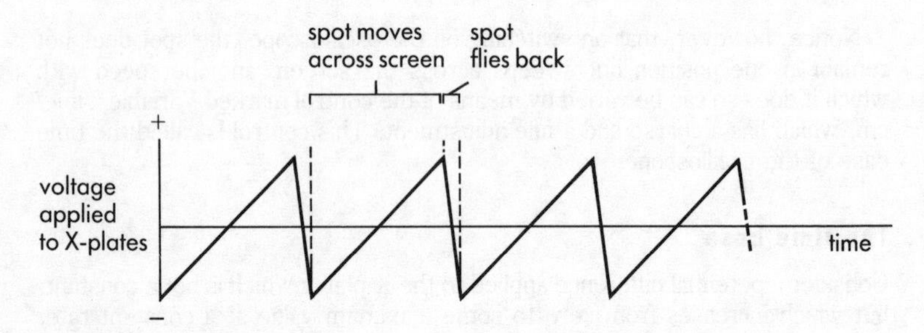

Fig. O.12 Saw-tooth waveform

together with a fast fly-back of the spot to its initial position. Such a linear time sweep on an oscilloscope is called a linear time base, and the frequency of this linear time base is controlled by the Time/cm switch which, on the coarse control, has a number of positions giving sweep times between 100 ms/cm to 1 s. There is usually a fine control which allows an overlap between the fixed speeds.

The time base can always be turned off and an external source of alternating voltage can be applied to the X-plates. On some models the terminals for doing this are at the rear of the oscilloscope.

Types of control

The usual controls which are provided are:

i) On/off and brightness control: The brightness control should be kept at the lowest possible intensity suitable for the time-base frequency being used so that damage to the screen does not occur.
ii) Focus control: The spot or line trace can be made sharp with this.
iii) X-gain control: This adjusts the length of the sweep of the spot or line trace in the x direction.

iv) X-shift control: This bodily moves the whole sweep in either x direction
and can be used to adjust which part of the screen is used for either starting or terminating the sweep.

v) Trig +/− control: To maintain a stable trace on the screen each horizontal sweep must start at the same point on the waveform being displayed (Fig. O.13). This is done by feeding part of the input signal to

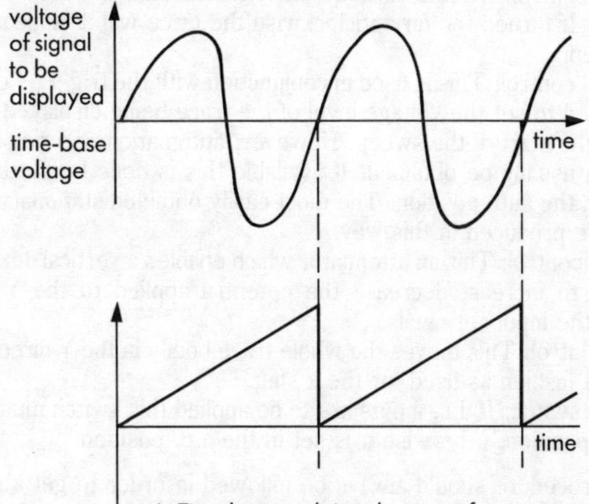

a) Time base and signal at same frequency

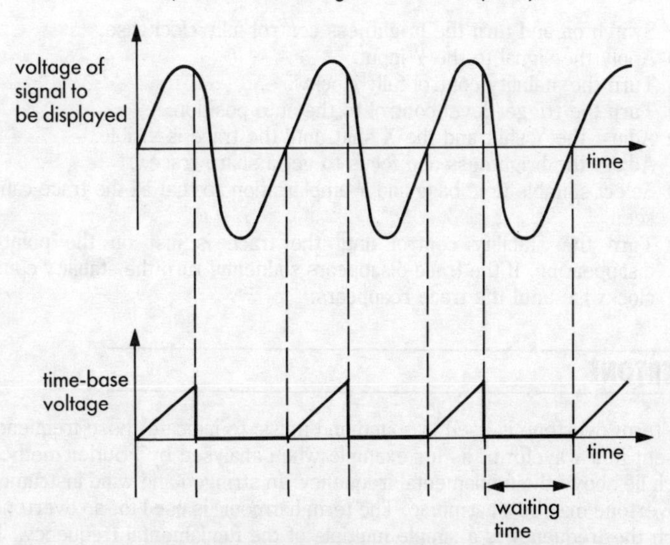

b) Time-base and signal at different frequencies

Fig. O.13 Action of the trigger: in case b) a steady trace would not be produced unless the time base 'waits' for the voltage on subsequent sweeps to be the same

a trigger circuit, which starts the movement of the spot from the left of the screen and at a point chosen by this control and the trig level control below. The control is normally set in the trig + position so that the time base is triggered on a rising waveform.

vi) Time/cm control: This usually has a coarse control with a number of fixed positions and a fine control to allow further variations. Often the time base can be switched off by turning it fully anticlockwise.

vii) Stability control: This is turned anticlockwise until a stable trace is obtained. If turned too far anticlockwise the trace will disappear from the screen.

viii) Trig level control: This is used in conjunction with the trig +/− control and is used to set the voltage level of the trace being displayed which initiates the start of the sweep. However, automatic triggering by the input can usually be obtained. If available this is done by putting the control in the auto position. The most easily obtained stationary wave traces are produced in this way.

ix) Volts/cm control: This an attenuator which enables a vertical deflection amplifier to increase/decrease the potential applied to the Y-plates through the input terminals.

x) Y-shift control: This moves the whole trace bodily in the Y direction in the same fashion as used for the x shift.

xi) D.c./a.c. switch: If d.c. inputs are to be applied this switch must be in the d.c. position, otherwise it is set in the a.c. position.

The following procedure should always be followed in order to get a steady trace on the screen.

a) Switch on and turn the brightness control fully clockwise.
b) Apply the signal to the Y input.
c) Turn the stability control fully clockwise.
d) Turn the trigger level control to the auto position.
e) Adjust the Y shift and the X shift until the trace is visible.
f) Adjust the brightness and focus to get a sharp trace.
g) Select suitable time base and Y amplification so that all the trace can be seen.
h) Turn the stability control until the trace is just on the point of disappearing. If the trace disappears suddenly, turn the stability control clockwise until the trace reappears.

OVERTONE

The term overtone is used in sound and music to indicate those frequencies present in a waveform, as for example when analysed by **Fourier methods**, which lie above the fundamental frequency. In stringed and wind instruments an overtone may be a harmonic. The term harmonic is used for an overtone in which the frequency is a simple multiple of the fundamental frequency. The overtones of percussion and reed instruments are not harmonics.

◀ Musical instruments ▶

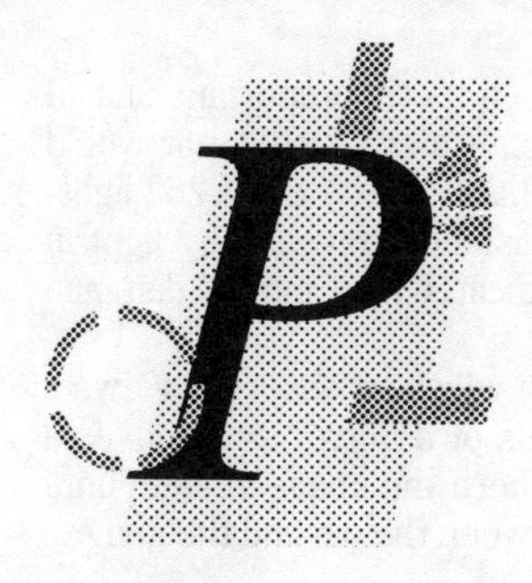

PARALLAX

Parallax is a term of astronomy and optics. An object has parallax if it appears to move relative to another object when the observer moves his vantage point.

In astrophysics this is used for the measurement of the distances of nearby stars (Fig. P.1). As the earth moves round the sun, a nearby star (one object) will appear to move relative to more distant stars (the second object). Hence the nearby star exhibits parallax. In fact in astronomy the angle θ, through which the nearby star moves, is defined as twice the parallax angle, and this angle is usually measured in seconds of arc. It should be clear from the simple geometry of Fig. P.1 that ESE′ forms a triangle of which the base line EE′ is known, and hence the distance of the star can be found.

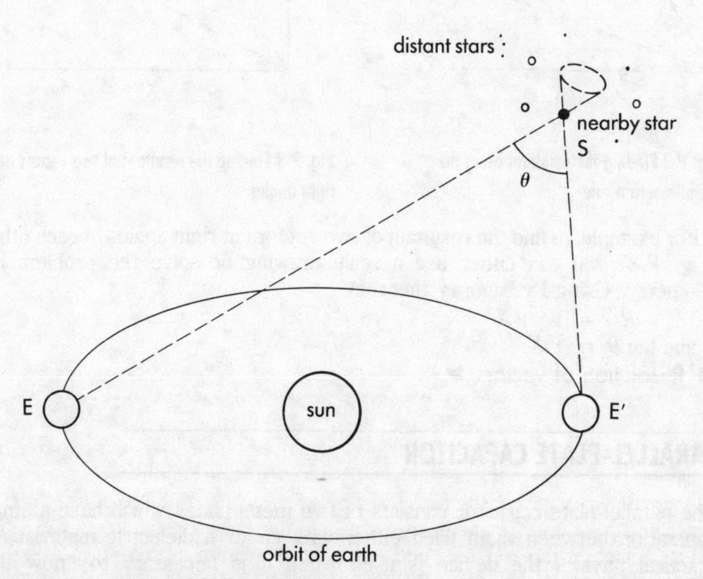

Fig. P.1 Stellar parallax. As the earth orbits the sun, a nearby star apparently moves relative to distant stars. θ is twice the parallax angle

The method of trigonometrical parallax has given us the important unit of distance known as the parsec (pc). This is the distance at which a star would have a parallax of 1 second of arc and is equal to 3.086×10^{16} m. 3.262 light-years is equal to a parsec (the light-year is the distance travelled by light in one year). In astronomy the parallax of a star is indicated by p and the distance d of a star in parsecs is given by $d = 1/p$.

In optics the 'no parallax' method is a method in which an observer views a virtual image through an optical system, i.e. a lens or a mirror, and moves a pointer, e.g. a pin, in the vicinity of the region where the image is seen until there is no parallax, i.e. no relative movement between the pin and the image.

PARALLELOGRAM OF VECTORS

The parallelogram of vectors is a way of adding **vectors.** Because they have direction as well as magnitude they cannot be added arithmetically.

The parallelogram rule states that if two vectors acting at a point are represented in magnitude and direction by the sides of a triangle, their resultant is represented by the diagonal of the parallelogram drawn from the point (Fig. P.2).

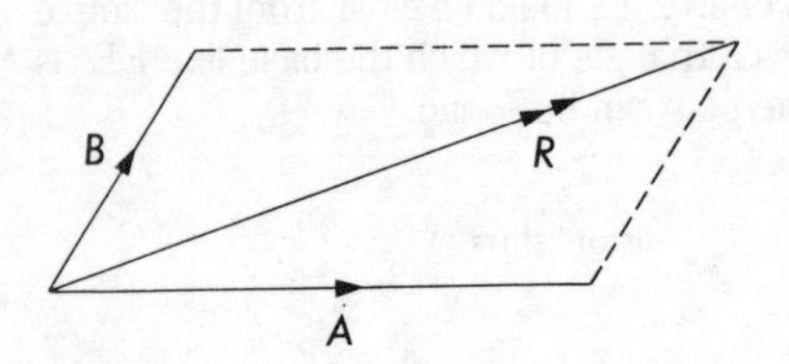

Fig. P.2 Finding the resultant using the parallelogram rule

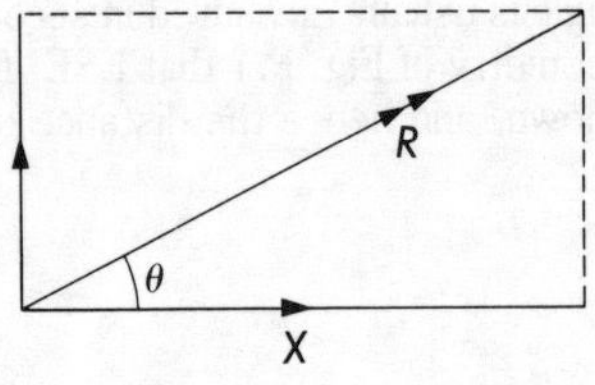

Fig. P.3 Finding the resultant of two vectors at right angles

For example, to find the resultant of two vectors at right angles to each other (Fig. P.3) you can either use a scale drawing or solve the problem by geometry. Using Pythagoras' theorem

$$R^2 = Y^2 + X^2$$

and $\tan \theta = Y/X$

◀ Resolution of vectors ▶

PARALLEL-PLATE CAPACITOR

The parallel-plate capacitor consists of two metal plates which have a small separation between them filled either with air or a dielectric material. In practical physics the device is used when it is necessary to know the capacitance exactly. There is a **uniform electric field** between the plates. With air between the plates the capacitance is given by the formula $C = Q/V$

$= A\epsilon_o/d$. Here ϵ_o is the permittivity of free space, A the plate area, and d the plate separation. Hence $Q/A = V/d$ = the field intensity between the plates.

If an insulator, that is a dielectric, is placed between the plates, the molecules of the dielectric become polarised by the electric field, and the effect is to increase the capacitance. When this happens the capacitance is given by

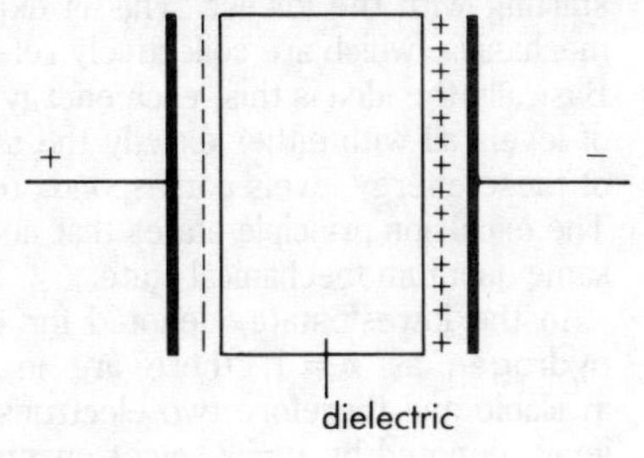

Fig. P.4

$$C = A\,\frac{\epsilon_r\,\epsilon_o}{d}$$

where ϵ_r is the relative permittivity of the dielectric.

If such a capacitor, once charged, is isolated, the charge upon it remains constant. If the capacitance is then increased by decreasing the separation of the plates, the potential difference must decrease. If the capacitor is not isolated, i.e. is connected to a battery, then if the plates separation is decreased, increasing the capacity, then the charge upon it will increase.

◀ Capacitors ▶

PARITY GATE

◀ Logic gates ▶

PASCHEN SERIES

◀ Energy levels in hydrogen ▶

PAULI EXCLUSION PRINCIPLE

The Pauli exclusion principle is the name given to the set of rules used in **quantum mechanics** to make sense of the fact that in spite of what would be expected from an understanding of energy, a multi-electron atom does not have all its electrons in the lowest energy level (state). In fact only two electrons are ever found with the lowest value of energy.

In general most physical and chemical systems find their equilibrium state to be the one with the lowest amount of energy. Put another way, they need energy to be shifted from their equilibrium state. (The exceptions are systems which are said to be unstable equilibrium: for example a circus acrobat walking on a tight-rope.) As an example of a stable equilibrium at the atomic level there is the case of the hydrogen atom, where the single electron finds its most stable state in the lowest energy level. However, in the case of multi-electron atoms the lowest energy state turns out to be one in which the electrons are distributed across a range of energy levels starting with the lowest. This is explained by the set of rules of quantum mechanics, which are collectively referred to as the Pauli exclusion principle. Basically the idea is this: each energy level of the atom is in fact a multiplicity of levels all with either exactly the same or closely similar levels. Each one of these energy levels corresponds to a so-called quantum mechanical state. The exclusion principle states that no two electrons in an atom may have the same quantum mechanical state.

In the lowest state, denoted for example in the entry **Energy levels in hydrogen** as $n = 1$, there are in fact two quantum mechanical states available and therefore two electrons are allowed on this level. In the next level, denoted by $n = 2$, eight quantum mechanical states are available and so up to eight electrons are allowed on this level (Fig. P.5). The collections of energy levels, $n = 1$, $n = 2$, etc., are sometimes referred to as 'shells'. The electrons in the lowest energy state are referred to as being in the K-shell, those in the next level the L-shell and so on.

Number of level n	1	2	3	4	. . . .
Maximum number of electrons in the level (shell)	2	8	18	32	. . . .
Letter code for shell	K	L	M	N	. . . .

Fig. P.5

PENDULUM

◀ **Simple pendulum** ▶

PERIOD

This is a term used in **oscillation**, wave and **alternating current** theory. In all these cases there is a periodic cycle of events. The period, T, is the time for one complete cycle. In the case of an oscillator it is the time for one return journey from and to an extreme position of the oscillator.

PERMEABILITY

μ is a constant of proportionality in magnetic theory, which relates the magnetic flux density, B, to the current producing it. For example, in a solenoid $B = \mu_o nI$, where n is the number of turns per metre of the coil and μ_o the permeability for empty space. The formula has to be modified if the material in the solenoid is other than empty space. The permeability in the equation is then that of the material and not a vacuum. The permeability of the material is written as μ, but it is usual to speak of the relative permeability of the material. This is the ratio of the permeability of the material to that of vacuum, and is written $\mu_r = \frac{\mu}{\mu_o}$. As such μ_r is a pure number with no units or **dimensions.**

Some values for relative permeabilities are given below. The value of iron is many thousands of that of air, which is why placing an iron core into a solenoid produces a very large increase in the field within it. The mechanism for the increase of the field is that once the iron is magnetised there are large circulating curents within the iron at an atomic level which all reinforce each other and the currents flowing in the wire of the solenoid. The overall effect of the atomic currents and the current in the wire is a huge magnetic field.

Material	*Relative permeability*
Iron	9000
Mild steel	2000
Super maloy	1 000 000

PERMEABILITY OF FREE SPACE

The permeability of free space, μ_o, is a constant which arises in a number of the equations of electromagnetism. For example, the magnetic field due to an electric current I flowing in a single wire is proportional to the current and inversely proportional to the distance r from the wire. In other words $B \propto I/r$. The constant of proportionality is $\mu_o/2\pi$ and hence $B = \mu_o\, I/2\pi r$.

The ampere is defined as that constant current which, flowing in two infinitely long parallel conductors of negligible cross-section, placed in a vacuum 1 metre apart, produces a force between them of 2×10^{-7}N m^{-1}, and this provides a definition of the permeability of free space.

Consider two parallel wires, as in Fig. P.6, 1 m apart, each with a current of 1 A flowing in them. The force on one wire in the presence of the field of the other is given by BIL. So considering a length of 1 metre we have $L = 1$ metre. As explained above $B = \mu_o I/2\pi r$, and hence we have

$$F = \frac{\mu_o I_1 I_2 L}{2\pi r} \text{ giving } \mu_o = 2\pi r F/I_1 I_2 L$$

Now with $I_1 = I_2 = 1$ A, $L = 1$ m, and $r = 1$ m we have $\frac{\mu_o}{2\pi}$ numerically equal

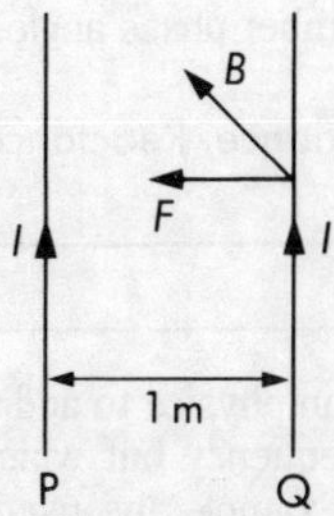

Fig. P.6 Force between two parallel current-carrying wires

to the force, which by definition has a value in newtons of 2×10^{-7}. Hence μ_o has a numerical value of $4\pi \times 10^{-7}$.

The units of μ_o are usually expresed as H m^{-1}. This is obtained as follows. Rearranging $B = \mu_o I/2\pi r$ we get $\mu_o = 2\pi rB/I$. This gives the units of μ_o as m T/A. But 1 T = 1 weber/metre^2, hence 1 m T/A = 1 m Wb/A m^2 = 1 Wb/m A.

To proceed further we need two equations from electromagnetic induction: Faraday's Law, $E = -\mathrm{d}\phi/\mathrm{d}t$, which implies that 1 Wb = 1 V s, and the equation for the e.m.f. generated in an inductor of L henries, $E = -L\mathrm{d}I/\mathrm{d}t$, which gives 1 H = 1 V s A^{-1}.

Hence from these two we get 1 H = 1 Wb/A, and substituting this into our earlier result we get 1 m T/A = 1 H m^{-1}, the units of permeability. Note that this unit compares with the unit of F m^{-1} for the permittivity of free space (see Uniform electric field).

PERMITTIVITY OF FREE SPACE

◄ Uniform electric field ►

PFUND SERIES

◄ Energy levels in hydrogen ►

PHASE

◄ Alternating current, Phase in alternating current circuits, Simple harmonic motion ►

PHASE IN ALTERNATING CURRENT CIRCUITS

In alternating current circuits current and voltage are usually not in phase. When a.c. is applied to a capacitor the current leads the voltage by $\pi/2$ radians (90°). With a pure inductor the current lags behind the voltage by $\pi/2$ radians (90°).

A useful mnemonic to remember phase angles in a.c. is CIVIL: I ahead of V for C; I after V for L.

◄ Alternating current, Impedance, Reactance ►

PHASORS

Phasors are used extensively in physics to add two quantities together which are oscillating at the same frequency but which are out of phase with each other. The method can, for example, be used to find the resultant of two coherent wave trains of light, both of the same frequency, travelling through a medium. It can also be used in the theory of alternating currents to add two alternating voltages or currents together. Here we shall simply consider its application in a.c. theory.

The entry **Simple harmonic motion** shows how the projection of a rotating point on to an axis produces a sinusoidal quantity. So the projection of a rotating vector along say the y-axis can represent a varying a.c. voltage $v = \sin \omega t$. Such a rotating vector is called a phasor. To add two voltages together, the phasors are added using the **parallelogram of vectors**, taking account of the phase angle between them (Fig. P.7). The resultant is the phasor, which represents the addition of the two out-of-phase voltages.

Although the method has been described in terms of peak values of voltage, the addition process can be done with r.m.s. values, provided it is remembered that the computed value is an r.m.s. value. This is because on a vector diagram the effect is simply to scale the lengths of all vectors down by a factor of $\frac{1}{\sqrt{2}}$. In the subsequent examples, whenever voltages and currents are referred to, it is the r.m.s. values that are considered. The method can of course also be used to add currents which are not in phase.

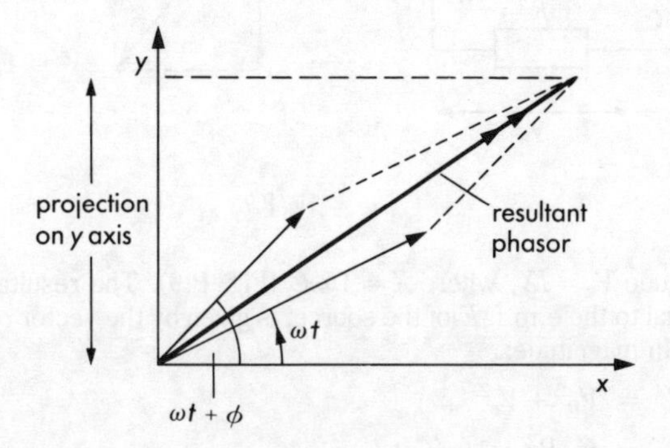

Fig. P.7 Adding two phasors using the parallelogram rule

Solving series circuit problems

In solving series circuits there are two key points to consider in working out voltages and currents:

a) At any instant the current is the same in each circuit component (because they are in series).
b) The sum of the p.d.s at any instant is equal to the source e.m.f. at that instant.

The following rules should then be adopted:

1) First draw the current vector, horizontally (for convenience).
2) Draw the vector representing voltage across a resistance in phase with the current vector (i.e. along the direction of the current vector).

3) Draw in the other voltage vectors at right angles, remembering the mnemonic CIVIL (see **Phase in alternating current circuits**).
4) Find the resultant voltage vector.
5) Compare the magnitude of this with the magnitude of the current vector in order to find the circuit **impedance** Z.
6) Compare its direction with the horizontal in order to establish the phase angle between current and voltage.

CR circuit

The voltage V_R $(= IR)$ is in phase with the current vector and is drawn horizontally (Fig. P.8). With the capacitor, the current leads the voltage by 90°, and so its voltage vector V is drawn downwards.

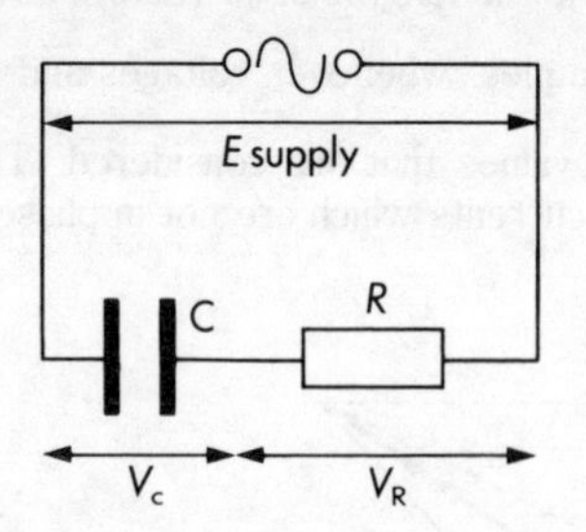

Fig. P.8

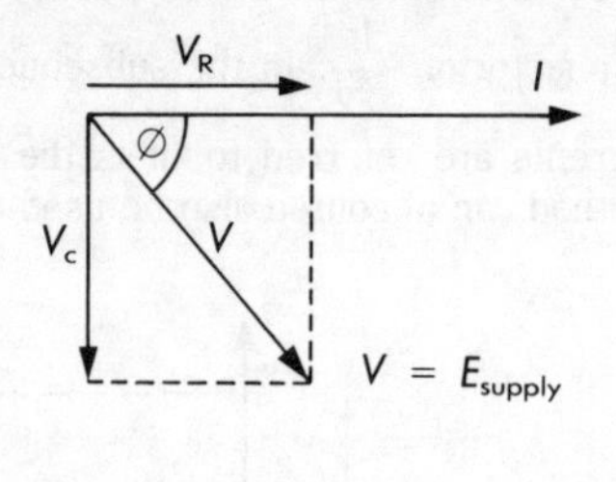

Fig. P.9

In magnitude $V_c = IX$, where $X = 1/\omega C$ (Fig. P.9). The resultant p.d. V, which is equal to the e.m.f. E of the source, is given by the vector resultant of V_R and V_c. In magnitude:

$$E^2 = V_R{}^2 + V_c{}^2$$

$$= I^2 (R^2 + 1/\omega^2 C^2)$$

$$\text{or} \quad E = IZ$$

where Z is the impedance and given by

$$Z = \sqrt{R^2 + 1/\omega^2 C^2}$$

$$\text{Phase: } \tan\phi = \frac{V_c}{V_R} = \frac{I}{\omega C} \cdot \frac{1}{IR}$$

$$\text{so } \tan\phi = \frac{1}{\omega RC}$$

RL circuit

For the inductance the applied voltage leads the current by 90°, so its voltage vector V_L is drawn upwards (Fig. P.10) In magnitude $V_L = IX$, where

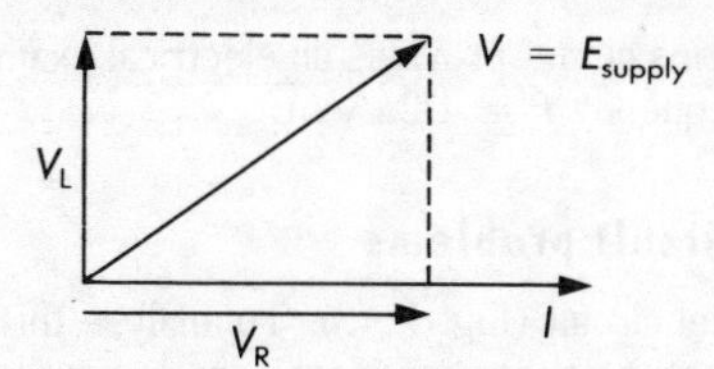

Fig. P.10

$X = \omega L$. The resultant p.d. V, equal to E, is then drawn in. Doing the same analysis as before we obtain

$$E^2 = V_R{}^2 + V_L{}^2$$
$$= I^2\,(R^2 + \omega^2 L^2)$$

or $\quad E = IZ$

where Z is the impedance and is given by

$$Z = \sqrt{R^2 + \omega^2 L^2}$$

$$\tan\phi = \frac{V_L}{V_R} = \frac{\omega L}{R}$$

LCR circuit

Note that in practice there may only be a coil and a capacitor. A real coil will always have some resistance and R is then the resistance of the coil. The phasor diagram is as shown in Fig. P.11 with V_L leading I by 90° and V_c lagging it by 90°. $V_L - V_c$ can then be drawn (in Fig. P.12 it is assumed that V_L is greater than V_c). The calculation is then as before:

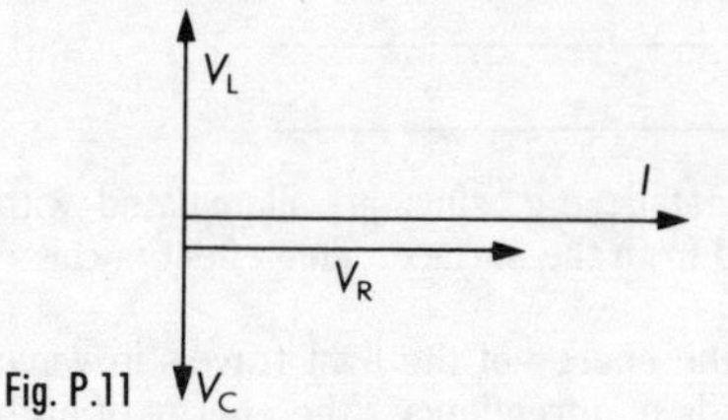

Fig. P.11

Fig. P.12

$$E^2 = V_R{}^2 + (V_L - V_c)^2$$
$$= I^2\left(R^2 + \left(\omega L - \frac{1}{\omega C}\right)^2\right)$$

or $\quad E = IZ$ where

$$Z = \sqrt{R^2 + \left(\omega L - \frac{1}{\omega C}\right)^2}$$

and $\tan\phi = \dfrac{V_L - V_C}{V_R}$

Note that the LCR series circuit provides an electrical example of **resonance**. This occurs at the frequency $f = 1/2\pi\sqrt{LC}$

Solving parallel-circuit problems

Consider an LC parallel circuit (Fig. P.13). To analyse this with phasors you need to know that because the components are in parallel it is the voltage which is now common and not the current. So in drawing a phasor diagram you start by drawing the voltage vector and then add the current vectors (Fig. P.14).

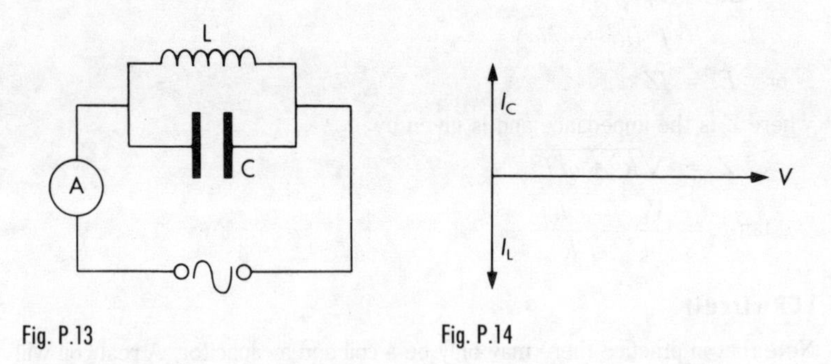

Fig. P.13

Fig. P.14

Note that this circuit also exhibits resonance. The resonance frequency is also $f = 1/2\pi\sqrt{LC}$.

◀ Alternating currents, Phase in alternating current circuits ▶

PHOTOELECTRIC EFFECT

When very clean surfaces of some metals, e.g. zinc, are illuminated with ultraviolet light, electrons are released from the surface. This effect is called the photoelectric effect.

According to **quantum mechanics** the energy of the light travels in wave packets known as photons. If the light is of a frequency f the energy of each photon is hf, where h is the **Planck constant**. A free (conducting) electron near the surface of the metal requires a minimum amount of energy, ϕ, the so-called work function of the metal, to escape. Provided the energy of the incoming photon is greater than this, electrons will be emitted.

An important and often misunderstood feature of the process is that the energy of a photon is either given up completely or not given up at all, and all the energy is transmitted to one electron. This 'quantum mechanical' behaviour is sometimes thought of as 'slot-machine physics'. It means that in order to get enough energy you can't wait for two photons to give up energy which could be added together to release an electron. If the incoming photon has insufficient energy the process just doesn't take place. The emitted electrons have a range of kinetic energies up to a maximum. This is because, although the photons each deliver the same amount of energy hf to the electrons, the electrons lose different amounts of energy while escaping. These differing amounts of energy depend upon factors such as how far away from the metal surface they are when they absorb the energy of the photon etc.

In general we have the equation

$$hf = \tfrac{1}{2}mv_{\max}^2 + \phi$$

where $\frac{1}{2}mv_{\max}^2$ is the maximum electron kinetic energy which is observed. The photoelectric effect is observed with visible light, but visible light has insufficient photon energy to cause a photoelectric effect with metals such as zinc. Instead, metals with a smaller work function such as sodium or potassium have to be used. These metals, which oxidise very easily, have to be kept in evacuated containers, and hence the experiments cannot be conducted except with specially prepared tubes in which the electrodes can be mounted.

PHOTOGRAPHIC FILM

The characteristics of black and white photographic film is of great importance to the astronomer because most astronomical data is still collected by the exposure of films or plates in a telescope.

Photographic film has a surface coating of a photographic emulsion. This contains microscopic crystals of silver bromide and silver iodide. The process of photography is an example of the quantum mechanical nature of light. Light has to be thought of not as a wave but as a stream of particles. When a film or plate is exposed to light, crystals in the emulsion will be activated only if a light photon passes through them and is absorbed. If absorption takes place some of the silver bromide (or iodide) will be reduced to silver. When the film is subsequently developed the whole crystal will be reduced if there is a small region which has been already reduced by the action of light. The developed crystal does not have the characteristic shiny appearance of silver on a comparatively large scale: instead it is black. A piece of film subjected to a modest exposure will therefore consist of a large number of black 'grains', depending upon where light photons have been absorbed. The image therefore is grainy. The difference between a high-speed film and a slower, less sensitive film is largely in the size of the grains in the developed image (and in the crystals in the undeveloped film). The faster the film the larger the grains.

Fig. P.15 shows the characteristic way in which the density of the image of a film, D, is related to the intensity of light E to which it is exposed. E is measured in $\mathrm{W\,m^{-2}\,s}$ or $\mathrm{J\,m^{-2}}$. Such a graph is called a **Hurter-Driffield curve**, or an HD curve for short. A film of higher contrast would have a steeper slope, and one of higher speed would be displaced to the left. The gross fog level is the minimum density the film has, even if it has not been exposed to light. The saturation level is the maximum density which can be achieved. Once this has occurred, more exposure has no effect. It corresponds to an activation of all the grains in the emulsion. The dynamic ranges of input and output should be self-explanatory.

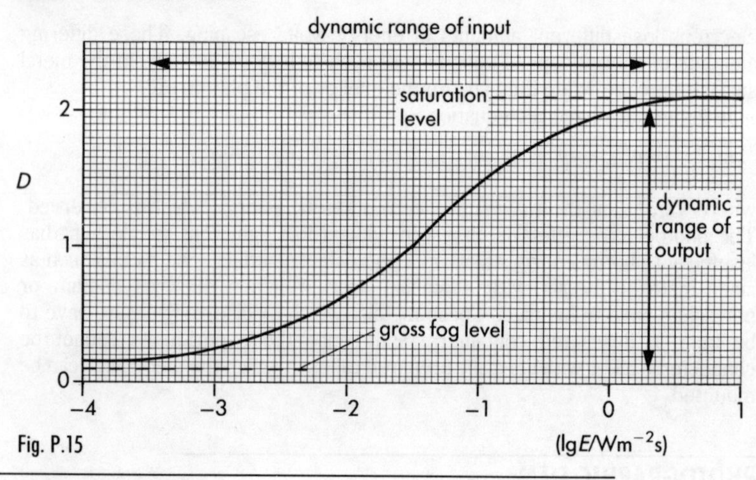

Fig. P.15

PHOTOMULTIPLIER

◀ Scintillation counter ▶

PHOTONS

The members of the electro-magnetic spectrum can be usefully considered as particles, called photons, whose energy $E = hf$, where h is the Planck constant (6.6×10^{-34} J s).

◀ Electromagnetic spectrum ▶

PHYSICAL QUANTITIES IN THE SI SYSTEM

Basic quantities and units

The name International System of Units (SI) has been adopted by the Conférence Générale des Poids et Mesures (CGPM) for a coherent system based on seven basic quantities. These are chosen for their convenience and are: *mass, length, time, electric current, temperature, luminous intensity* and *amount of substance*. All other quantities are derived from one or more of the basic quantities.

The base units for each of these quantities are listed below:

metre (m) The metre is the length equal to 1 650 763.73 wavelengths in vacuum corresponding to the transition between the levels $2p_{10}$ and $5d_5$ of the krypton-86 atom.

kilogram (kg) The kilogram is the unit of mass; it is equal to the mass of the international prototype of the kilogram. (This prototype is in the custody of the Bureau International des Poids et Mesures at Sèvres, France.)

second (s) The second is the duration of 9 192 631 770 periods of the radiation corresponding to the transition between the two hyperfine levels of the ground state of the caesium-133 atom.

ampere (A) The ampere is that constant current which, if maintained in two straight parallel conductors of infinite length, of negligible circular cross-section and placed 1 metre apart in vacuum, would produce between these conductors a force equal to 2×10^{-7} newton per metre of length.

kelvin (K) The kelvin, unit of thermodynamic temperature, is the fraction 1/273.16 of the thermodynamic temperature of the triple point of water.

candela (cd) The candela is the luminous intensity, in a perpendicular direction, of a surface of 1/600 000 square metre of a black body at the temperature of freezing platinum under a pressure of 101 325 pascals (newton per square metre).

mole (mol) The mole is the amount of substance of a system which contains as many 'elementary entities' as there are atoms in 0.012 kilogram of carbon-12. By 'elementary entity' is meant an atom, molecule, ion, electron, etc.

There are two supplementary units, the radian (rad) and the steradian (sr), which are dimensionless. Units for all other physical quantities are derived units based entirely on the nine units given above.

Derived quantities and units

Examples of derived quantities and their units are given below. Derived quantities are obtained from the base units by simple multiplication or division: no numerical factors are involved.

Derived quantity	*Unit*	
	Name	*Symbol*
velocity	metre per second	$m\,s^{-1}$
acceleration	metre per second squared	$m\,s^{-2}$
momentum	kilogram metre per second	$kg\,m\,s^{-1}$
volume	cubic metre	m^3
density	kilogram per cubic metre	$kg\,m^{-3}$

Special names and symbols exist for some derived SI units

Physical quantity	*Name of derived SI unit*	*Symbol for unit*	*Unit expressed in terms of base, supplementary or derived unit*
frequency	hertz	Hz	s^{-1}
force	newton	N	$kg\,m\,s^{-2}$
pressure and stress	pascal	Pa	$N\,m^{-2}$
work, energy, heat	joule	J	Nm
power	watt	W	$J\,s^{-1}$

Physical quantity	*Name of derived SI unit*	*Symbol for unit*	*Unit expressed in terms of base, supplementary or derived unit*
magnetic flux	weber	Wb	V s
magnetic flux density (magnetic induction)	tesla	T	Wb m^{-2}
inductance	henry	H	Wb A^{-1}
luminous flux	humen	lm	cd sr
illuminance	lux	lx	lm m^{-2}
electric charge	coulomb	C	A s
electric potential, potential difference, electromotive force	volt	V	J C^{-1}
electric capacitance	farad	F	C V^{-1}
electric resistance	ohm	Ω	V A^{-1}
electric conductance	siemens	S	Ω^{-1}

When the unit is named after a person the symbol has a capital letter.

Multiples of SI units

The following prefixes may be used to indicate decimal sub-multiples or multiples of both base and derived units.

Sub-multiple	*Prefix*	*Symbol*	*Multiple*	*Prefix*	*Symbol*
10^{-1}	deci	d	10^{1}	deca	da
10^{-2}	centi	c	10^{2}	hecto	h
10^{-3}	milli	m	10^{3}	kilo	k
10^{-6}	micro	μ	10^{6}	mega	M
10^{-9}	nano	n	10^{9}	giga	G
10^{-12}	pico	p	10^{12}	tera	T
10^{-15}	femto	f			
10^{-18}	atto	a			

It will be noted here that the kilogram for an SI base unit is anomalous, but it is self-evident how fractions and multiples of the kilogram should be expressed.

Coherence of the SI system

SI units are coherent. This means that there is only *one* unit for each quantity (ignoring multiples and submultiples) and if these are used for the quantities in an expression, the answer is obtained in the correct SI unit. For example if in $F = ma$, m is expressed in kg and a in m s^{-2} then F will be automatically in newtons.

◀ Dimensions, Fundamental constants ▶

PION

◀ Quarks ▶

PITCH

Pitch is a term used in music to describe how 'high' or 'low' a note which is played or sung seems to be. In physics terms, high pitch corresponds to a high frequency and low pitch to a low frequency. Two notes from different instruments are said to be of the same pitch if they seem to a listener to be of the same predominant frequency.

To find the predominant frequency of a note it would be necessary to analyse it by **Fourier methods** to determine the sinusoidal waves out of which it could be constructed. The sine wave with the largest amplitude would be the predominant one.

◀ Musical instruments ▶

PITOT STATIC TUBE

This is an instrument used in transport for measuring the velocity of a vehicle, such as a ship, moving through a fluid.

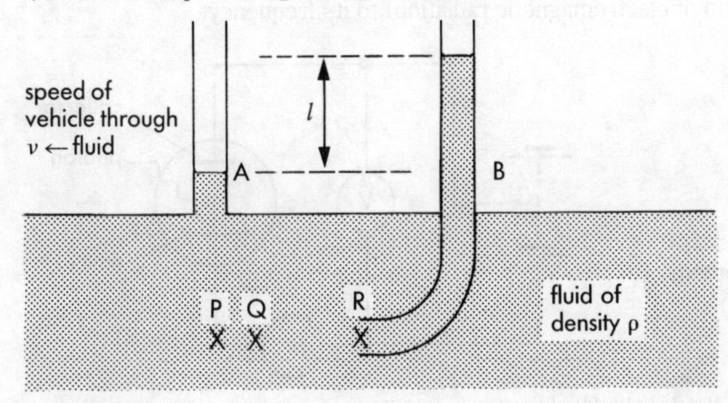

Fig. P.16 Pitot static tube

In Fig. P.16, v is the speed of the vehicle through the fluid and ρ is the density of the fluid. However, we can regard the fluid as moving and the vehicle as being at rest. The physics is obviously the same.

The **manometer** A, being connected to a surface layer, measures the static pressure of the fluid. This is sometimes called the hydrostatic pressure. B is the Pitot tube.

To apply **Bernouilli's principle**, i.e.

$p + \frac{1}{2}\rho v^2 + \rho g h = \text{constant}$

consider horizontal flow and measurements made at the level of the flow.

Bernouilli's equation becomes

$$p + \tfrac{1}{2}\rho v^2 = \text{constant}$$

If p is the pressure at P and Q and p' the pressure at R, manometer A measures the static pressure p and the Pitot tube B the pressure p'. As it enters the tube at R the fluid must be at rest. Thus we have

$$p + \tfrac{1}{2}\rho v^2 = p'$$

$$\text{so } p - p' = \tfrac{1}{2}\rho v^2$$

The height l is measured and we obtain

$$\tfrac{1}{2}\rho v^2 = h\rho l \text{ using the manometer formula}$$

Hence $v = \sqrt{2hl}$ enabling v to be found.

PIXEL

◀ Charge-coupled device ▶

PLANCK CONSTANT

The Planck constant is the ratio of the energy of a **photon** (packet or quantum of electromagnetic radiation) to its frequency.

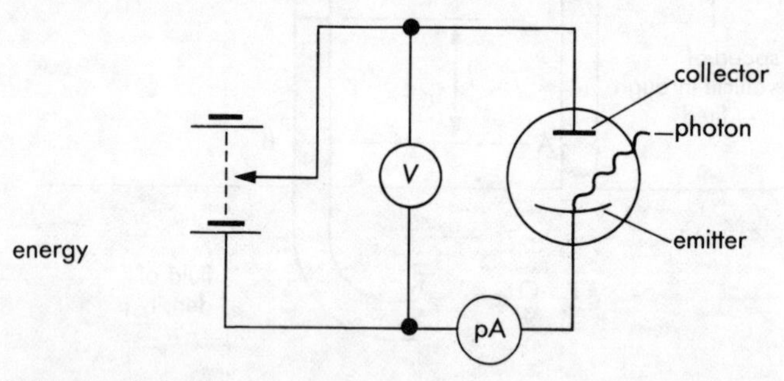

Fig. P.17 Measuring the Planck constant

As explained in the entry **Photoelectric effect**, ordinary visible light can cause the emission of electrons from metals such as sodium and potassium. In the apparatus shown in Fig. P.17 an evacuated cell with a collector electrode and an emitting electrode which has a surface of sodium or potassium is used. The electrons are generated on the surface of the sodium or potassium metal and travel towards the collector. In the experiment an electric field is supplied to decelerate and stop them. If the potential difference is steadily increased, gradually fewer and fewer electrons will be able to get across to the collector, until eventually even the most energetic electrons are stopped. The flow of electrons is determined by the use of the picoammeter in series with the photocell. The maximum stopping potential V_{max} is recorded when this meter reads zero. When this occurs the energy condition is:

$$\tfrac{1}{2}mv_{max}^2 = eV_{max}$$

Note that in this experiment it is important to use a very high-impedance (resistance) voltmeter so that only a neglible current is drawn from the photocell. If we consider the most energetic electrons, the energy of the incoming photon is equal to eV_{max} + the work function ϕ. i.e.

$$hf = eV_{max} + \phi$$

The frequency of light used has to be known, and the usual procedure is to take a number of measurements with a series of filters and a white light source. The filters have to be narrow-band filters for which the mean wavelength is known. If a graph of V_{max} against frequency, f, is plotted Fig. P.18 is obtained. From the gradient the Planck constant can be found, and also the threshold frequency f_o, which is the smallest frequency which will release electrons from the metal.

◀ Electromagnetic spectrum, Photon ▶

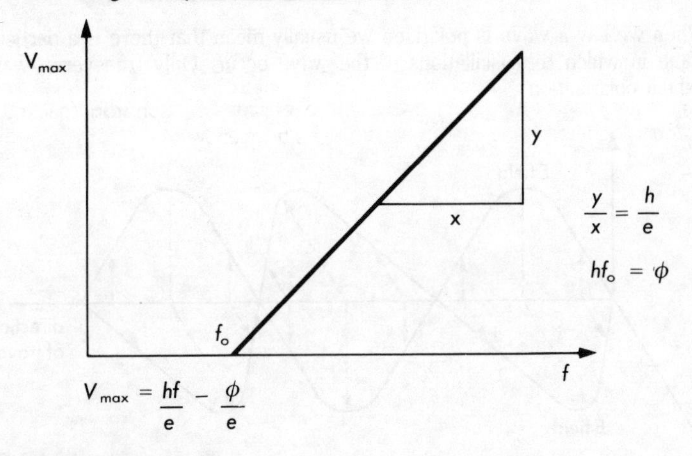

Fig. P.18 Graph of V_{max} against f

PLASMA

◀ Gases, liquids, vapours and plasmas ▶

POISEUILLE'S FORMULA

This is a formula which applies to the steady flow of a fluid through a circular pipe. By steady flow we mean **streamline flow** without the onset of turbulence. Poiseuille's formula states that the volume of liquid passing per second, V, is proportional to the fourth power of the radius r of the pipe. The complete expression for the formula is

$$V = \frac{\pi P r^4}{8\eta l}$$

where P is the pressure difference between the ends of the pipe, l its length and η a constant called the coefficient of viscosity of the fluid.

The sharp dependence upon the fourth power of the radius is of particular importance in medical physics. Patients who suffer from angina experience a narrowing of the arteries. It should be clear that the halving in the effective diameter of the arteries decreases the rate of flow of liquid by a factor of 16. In some circumstances it is necessary to apply drugs which reduce the viscosity of the blood, i.e. provide a smaller value of η, and hence allow a reasonable liquid flow without having to increase the heart pressure.

◀ Millikan's experiment, Turbulent flow ▶

POLARISATION

When we say a wave is polarised we usually mean that there is a particular plane in which the oscillations of the wave occur. Only transverse waves exhibit polarisation.

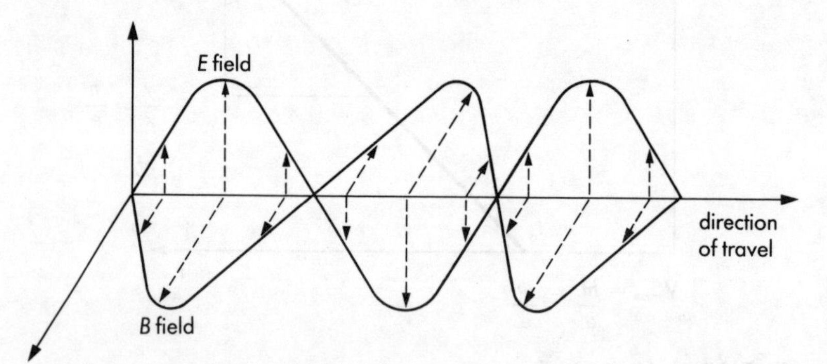

Fig. P.19 Electromagnetic waves

Fig. P.19 shows the oscillations of an electromagnetic wave which is polarised. In such a wave there are two simultaneous oscillations: one of the local electric field E, and at right angles to this one of the local magnetic field B. The diagram shows these oscillations with those of the E field in a vertical plane and those of the B field in a horizontal plane. (Note that the eye or a photographic film responds only to the effect of the E field, but both E and B fields are necessary for the propagation of the wave.) Because the wave has its electric field in one plane only, it is said to be plane-polarised. An unpolarised wave would generally consist of a large number of simultaneous waves (photons), each with electric fields in all planes perpendicular to the direction of travel. Light waves coming from the sun or from an ordinary reading lamp are of this kind. The light may be polarised by scattering or by passing it through a sheet of **polaroid**, or it may become partly polarised by reflection.

POLAROID

Polaroid is a special kind of filter which causes **polarisation** of a light beam incident upon it. If light is passed through one piece of polaroid and a second sheet of polaroid is rotated in this beam, the intensity of the light emerging from the second polaroid varies, reaching zero twice in one revolution when the polaroids are said to be crossed.

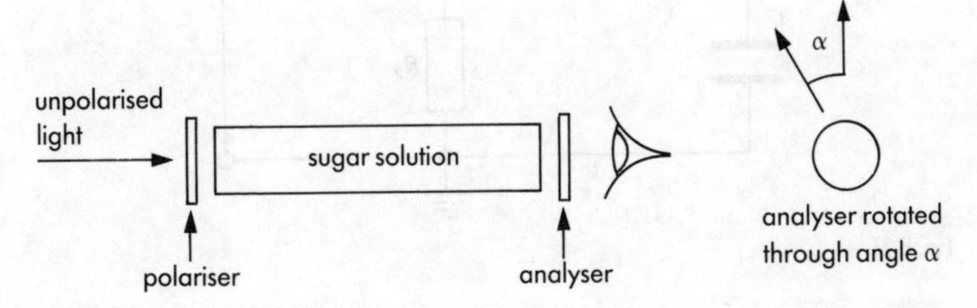

Fig. P.20 Polarimeter

If polarised light generated by passing unpolarised light through a polaroid is then allowed to pass through a long tube containing certain sugar solutions, it is found that the plane of polarisation is rotated by the solution (Fig. P.20). The amount of rotation can be found by viewing the light with a second polaroid at the far end of the solution. In order for light to be seen at maximum brightness the second polaroid has to be rotated through an angle α. However, it is usually easier to detect total extinction of light. So to do this the polaroids are initially 'crossed'. The solution is added and the angle α found by rotating the analysing polaroid in order to obtain extinction again. Such an instrument is called a polarimeter. The first polaroid used in this way is called a polariser and the second polaroid an analyser.

POLYMERS

◀ Solids ▶

POSITIVE FEEDBACK AND ELECTRICAL OSCILLATIONS

Electronic oscillating circuits are an important use of electronics technology. By using positive feedback, i.e. feedback where the output enhances the input, a free-running oscillator can be produced.

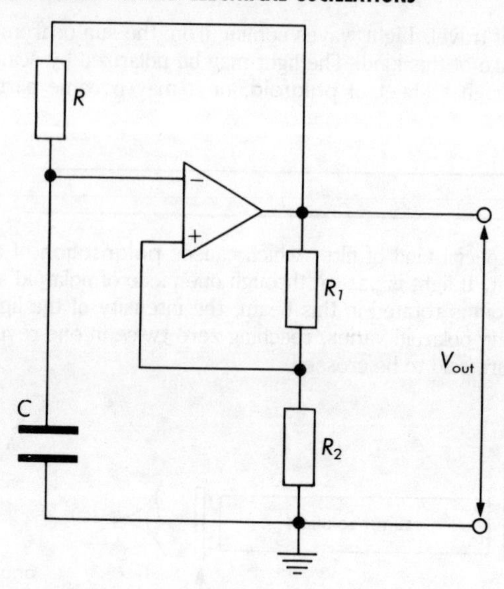

Fig. P.21

The simplest circuit to understand and the easiest to set up is the **relaxation oscillator** (Fig. P.21), which produces a square-wave output and uses an **operational amplifier**. It has the following properties:

a) The circuit has two possible output states.
b) Except at cross-over points the op. amp. operates as a differential amplifier with a saturated output which is either positive or negative.
c) The resistors R_1 and R_2 act as a voltage divider to determine the point at which cross-over occurs.
d) The switching frequency is determined by the time constant RC.

Consider the following simple example. If the capacitor is initially uncharged the voltage at the inverting terminal, V_-, is zero. V_{out} may be either positive or negative. If positive, a fraction of its voltage will be fed back to the non-inverting terminal holding this positive. Because of the high gain of the op.amp. the effect of this will be to hold V_{out} in a saturated state at + V_s. Equally V_{out} may be negative. The same argument then holds and V_{out} will be held at $-V_s$ by this positive feedback loop.

Suppose the output voltage is initially $+V_s$ The behaviour with time is as shown in Fig. P.22. With V_{out} at $+V_s$ volts the capacitor steadily charges through R. As it does, V_- rises until at the moment when it reaches (and just exceeds) the steady value at V_+, $(V_+ - V_-)$ goes negative and so the amplifier switches into its negative saturated state. Because V_{out} is negative V_+ must also be negative, reinforcing this. The capacitor then begins to discharge through R, and continues to do so until it has become negatively charged and reaches (and just gets lower than) the (negative) steady value at V_+. The op. amp. then switches to the positive saturated state.

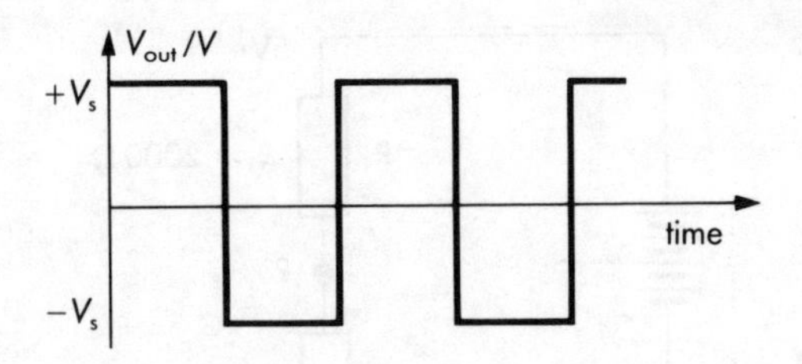

Fig. P.22

Changing the capacitor C will change the cycle time of the oscillator. This is because this depends upon the time constant for discharging the capacitor. Doubling the value of the capacitance will double the cycle time. Changing the ratio of R_1 and R_2 will also change the cycle time. This is because the ratio sets the magnitude of the voltage of V_-, above and below zero at which the system changes state. As R_1 gets smaller with respect to R_2 this voltage gets smaller and so the cycle time will get shorter.

POSITRON

◀ A positive electron ▶

POTENTIAL

◀ Inverse square law fields ▶

POTENTIAL DIFFERENCE (P.D.)

The term potential difference is applied to resistors, light bulbs, motors, heaters, batteries being charged, etc., i.e. devices in which there is a conversion of energy from electrical form to non-electrical. For example, when a lead acid accumulator is charged, energy is converted from electrical form to chemical form. In a light bulb electrical energy is converted into heat and light. The p.d. of the circuit item is measured in volts and is the electrical energy (in joules) given up by one coulomb of electricity passing through the circuit when a current flows. Thus one volt is one joule/coulomb.
◀ Electromotive force (e.m.f.), Internal resistance ▶

POTENTIAL DIVIDER

A potential divider is part of an electrical circuit designed to split up the supply potential difference into more appropriate values. It is essentially two **resistors** in series connected across the power rails of a circuit. Because the resistors are in series the current through both resistors is the same and

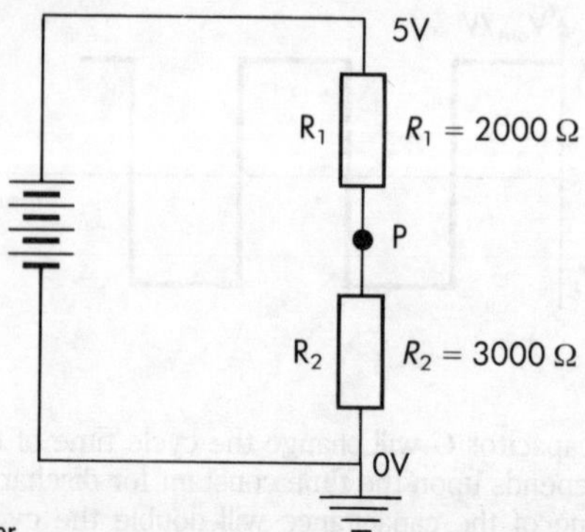

Fig. P.23 Potential divider

hence the potential difference across each resistance is proportional to its resistance.

In Fig. P.23 the p.d. across R_1 will be 2 volts and that across R_2 will be 3 volts. In electronic circuits the midpoint P will be connected to some other component such as one of the inputs of an operational amplifier or the base of a transistor. R_2 might be a variable resistor, such as a light-dependent resistor (LDR). When light shines on the LDR the resistance falls, and so as the ratio of resistances changes the potential at P changes.

◀ Potentiometer, Resistors in series ▶

POTENTIAL ENERGY

The term potential energy is first encountered in mechanics, where it is the **energy** due to the position of a body in a gravitational field, and referred to some level chosen as zero. The higher a body is up a hill the more potential energy it has. Hence in elementary books it is sometimes called 'uphill energy'.

The weight of a body of mass m is mg. So to raise it a height h, work of amount $Fh = mgh$ has to be done. This is then the potential energy stored in joules and available for release if the mass were to revert to its lower position. Writing this potential energy as U we have the formula $U = mgh$, where h is the height above the (arbitrary) zero position.

More generally, potential energy can be a term which is used with other types of stored energy, e.g. energy stored in a spring, in an electric field or in a magnetic field.

◀ Inverse square law fields ▶

POTENTIOMETER

The potentiometer is essentially the same as the **potential divider** but uses one resistance with a slide contact to divide it effectively into two **resistors**. The potential at the point P connected to the slider depends upon the ratio of

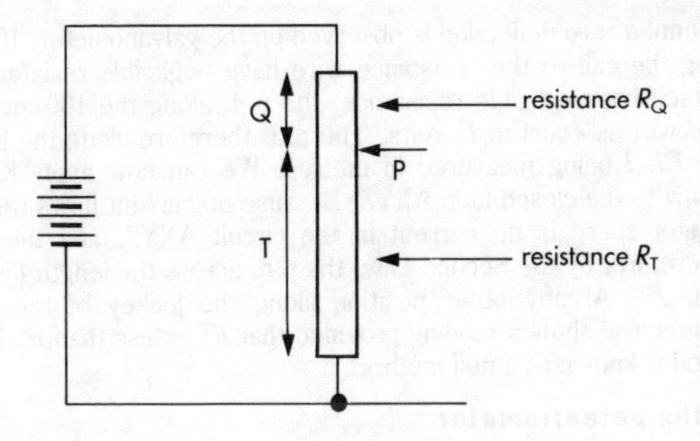

Fig. P.24 Potentiometer

the two effective resistances R_Q and R_T so formed (Fig. P.24). As with the potential divider a current flowing through from P must be negligible, so that the two resistors can be treated as though they are in series. In practical physics the potentiometer is encountered in two forms. In electronics it will take the form of a miniature device with a carbon track and will be used in circuits to generate a varying voltage which can be supplied through some other component such as a **logic gate**, an **operational amplifier**, or the base of a **transistor**.

It will be also encountered as a piece of resistance wire, usually a metre long, fixed between two points A and B with a cell (battery) of e.m.f. E connected between the two ends. And in this form it is used for a number of measurements in d.c. electrical work.

Consider the circuit shown in Fig. P.25. The potentiometer, i.e. the metre bridge wire and the cell, is connected to another source of e.m.f. E', a galvanometer and a sliding contact (or jockey). The position of the jockey

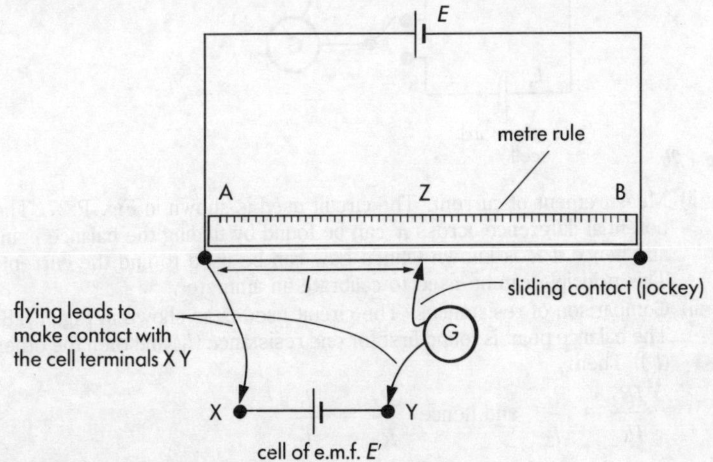

Fig. P.25 Slide-wire potentiometer

is varied until a zero deflection is observed on the galvanometer. If the leads connecting the cell to the resistance wire have negligible resistance and if the cell itself has negligible resistance, the p.d. along the 100 cm length of resistance wire is equal to E volts. The p.d. therefore along the length l is therefore El, l being measured in metres. We can now apply **Kirchhoff's** Second Law to the closed loop AXYZ. Because no current flows through the galvanometer there is no current in the circuit AXYZ, and therefore no p.d.s. Therefore, by the Second Law, the p.d. across the length l is equal to the e.m.f. E'. At any other position along the jockey of the wire the galvanometer will show a reading provided that E' is less than E. Note that this method is known as a **null method**.

Uses of the potentiometer

i) Absolute measurement of e.m.f. The circuit used is shown in Fig. P.26. E' is the unknown e.m.f. and E_s is the e.m.f. of a standard cell, usually a weston cadmium cell having an e.m.f. of 1.0186 V. The balance point is first found with the standard cell and then with the unknown cell. The ratio of e.m.f.s is then found from: $E'/E_s = l'/l_s$, where l_s is the balance point with the standard cell and l' is the balance point with the unknown cell.

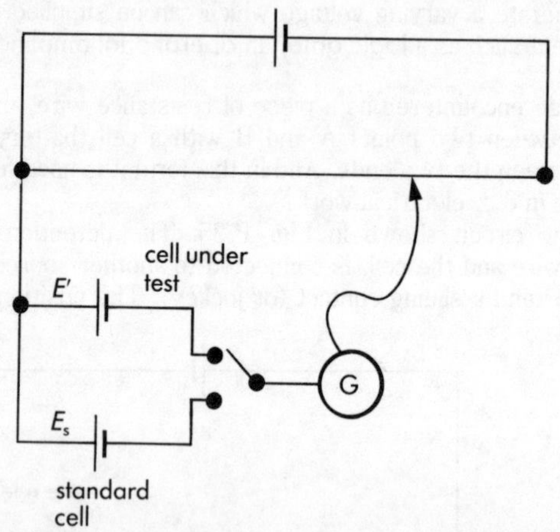

Fig. P.26

ii) Measurement of current. The circuit used is shown in Fig. P.27. The potential difference across R can be found by finding the balance point and hence if R is known Ohm's Law can be used to find the current. This principle can be used to calibrate an ammeter.

iii) Comparison of resistances. The circuit used is as shown in Fig. P.28. The balance point is found first for one resistance (l_1) and then the other (l_2). Then:

$$\frac{IR_1}{IR_2} = \frac{l_1}{l_2} \quad \text{and hence} \quad \frac{R_1}{R_2} = \frac{l_1}{l_2}$$

where I is the current flowing.

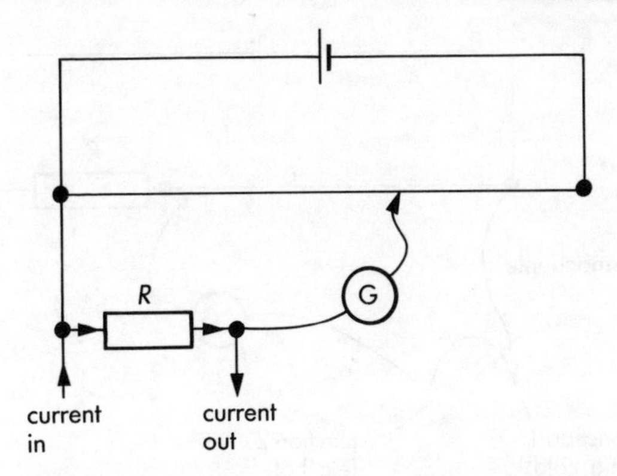

Fig. P.27

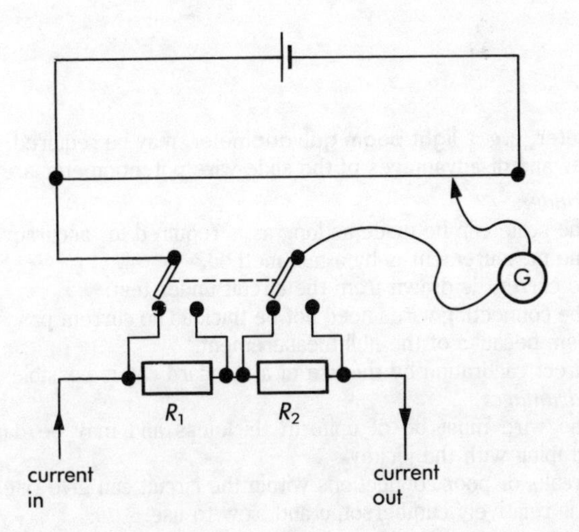

Fig. P.28

iv) The measurement of very small e.m.f.s. With a very small e.m.f. of only a few mV like that produced by a **thermocouple** the balance point would be very close to one end of the wire and therefore very difficult to measure. In order to increase the sensitivity a resistance R is placed in series with the potentiometer wire (Fig. P.29). The resistance of the wire and the resistance R have to be known. Suppose the resistance of the wire is 2 Ω and that of the series resistor 998 Ω, then the total resistance is 1,000 Ω making it equivalent to a wire 1000/2 = 500 m long. With a cell of e.m.f. 2V the balance point of 40.6 cm corresponds therefore to a voltage of $\frac{0.406}{500} \times 2 = 1.62\,\text{mV}$. The currents which flow in off-balance positions are very small and so a very sensitive

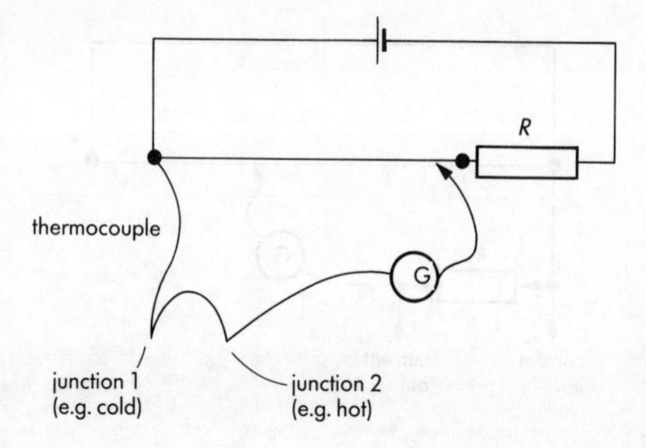

Fig. P.29

galvanometer, e.g. a **light-beam galvanometer**, may be required. The advantages and disadvantages of the slide-wire potentiometer are:

- *Advantages*
  1 The scale can be made as long as is required for accuracy.
  2 The measurement is by a null method.
  3 No current is drawn from the circuit under test.
  4 The connecting wires need not be thick as no current passes through them because of the null measurement.
  5 Direct calibration by the use of a standard cell is possible.
- *Disadvantages*
  1 The wire must be of uniform thickness and may be damaged by scraping with the jockey.
  2 Breaks or poor connections within the circuit can give rise to faults.
  3 It is relatively cumbersome and slow to use.

POWER

This is a term used in mechanics and energy theory. It is defined as the rate of doing **work**. Its unit is the watt which is a rate of doing work of $1 \mathrm{J\,s^{-1}}$. When a force moves forward at a constant velocity v

Power $= F \times v$.

PRESSURE

This is defined as force/area over which the force acts. The units are pascals (Pa) or $\mathrm{N\,m^{-2}}$

◀ Pressure in fluids ▶

PRESSURE IN FLUIDS

Pressure is force/area. Application of this principle to a right circular cylinder gives the **manometer** formula (Fig. P.30).

If the cylinder is filled with a liquid of density ρ we get

$$\text{mass} = \text{volume} \times \text{density}$$
$$= Ah \times \rho$$
$$\text{weight} = Ah\rho g, \text{ so pressure } p = Ah\rho g/A = h\rho g$$

Empirically it is found

i) that $p = h\rho g$ applies for all geometries, not just a circular cylinder (Fig. P.32);
ii) that the pressure acts equally in all directions; (Fig. P.31);
iii) that the same results hold for gases.

Note that because of iii) the term 'fluids' is used, which means both liquids and gases.

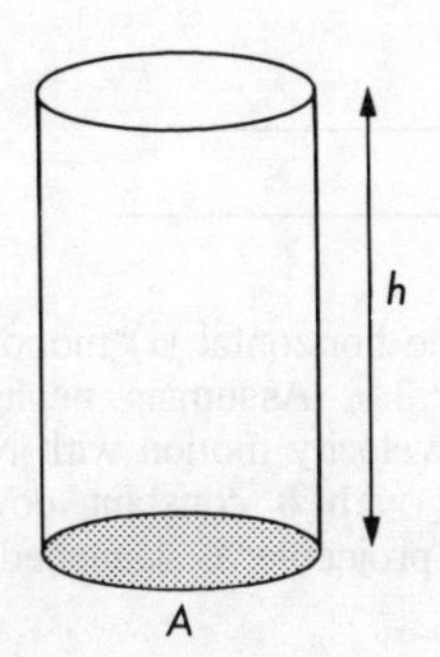

Fig. P.30 Right circular cylinder

Fig. P.31 Pressure acts equally in all directions

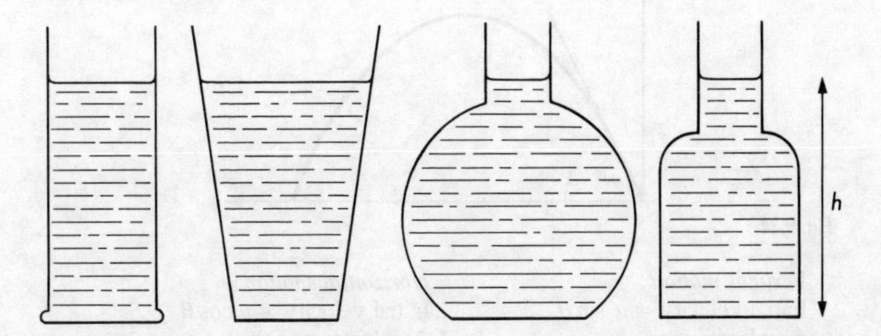

Fig. P.32 Containers of various geometries

PRINCIPAL AXIS

This is a term used in ray optics. It is a line which runs through the midpoint of lenses, mirrors and telescopes etc., and is defined by the fact that rays that are coincident with the principal axis are not deviated in any way, i.e they are not changed in direction. The case of a mirror where a ray travelling along the principal axis is reflected along its incident path is not considered an example of deviation.

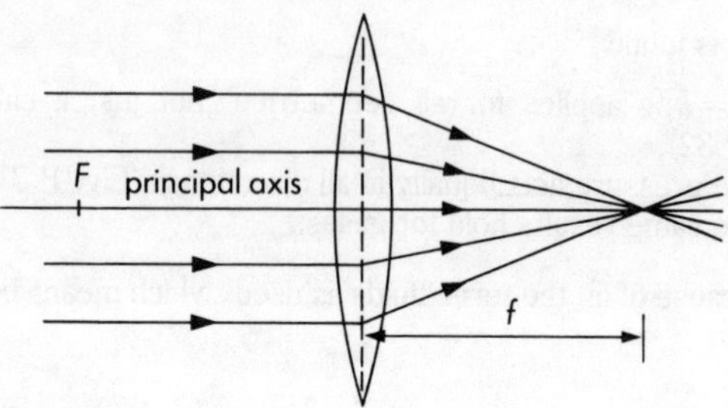

Fig. P.33 Principal axis

PROJECTILE MOTION

This is the motion of bullets, shells etc.

Projectile motion is handled by treating the horizontal (x) motion separately from the vertical (y) motion (Fig. P.34). Assuming negligible air resistance the horizontal motion is constant velocity motion with Newton's First Law. The vertical motion is motion with a constant downwards gravitational acceleration, g. Suppose the projectile is launched with a velocity u at angle θ to the horizontal:

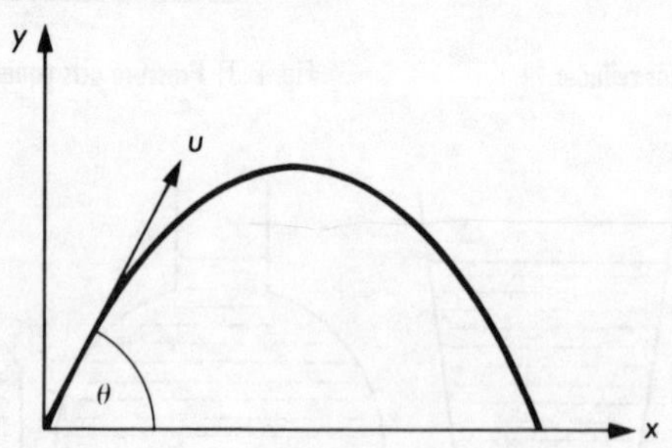

Fig. P.34

Vertical motion
Initial velocity $= u \sin\theta$
Acceleration $= -g$
(minus as positive is taken as upwards)

Horizontal motion
Initial velocity $= u \cos\theta$
Acceleration $= 0$

Vertical motion	*Horizontal motion*
Time taken = t	Time taken = t
Displacement = y	Displacement = x
Using $s = ut + \frac{1}{2}at^2$	Using $s = ut + \frac{1}{2}at^2$
we get $y = u \sin\theta.t - \frac{1}{2}gt^2$	we get $x = u \cos\theta.t$

Eliminating t between these two equations gives the equation of the parabola shown in the diagram above.

From this it can also be shown that, for a level surface, range (maximum horizontal distance travelled) = $u^2 \sin 2\theta/g$, maximum height = $u^2 \sin^2 \theta/2g$ and the time of flight = $2u \sin\theta/g$

◀ Newton's Laws of motion ▶

PROJECTION LENS SYSTEM

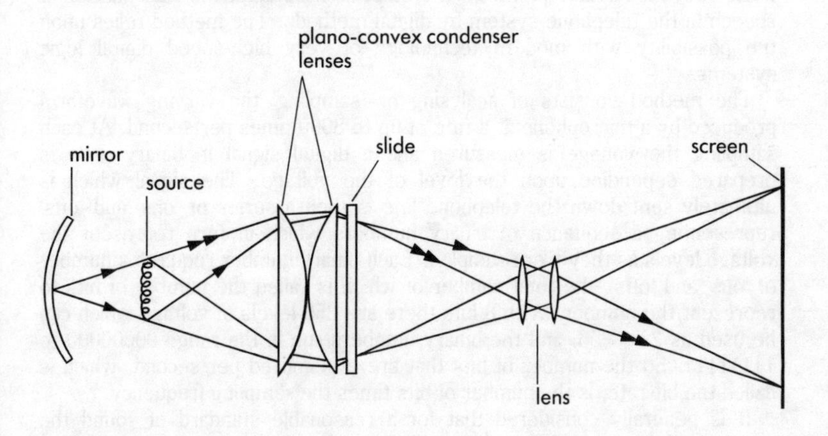

Fig. P.35 Projection lens system (not to scale)

Fig. P.35 shows the layout of lenses in a typical slide projector. A photographic enlarger has a similar arrangement but is usually engineered so that the slide is held horizontally and the screen is replaced by a sheet of photographic paper on a base or table.

Most systems use an intense tungsten light source behind which is a mirror, the source being set at the centre of curvature of the mirror. In this way light emitted from the source both in the forward and backward directions is utilised. The rays from the light source are focused into a parallel beam by two large plano-convex condenser lenses. This ensures that the slide is evenly illuminated. The light passes through the slide, which acts as an object for the lens system which focuses it on to a screen.

◀ Converging lens ▶

PROTON

A positively charged particle found in the nucleus of all atoms.
◀ Nucleus ▶

PROTON NUMBER

The name given to the number of protons in a **nucleus**. It is denoted by Z. The number of protons in the nucleus determines the number of electrons in a neutral atom and this gives rise to the chemical properties of the atom.

PULSE CODE MODULATION

Pulse code modulation (p.c.m.) is a system developed for the transmission of speech in the telephone system by digital methods. The method relies upon the possibility with modern technology of very high-speed digital logic systems.

The method consists of analysing or 'sampling' the varying waveform produced by a microphone at a rate of up to 8000 times per second. At each sampling the voltage is measured and a digital signal in binary code is prepared depending upon the level of the voltage. The signal which is ultimately sent down the telephone line is then a series of 'ons' and 'offs' representing a sequence of binary numbers which in turn represent the voltage levels as they were sampled. Each binary number requires a number of 'ons' and 'offs', the total number of which is called the number of bits to represent the number. With 8 bits there are 256 levels of voltage which can be used as $2^8 = 256$, and the binary numbers run in the range 00000000 to 11111111. So the number of bits that are transmitted per second, which is called the bit-rate, is the number of bits times the sampling frequency.

It is generally considered that for a reasonable standard of sound the sampling frequency should be at least twice as great as the highest frequency in the initially received signal.

At the receiving end of the system the process is carried out in reverse and the analogue signal is reconstructed.

The disadvantage of sending an analogue signal down a telephone line is that over very long distances the signal may be distorted because of noise and the fact that different frequencies may be attenuated by different amounts or even travel at slightly different speeds. Once a signal has become distorted in this way it is very difficult to improve it. However, if a digital signal is sent down a line, noise and distortion is not such a problem. Even if the signal is badly distorted, as long as the 'ons' and the 'offs' can be recognised, even in a dirty signal, it is possible to regenerate the pattern of pulses so that the overall effect is that there has been no distortion at all. Thus in a very long telephone line there might be several stations at which this kind of regeneration took place. In this way there is no distortion of the signal after reconversion to analogue form at the receiving station.

Q-FACTOR

◀ Forced oscillations, Radio ▶

QUANTUM MECHANICAL MODEL OF THE ATOM

This is the modern model of the atom in which the electrons are treated as **standing waves** trapped in the atom.

The idea developed in the 1920s from de Broglie's suggestion that matter can behave either as particles or as waves. The idea became called wave mechanics or quantum mechanics: quantum because only certain limited states or standing waves are allowed. We can consider the case of hydrogen. This is a comparatively simple system because there is only one electron in the atom. The electron is trapped by a $1/r$ potential well.

The curve in Fig. Q.1 represents the variation of potential energy of the electron at a distance r from the nucleus. The dotted line represents the total energy of the electron. Thus its kinetic energy is the difference between the total energy and the potential energy. Two values of kinetic energy are shown on the diagram: these clearly indicate that the kinetic energy of the electron must increase as it approaches the nucleus. De Broglie's relation is

$$mv = h/\lambda$$

where m is the mass of the electron, v its velocity, h the Planck constant and λ the wavelength. Thus as the electron approaches the nucleus the momentum, mv, increases and so the wavelength of the electron decreases. The standing wave is therefore unlike those studied in mechanical vibrations and sound, as it is a standing wave with a wavelength which varies with the distance from the centre of the atom.

Fig. Q.2 shows a typical possible standing wave for an electron in the hydrogen atom. It should be apparent from this diagram that the wavelength is increasing with distance from the centre of the atom.

Once such a standing wave like this has been calculated it needs to be given some meaning, and here we move into an area which has always been a source of controversy in physics. In the standard interpretation of quantum

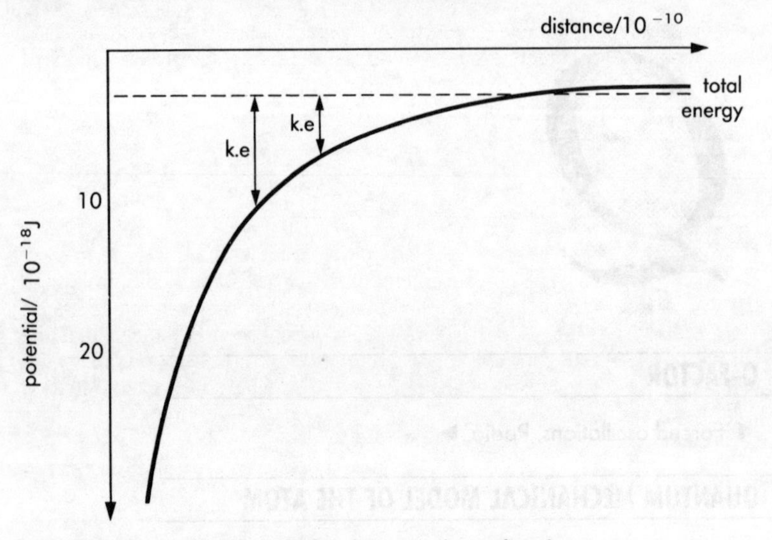

Fig. Q1 Variations of potential energy of an electron at a distance from the proton

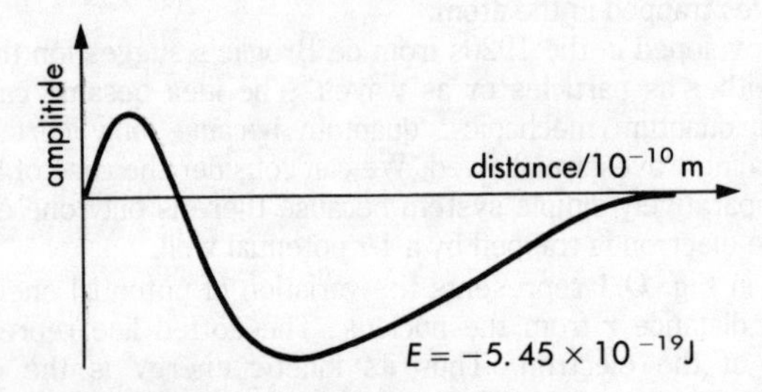

Fig. Q2 Electron two loop standing wave within the hydrogen atom

mechanics the standing wave is understood to be a 'probability' wave. That is to say the amplitude is an indication of the probability of finding the electron at any point in the atom. So, interpreting the diagram of Fig. Q.2, we would say that there was a strong probability of finding the electron at an x-value corresponding to the peak of the curve, a zero probability where the graph crosses the x-axis and a high probability of finding it further out still. This interpretation arises from the fact that when we go looking for electrons we find either 'whole' electrons or none at all: we never find 'half-electrons'.

It should be noted that the probability of finding the electron is greatest at 5×10^{-10} m, which is sometimes regarded as the 'radius' of the atom.

In quantum mechanics the standing waves are found by solving differential equations which were first developed by the German physicist Schrodinger. Such equations are called *Schrodinger equations*. The detail of this theory lies outside the scope of this book. Suffice it to say that quantum mechanics based upon the Schrodinger equations provide very exact descriptions of the experimentally measurable properties of atoms. These properties include ionisation and excitation energies, the optical and X-ray spectra, and much of the chemistry of atoms in combination with each other.

◀ Matter waves, Pauli exclusion principle ▶

QUARKS

By the early 1960s thirty or so **elementary particles** had become known. Recurring patterns were noticed among these particles in a similar fashion to the way patterns had been seen among the atomic **elements** in the 1860s. In 1964 Murray Gell-Mann and George Zweig independently noticed that the patterns would arise naturally if all the elementary particles were built from just three varieties of 'sub-elementary' particles which they called quarks. Two of these were known as 'up' and 'down' quarks. The third variety was called the strange quark.

Quarks are unusual in that they have electric charges that are fractions of the charge on a proton. For example the 'up' quark has charge of +2/3 and the 'down' quark has charge of –1/3. So in this model the proton with charge +1 is formed from two 'up' quarks and one 'down' quark, and the neutron with charge 0 from two 'down' quarks and one 'up' quark. All the **hadrons** have three quarks and particles such as the pions are made from a quark and an antiquark.

Fig. Q.3 shows the use of icons for depicting quark combinations as developed by Alvaro de Rujula and Frank Close.

Quarks remain elusive entities in that they have never been seen individually. Since quark theory began other quarks have been added to the original three described here in order to explain the increasing number of 'elementary particles' which have been discovered.

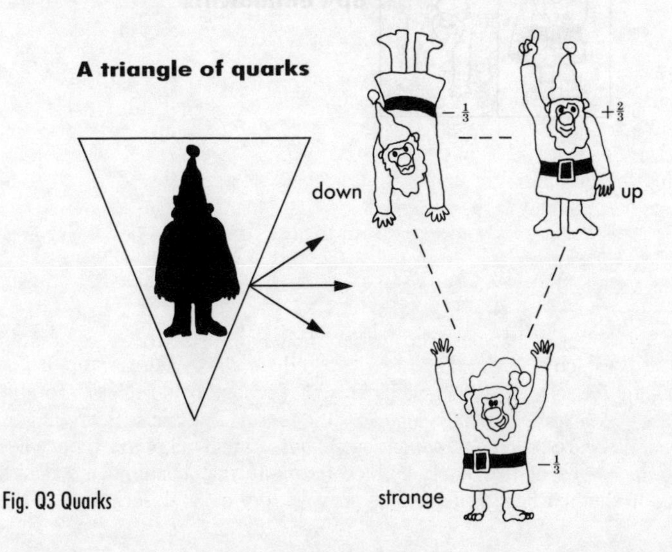

Fig. Q3 Quarks

The existence of strange particles is due to the fact that quarks as originally conceived occur in three varieties: up, down, or strange. In this scheme quark plus antiquark yield nine possibilities. Examples are the proton and the neutron.

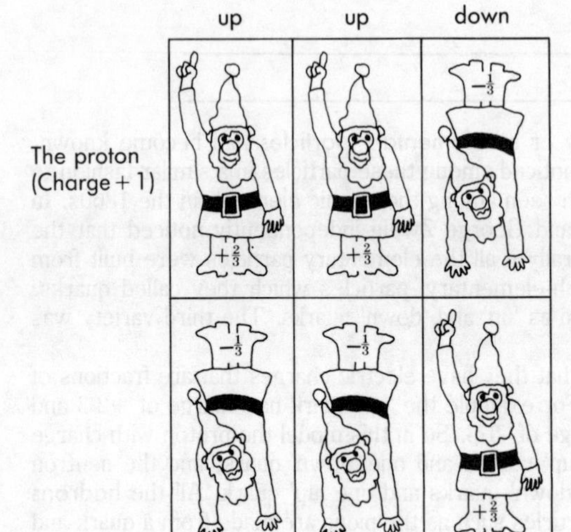

Up and down quarks and antiquarks build the pi-mesons.

up + antidown:π^+

RAD

◀ Radioactivity: units of measurement ▶

RADIAL ELECTRICAL FIELDS

The electric field of a single point charge is radial, with field lines radiating away from the charge if it is positive and towards it if it is negative. Fig. I.16 (page 200) shows an example of the case of positive charge. A much more important case is the field of a sphere of charge. The sphere might be a metal sphere, a planet made of conducting material or the dome of a Van de Graaff generator.

It is an interesting and direct consequence of the inverse square law that: i) in the region outside the sphere, the field is exactly the same as if all the charge were concentrated at the centre of the sphere; ii) within the sphere itself the field is zero. For this second point refer to Fig. R.1. Consider the point P in this diagram. Two cones have been drawn outwards in opposite directions from this point, one intersecting the sphere at X and the other at Y. The charge on the surface at X will exert a force in the direction XPY and that at Y will exert a force in the direction YPX. It is obvious that there is more charge at the cone/sphere intersection at X than there is at the equivalent intersection at Y. But the charge at X is further away from P than that at Y. It can be shown mathematically that the effect of the inverse square law is to give exact cancellation of the effects of the charge at X and at Y. The total effect of all the charge on the sphere can be found by

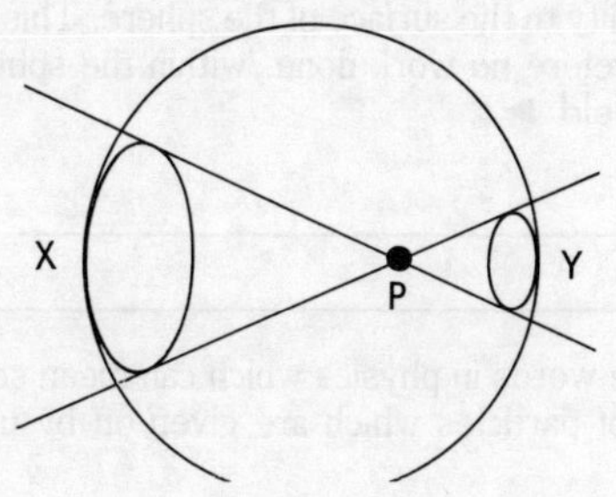

Fig. R.1

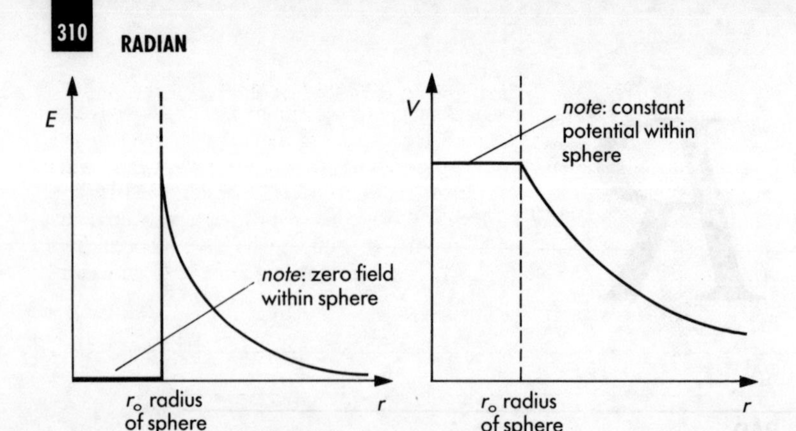

Fig. R.2

Fig. R.3

considering all the possible cones in all the directions of three-dimensional space.

As a result the graphs of field and potential as a function of a distance, r, from the centre of such a sphere are shown in Figs. R.2 and R.3. The entry **Inverse square law fields** explains that the field is always equal to minus the rate of change of potential with distance, i.e.

$$E = \frac{-\mathrm{d}V}{\mathrm{d}r}$$

There are two important consequences of this result for the potential, V.

i) At external points V is inversely proportional to the distance from the centre of the sphere, i.e.
$V = Q/4\pi\epsilon_0 r$
where Q is the charge on the sphere. (Note a $1/r$ dependence, unlike the $1/r^2$ dependence for E).

ii) The potential within the sphere is constant at the value at the surface. This is because in accordance with the definition of potential and potential energy no further work is done in moving a test charge once it has been brought from infinity to the surface of the sphere. This is because there is no field, and therefore no work done, within the sphere.

◀ Uniform electric field ▶

RADIATION

Radiation is one of the words in physics which can mean several things. It can mean the emissions of particles which are given off by unstable radioactive atoms, i.e. it can mean **alpha, beta**, or **gamma radiation**. It is also used to mean one of the forms of electromagnetic radiation, i.e. radio emission, microwaves, light, X-rays. Often it means one of the ways in which heat is transferred from one body to another. This is **thermal radiation**, and when this term is used it is electromagnetic radiation having wavelengths largely in the infrared region that is implied. It should, however, be remembered that all electromagnetic radiations carry energy. People who have stood in front of radar beams at RAF stations say it is like standing in front of an electric fire!

RADIO

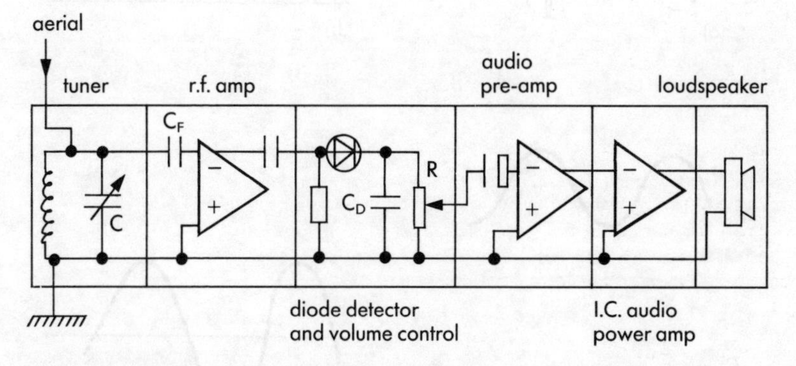

Fig. R.4 Simple radio

Fig. R.4 shows the block diagram of a simple **amplitude modulation** radio receiver. It has been drawn as a series of interconnecting modules each of which has a specific function.

From the left, the first module is the tuner. This consists of an inductor and a capacitor which form an a.c. resonant circuit (see **Resonance**). The frequency of resonance is determined by the amount of the inductance and the capacitance. In most radio sets this is adjusted by the use of a variable air-core capacitor. The circuit then responds to a particular frequency. Electromagnetic waves pass the aerial and the electric field of such waves causes currents in the aerial. Those which are at the frequency of resonance of the tuner circuit caused **forced oscillations** of that circuit. Because of amplitude modulation the signal received is that shown in Fig. R.5a). The Q-factor of the tuner must not be so large that the circuit is unable to accept the band width of the radio frequency signal.

The tuner is coupled to the next module, which is the radio frequency amplifier. Coupling is done by the capacitor C_F. The function of this module is simply to amplify the radio frequency signal, which is then passed to the **diode** detector and volume control module. Diode detection is sometimes called demodulation. The effect of the diode is simply to cut off the bottom part of the received r.f. signal so that it now looks like that shown in Fig.

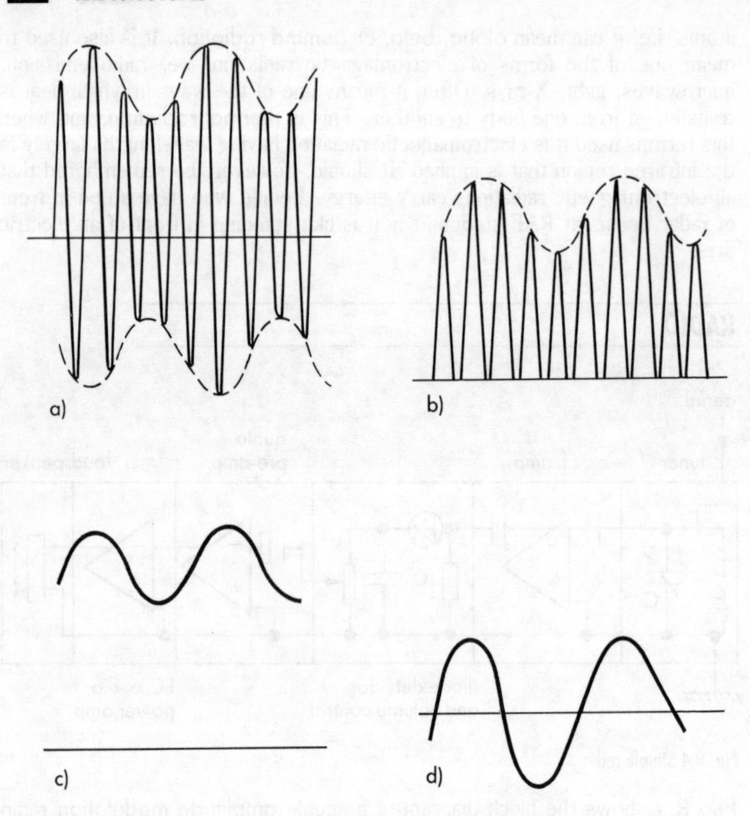

Fig. R.5

R.5b). It is then smoothed by the action of the capacitor C_D, so that the signal which is then formed is like that shown in Fig. R.5 c). This voltage is developed across the resistor R and the volume control is achieved by moving the slider up and down to tap off what is needed for the next stage. This next module is the audio frequency preamplifier. Again there is coupling by a capacitor, this time an electrolytic one of high value, so that the audiofrequency signal is passed but the d.c. component is eliminated (Fig. R.5 d)). This amplified signal is then passed to a power amplifier, the output of which develops sufficient current to drive the loudspeaker.

◀ Half-wave dipole aerial ▶

RADIOISOTOPES

◀ Isotopes ▶

RADIO TELESCOPE

Radio astronomers use both dish and antennae type telescopes. The latter are very similar to the kinds of aerial used to receive television signals, except that a radio astronomer will use a large array of these. Sometimes they are laid out along a track of several kilometres and used as an interferometer in a method with some similarity to that used for dishes as described below.

By contrast the dish telescope is very similar to an optical **reflecting telescope**. The dish replaces the objective mirror of the telescope. It has to be constructed either of wire mesh or solid metal plates. Either way the dish needs to be fashioned to within about 1/20 of the wavelength of radiation to be detected. The electronic technology of the detector is very similar to that used in domestic satellite dish aerial systems.

The main difference between the radio and the optical telescope is the poor resolution of a radio telescope compared with an optical one. For resolving power see **Rayleigh's criterion**, where it is shown that the limit of resolution is $= 1.22\ \lambda/d$. This same formula applies to a radio telescope and indicates that as radio waves are so very much longer than light waves huge diameters would be necessary to obtain the same resolution.

To overcome this kind of problem astronomers have sought alternative solutions which involve the use of interferometry. In its simplest form this method involves using two dish telescopes at separate locations a distance D apart. D may be as low as tens of metres but can be as high as the diameter of the earth. The telescopes are pointed to the same place in the sky. The signals received by the two receivers are out of phase because of the differences in the optical path length back to the source being detected. As the earth rotates on its axis this phase difference changes.

The technique, therefore, requires equipment which can detect and store this phase difference. This either requires the use of cables linking the two telescopes or the recording of the data on magnetic storage systems (i.e. tape or floppy disks). If the latter method is used it is necessary to also record pulses from a standard electronic clock. In this way the two separate recordings can be 'lined up' with each other when the data is subsequently analysed and the phase differences can be extracted. Several experiments are usually performed with a range of different values of D. All the information collected is then processed by a computer. The overall effect is that of having resolution of a telescope of diameter of the same order of magnitude as the maximum value of D.

RADIO TRANSMISSION

Radio waves travel between a transmitter and a receiver by four different routes depending upon wavelengths. They can travel over the surface of the earth in what is called a 'ground' wave; directly from the transmitter to the receiver in what is called a 'space' wave; and by reflection from the ionosphere by what is called a 'sky' wave; or waves may be reflected or relayed from a satellite.

Ground wave

A ground wave travels along the surface of the earth, following its curvature. The range is fairly small and is limited by the extent to which there is attenuation, that is a steady reduction of the signal with distance, due to energy absorption. Absorption increases with frequency, and so although the range may be about 1,000 km for low frequencies it is very short for very high frequency (v.h.f.)

Space wave

Space waves are used with v.h.f., ultra high frequency (u.h.f.) and microwave signals. There has to be a clear line of sight between the aerial and the transmitter, so that the range is fairly limited and depends upon the positioning of both the aerial and the receiver.

Sky wave

Before the advent of satellite communication sky waves were the only way of transmitting signals right the way round the earth. The method depends upon the signals bouncing backwards and forwards between the ground and the *ionosphere*. The ionosphere consists of a number of layers of ionised air molecules which will become charged through the action of solar ultraviolet radiation. V.h.f. waves travel through the ionosphere into outer space but waves of lower frequency, typically those of the long, medium and short wave systems used in radio, are reflected. When signals are sent over very long distances with many reflections, the quality of signal depends heavily upon a state of ionisation of the ionosphere and reception can change markedly over a time scale of only a few minutes.

Reflection or retransmission by satellite

Radio signals can be reflected by satellite but more commonly are received by satellite and retransmitted back to earth. An important kind of satellite is the geostationary satellite which orbits above the earth's equator once every twenty-four hours and thus is stationary with respect to the earth. In order to do this, the satellite has to be at a height of approximately 36 000 km and thus can be seen over a wide range of latitudes. Because of this great altitude it would only be necessary to have three satellites to cover the entire surface of the earth.

RADIOACTIVE DECAY LAW

The radioactive decay law is a way of describing macroscopically the process of radioactive decay which occurs randomly at the microscopic level.

The decay process is a random one in the sense that each atom of a particular source has a fixed chance of decaying in any second. This chance is called the decay constant, λ. It seems that there is no way of knowing which particular atoms will disintegrate in any second, but with a source containing a very large number of atoms it is possible to predict how many on average will decay in a second. It can be compared with throwing a very large number of dice and knowing there is no way of forseeing which particular dice will turn up as sixes. Nevertheless it is possible to predict that on average one sixth of them will be sixes because each die has the same one sixth chance of being a six.

We assume that the number of radioactive nuclei, dN, decaying in time dt, is proportional to the number, N, present at that instant in time. Thus we write $\mathrm{d}N = -\lambda N\,\mathrm{d}t$. The negative sign shows that the number of radioactive nuclei decreases with time. Note that $\mathrm{d}N/\mathrm{d}t$ is called the activity of the sample. Thus we get

$$\int \frac{\mathrm{d}N}{N} = -\int \lambda\,\mathrm{d}t$$

which on integration gives

$$N = N_0\,\mathrm{e}^{-\lambda t}$$

where N_0 is the number of undecayed nuclei at time $t = 0$.

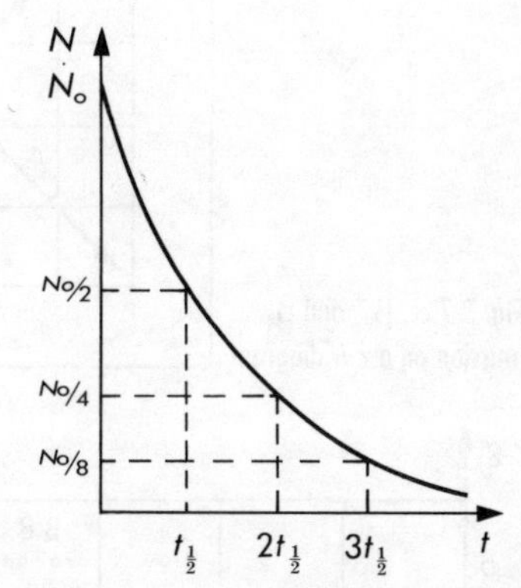

Fig. R.6 Radioactive decay curve

Fig. R.6 shows the graph of $N = N_0\,\mathrm{e}^{-\lambda t}$. The curve is a falling exponential curve. Note that after a time of one half-life, $t_{\frac{1}{2}}$, the number of atoms remaining is $N_0/2$. This feature characterises the whole curve, so that after $2t_{\frac{1}{2}}$ there are $N_0/4$ atoms remaining and so on. So, $N_0/2 = \mathrm{N}_0\mathrm{e}^{-\lambda t_{\frac{1}{2}}}$ and hence $t_{\frac{1}{2}} = \ln 2/\lambda$. Note that a large value of λ means a short half-life, because at any particular time there is a large rate of decay for a given number of atoms. Another way of handling the data is to plot ln (N) against t. This gives a straight-line graph of the negative gradient.

The term half-life, $t_{\frac{1}{2}}$, is usually applied to isotopes which are alpha and beta emitters. In gamma ray physics it is more common to use the term life time, τ. Here the exponential decay law is described by $N = \mathrm{N}_0\mathrm{e}^{-t/\tau}$ and hence τ is the time for the number of atoms N to fall to N_0/e.

◀ Alpha radiation, Beta radiation, Gamma radiation ▶

RADIOACTIVE DECAY SERIES

When a radioactive isotope decays it produces a daughter product which, if also radioactive, will decay and produce a daughter product and so on. Eventually this process will cease with the production of a stable isotope. This is called a radioactive decay series.

The emission of an alpha particle from a radioisotope reduces the **proton number** Z by 2 and the **neutron number** N by two. In β^- emission a neutron turns into a proton. Consequently N decreases by 1 and Z increases by 1. β^+ emission increases N by 1 and reduces Z by 1. α emission reduces both Z and N by 2. The emission of gamma radiation has no effect on N or Z. These movements are shown in Fig. R.7.

As an example, helium-6 decays by β-emission to lithium-6, one of the two stable isotopes of lithium (Fig. R.8). The half-life for this process is 802 ms.

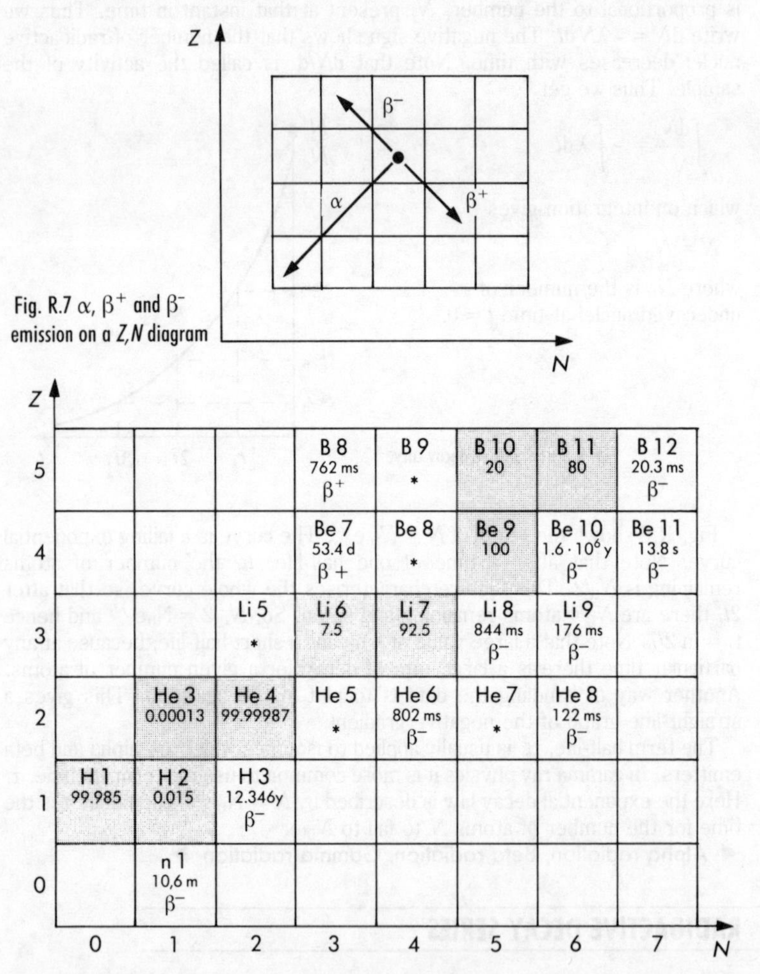

Fig. R.7 α, β^+ and β^- emission on a Z,N diagram

Fig. R.8 Z,N diagram for light isotopes. Stable isotopes are indicated in grey and percentage abundances are marked. For example, 7.5 per cent of lithium is lithium-6. The half-lives of unstable isotopes are given. Isotopes marked with an asterisk have exceedingly short half-lives but are thought to exist.

(Note that diagrams of Z against nucleon number A are sometimes used. On a Z,A diagram β^- emission causes an upward movement of one space, β^+ emission causes a downward movement of one space, and α emission causes a movement down two places and four places to the left. This is shown in Fig. R.9.)

Sometime after the creation of the starting (parent) isotope all the members of the series will be in equilibrium, that is to say they will be being produced from their own immediate parent at the same rate at which they are decaying and producing their own immediate daughter product, i.e. $N_1\lambda_1 = N_2\lambda_2 = N_3\lambda_3 = \ldots$, where N_1, $N_2, \ldots$ are the equilibrium numbers of atoms of each member of the series and λ_1, λ_2 the respective decay constants. Fig. R.10 shows two radioactive series. Note that to measure the half-life of a member of a series it has to be isolated from its parent, so that when it is decaying it is not also being reproduced at the same time.

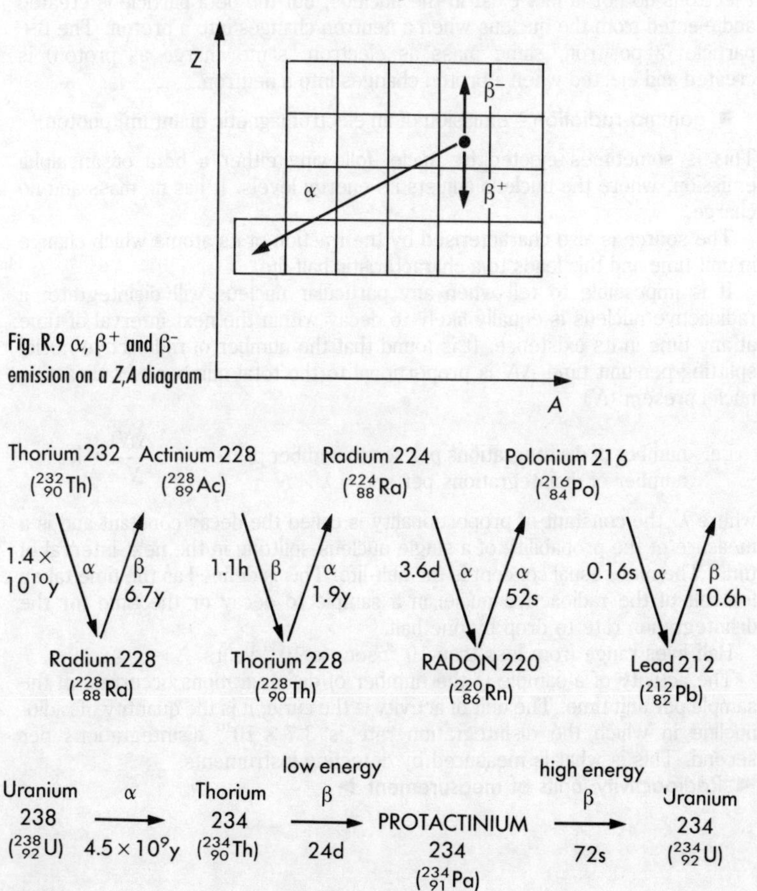

Fig. R.9 α, β^+ and β^- emission on a Z,A diagram

Fig. R.10

RADIOACTIVITY

A radioactive source is a collection of atoms whose nuclei are unstable and have the property of randomly but spontaneously emitting radiation.

Such a source is characterised by its radiations which may be:

- **alpha-radiation** – ejection of a fast moving massive particle

This is a particle, comprising two protons and two neutrons. Hence it has a mass about 8000 times that of the electron and a charge of 3.2×10^{-9} C.

- **beta-radiation** – particle ejection accompanied by anti-neutrino particle

There are in fact two β particles the β− and the β+. The β− is the beta particle normally referred to in A-level questions and it is an electron. Electrons do not in fact exist in the nucleus, but the beta particle is created and ejected from the nucleus when a neutron changes into a proton. The β+ particle (a positron, same mass as electron, same charge as proton) is created and ejected when a proton changes into a neutron.

- **gamma-radiation** – emission of an electromagnetic quantum (photon)

This is sometimes ejected by nuclei following either a beta or an alpha emission, where the nucleus adjusts its energy levels. It has no mass and no charge.

The source is also characterised by the fraction of its atoms which change in unit time and this leads to a characteristic half-life.

It is impossible to tell when any particular nucleus will disintegrate; a radioactive nucleus is equally likely to decay within the next interval of time at any time in its existence. It is found that the number of radioactive nuclei splitting per unit time ΔN is proportional to the total number of radioactive nuclei present (N)

i.e. number of disintegrations per sec to number present $= \dfrac{\Delta N}{N} = \lambda$

number of disintegrations per sec $= \lambda \times N$

where λ, the constant of proportionality is called the decay constant and is a measure of the probability of a single nucleus splitting in the next interval of time. The more usual concept is the half-life. This is defined as the time taken for half of the radioactive nuclei in a sample to decay or the time for the disintegration rate to drop by one half.

Half lives range from less than 10^{-20} sec. to 10^{20} years.

The activity of a sample is the number of disintegrations occurring in the sample per unit time. The unit of activity is the curie; it is the quantity of radionuclide in which the disintegration rate is 3.7×10^{10} disintegrations per second. This is what is measured by detecting instruments.

◀ Radioactivity: units of measurement ▶

RADIOACTIVITY: UNITS OF MEASUREMENT

Measurement of the activity of a source

The activity of any radioactive sample may be measured by photographic films, Geiger counters or scintillation counters, etc. It is measured in disintegrations, of any type, α, β or γ, per second. 1 disintegration per second (d.p.s.) is known as a *Becquerel* (Bq). 3.7×10^{10} Bq is termed 1 *Curie* (Ci). This is roughly equivalent to the activity of 1 g pure radium, and is a very high activity. Biologists often use the μCi, which is a million times smaller (3.7×10^4 Bq). Notice that Bq and Ci are independent of the size of the sample. They are not specific activities.

Measurement of biological effects

We first need to measure the amount of radiation to which the tissue has been subjected. This can be expressed as the amount of energy given to a unit mass of tissue. It is called the Absorbed Dose and its unit is the *Gray* (Gy), which is equivalent to 1 joule per kilogram. The previously used unit was the *rad*, standing for *r*adiation *a*bsorbed *d*ose. It is equivalent to 0.01 joule per kilogram. These units depend only on the energy of the radiation, irrespective of whether it comes from α, β or γ rays.

But α, β or γ rays have different physical properties, so that equal absorbed doses do not produce the same biological effect. α particles, because they are slower and have a greater charge, travel a shorter distance in the tissue and so cause greater damage in a localised area. To obtain a more realistic measure of the radiation dose sustained by the tissue, the absorbed dose (in Gy) is multiplied by a factor of 20 for α particles, and by a factor of 1 for β and γ rays. This gives the *dose equivalent* in units called *Sievert* (Sv). The previously used unit was the *rem*, standing for *r*oentgen *e*quivalent in *m*an, and was similarly derived from the rad.

Summary

Quantity measured	*Old unit*	*New unit*	*Relationship*
Radiation given off by a source	curie (Ci)	becquerel (Bq)	$1\text{Ci} = 3.7 \times 10^{10}$ Bq
Energy received by a unit mass of tissue	rad (rad)	gray (Gy)	1 rad = 0.01 Gy
Biologically damaging energy received by a unit mass of tissue	rem (rem)	sievert (Sv)	1 rem = 0.01 Sv

◀ Biological effects of ionising radiation, Radioactivity ▶

RADIOGRAPHY

This is the term used in medical physics to describe the use of **X-rays** for medical examination.

The usefulness of X-rays, i.e. the fact that they can travel through matter, is a disadvantage when it comes to trying to focus them. Instead of being refracted by a lens or reflected by a mirror they pass straight through. (The exception is in the case of X-rays incident at glancing angles – i.e. i is just less than 90° – at metal surfaces, and as used in X-ray telescopes in astronomy.)

Consequently taking an X-ray photograph of the body is essentially like making a shadowgraph in optics. The source needs to be fairly small and at some distance from the body being examined, and a large photographic plate has to be placed beneath the body. X-rays passing through the body are either absorbed or scattered. The absorption of X-rays by matter depends upon the atomic number, Z, and so bones which contain substances of comparatively high Z number produce comparatively high X-ray absorption. Scattering of X-ray photons also occurs. This is a result of a process called Compton scattering. The scattered X-ray light can be removed by the use of grid as shown in Fig. R.11. This technique is used in the majority of radiographic techniques. By limiting the amount of scattered radiation reaching the film the contrast of the final image is improved. A grid normally has about two or three strips of fine lead per millimetre, about 0.05 mm thick and 5 mm deep.

Prolonged exposure to X-rays is dangerous and so in order to reduce the time for which a patient would have to be exposed to X-rays an *intensifying*

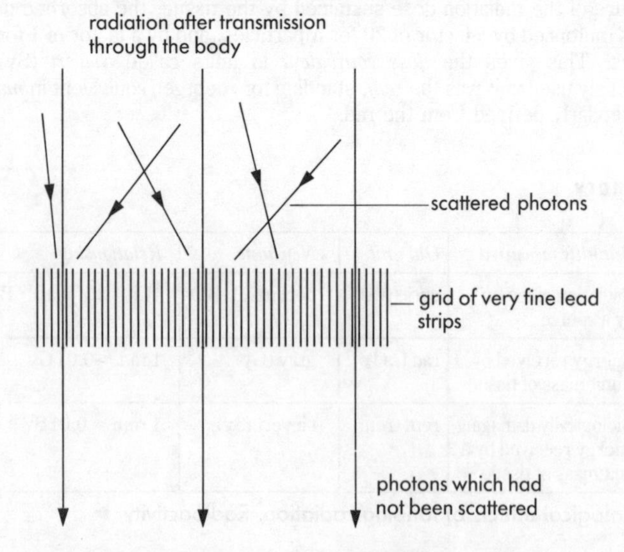

Fig. R.11 Schematic diagram of grid used in radiography to eliminate scattered X-rays

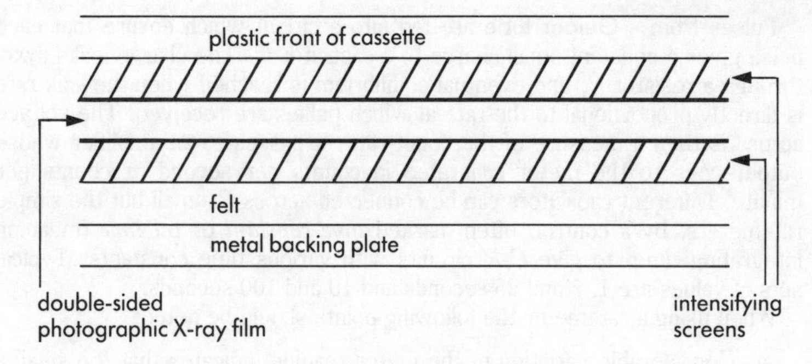

Fig. R.12 Cassette of double-coated X-ray film with intensifying screens

screen is used. An intensifying screen consists of a sheet of card upon which is spread a layer of a fluorescent material in the form of small crystals. The common practice is to use two intensifying screens in a pair held in a sandwich arrangement, with the emulsion on each side of a double-coated X-ray film (Fig. R.12). The X-rays then affect the photographic film directly, but also indirectly as a result of the action of the two screens. X-rays are absorbed in the screen material, which fluoresces giving off visible light which affects the photographic film. Typical intensifying reduces the exposure which would otherwise be necessary by a factor of about 30.

RANGE

The average distance travelled by an ionising particle before it stops.

◀ Alpha radiation, Beta radiation, Gamma radiation ▶

RATEMETER

The ratemeter (Fig. R.13) is an instrument used in the school or college laboratory for measuring the activity of a radioactivity source. It gives a direct reading of counts/second. The count-rate is read directly from a moving-coil meter in the instrument, and usually a loudspeaker is incorporated to register individual clicks as each pulse is registered.

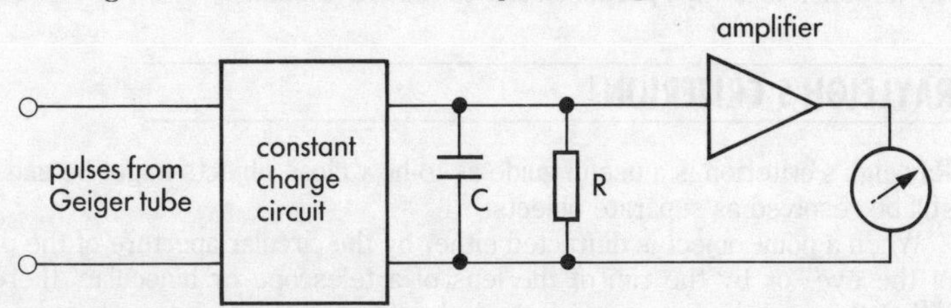

Fig. R.13 Schematic diagram of a ratemeter

Pulses from a **Geiger tube** are fed into a circuit which ensure that each pulse gives a constant small charge to a capacitor C. The charge leaks away through a resistor R, and eventual equilibrium is reached when the leak rate is directly proportional to the rate at which pulses are received. The voltage across is then a measure of the count-rate; it passes to an amplifier whose output goes to the meter calibrated in counts per second or counts per minute. Different capacitors can be connected across R, in all but the simple ratemeters, by a control, often marked *time constant* or *int time* (meaning integrating time) to give C-R circuits with various time constants. Typical sets of values are 1, 5 and 25 seconds and 10 and 100 seconds.

When using a ratemeter the following points should be noted:

a) Considerable variation of the meter reading indicates that too small a time constant is being used, making it difficult to estimate the count-rate. Low count-rates require a large time constant.
b) Once the time constant has been selected, a reading cannot be taken until equilibrium is attained. For this, five time constants must elapse, i.e., about 2 minutes for a time constant of 25 seconds.
c) When the ratemeter has been brought into equilibrium the problem remains of taking a reading which is varying because of the random nature of radioactive decay. A convenient procedure is to make an estimate of the average reading over a period equal to about twice the time constant in use.

Modern **scalars** often have a device for counting for a fixed interval of time before pausing to display the count. Such devices can replace the ratemeter.

RAY

This is a term used in the theory of light. A ray is a narrow pencil of light which travels in a straight line except at places where it is reflected or refracted. Most of the behaviour of lenses, mirrors and optical instruments can be explained in terms of rays.

Ray theory can only really be applied when **diffraction** effects can be neglected. This is because diffraction is the very opposite of ray behaviour. It is the spreading out of light and the bending of light round corners.

The link between ray optics and wave optics is made by considering the ray at the direction in which the waves propagate. In simple wave theory the ray direction is always perpendicular to the **wavefront**.

RAYLEIGH'S CRITERION

Rayleigh's criterion is a useful guide as to how close objects might be and yet still be resolved as separate objects.

When a point object is diffracted either by the circular aperture of the pupil of the eye, or by the rim of the lens of a telescope or binocular, there is **diffraction** and the image consists of a bright central circular patch surrounded by alternate dark and bright rings. This means that if there are two objects very close to each other it might be difficult to distinguish them if their diffracted patterns overlap. Rayleigh suggested that the limit on resolution would be when the first minimum of one pattern overlapped the central maximum of the other (Fig. R.14). Thus if θ is the angle between the two point objects, we have in this limit $\theta = \sin^{-1}(1.22\ \lambda/d)$, where d is the diameter of the viewing aperture.

This criterion is important in astronomy. The result extends to radio-astronomy. Here the wavelengths used are much longer than those of light, e.g. 60 cm rather than 600 nm. In radioastronomy a reflecting telescope is used rather than one with a 'lens'. Nevertheless it is the diameter of the reflector which determines the resolution. Application of the formula $\theta = \sin^{-1}\left(1.22\frac{\lambda}{d}\right)$ shows why very large dishes have to be used if anything like the resolution of the eye or an optical telescope is to be obtained.

◀ Diffraction from a circular aperture ▶

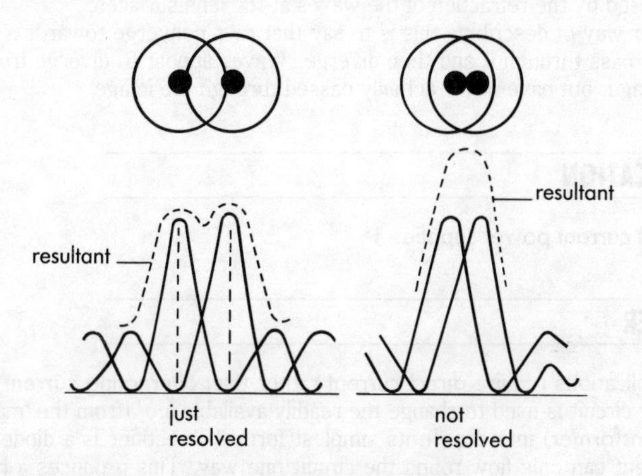

Fig. R.14 Rayleigh's criterion for the resolution of two point objects

REACTANCE

Reactance is the ratio of voltage to current (peak or r.m.s.) in an **alternating current** circuit which contains either a pure capacitor or a pure inductor. It is analogous to **resistance** in d.c. theory, i.e. reactance, $X = V_0/I_0 = V_{\text{r.m.s.}}/I_{\text{r.m.s.}}$.

It has the same units as resistance, i.e. it is measured in ohms. Note that in these cases the current and voltage are 90 degrees ($\pi/2$ radians) out of phase.

For an inductor $X = \omega L = 2\pi f L$

For a capacitor $X = \dfrac{1}{\omega C} = \dfrac{1}{2\pi f C}$

◀ Impedance ▶

REAL IMAGE

Real image is a term used in ray optics to describe an image through which rays actually travel. It is an image which can be formed on a screen. For example, when a magnifying lens (burning glass) focuses the sun's rays on a piece of paper the image is a real image. Such an image is in contrast with a **virtual image**, which is a point from which rays seem to come. For example, if the same magnifying glass is used to inspect a close object the rays appear to come from a very large object behind the lens. This is just an apparent effect caused by the refraction of the waves at the lens surfaces.

Another way of describing this is to say that rays converge towards a real image, to pass through it and then diverge. Waves appear to diverge from a virtual image, but have never actually passed through the image.

RECTIFICATION

◀ Direct current power supplies ▶

RECTIFIER

Many applications require **direct current** rather than **alternating current** and a rectifier circuit is used to change the readily available a.c. (from the 'mains' and a **transformer**) into d.c. In its simplest form the rectifier is a diode, so that current can only flow round the circuit one way. This produces a **half-wave rectifier**. This is wasteful as half the a.c. supplied is not used and a **full-wave rectifier** can produce a much better result.

RED SHIFT

◀ Doppler effect, Hubble's Law ▶

REED SWITCH

This is a switch used as a sensor in microelectronics and in experiments for the rapid charging and discharging of **capacitors**, as, for example, in experiments to determine capacitance.

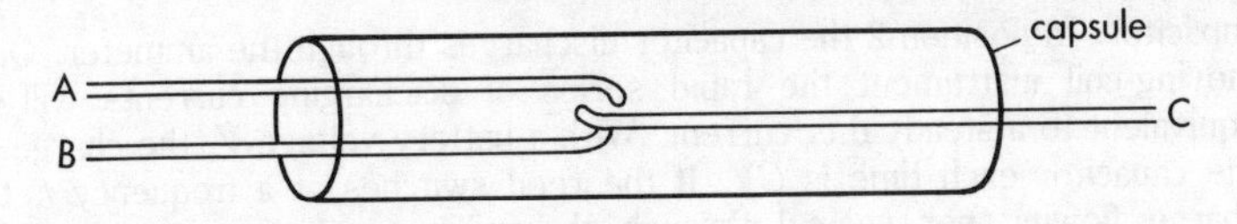

Fig. R.15 The basic reed switch

In its simplest form (Fig. R.15) it consists of a small glass capsule containing three metal strips A, B, and C. C is the 'reed', a springy strip which flips from B to A when a magnetic field is applied. This is because A and C become magnetised and attract one another into contact. B is made of a material which is not magnetic. Thus, in the absence of a field C is connected to B and in the presence of a field A and C are connected. Thus, in microelectronics, the switch can detect the proximity of an object carrying a magnet. The switch could for example be laid in the middle of a model railway track to detect the passage of a truck fitted with a magnet on its underneath.

In another form of the switch the capsule is enclosed in a coil. The field generated by the coil causes the switch to operate if the current is big enough. If a large enough fluctuating current is fed to the coil, the switch contacts will be continually opening and closing as the current rises and falls. If the coil is fed from an alternating supply with a diode rectifier in the circuit, so that current only flows during one-half of each cycle, then the switch operates once in each cycle. Thus, if the frequency of the alternating current is 50 Hz, the switch will operate fifty times a second.

It is this type of switch which is used in capacitance determination. The rapid succession of capacitor discharge pulses, each carrying a charge Q, at the rate f, passes through a meter which deflects as if a steady current $I = Qf$ were flowing. If I and f are known, Q can be found. If the capacitor used has capacitance C, then $C = Q/V$ (V being the voltage to which it was charged).

◀ Reed switch capacitance determination ▶

REED SWITCH CAPACITANCE DETERMINATION

The **reed switch** consists of a very thin piece of steel, the reed, set inside a glass encapsulation where it can flip between two contacts. The flipping is done by means of a magnetic field and in the form of reed switch used in this experiment the glass encapsulation is surrounded by a coil through which an unsmoothed d.c. supply can be passed. An unsmoothed d.c. supply generated from a 50 Hz a.c. supply with a bridge rectifier will have two current surges every 1/50 second. This will cause the switch to move from position 1 to position 2 and back again one hundred times a second.

To measure the capacitance of a capacitor the circuit figure shown in Fig. R.16 is used. When the reed switch is in position 1 the battery charges the capacitor. In position 2 the capacitor discharges through the ammeter. On a moving-coil instrument the rapid series of discharging currents will be equivalent to a steady d.c. current. With a battery voltage V, the charge on the capacitor each time is CV. If the reed switches at a frequency f, the charge flowing per second through the milliammeter is given by CVf. Because this is the charge in 1 second, it is also the current, I. By measuring the current on the milliammeter and with knowledge of f, C can be found.

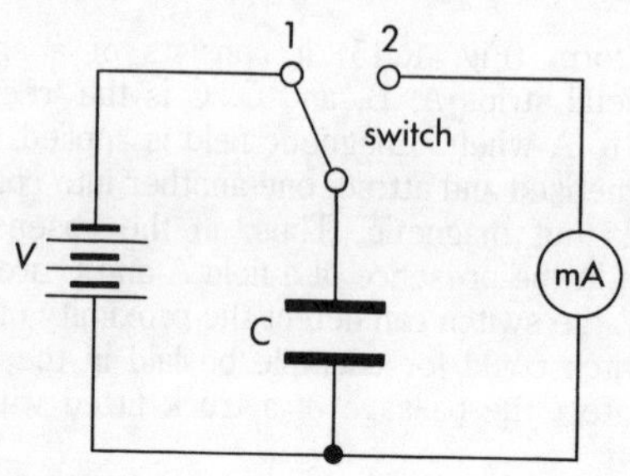

Fig. R.16 Reed switch in circuit

Note that with very small capacitors, such as a laboratory **parallel-plate capacitor**, it would be necessary to use a sensitive **light-beam galvanometer** for this measurement. It is also useful practice to monitor the discharging of the capacitor by connecting an oscilloscope across the capacitor. It is then possible to check that the voltage falls to zero each time the reed switch switches to position 2, ensuring that all the charge on the capacitor is discharged through the meter.

◀ Ammeters and voltmeters ▶

REFLECTING TELESCOPE

Fig. R.17 shows a form of reflecting telescope usually called a Newtonian reflector after its inventor Isaac Newton.

The principle of the telescope is very similar to that of the **astronomical telescope** except that in this case a **concave mirror** is used instead of a **converging lens.** Just before the parallel rays from a distant object are focused to a focal point of the mirror F, they are deflected through an angle of 90° by a small plane mirror. By placing the mirror close to F, only a small fraction of the incident beam is obstructed by this mirror. The remainder of the arrangement is similar to that of the astronomical telescope, with the eyepiece lens set with its focal point at the point where the intermediate image is formed. In this way the telescope is in 'normal adjustment'.

As in the case of the refracting telescope the function of the device is to increase the angular size of a distant object in the field of view. However, in order not to make figure R.17 over-complicated only rays from one point on the object have been drawn.

◀ Galilean telescope ▶

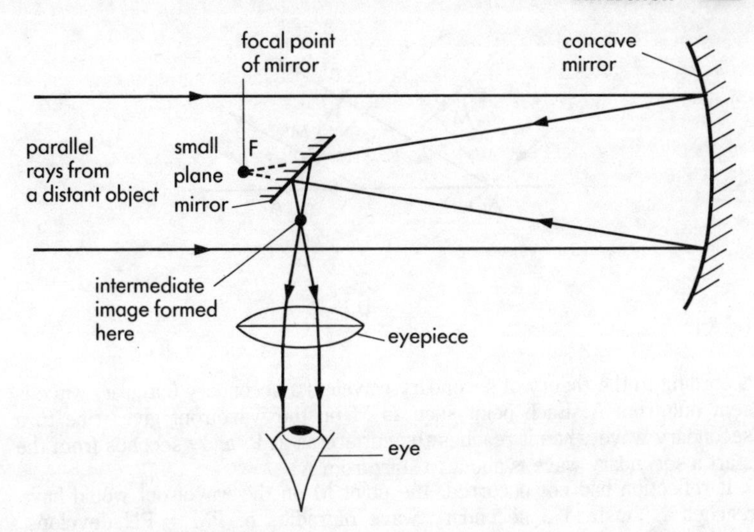

Fig. R.17 Newtonian reflecting telescope

REFLECTION

This is the term used in the theory of light, and in wave theory generally, to describe the 'bouncing-off' of a wave from a surface.

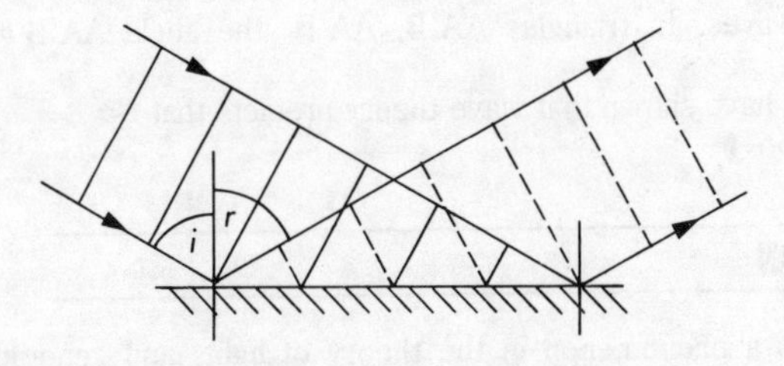

Fig. R.18 Plane waves (and rays) reflecting from a plane surface

Fig. R.18 shows plane waves (and rays) reflecting off a plane (flat) surface. The law of reflection is that the angle of incidence, i, is equal to the angle of reflection, r. Notice that these angles are measured with respect to the normal to the surface.

The phenomenon of the reflection of plane waves with $i = r$ can be explained using Huygens's theory of secondary wavelets (see **Diffraction**). Consider Fig. R.19. Let us suppose that the velocity of the wave is v. AB represents a plane wave striking the reflecting surface at A. Suppose t is the time for the edge B of the wavefront to reach the surface at A′. As soon as the wave first strikes the surface a disturbance is generated at A and

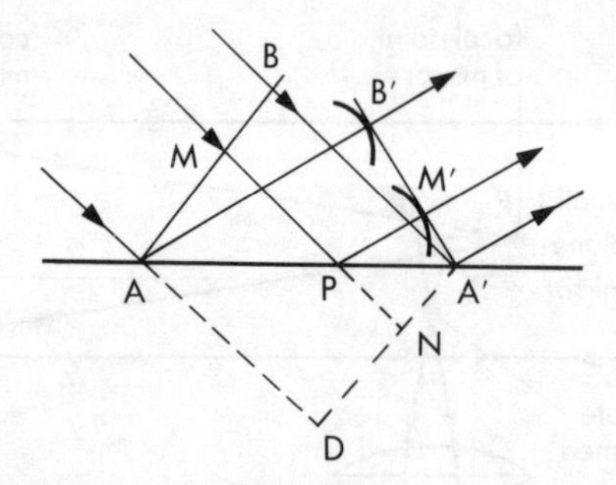

Fig. R.19

according to the theory of secondary wavelets a secondary (circular) wave is sent out from A. Each point such as M on the wavefront gives rise to a secondary wave when it reaches the surface as at P, and t seconds from the start a secondary wave is about to start from A′.

If reflection had not occurred, the point M on the wavefront would have reached N; instead a secondary wave of radius of PM′ = PN develops. Similarly the reflected wave at A gives rise to a secondary wave of radius AB′ = AD.

The rest of the argument requires some geometry. Through A′ draw a line representing a plane touching the secondary wave diverging from A at B′. Now since AB′ = BA′ = AD = vt, and AA′ is a common side, triangles AA′B, AA′B′, AA′D are equal in all respects. So in triangles AA′B′, AA′D the perpendicular PM′ dropped to B′A′ = PN; and the reflected wave diverging from P would touch A′B′. This would be true for all similar secondary waves. In triangles AA′B, AA′B′ the angle AA′B = the angle A′AB.

Hence we have shown that wave theory predicts that $i = r$.

◀ Refraction ▶

REFRACTION

Refraction is a phenomenon in the theory of light, and generally in wave theory, whereby the direction of propagation changes when the wave crosses a boundary. A change of direction does not occur when the wave travels at right angles to the boundary.

The reason for refraction is that the speed of a wave changes as it crosses a boundary. For example, water waves slow down when moving into a shallower region and light waves slow down on entering glass or water from air.

Fig. R.20 shows a plane wave crossing a boundary and slowing down. The left-hand end at A reaches the boundary first and then travels more slowly. While this is occurring, the right-hand end is still travelling towards the boundary. The diagram shows wavefronts corresponding to crests of wave. The wavelength of the upper side of the boundary is λ_1, and that on the lower side of the boundary is λ_2. The frequency of the waves on both sides

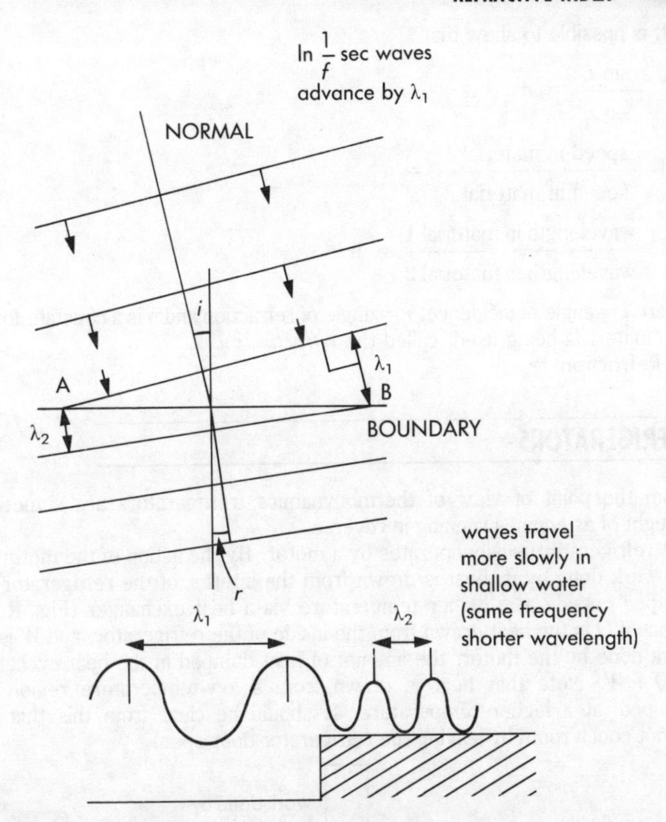

Fig. R.20 Refraction of water waves on entering a region of shallow water

of the boundary is the same. On the upper side of the boundary the waves advance a distance λ_1 in a time $1/f$ seconds. A complete analysis in the kind of detail given in the entry **Reflection** shows that sin i/sin r = constant, and sin i/sin $r = \lambda_1/\lambda_2 = v_1/v_2$, where v_1 and v_2 are the velocities on either side of the boundary.

The constancy of the ratio sin i/sin r is called **Snell's Law**, and in the application of refraction to light rays is used to define the **refractive index** of a medium.

REFRACTIVE INDEX

The angle of incidence is the angle between the ray going towards the boundary and the normal. The angle of **refraction** is the angle between the ray leaving the boundary and the normal. It is important to remember to measure the angles *from the normal* and *not* from the boundary.

It is possible to show that

$$\frac{\sin i}{\sin r} = n$$

and $$\frac{\text{speed in material 1}}{\text{speed in material 2}} = n$$

and $$\frac{\text{wavelength in material 1}}{\text{wavelength in material 2}} = n$$

where i = angle of incidence, r = angle of refraction and n is a constant for the two materials being used, called the *refractive index*.

◀ Refraction ▶

REFRIGERATORS

From the point of view of thermodynamics, refrigerators are sometimes thought of as engines running in reverse.

A refrigerator usually operates by a motor. By the action of the motor and the work done by it, heat is drawn from the interior of the refrigerator and dumped outside at a higher temperature via a heat exchanger (Fig. R.21). Hence if Q is the heat drawn from the inside of the refrigerator, and W is the work done by the motor, the amount of heat dumped in the heat exchanger is $Q + W$. Note that heat is drawn from a low-temperature region and 'dumped' at a higher temperature. It should be clear from this that you cannot cool a room by leaving the refrigerator door open!

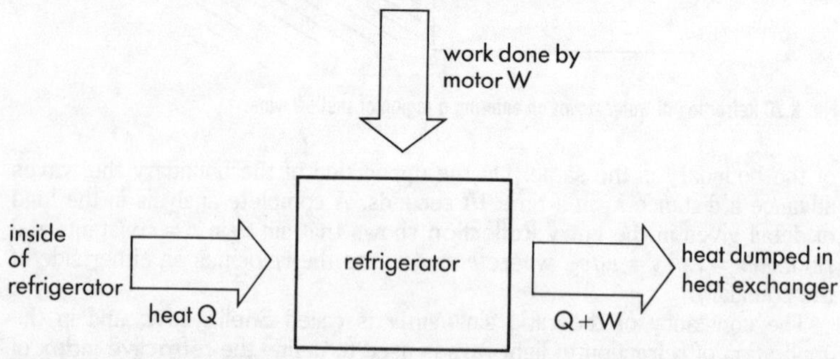

Fig. R.21 Heat flow in a refrigerator

RELATIVE ATOMIC MASS

Relative atomic mass is defined as:

$$\frac{\text{mass of an atom}}{1/12 \text{ of mass of a } {}^{12}_{6}\text{C atom}}$$

RELATIVITY

There are two theories of relativity: special relativity, developed by Einstein in 1905, and general relativity, developed in 1915.

Special relativity is based upon the idea that the laws of physics should be the same for all observers moving with constant relative motion, no matter what their speed. In particular, in Einstein's theory two observers should obtain the same value for the velocity of light when they measure it. By this Einstein means that we could conceive of a situation in principle of a single beam of light that two observers separately measure. One observer could be travelling at a constant speed with the respect to the other along the direction of the light beam. Now velocity is a derived quantity: it is obtained by measuring a time to travel a certain distance. So in principle both observers measure a distance and measure a time, and punch both pairs of numbers into their calculators to get a value of velocity. According to Einstein the same answer comes out of both calculators.

Clearly there is something of a paradox here which can only be resolved by recognising that the measuring scale of one observer for distance must be different from that of the other observer, or the rate of progress of clocks for one observer must be different for the other observer, or both distance and time must be different for both observers. The special theory of relativity makes this claim and says that for moving observers, compared with observers at rest, lengths contract and clocks move more slowly.

General relativity extends the idea of special relativity from the consideration of two observers moving with constant relative motion to the case of all observers no matter how they are moving. It becomes a theory of gravity which explains the force of gravity in terms of the curvature of a four-dimensional space/time, the description of which is outside the terms of reference of this book.

Both theories of relativity have been verified by experiment.

RELAXATION OSCILLATOR

◀ Positive feedback and electrical oscillations ▶

RELAY

The relay is an electromagnetic device for switching one electric current by the action of another much smaller one.

Fig. R.22 shows the typical layout of a small modern relay. When a d.c. current of the order of milliamperes is passed through the coil, the armature made of iron is pulled by the magnetic field which is created and the effect of this is to switch a pair of electric contacts. Thus the relay is essentially a switch controlled by an electric current.

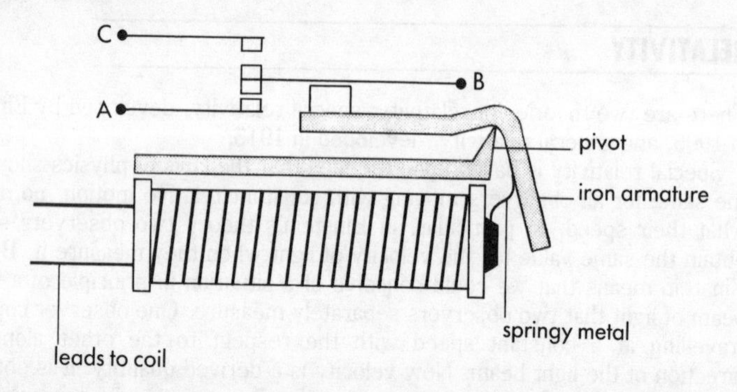

Fig. R.22 Typical relay. A, B and C are springy pieces of copper. As drawn, B is connected to A, but if the coil is energised the movement of the armature pushes B into contact with C

The name 'relay' derives from the use in telegraphy in the nineteenth century. It was found that with very long distances between a transmitting and a receiving station the currents would be too small to work directly the armature of a morse-code receiving set. So the current would be passed through a relay in order to switch a larger current powerful enough to work equipment, or to switch the current in the wire of a further 'leg' of the telegraphy network.

Sometimes the need for a relay is different from the situation described above. Electronic switching circuits generally use small d.c. currents, but they may be needed to control a.c. circuits. In order not to mix the d.c. and the a.c. a relay is used to couple between the two parts of a system.

◀ Reed switch ▶

RELUCTANCE

◀ Magnetic circuits ▶

REM

◀ Radioactivity: units of measurement ▶

RESET-SET LATCH

◀ Bistable ▶

RESISTANCE

The resistance R of a conductor is the ratio of the potential difference V across it to the current I passing through it ($R = V/I$).

When a given potential difference is applied across different conductors different currents will flow. Some conductors allow comparatively large currents to flow for a given potential difference and are said to have low resistance, others comparatively small currents and high resistance.

For some components such as carbon **resistors,** and wires held at constant temperature, the resistance is independent of the current. Components such as this are called Ohmic and are to be distinguished from devices such as **diodes** and **transistors,** which are non-Ohmic. For most metals the resistance increases with temperature and the resistance is given by the formula $R = R_0(1 + \alpha\theta)$, where R is the resistance at a temperature and R_0 is the resistance at 0°C. α is the temperature coefficient of the resistance and has units $°C^{-1}$ (Fig. R.23).

◀ Ohm's Law, Resistivity, Thermistor ▶

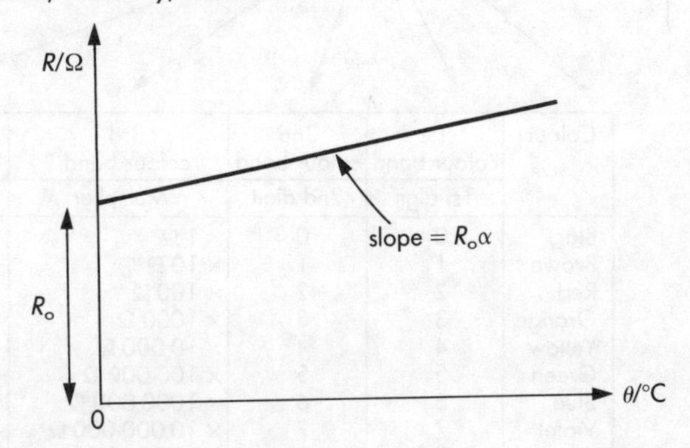

Fig. R.23 Temperature dependence of a metallic conductor

RESISTIVITY

The resistivity of a material is the resistance of a 1 metre length of the material with cross-sectional area 1 m^2 at a certain temperature.

The resistance R of a wire is proportional to its length, L, and inversely proportional to the cross-sectional area, A. So doubling the length of a wire doubles the resistance, and doubling the diameter quadruples the cross-sectional area and reduces the resistance to a quarter of its initial value. The term resistivity, ρ, is used to compare the conducting properties of materials in a way which is independent of the particular geometry of the sample used. It is defined by the formula $R = \rho L/A$, and hence $\rho = R\,A/L$.

The units of resistivity are Ω m.

◀ Conductivity, Conductors and insulators ▶

RESISTORS

Practical resistors come in three types:

Carbon-composite resistors

These usually have comparatively poor stability.

Carbon-film resistors

These are ceramic rods on which a thin film of carbon has been deposited.
Resistors are colour-coded, as shown in Fig. R.24.

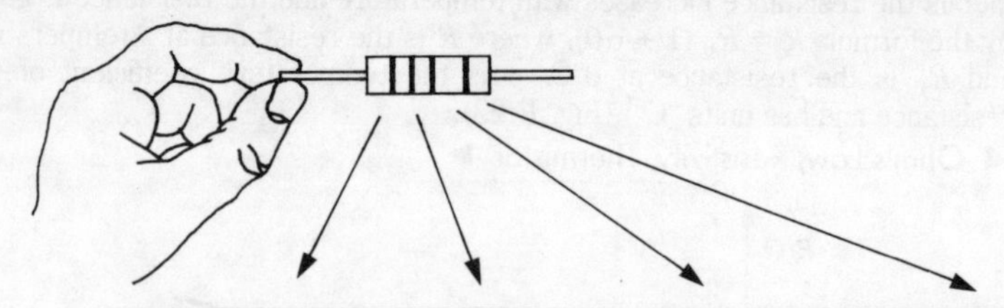

Colour	1st colour band	2nd colour band	3rd colour band	4th colour band
	1st digit	2nd digit	Multiplier	Tolerance
Black	0	0	× 1 Ω	± 1%
Brown	1	1	× 10 Ω	± 2%
Red	2	2	× 100 Ω	
Orange	3	3	× 1000 Ω	
Yellow	4	4	× 10 000 Ω	
Green	5	5	× 100 000 Ω	
Blue	6	6	× 1000 000 Ω	
Violet	7	7	× 10 000 000 Ω	
Grey	8	8	× 100 000 000 Ω	
White	9	9	× 1 000 000 000 Ω	
Gold			× 0.1 Ω	± 5%
Silver			× 0.01 Ω	± 10%

Example:

green blue orange

silver

1st colour band: green = 5

2nd colour band: blue = 6

3rd colour band: orange = × 1000 Ω

4th colour band: silver = ± 10%

Therefore resistor is 56 000 Ω ± 10%

Fig. R.24 Common resistor colour code

Wire-wound resistors

These are usually made with nichrome or constantan wire wound non-inductively in order to eliminate self-inductance. (This is done by having as many turns in one sense as in the other sense.)

In electronics the method of writing resistance values is as follows
2.5 Ω is written 2R5
3.5 k Ω is written 3K5
650 k Ω is written 650 k or M65

◀ Resistance ▶

RESISTORS IN PARALLEL

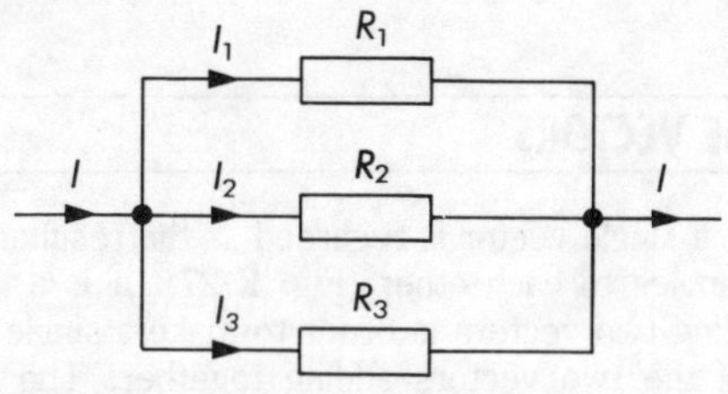

Fig. R.25 Resistors in parallel

The total current is equal to the sum of all the currents passing through the resistors (Fig. R.25). This gives:

$$I = I_1 + I_2 + I_3$$

The p.d. across each resistor is the same, giving:

$$V = I_1R_1 = I_2R_2 = I_3R_3 \text{ so } I_1 = V/R_1,\ I_2 = V/R_2,\ I_3 = V/R_3$$

hence the total current is equal to

$$\frac{V}{R_1} + \frac{V}{R_2} + \frac{V}{R_3} = V\left(\frac{1}{R_1} + \frac{1}{R_2} + \frac{1}{R_3}\right)$$

and hence if R is the resistance of the single resistor which could replace the three resistors, its value is given by

$$\frac{1}{R} = \frac{1}{R_1} + \frac{1}{R_2} + \frac{1}{R_3}$$

◀ Resistors in series ▶

RESISTORS IN SERIES

If several resistors are placed in series the current I passing through each of them is the same (Fig. R.26). The total potential difference across them is

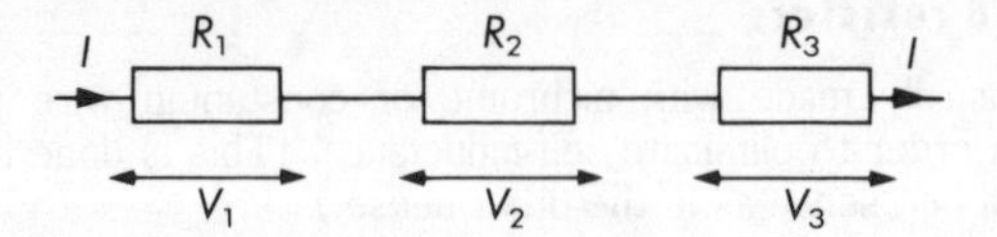

Fig. R.26 Resistors in series

equal to the sum of the individual p.d.s and the total resistance is the sum of all resistances. Hence:

$$V = V_1 + V_2 + V_3$$
and $$R = R_1 + R_2 + R_3$$

Note also that in such a resistor chain the potential difference across any individual resistor is proportional to its resistance.

◀ Resistance ▶

RESOLUTION OF VECTORS

In this procedure a single vector is regarded as the resultant of two vectors usually at right angles to each other (Fig. R.27). It is a kind of 'opposite' procedure to adding two vectors in order to make a single vector, which is the equivalent of the two vectors adding together. The two vectors are called components.

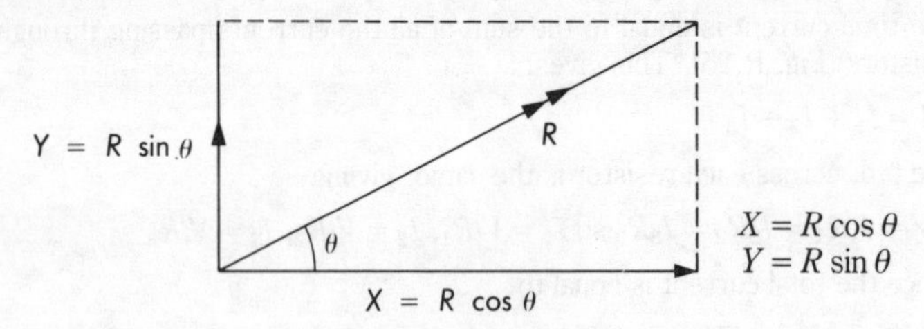

Fig. R.27 Resolving vectors into two components at right angles

An example is the weight W of a car standing on a hill of angle θ (Fig. R.28). The weight W resolves into a component $W \sin\theta$ down the hill and $W \cos\theta$ normal to the hill surface.

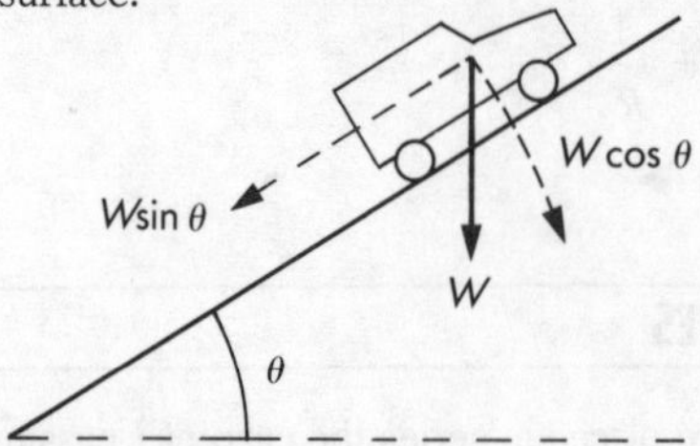

Fig. R.28 Resolving the weight of a car down an incline

RESONANCE

In one of the stories of the Bible the walls of Jericho were supposed to have been brought down by the sounding of trumpets. If such an event did take place it would have been an example of resonance. For resonance to occur it is necessary to have a system which can oscillate. It must have one or more frequencies at which it will oscillate naturally, and an external vibration must be supplied at one of these frequencies. A comparatively large-amplitude oscillation will then occur and this is called resonance.

In considering the detail of resonance it is useful to consider separately systems where there is only one frequency of resonance from those where there are several, or even an infinite number of resonant frequencies. The former case is considered in the entry **Forced oscillations** and the latter case in the entry **Standing waves**.

REVERBERATION

This is a term used in the theory of sound.

If a musical instrument is sounded in an empty hall the note is heard long after the instrumentalist has stopped playing. The sound waves produced bounce backwards and forwards from the surfaces of the room, gradually dying away as energy is lost by the interaction of the sound waves with the surfaces. This is called reverberation.

The reverberation time is conventionally defined as the time for the intensity level of the sound to fall by a factor of 10^6, or in decibels for the sound to diminish by 60 decibels. Reverberation time is reduced substantially by filling a room with soft furnishings. An empty hall can produce a very long reverberation time and so if an orchestra is to rehearse in a hall under such conditions it is common practice for cushions and fabric to be placed on the seats to reduce the reverberation time to what it would be if an audience was present.

◀ Musical instruments, Resonance ▶

RIGHT-HAND GRIP RULE

◀ Corkscrew rule ▶

RIGID-BODY ROTATION

The motion of wheels, flywheels, lathes, etc. are all examples of rigid-body rotation in engineering. The earth itself largely behaves as a rigid body and so its rotation on its axis is an astrophysical example of rigid-body rotation.

Rigid-body kinematics

For all the concepts used in straight-line kinematics there are equivalent quantities in rotational motion. The key idea is the use of an angle as a measure of displacement rather than a distance. The other concepts then follow from this. For example, instead of velocity we have angular velocity, which is the rate of change of angle. The equivalent quantities are:

Concept in linear motion	*Equivalent in rigid body motion*
displacement (s)	angular displacement (θ)
velocity ($v = \mathrm{d}s/\mathrm{d}t$)	angular velocity $\left(\omega = \dfrac{\mathrm{d}\theta}{\mathrm{d}t}\right)$
acceleration ($a = \mathrm{d}v/\mathrm{d}t$)	angular acceleration $\left(\alpha = \dfrac{\mathrm{d}\omega}{\mathrm{d}t}\right)$

The units of ω are radians s^{-1} and the units of α are radians s^{-2}. Similarly, the formulae for uniform acceleration in straight-line motion have exact circular motion equivalents.

Formula in linear motion	*Equivalent in rigid-body motion*
$v = u + at$	$\omega_{\text{final}} = \omega_{\text{initial}} + \alpha t$
$s = ut + \frac{1}{2}at^2$	$\theta = \omega_{\text{initial}}\, t + \frac{1}{2}\alpha t^2$
$s = \dfrac{(u+v)}{2}t$	$\theta = \dfrac{(\omega_{\text{initial}} + \omega_{\text{final}})}{2}t$
$v^2 = u^2 + 2as$	$\omega^2_{\text{final}} = \omega^2_{\text{initial}} + 2\alpha\theta$

Dynamics

To increase the angular velocity of a rotating body a **couple** or **torque** must be applied. The torque, T, takes the place of force in straight-line motion and the **moment of inertia** I takes the place of mass. So instead of Newton's Second Law in the form

$$F = m\frac{\mathrm{d}v}{\mathrm{d}t} = ma$$

we have

$$T = I\frac{\mathrm{d}\omega}{\mathrm{d}t} = I\alpha$$

(Note that α, the angular acceleration referred to here, must not be confused with the term centripetal acceleration described in the entry **Circular motion**.)

As an example, consider a weight acting on a string wrapped round an axle so that it angularly accelerates a dumb-bell of moment of inertia I (Fig. R.29). Because there is no upward or downward motion, the downward force W must be balanced by the upward normal reaction force N at the support. So

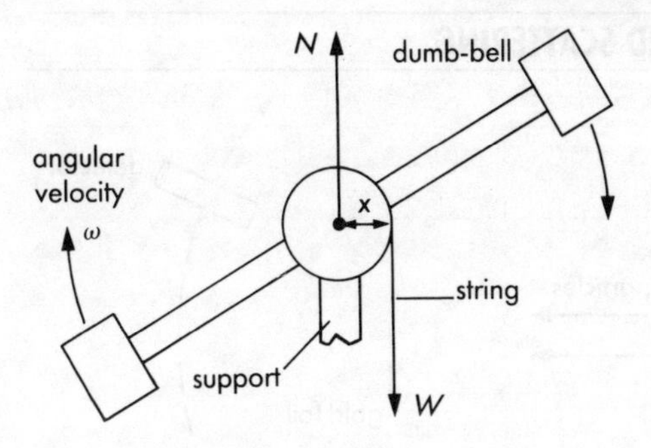

Fig. R.29 Weight acting on a string wrapped round an axle

$N = W$. These two forces form a couple, the torque T of which is Nx, where x is the distance between the lines of action, i.e. the radius of the axle. So $T = I \dfrac{d\omega}{dt}$, where ω is the angular velocity of the dumb-bell.

Note that measurements made in this experiment could be used to determine the moment of inertia of the dumb-bell.

The remaining dynamical quantities which have equivalents in rotational motion are those of momentum and energy. The details are summarised in the table below:

Quantity or formula in linear motion	*Equivalent in rigid-body motion*
momentum (mv)	angular momentum $L = I\omega$
kinetic energy ($\frac{1}{2}mv^2$)	kinetic energy $\frac{1}{2}I\omega^2$
work done Fs	work done $T\theta$
$m_1v_1 + m_2v_2 = \text{constant}$	$I_1\omega_1 + I_2\omega_2 = \text{constant}$

◀ Angular momentum ▶

R.M.S. VALUES

◀ Alternating current ▶

ROTATIONAL MOTION

◀ Moment of inertia ▶

RUTHERFORD SCATTERING

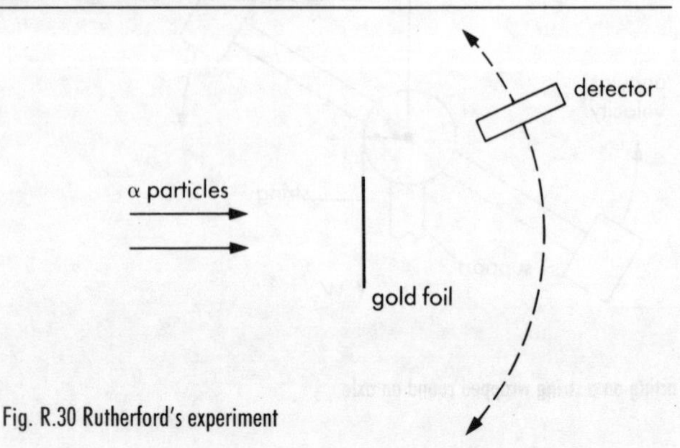

Fig. R.30 Rutherford's experiment

This is a classic experiment of early nuclear physics which led to the adoption of the **nuclear model of the atom**. The experiment was performed by Geiger and Marsden, who were working under Lord Rutherford. In the experiment (Fig. R.30) alpha particles were directed at a thin sheet of gold foil. Most of the alpha particles went straight through, implying that most of the foil was empty space, but a small number were deflected, and a significant number, about one in 8000, were deflected through angles greater than 90°. At the time Rutherford said that the discovery was like firing a shell at a piece of tissue paper and discovering that the shell bounced back towards the firer. Rutherford's explanation was that the atoms of gold had very small massive centres, called nuclei, with a positive charge. Surrounding the nucleus were electrons in orbits a long way from the nucleus. Consequently if an alpha particle came near the nucleus it was repelled by the positive charge and deflected. The nearer it was to hitting the nucleus the greater the deflection (Fig. R.31).

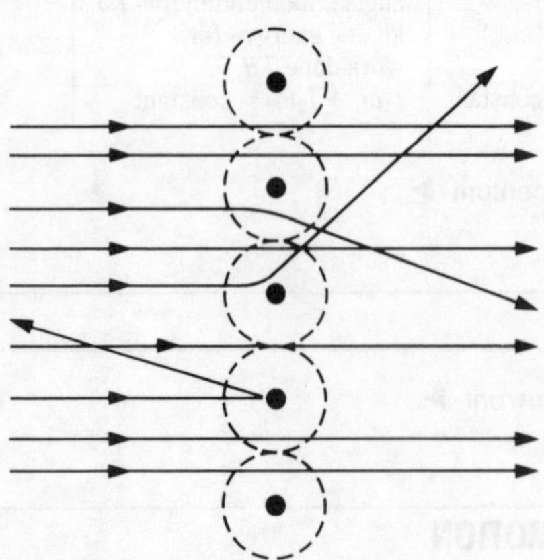

Fig. R.31 Deflection and passage of alpha particles through gold nuclei

SATELLITES LAUNCHED FROM THE EARTH

A stone thrown upwards from the surface of the earth eventually falls down again. As something leaves the surface of the earth it gains gravitational potential energy while simultaneously losing kinetic energy. The gravitational potential, i.e. the potential energy possessed by unit mass, at a distance r from the centre of the earth is given by $V = -GM/r$, where G is the gravitational constant, M is the mass of the earth and r is the distance from the centre of the earth. The gravitational potential at the earth's surface is therefore $-GM/R_E$, where R_E is the radius of the earth. In principle therefore if an object were given a kinetic energy equal to the magnitude of the gravitational potential energy at the earth's surface, and a corresponding velocity in the direction away from the field, it will travel away from the earth, slowly losing kinetic energy until at an infinite distance from the earth it is stopped. The velocity necessary for this kind of journey is called the *escape velocity*. This is the minimum speed away from the gravitational field that an object must be given in order to complete and escape the influence of the field. In the case of a satellite leaving the earth we have

$$\tfrac{1}{2}mv^2 = GMm/R_E$$

which gives

$$v = \sqrt{\frac{2GM}{R_E}}$$

where v is the escape velocity in $m\,s^{-1}$. The escape velocity in the earth's gravitational field is about $11\,km\,s^{-1}$.

Satellites which are sent into orbits round the earth (Fig. S.1) are given a smaller velocity than this.

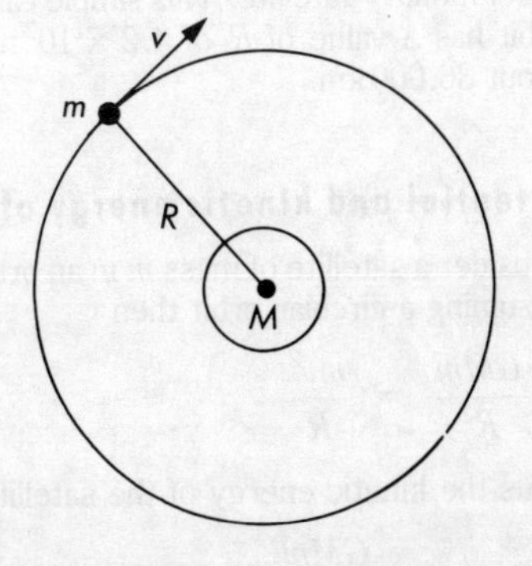

Fig. S.1 Mass m in orbit about a planet of mass M

For a circular orbit the condition governing the motion is that there should be a constant force towards the centre of the circle of the orbit equal to the mass times the constant centripetal acceleration. The acceleration is given by

$$a = \frac{v^2}{r} = \omega^2 r$$

where ω is the angular velocity and r is the radius of the circle. Hence applying Newton's Second Law in the form $F = ma$ we have

$$F = mv^2/r = m\omega^2 r$$

For satellites orbiting the earth it is the gravitational force of attraction which provides the centrifugal acceleration. Hence:

$$\frac{GMm}{r^2} = m\frac{v^2}{r} = mr\omega^2$$

For a satellite of mass m in an orbit of radius R about the earth of mass M, v the velocity of the mass in orbit is thus determined by the radius R of the orbit as G,M are constant. So mathematical manipulation gives the following equations: the period T is given by

$$T^2 = 4\pi R^3/GM$$

$$\text{hence } T = \sqrt{\frac{4\pi R^3}{GM}}$$

It should be noted that the period squared is proportional to the radius cubed. Also that the higher the orbit the greater the value of R and so the smaller the values of v and ω.

Using these equations it is possible to calculate the period of an orbit such that the satellite rotates with the same angular velocity as the earth on its axis. A satellite in such an orbit stays stationary on a fixed point on the earth. Such an orbit is called a parking orbit or the satellite is said to be a geostationary satellite. This simple calculation shows that the height of such an orbit has a value of R of 4.2×10^7 m, giving the height above the earth of about 36,000 km.

Potential and kinetic energy of satellites in orbit

Consider a satellite of mass m in an orbit of radius R about a planet of mass M. Assuming a circular orbit then

$$\frac{GMm}{R^2} = \frac{mv^2}{R}$$

Thus the kinetic energy of the satellite is:

$$\tfrac{1}{2}mv^2 = \frac{GMm}{2R}$$

The potential energy is:

$$-\frac{GMm}{R}$$

Adding these two energies we get the total energy of the satellite, the potential energy plus the kinetic energy:

$$\text{Total energy} = -\frac{GMm}{R} + \frac{GMm}{2R} = -\frac{GMm}{2R}$$

Note that this is negative and exactly half the potential energy.

SATURATED VAPOUR

The term saturated vapour is applied to a vapour which is confined inside a container together with some of its parent liquid. Thus in the container are both liquid and vapour, which find themselves in dynamic equilibrium with each other.

This equilibrium situation is one in which molecules in the liquid have a range of velocities and those which are very energetic and achieve an 'escape' velocity leave the liquid and become part of the vapour. The molecules in the vapour also have a range of velocities and those which as a result of collisions acquire a very slow velocity find their way back into the liquid. Thus there is a dynamic equilibrium between molecules leaving the liquid and molecules returning into the liquid from the vapour. The saturated vapour pressure of a material is the pressure exerted by the vapour in equilibrium with the liquid. Unsaturated vapours obey *Boyle's law*. However, as soon as the vapour becomes saturated the pressure remains the same independent of the volume. Reducing the volume of a container will force proportionately more and more vapour into the liquid state at constant pressure until all the vapour has become liquid. Fig. S.2 shows a pressure–volume (p, V) curve for a vapour as the volume of the container is steadily reduced.

◀ Gases, liquids, vapours and plasmas ▶

SCALAR

A scalar quantity is a quantity in physics which has magnitude only and is completely described by a number and an appropriate unit. Examples are mass (e.g. $m = 500.034$ kg) or temperature (e.g $\theta = 467$ K).

A scalar quantity contrasts with a **vector** quantity, a quantity which has magnitude and direction.

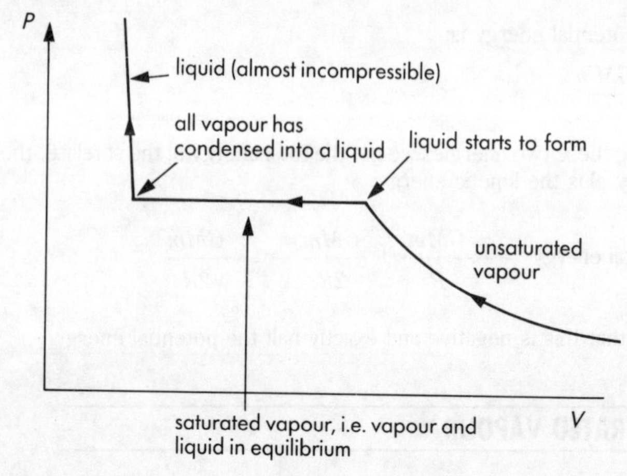

Fig. S.2 Graph of p against V for an unsaturated vapour as the volume of the container is reduced at constant temperature so that it eventually forms a liquid. (T is below the critical temperature)

SCALER

This is an instrument found in the school or college laboratory for counting pulses, such as those received from a **Geiger tube** in experiments in radioactivity.

Many older pieces of equipment use two dekatron tubes, the first for recording units and the second for tens, followed by a mechanical register for hundreds. The *dekatron* is a tube which can record counts up to ten, displaying the number as a glow discharge across a labelled set of electrodes.

More modern instruments use a display which gives a direct digital readout. Some also include electronic circuitry which enables the device to count for a fixed time, typically 1, 10 or 100 s, and then to pause and display the count for that period. Such an instrument can then replace the **ratemeter**.

Some scalers also include an electronic oscillator which generates pulses at a regular rate. These can be sent to the display and the device then acts as a clock.

SCATTERING OF LIGHT

When unpolarised light is passed through a cloudy medium, e.g. an atmosphere with a lot of dust or tiny water particles in it, cloudy water, i.e. water to which has been added a drop of milk, or sodium thiosulphate solution to which has been added a little acid, it will be found that the light viewed from above or from the side is plane polarised. The light viewed from the side is scattered by the particles in the medium. As the light consists of transverse oscillations, there are no oscillations in the original beam parallel to the original direction and so there can be no oscillations in this direction in the

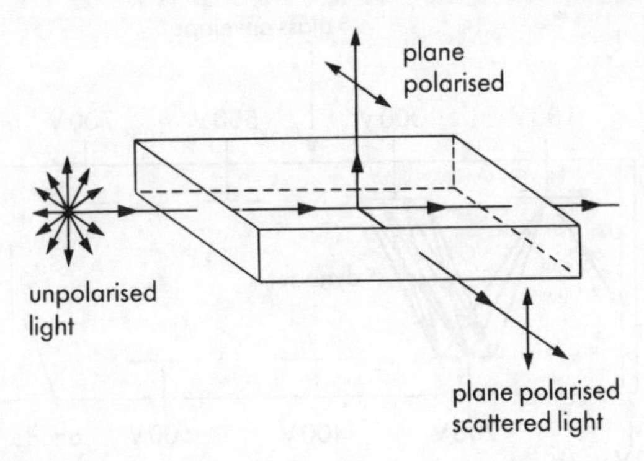

Fig. S.3 Scattering of light

scattered beam. The oscillations in the scattered beam can only be perpendicular to the new direction and so can only be as shown in Fig. S.3. A similar argument can be applied to the beam scattered upwards. The detection of polarisation can be carried out by using polaroid.

◀ Polarisation, Polaroid ▶

SCHRODINGER EQUATIONS

◀ Quantum mechanical model of the atom ▶

SCINTILLATION COUNTER

The scintillation counter is an instrument used in radioactivity, particle physics and medical physics for detecting ionising radiation.

When ionising radiation falls on certain crystals, for example sodium iodide activated with thallium, and certain plastic materials flashes of light are produced. In a scintillation counter these flashes are used to generate a pulse of electricity by means of a photomultiplier tube whose photocathode emits electrons when light falls upon it.

Fig. S.4 shows schematically an arrangement of a photomultiplier tube. The electrodes (dynodes) are held at increasing potentials. An electron emitted by the photocathode is accelerated to the first of these. On collision it generates several 'secondary' electrons which in turn are accelerated to the second dynode, where the process is repeated. This successive multiplication results in an avalanche of electrodes arriving at the final collector.

SEARCH COIL

The search coil is a small flat coil of fine insulated wire with a very large number of turns. Those in use in schools and colleges have up to 2000 turns.

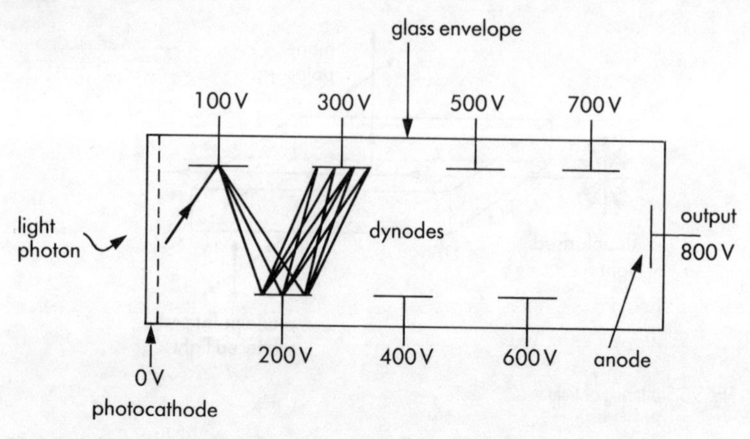

Fig. S.4 Schematic diagram of a photomultiplier used with a scintillation counter

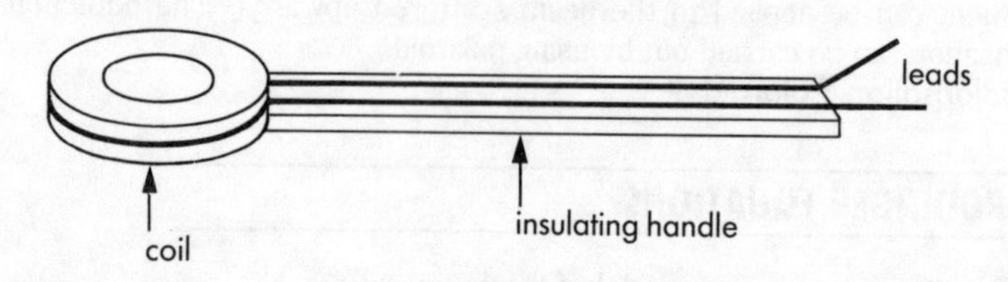

Fig. S.5 Search coil

The diameter is usually about 0.5 cm and the device is mounted with an insulated handle as shown in Fig. S.5.

The search coil is particularly useful for measuring the magnetic field of an electric circuit which can be supplied with alternating current. For example, one can investigate the magnetic field of a solenoid by driving the solenoid with an alternating current. When the coil is placed in such a sinusoidal magnetic field an e.m.f. is induced in it which is directly proportional to the rate of change of the magnetic field, dB/dt. The search coil is usually connected to an **oscilloscope**, and the amplitude of the trace on the oscilloscope is therefore proportional to the amplitude of the magnetic field. Such a trace is proportional to the steady magnetic field that the circuit would have if it were driven by a direct current. The coil has to be placed perpendicular to the field being investigated. If the number of turns N of the coil is known and the area, A, we have the e.m.f., E, is equal to $-NAdB/dt$. Hence with a sinusoidal variation of B, $B = B_0 \sin \omega t$ and hence $E = -NA\omega B_0 \cos \omega t$.

The search coil can also be used to measure steady magnetic fields. In this method it is connected to a **ballistic galvanometer**. For example, consider a coil of N turns in an area A. Suppose it is at right angles to a field of flux density B. In the method the coil has to be removed suddenly to a large distance from the field and when this occurs the change in flux in the coil is NAB. The e.m.f. B produced as the coil is removed is given by $E = -NA\mathrm{d}B/\mathrm{d}t.i$, the current flowing at any instant in time, is given by $i = E/R$ where R is the total resistance of the complete circuit, including the resistance of the ballistic galvanometer. Integrating this equation gives

$$\int i\mathrm{d}t = -\int \frac{NA}{R}\mathrm{d}B \quad \text{or} \quad \int i\mathrm{d}t = \frac{NAB}{R}, \text{ neglecting signs}$$

$\int i\mathrm{d}t$ is the charge Q which flows in the coil and hence we obtain $Q = NAB/R$. Notice that the charge does not depend upon the time taken to remove the search coil from the field. However, in ballistic galvanometer use the coil should be removed as quickly as possible. If the maximum deflection of the ballistic galvanometer is θ then: $B = \theta R/SNA$, where S is the charge sensitivity of the ballistic galvanometer in degrees C^{-1}. If this charge sensitivity is known, the value of B may be found.

◀ Magnetic flux density measurement ▶

SEARLE'S BAR

◀ Thermal conductivity determination ▶

SELF-INDUCTANCE

The current in a coil causes a magnetic field and hence a magnetic flux which is linked with the coil. That is to say the magnetic flux threads its way through the coil. As a result, if the current in the coil itself is changing, so the flux linked with the coil changes. Because of the laws of induction an e.m.f. is induced in the coil. Such an e.m.f. is said to be self-induced.

In the case of an air-cored coil the flux linked, Φ, is proportional to the current, I, in the coil. We write $\Phi = LI$, where L is the constant of proportionality called the self-inductance of the coil. (Note that if the coil contains iron, Φ is not directly proportional to I, but an average value of L can still be quoted.) The laws of induction give $E = -\mathrm{d}\Phi/\mathrm{d}t$ and hence the e.m.f. is given by $E = -L\,\mathrm{d}I/\mathrm{d}t$.

The self-induced e.m.f. must oppose the change in current causing it and is said, therefore, to be a 'back e.m.f.'.

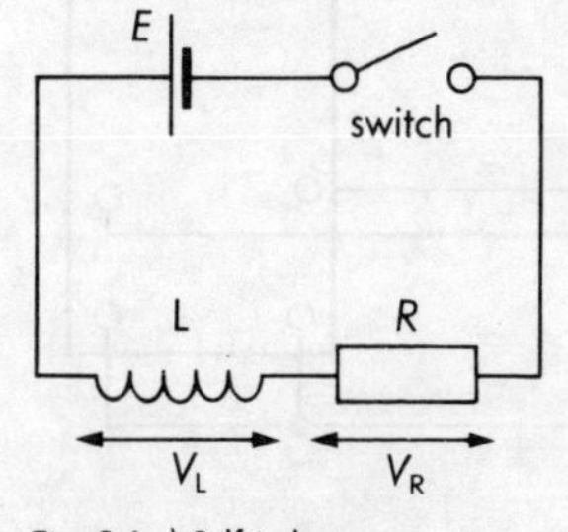

Fig. S.6 a) Self-inductance

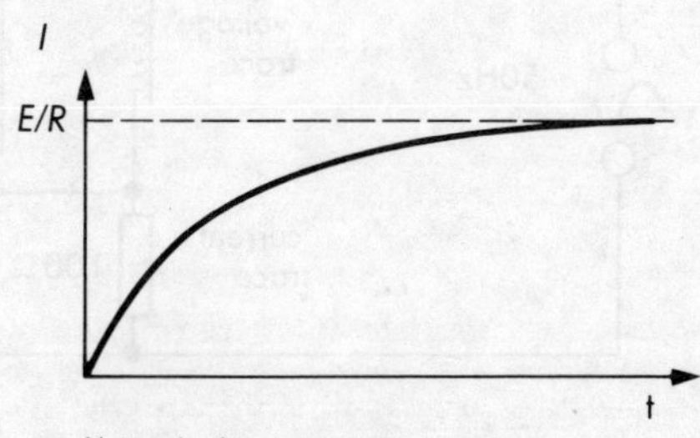

b) Graph of current against time

When a battery is connected across an inductor of inductance L and the switch is closed, the initial current is zero (Fig. S.6a). There are two e.m.f.s in the circuit: the forward e.m.f., E, from the cell or battery, and the back e.m.f., $-L\,dI/dt$, from the inductance. The net e.m.f. in the circuit is therefore $E - L\frac{dI}{dt}$. And this is equal to the p.d. round the circuit. The only p.d. in the circuit is that across the resistance ($V = IR$). Hence we have

$$E - L\frac{dI}{dt} = IR$$

The current grows as shown in Fig. S.6b. Eventually the current will be such that the p.d. across the resistor equals the e.m.f. of the supply. At that point there is no back e.m.f. because the current has stopped growing.

Measurement of the self-inductance of a coil

The simplest way to measure the self-inductance of a coil is to use an a.c. supply, a double-beam **oscilloscope** and the circuit shown in Fig. S.7. The method relies on the measurement of **impedances**. Two voltages are sent to the oscilloscope, one from the resistor, V_R, and one which is the voltage across both resistor and inductor. The resistance has to be chosen so that the former is much smaller than the latter, and so that the latter is effectively the voltage across the inductance, V_L. Typical traces might be as shown in Fig. S.8.

$V = -L\,dI/dt$. dI/dt, the rate of change of current, can be found from the trace of V_R. This is because in an a.c. circuit the current in and p.d. across a resistor are in phase. In the example above, the maximum rate of change of current is given by 0.4 V across 100 Ω in 2 ms, which is 2.0 A s^{-1}. This rate of change has been chosen because at this instant V_L is a maximum. In the example this is 20 V. So using these magnitudes L = 20 V/2.0 A s^{-1} = 10 H.

◀ **Alternating current, Electromagnetic induction, Mutual inductance** ▶

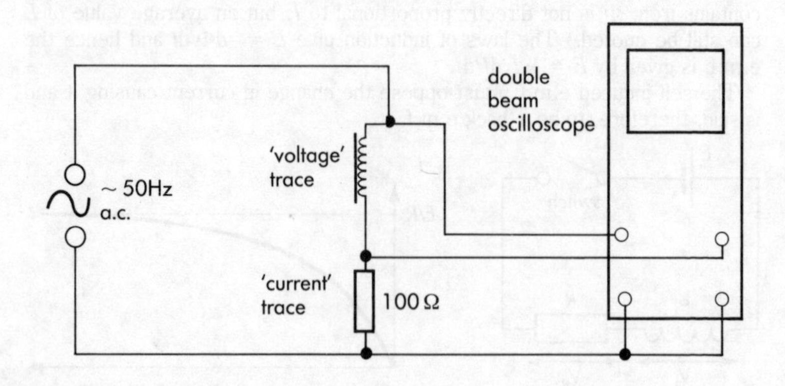

Fig. S.7 Measurement of inductance

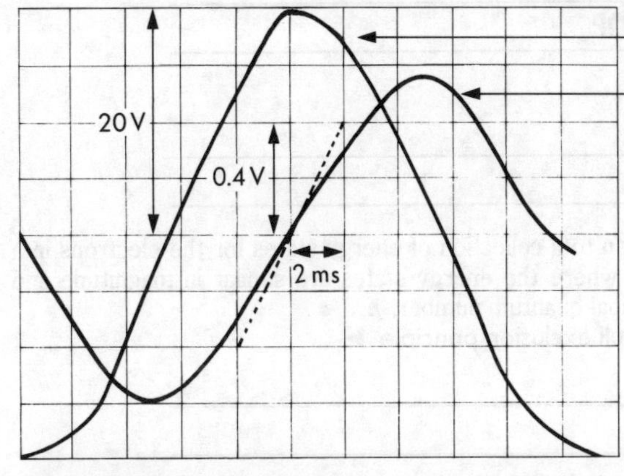

Fig. S.8 'Current' and 'voltage' traces

SEQUENTIAL LOGIC

The logic gates NOT, NAND, NOR (see **Digital logic**) are examples of what is properly called 'combinational logic'. This term means that the outputs depend only on the current input states. By contrast, the term sequential logic applies to circuits whose outputs depend not only on the current inputs but on the past ones as well. A sequential logic circuit therefore has some kind of memory in order that the earlier input states can be 'recalled'. The memory is obtained by the use of feedback, which ensures that when the input changes the effect of the previous input is not lost. The simplest example of such a circuit is the **bistable**, but generally more sophisticated flip-flops such as the **D-type flip-flop** or the **JK flip-flop** are used.

Data is usually handled in binary code, the two stable states of a flip-flop representing the two binary digits 0 and 1. Most flip-flops, including both the D and JK types, use clocked logic. That is to say they do not respond immediately to a piece of data but wait until a clock or enabling pulse is received at a clock (CK) or enabling (E) input. A complicated sequential logic system such as a computer is regulated by a clock in the form of a pulse generator. Changes throughout the system then occur in an orderly way, a step at a time, according to the sequence of pulses from the clock. Typically the pulses will be at a very steady rate, 10 MHz or higher being typical. The usual way of clocking is to have changes occurring when the clock pulse is rising (from logic 0 to logic 1) or falling (from 1 to 0). The former is called positive-edge triggering and the latter negative-edge triggering. The former is described in the **JK flip-flop**.

SERIES-WOUND MOTOR

◀ Direct current electric motor ▶

SET-RESET FLIP-FLOP

◀ Bistable ▶

SHELL

This is the name given to a collection of energy states for the electrons in a multi-electron atom, where the energy states are similar in magnitude and share the same principal quantum number, n.
◀ Energy levels, Pauli exclusion principle ▶

S.H.M.

◀ Simple harmonic motion ▶

SHORT-SIGHTEDNESS

◀ Defects of vision ▶

SHUNT

◀ Ammeters and voltmeters ▶

SHUNT-WOUND MOTOR

◀ Direct current electric motor ▶

S I SYSTEM

◀ Physical quantities in the SI system ▶

SIEVERT

◀ Radioactivity: units of measurement ▶

SIGNAL TO NOISE RATIO

This is a term used in communication physics. In communication physics noise is a technical word which refers to electrical disturbances which, for example in a radio, causes audible and unwanted noise when heard on a receiver. Noise on a television system gives rise to similar objectionable effects, in this case unwanted graininess or 'snow'.

Some noise is picked up from external electrical equipment. The public electricity supply produces mains hum at 50 Hz. Switching circuits, thermostats, contacts, electric motors, faulty lighting: all these items can cause noise in a communication circuit. Even if all these were eliminated there is still the problem that an electric current is not a smoothly continuous flow of charge; instead it is made up of individual electrons and their random kinetic movements are equivalent to tiny random currents. Several stages of amplification will magnify these until on a radio set they are heard as a hissing sound. The only way of eliminating this effect is to keep electronic equipment at temperatures near absolute zero, which is impracticable.

The signal to noise ratio is used in connection with the input or the output of a piece of equipment and is defined as the amplitude of the signal divided by the mean amplitude of the noise.

SILICON CHIP

◀ Integrated circuit ▶

SIMPLE HARMONIC MOTION (S.H.M.)

This is a special class of **oscillation** in which the period, T, is the same for all amplitudes be they large or small. If and only if an oscillator has this property, it follows that:

i) The oscillation is sinusoidal.
ii) The acceleration is proportional to the magnitude of the displacement but directed always towards the equilibrium position, that is the mid-point of the motion.

S.H.M. considered mathematically

The simplest example of s.h.m. is the idealised motion of a trolley tethered by two springs. In the ideal case there is no friction and so the oscillation goes on indefinitely: the motion is horizontal and the only horizontal forces acting are the restoring forces of the springs (Fig. S.9). The displacement/time graph is shown in Fig. S.10, the corresponding velocity/time graph in Fig. S.11 and the acceleration/time graph in Fig. S.12.

Fig. S.9 Tethered trolley

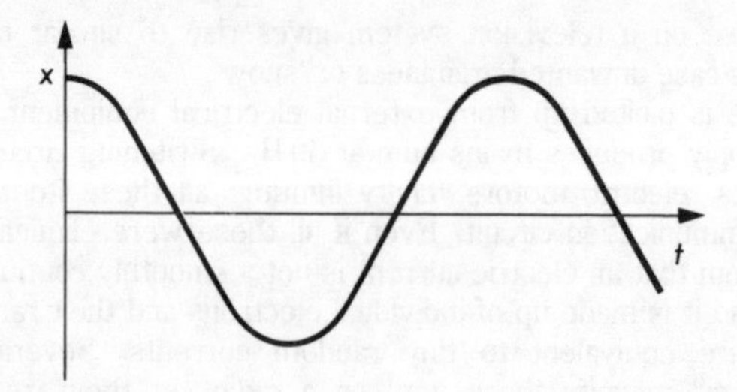

Fig. S.10 Displacement in s.h.m.

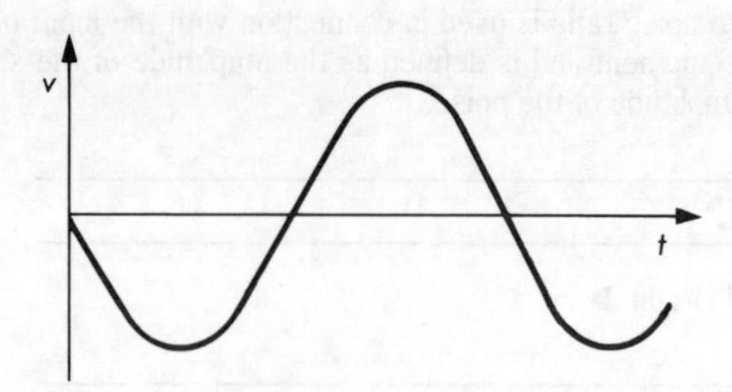

Fig. S.11 Velocity in s.h.m.

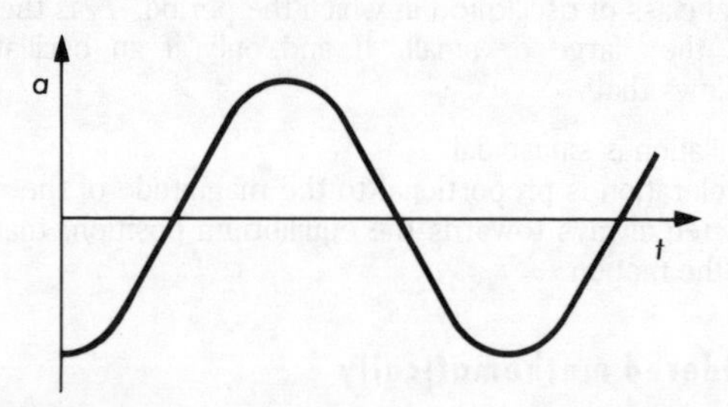

Fig. S.12 Acceleration in s.h.m.

Note that in the special case of s.h.m. all the three graphs are sinusoidal. The velocity/time and acceleration/time graphs are 90° and 180° out of phase respectively with the displacement/time graph. Note the term 'phase'. The sine and cosine functions are 'circular' functions, repeating themselves every 360° (or 2π radians). A complete cycle of oscillation is therefore 360°, a quarter of a cycle 90°. When two oscillations are '90° out of phase' we mean they are out of step by a quarter of a complete cycle.

Because of **Hooke's Law**, the elasticity of the springs provides a restoring force, F, given by $F = -kx$, where k is the force per unit displacement. k is found experimentally by displacing the trolley from its equilibrium position, measuring the restoring force with a newtonmeter and dividing the force by the displacement. (See also **Hooke's Law and simple harmonic motion.**)

Newton's Second Law gives $F = ma$, so we get

$$a = -\frac{kx}{m}$$, which is usually simplified as

$$a = -\omega^2 x$$

where $\omega^2 = k/m$.

Note that as the trolley is displaced more and more to the right the net force to the left gets more and more. Because of the **vector** nature of force, this means that the net force in the direction of increasing x is negative, and hence so is the acceleration. In simple language it means the trolley decelerates.

Assuming that the trolley is released with a displacement $x = x_0$ at $t = 0$ the solution of this equation is: $x = x_0 \cos \omega t$, where x_0 is the amplitude of oscillation.

The graphs that result are then those shown in Figs S.13 and S.14, described by the equations below:

velocity $\quad v = \omega x_0 \sin \omega t = v_{max} \sin \omega t = \omega \sqrt{x_0^2 - x^2}$

acceleration $\quad a = -\omega^2 x_0 \cos \omega t = -\omega^2 x$

with $T = 2\pi/\omega$ and $f = 1/T = \omega/2\pi$

Other mechanical examples of s.h.m. include the various types of pendulum, including torsional ones, a mass rolling on a parabolic track, liquid oscillating in a U-tube, and so on (Fig. S.13). Capacitor-inductor circuits provide an electrical example.

To solve problems in s.h.m. you need to establish the relationship between the restoring force F and the displacement in order to set up an equation corresponding to $F = -kx$. Then using $F = ma$ you can obtain $a = -\omega^2 x$ and find T from $\omega^2 = k/m$. Your value of ω can then be substituted into the other equations. Note that in all these cases you 'idealise' the problem by ignoring frictional forces. For illustrations of the method, see **Mass-spring oscillator** and **Simple pendulum**.

Energy considerations

In s.h.m. there is a constant interchange of energy between the **kinetic** and **potential** forms, the total energy staying constant. If $x = x_0 \cos \omega t$, the kinetic energy is given by

$$E_k = \tfrac{1}{2} mv^2 = \tfrac{1}{2} mv^2_{max} \sin^2 \omega t = \tfrac{1}{2} m\omega^2 (x_0^2 - x^2)$$

and the potential energy is given by

$$E_p = \tfrac{1}{2} m\omega^2 x^2$$

E_k is a maximum at the equilibrium position, where it is $\tfrac{1}{2} mv^2_{max}$. The total energy is constant and is always the sum of E_k and E_p, i.e.

Total energy $= \tfrac{1}{2} m\omega^2 x_0^2$

Fig. S.14 shows the behaviour as the oscillator goes through a complete cycle. Note the dependence on amplitude squared. If the amplitude is doubled the system stores quadruple the energy.

◀ Damped s.h.m., Newton's Laws of Motion ▶

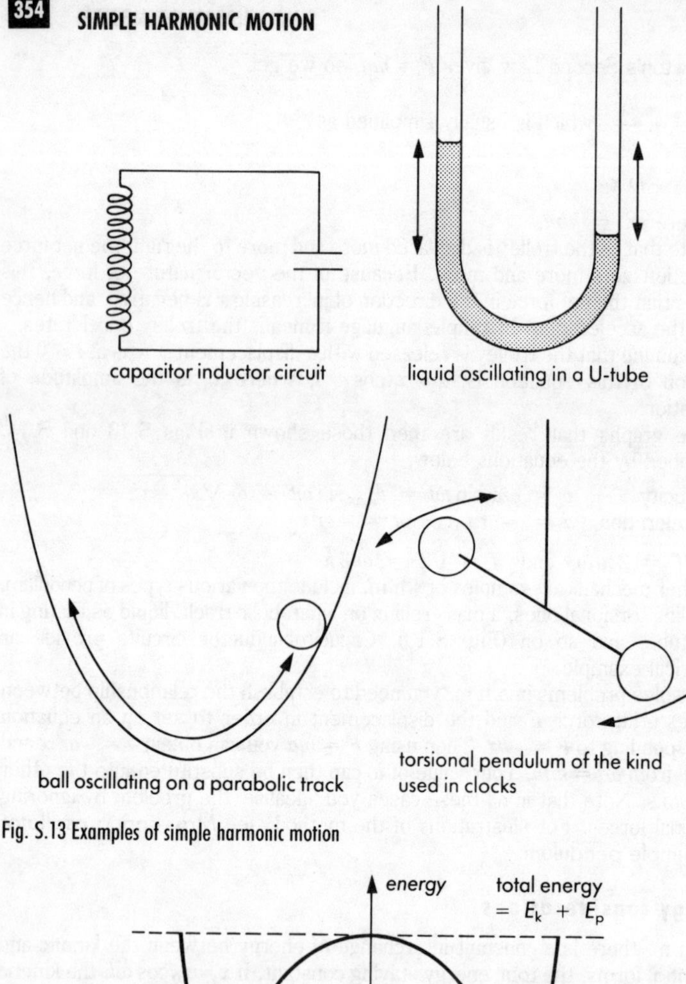

capacitor inductor circuit
liquid oscillating in a U-tube
ball oscillating on a parabolic track
torsional pendulum of the kind used in clocks

Fig. S.13 Examples of simple harmonic motion

energy
total energy = $E_k + E_p$
E_p
E_k
$-x_o$
x_o
displacement

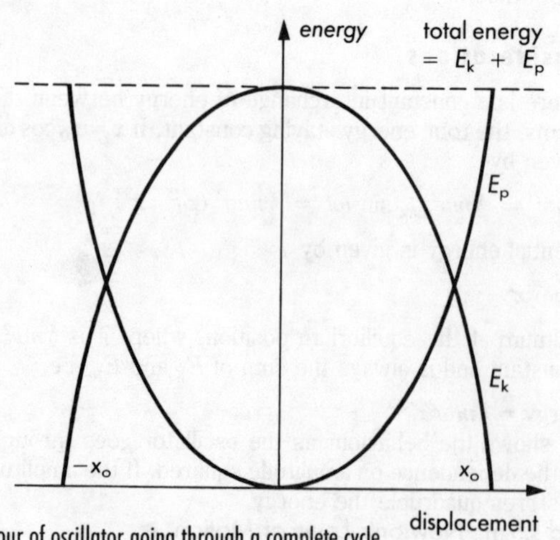

Fig. S.14 Behaviour of oscillator going through a complete cycle

SIMPLE PENDULUM

It is the regularity of the pendulum which provides the timekeeping mechanism of a grandfather clock. The pendulum is a simple example of an oscillator with **simple harmonic motion.**

In physics several types of pendulum are encountered. The term 'simple' pendulum is used to describe a pendulum in which all the mass acts at one point at the end of the pendulum. To analyse the motion from first principles it is necessary to resolve forces in the direction of motion and to make a small angle approximation.

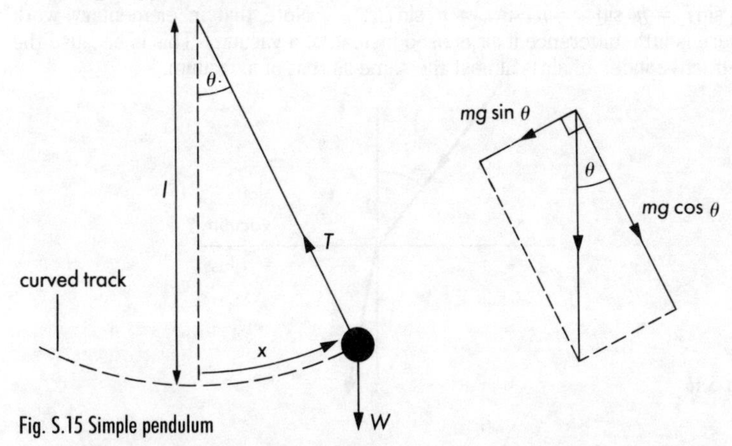

Fig. S.15 Simple pendulum

In Fig. S.15 the fixed length of the string, l, constrains the motion of the bob to the arc of a circle. It is helpful therefore to think of the bob moving on a curved track the steepness of which increases as the distance from the equilibrium position increases.

Two forces act on the bob, the tension T in the string and the weight W. The tension is always at right angles to the 'track', while W has to be resolved into two components, as shown in the smaller diagram. Here the component along the 'track' is $W \sin \theta$, or $mg \sin \theta$.

Let x be the distance along the arc of the track. Then in radians $\theta = x/l$. For small angles $\sin \theta \approx \theta$ and so $\sin \theta = x/l$. The restoring force, in the direction of increasing x, is therefore $-mgx/l$.

$$F = ma,$$
so $$ma = -mgx/l$$
or $$a = -\omega^2 x \quad \text{where} \quad \omega^2 = g/l$$
so $$x = x_0 \cos \omega t$$ and the period T is given by $T = 2\pi\sqrt{l/g}$.

SINUSOIDAL WAVE

◄ Travelling (progressive) wave ►

SNELL'S LAW

Fig. S.16 shows a ray travelling from a vacuum into glass and being refracted. Snell's Law states that $\sin i/\sin r$ = constant. The constant is written as n_g/n_v. n_g is the refractive index of the glass and n_v is the refractive index of vacuo taken to be 1. So we have $n_g = \sin i/\sin r$.

The refractive index must be equal to the ratio of the wavelength in vacuo in relation to the wavelength in the medium. (See **Refraction**.)

Fig. S.17 shows a ray travelling from a vacuum to glass to water to a different glass and so on. The product $n_i \sin i_i$ is constant and hence we have $n_1 \sin i_1 = n_2 \sin i_2 = n_3 \sin i_3 = n_4 \sin i_4 \ldots$ Note that in elementary work there is little difference if air is used instead of a vacuum. This is because the refractive index of air is almost the same as that of a vacuum.

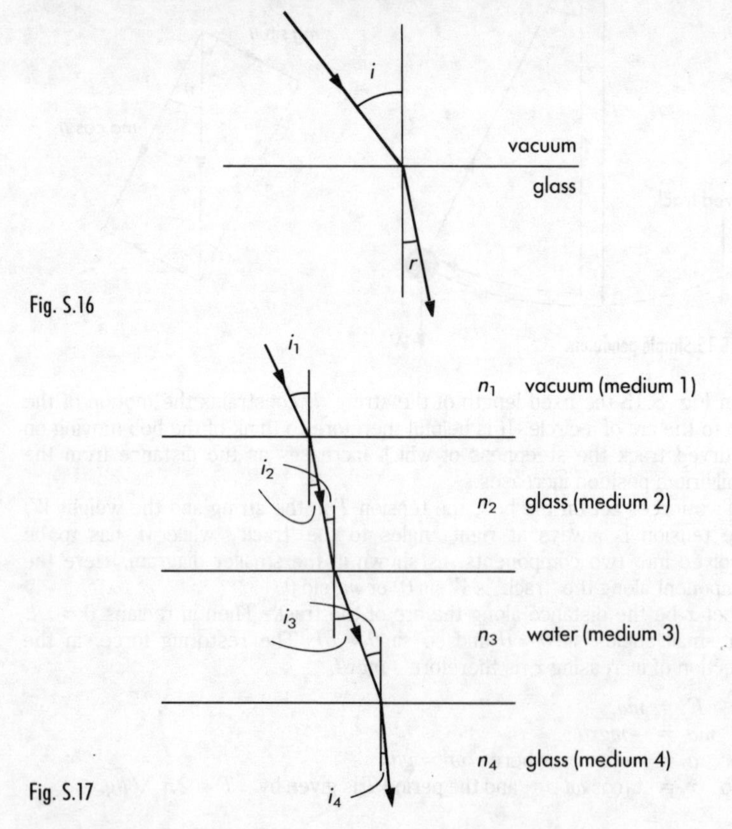

Fig. S.16

Fig. S.17

SOLENOID

◀ Magnetic field configurations ▶

SOLID-STATE DETECTOR

This is a method of detecting radioactive particles. It consists of a p–n junction of semiconducting material. When ionising radiation falls upon it, ion pairs are formed at the junction and the current through it increases. As with other detectors the signal has to be sent to an amplifier and a **scaler** or **ratemeter**.

SOLIDS

Solids may be crystalline, amorphous or polymeric. The structure of solids is more complex than that of gases, but less complicated than liquids. Solids are the most ordered state of matter and gases the most disordered, with liquids in between.

Crystalline solids

These are solids in which the atoms, ions or molecules are found in a regular repeating structure called a *lattice*. Crystals are usually three-dimensional, but two-dimensional ones, such as graphite and those used in liquid crystal displays in electronics, exist. Examples of crystal structure are shown, somewhat schematically, in Figs. S.18, S.19 and S.20.

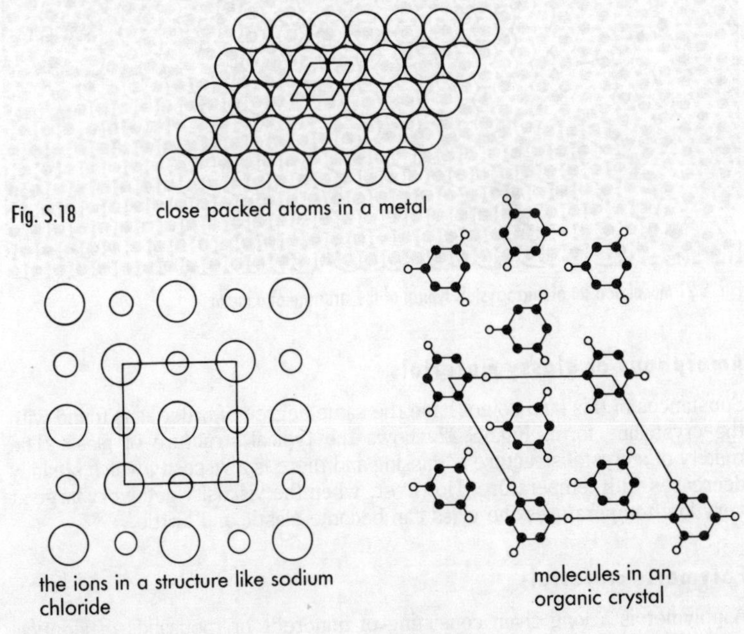

Fig. S.18 close packed atoms in a metal

the ions in a structure like sodium chloride

Fig. S.19

molecules in an organic crystal

Fig. S.20

The heavy line indicates the *unit cell* or the basic repeat unit. Bonding may be of several types, *ionic, covalent, metallic* or *van der Waals*. Ionic bonding is caused by electrostatic attraction between ions of opposite charge. The bond is non-directional. *Covalent bonding* is a quantum-mechanical effect which results from atoms sharing electrons, and is a directional bond. *Metallic bonding* is an even more complicated quantum-mechanical effect resulting from interactions between the 'sea' of conduction electrons and the lattice of ions. Van der Waals bonding is due to molecules behaving as electric dipoles which can weakly attract one another.

Many solids, including most metals, are actually crystalline, but with the crystal structure only apparent at a microscopic level. A piece of copper, for example, consists of a large number of microcrystals, each much smaller than a millimetre in length (Fig. S.21).

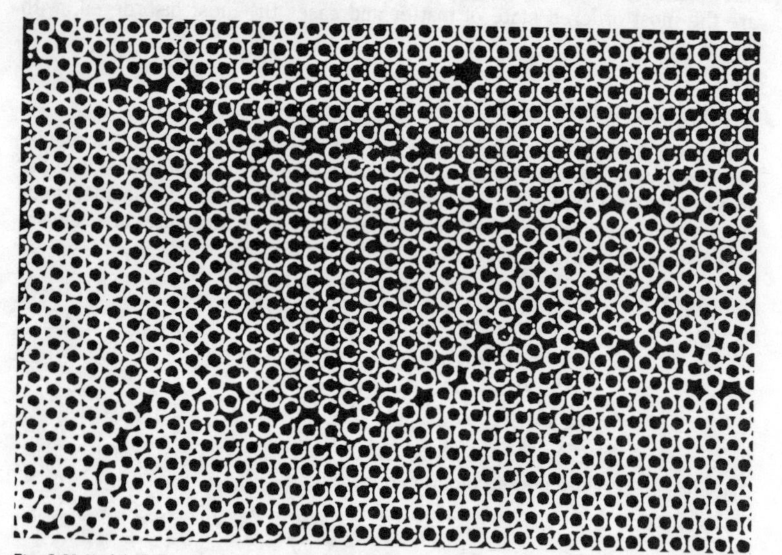

Fig. S.21 Model of a set of microcrystals typical of the structure of a metal

Amorphous or glassy materials

Substances of this kind do not have the same degree of order as is found with the crystalline form. Fig. S.22 shows the typical structure of glass. The rigidity of a crystal structure is missing and there is a viscosity which steadily decreases with temperature. However, when the viscosity gets very large at very low temperatures the glass can become elastic and brittle.

Polymeric materials

A polymer is a long chain consisting of hundreds or thousands of identical units. Each unit is basically itself a small molecule, and the chain is formed

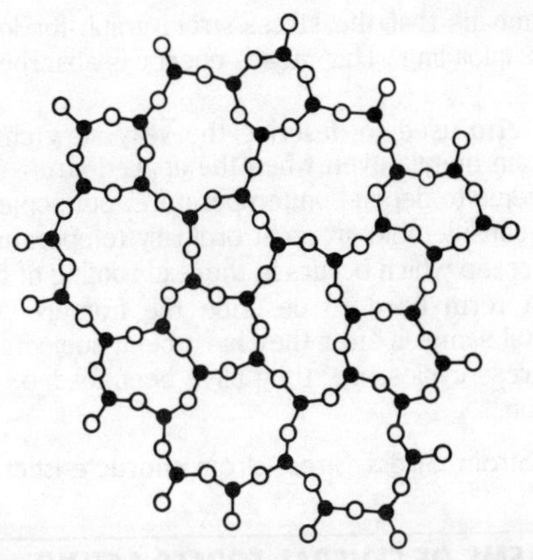

Fig. S.22 Structure of glass

when these molecules link together. The distance between units is fixed, but the chain can be bent and can curl up. Chains can slide past each other as the forces between them are weak. In some polymers the chains are tangled. An everyday example is rubber, in which on being strained the individual polymer chains straighten out and slide past parallel chains. As a result there is a much larger deformation before breaking than in a crystal. However, once the chains are fully stretched out it becomes difficult to stretch the substance further and it then breaks.

SOLIDS, PROPERTIES OF

Solids come in lots of shapes and sizes. Some are soft and spongy. Some hard and strong. The first stage in studying solids is to have a vocabulary to describe them. Physicists and engineers use a range of terms to characterise the properties solids may have. The more important ones are described below.

- 'Strong' means that the material can stand a large applied stress before breaking.
- 'Stiff' means that a large force is needed to bend the material.
- 'Ductile' means that the material can be easily rolled or pressed or drawn into wires.
- 'Brittle' means that the material cracks easily, and the broken pieces fit together showing no plastic deformation.
- 'Malleable' means that the material can be hammered into shape.
- 'Plastic' means that atoms of the material 'flow' past each other when a large stress is applied. If the stress is removed it is found that the material has acquired a permanent extension or 'set'.
- 'Elastic' means that the material returns to its original shape when a stress is removed. A plastic material cannot be elastic.

- 'Hysteresis' means that the stress/strain graph for loading is different from that for unloading. This means energy is absorbed in a loading/unloading cycle.
- 'Creep' is a term used to describe the very slow change in length or shape of certain metals even when the applied stress does not change. The effect seems to depend on temperature, but some soft metals such as lead have considerable creep at ordinary temperatures. An example of this is the creep which occurs in the lead roofing of cathedrals.
- 'Fatigue' is a term used to describe the fracture which sometimes occurs in metal samples after they have been subjected to a very large number of stress cycles, i.e. they have been loaded, unloaded, loaded again and so on.

◀ Hooke's Law, Strain, Stress, Stress-strain characteristics ▶

SOLVING PROBLEMS OF SEVERAL FORCES ACTING ON A BODY

i) Start with a sketch diagram showing all the forces acting on a body.
ii) Resolve the forces into two components in two mutually perpendicular directions chosen at your convenience (e.g. along a slope and normal to it).
iii) Then apply the rule that the net (resultant) force in any particular direction is zero. At this stage, if you find an unbalanced force, either you have missed out one or more forces at step i) or else you don't have equilibrium.
iv) Apply the principle of moments through the most convenient axis.

If step iii) yields an unbalanced force the object will accelerate in a straight line in the direction of that force. If on the other hand step iv) suggests an unbalanced moment the body will undergo rotational acceleration in the same sense as the moment.

Note that a single force which acts on a rigid body, but not through its centre of mass, can always be replaced by a force through the centre of mass and a couple (See fig. S.23). The effect is 'translational' or straight-line motion in the direction of the force through the **centre of mass**, and simultaneous rotation in the sense of the **couple**. An example is that of pulling on the end of a boat with a rope. The boat is both pulled nearer the bank and swung round.

◀ Forces, Moment, Parallelogram of vectors, Resolution of vectors ▶

SPACE DIAGRAM

This is a diagram used in the solution of problems in **statics** (mechanics). A space diagram is one in which forces on a body are drawn acting from a point.

◀ Static equilibrium ▶

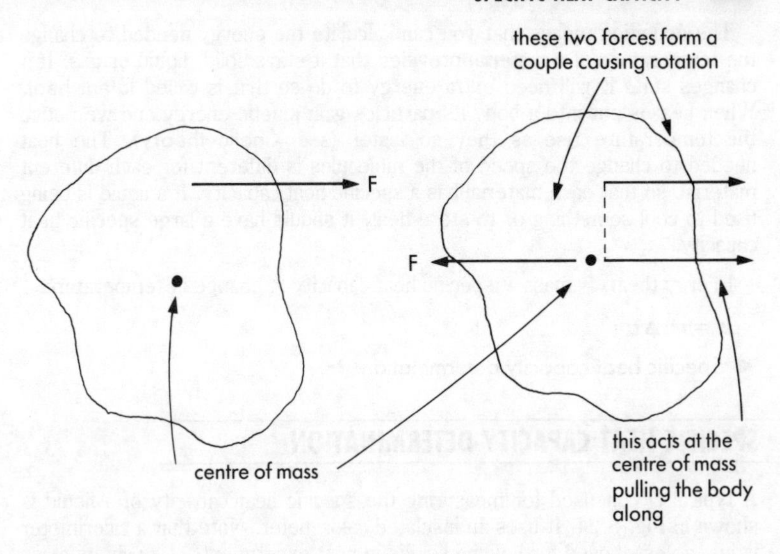

Fig. S.23

SPARK COUNTER

This is another method of detecting radioactive particles (see **Geiger tube, Ionisation chamber**). In its simplest form it consists of a fine metal gauze mounted about 1 mm away from a metal plate. An extra high tension (e.h.t.) supply is connected between the two and the voltage is adjusted so that sparking has just stopped taking place. The voltage required is about 5 kV. The device is particularly suitable for detecting **alpha radiation**. If an alpha source is brought up to the gauze, ionisation occurs and sparks will be seen between the gauze and the plate.

In a more sophisticated form the spark counter consists of a large number of wires separated from a plate each with their own individual e.h.t. supply. If a radioactive particle passes across the series of wires, a series of sparks are produced marking the track at the particle. In experiments in nuclear and particle physics each wire can be connected to a computer, so that the data can be automatically collected for subsequent analysis.

SPECIFIC HEAT CAPACITY

The specific heat capacity of a material is the quantity of heat energy that will raise the temperature of 1 kg of the material by 1 K without changing its state.

Since the energy goes 'inside' the body, we say that the heat energy has become *internal energy*. The specific heat capacity will be measured in $\mathrm{J kg^{-1} K^{-1}}$.

The definition means that you can calculate the energy needed to change the temperature of a material provided that it stays solid, liquid or gas. If it changes state it will need extra energy to do so that is called **latent heat.** When heat is put into a body its particles gain kinetic energy and we notice the temperature rise as they go faster (see **Kinetic theory**). The heat needed to change the speed of the molecules is different for each different material, so that each material has a specific heat capacity. If a liquid is being used to cool something or to store heat, it should have a large specific heat capacity.

Energy (heat) = mass × specific heat capacity × change in temperature.

$E = mc\Delta\theta$

◀ Specific heat capacity determination ▶

SPECIFIC HEAT CAPACITY DETERMINATION

A typical circuit used for measuring the specific heat capacity of a liquid is shown in Fig. S.24. It uses an insulated calorimeter. Note that a calorimeter is just a vessel used for holding liquids in heat experiments. Usually its mass and specific heat capacity should be known.

The liquid is heated for a time, t, using the heating element. The temperature increase should be measured with a thermocouple **thermometer** as this will have a very low thermal capacity. The thermal capacity, C, of the calorimeter needs to be known.

The specific heat capacity, c, of the liquid is then found from

$$IVt = mc\Delta\theta + C\Delta\theta$$

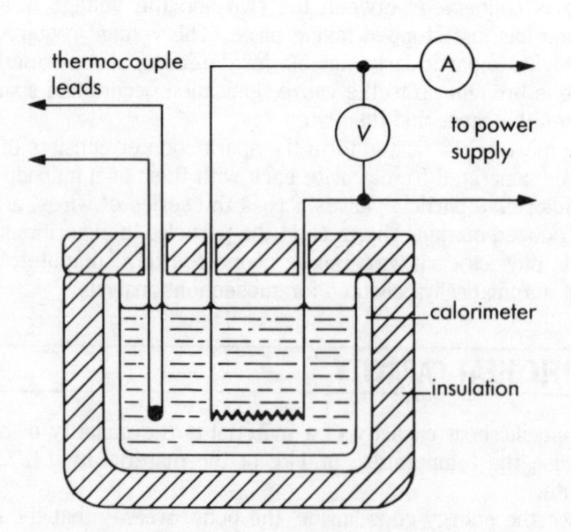

Fig. S.24 Circuit for measuring the specific heat capacity of a liquid

where I is the current, V the potential difference, t the time, m the mass of liquid under test, $\Delta\theta$ the temperature rise and C is the thermal capacity of the calorimeter.

Some correction for heat loss is needed for accurate work. The simplest way of avoiding a heat loss correction is to begin heating with the calorimeter and liquid at a temperature $\frac{\Delta\theta}{2}$ below room temperature and to heat to $\frac{\Delta\theta}{2}$ above it. The heat gained from the background in the first half of the heating cycle is then equal to that lost in the second half.

The specific heat, c_s, of an insoluble solid of mass, m_s, can be found using the same apparatus by adding a small sample of the solid to the liquid. Then,

$$IVt = (mc + m_s c_s)\Delta\theta + C\Delta\theta$$

SPECTROMETER

As the name implies the spectrometer is basically an instrument for observing spectra, but it can be used to view other optical effects such as the deviation of light by a prism, the diffraction of a single slit, etc. Fig. S.25 shows the essential parts of a type of spectrometer used in schools and colleges. It consists of:

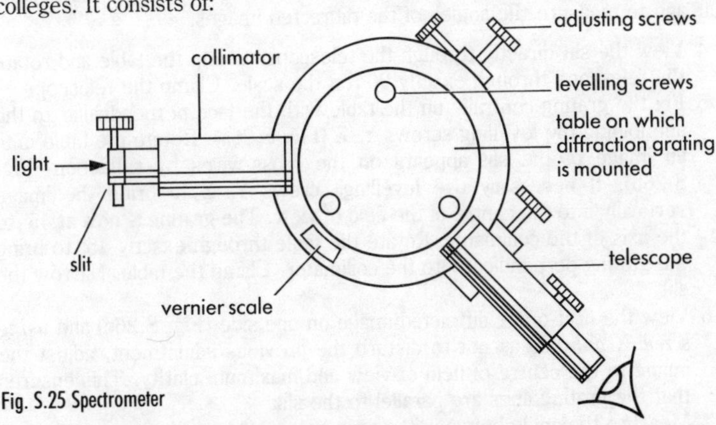

Fig. S.25 Spectrometer

i) The collimator. This is a tube with an adjustable slit at one end and a converging lens at the other. The distance between the slits and the lens can be varied. The collimator is usually adjusted so that the slit is at the focal point of the lens, so that when light is shown on the slit a beam of parallel light emerges from the lens.
ii) The table. This is a circular metal plate that can be rotated round a vertical axis. It can be levelled by means of three adjusting screws. In use a prism, diffraction grating or slit can be placed upon the table.
iii) The telescope. This is mounted horizontally and is free to rotate about the same vertical axis as the table. It is usually focused to receive parallel light from the collimator.

iv) **Vernier scale.** The base of the table is fixed to a vernier scale. It enables movements of the table to be read to high precision.

The most common use of the spectrometer in A-level physics would be for the determination of the wavelength of light, e.g. the measurement of the wavelength of the bright yellow lines of the sodium spectrum. The method of doing this using a diffraction grating is outlined below.

Preliminary adjustment of spectrometer

1 Focus the telescope eyepiece on the cross -wires.
2 Focus the telescope on a distant object.
3 Adjust the slit until it is vertical and open it until it is about 2 or 3 mm wide. Illuminate it with the sodium source. Now, with the telescope and collimator in the same straight line, observe the illuminated slit and focus the collimator. The collimator is now focused to produce parallel light and the telescope to receive it.

Use of diffraction grating

You now have to set the face of the grating perpendicular to the incident light from the collimator; to ensure that the grating lines are exactly parallel to the slit; and to measure the angles of the diffracted images.

4 View the slit directly through the telescope. Clamp the table and rotate the telescope through exactly 90° on the scale. Clamp the telescope.
5 Fix the grating centrally on the table with the face perpendicular to the line joining the levelling screws Y, Z (Fig. S.26a). Rotate the table until an image of the slit appears on the cross-wires by reflection (Fig. S.26b). If necessary use levelling screws Y, Z to bring the image vertically into the centre of the field of view. The grating is now at 45° to the axis of the collimator. Rotate the table through exactly 45° to bring the grating perpendicular to the collimator. Clamp the table. Narrow the slit.
6 View the first-order diffracted image on one side (Fig. S.26c) and *using screw X only,* so as not to disturb the previous adjustment, adjust the image to the centre of field of view and maximum clarity. This ensures that the grating lines are parallel to the slit.
7 Measure the angle between the first-order diffracted images on the two sides, for the yellow D-line. This angle is 2θ, where
$$\lambda = s \sin \theta$$
s being the known grating spacing, the reciprocal of the number of lines per metre, and $n = 1$ for first order.
8 Repeat, using the second order spectrum on both sides. In this case $n = 2$ and λ is found from
$$2\lambda = s \sin \theta$$
9 If possible use the best grating you have (in terms of the number of lines per metre) with the highest-order spectrum you can achieve with it, and with the narrowest possible slit. See whether you can resolve the line into the doublet which it really is.

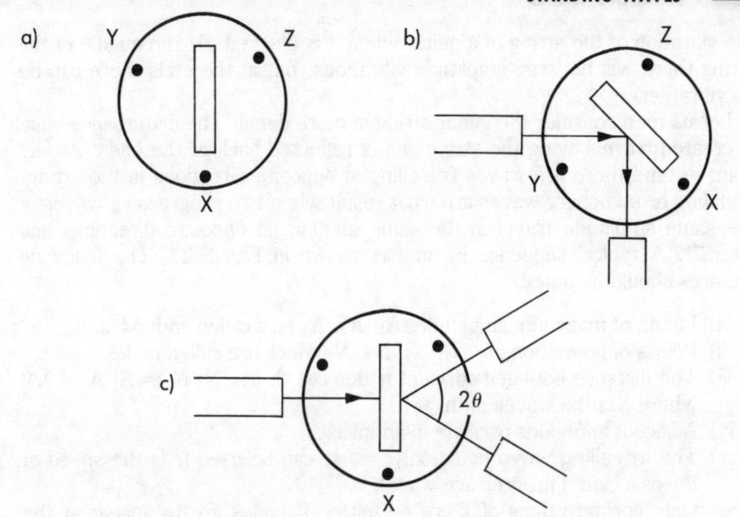

Fig. S.26 Adjusting the spectrometer

SPECTRUM

◀ Absorption spectrum, Band spectrum, Continuous spectrum, Electromagnetic spectrum, Line spectrum, Spectrometer ▶

SPHERICAL ABERRATION

◀ Camera ▶

SPIN

Spin is the intrinsic **angular momentum** possessed by **elementary particles.** In saying that a particle such as an electron has spin, we mean that at a fundamental level there is an asymmetry about the particle. In the case of the electron this means that if we were to rotate it through 180° its physical properties would be different from what they were before we carried out the rotation. In order to return to a physical state which was the same as when we began we could do so by a further rotation of 180°. See 'up' and 'down' quarks in the entry **Quarks.**

STANDING WAVES

Standing waves (sometimes called *stationary waves*) are a wave pattern which occurs in a system in which the waves do not move. An example is the vibration of the string of a guitar when it is plucked. At the middle of the string there will be large-amplitude vibrations, but at the ends there can be no vibration.

Let us then consider the guitar string in more detail. The disturbance which is created travels along the string and is reflected back at the ends. At any point in time there are waves travelling in opposite directions in the string. Standing or stationary waves are what result when two progressive waves of the same amplitude travel in the same medium in opposite directions and interact. A typical sequence in time is shown in Fig. S.27. The following features should be noted:

i) Points of maximum amplitude, A_1, A_2, A_3, are called antinodes.
ii) Points of no motion are N_1, N_2, N_3, N_4 which are called nodes.
iii) The distance between adjacent nodes is $\lambda/2$, i.e. $N_1 N_2 = A_1 A_2 = \lambda/2$ where λ is the wavelength.
iv) Adjacent antinodes oscillate in antiphase.
v) The **travelling wave** equation, $c = f\lambda$, can be used (c is the speed of the associated progressive wave).
vi) Only certain values of λ are permitted if nodes are to appear at the ends. The simplest example is the guitar string mentioned above. The system vibrates at the frequency given by $f = c/\lambda$.

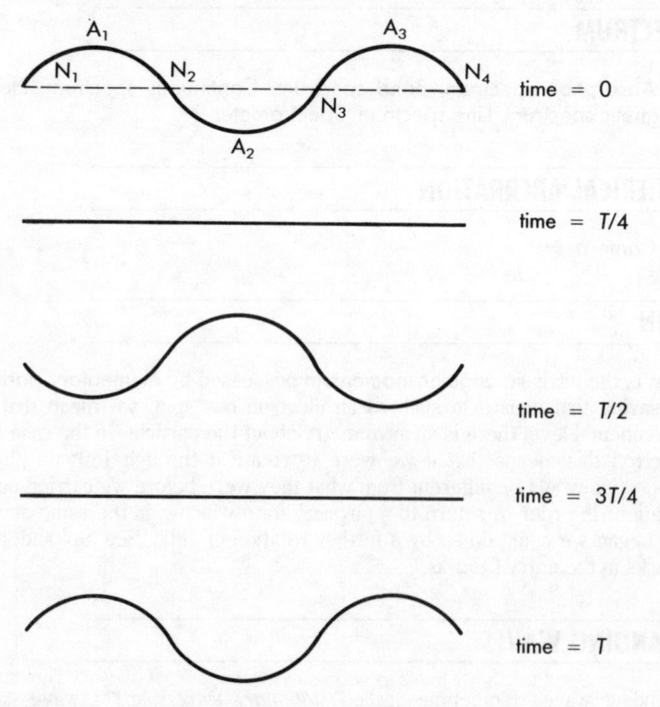

Fig. S.27 'Snapshots' of a standing wave system

Resonance

If an external vibration corresponding to one of the permitted frequencies can be applied, the standing wave may be produced. This is an example of **resonance.** Melde's apparatus provides an example (Fig. S.28). The frequency of the vibrator is adjusted until a resonance is obtained, i.e. a stationary wave pattern is produced. The speed of such waves is given by

$$c = \sqrt{T/\mu}$$

where T is the tension in the string and μ the mass per unit length. Using the fact that l, the node–node distance, is $\lambda/2$, and $c = f\lambda$, we find

$$f = \frac{1}{2l}\sqrt{T/\mu}$$

Another way of producing this type of resonance is to send a.c. from a variable frequency signal generator along a wire with a magnetic field across the wire at its centre (Fig. S.29). Oscillations will be induced through the **catapult field** force at the centre. Note that only resonances associated with nodes at the ends and an antinode at the centre will be obtained.

The difference between these resonances and the resonance of s.h.m. systems is that in this case there will be many resonant frequencies.

Further examples of resonance in sound are common.

◀ Air columns, Musical instruments ▶

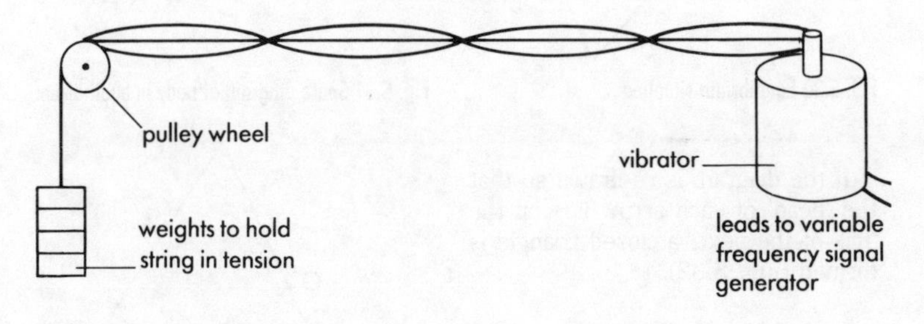

Fig. S.28 Melde's apparatus

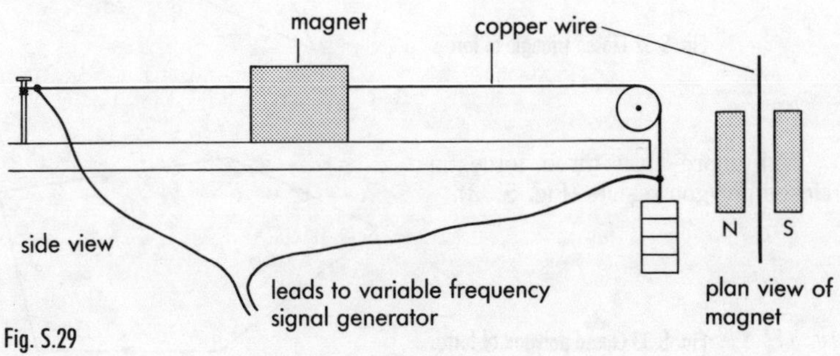

Fig. S.29

STATIC EQUILIBRIUM

An object is said to be in static equilibrium if it remains at rest even though it is acted on by several forces.

There are two types of static equilibrium: that which results from a set of non-parallel forces, and that from a set of forces which are parallel.

Equilibrium with several non-parallel forces

The two forces in Fig. S.30 add by the parallelogram rule to produce R. The body would be in equilibrium if a third force equal to R, but in the opposite direction, was also acting. A diagram with the three forces acting at a point is called a space diagram (Fig. S.31).

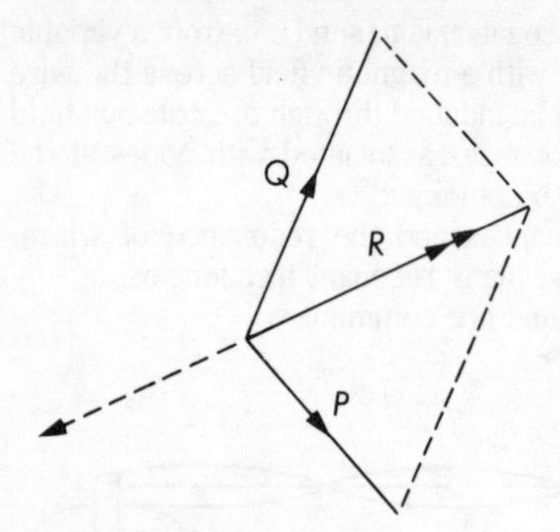

Fig. S.30 Equilibrium situation

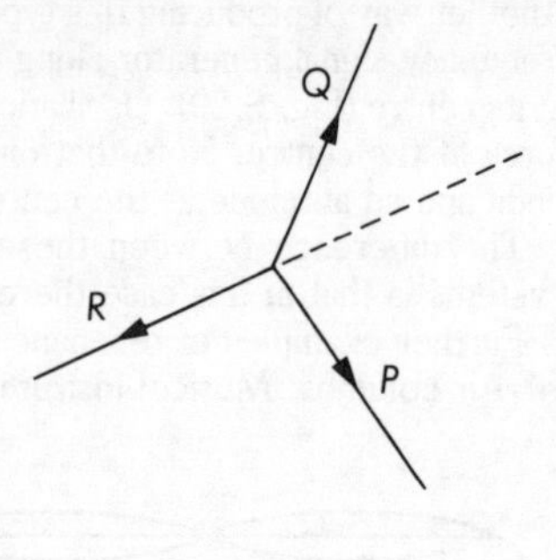

Fig. S.31 Space diagram of body in equilibrium

If the diagram is re-drawn so that the 'head' of each arrow lies on the 'tail' of the next, a closed triangle is formed (Fig. S.32).

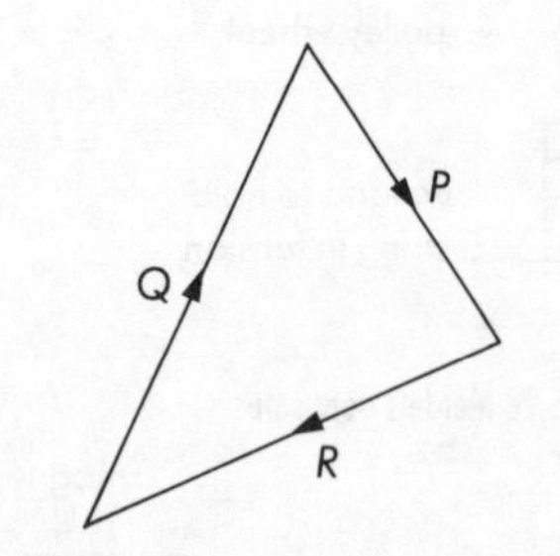

Fig. S.32 Closed triangle of forces

With more than three forces a closed polygon results (Fig. S.33).

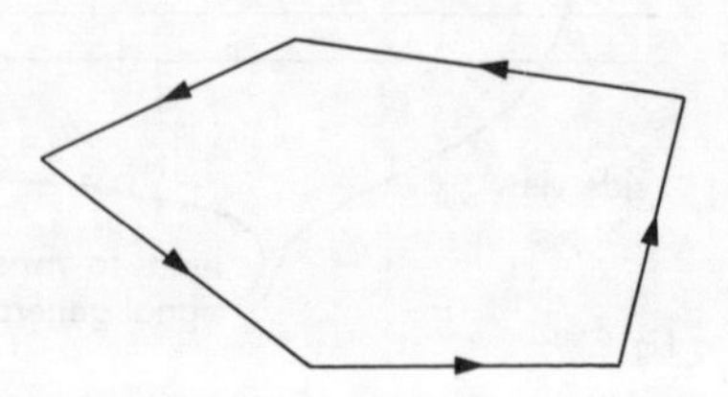

Fig. S.33 Closed polygon of forces

An example of this is the method of supporting the conducting cable on overhead-wire electrified railways (Fig. S.34).

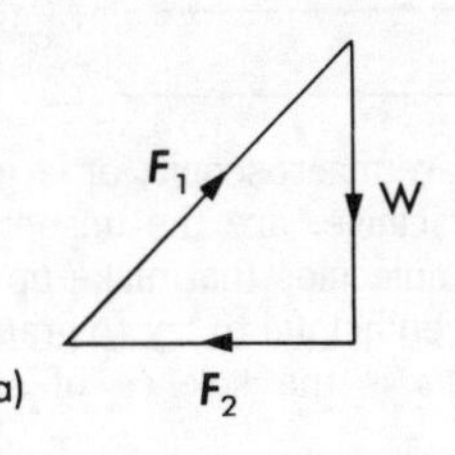

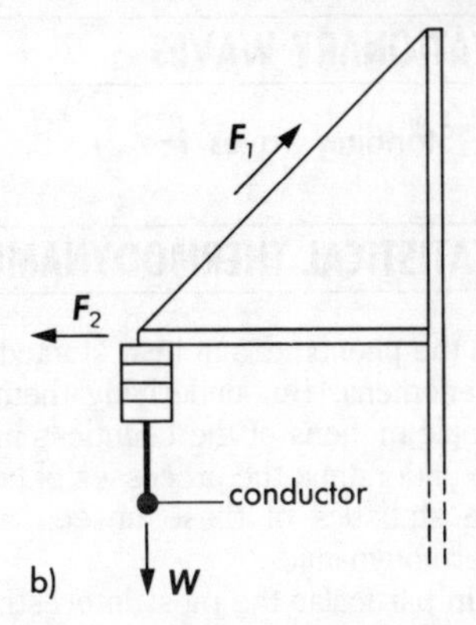

Fig. S.34

Equilibrium with several parallel forces

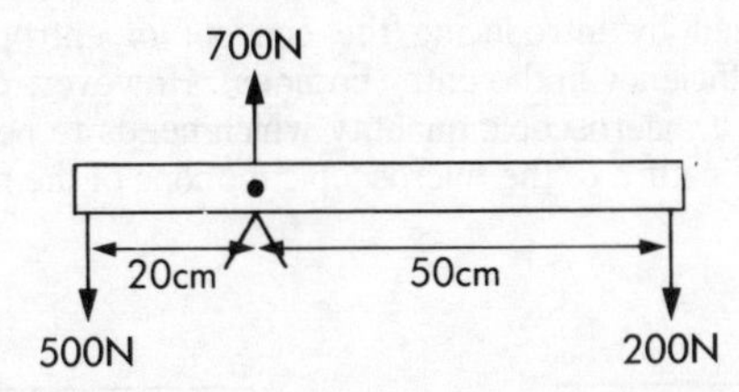

Fig. S.35

A see-saw is in equilibrium when acted on by a set of parallel forces. Each force produces a **torque** or **moment** about a fixed axis (Fig. S.35). For equilibrium the sum of the clockwise moments about any point on the body must be equal to the sum of the anticlockwise moments. This is usually called the principle of moments. (Note that in this example any point could be used for the analysis, not just the pivot. But if a point other than the pivot is chosen, the upward normal reaction force of 700 N has to be included.)

◀ Solving problems of several forces acting on a body ▶

STATIC PRESSURE

◀ Pitot static tube ▶

STATICS

Statics is the name generally given to that branch of mechanics which deals with what happens when the forces acting on a body are in equilibrium and the body is at rest.

STATIONARY WAVES

◀ Standing waves ▶

STATISTICAL THERMODYNAMICS

All the phenomena of heat studied at A-level are macroscopic, or large-scale, phenomena. But underlying them, and their cause, are the unseen microscopic motions of the countless numbers of molecules that make up matter. To understand the processes of heat it has been helpful to try to grapple with the statistics of these unseen motions. This is the science of statistical thermodynamics.

In particular the most interesting feature of **thermodynamics** is the 'one-way' processes that occur. For example, heat always flows *down* a thermal gradient, i.e. from a high-temperature region to one at low temperature: it never flows upwards. Then, for example, we can only convert some heat into work in a heat engine, but we can always convert work into heat. These problems are studied by introducing the concept of entropy, S (see the section on engine efficiency in the entry **Engines**). However, entropy defined in this way is itself a macroscopic quantity which needs to be understood in terms of the chance nature of the microscopic motions of the molecules.

Chance

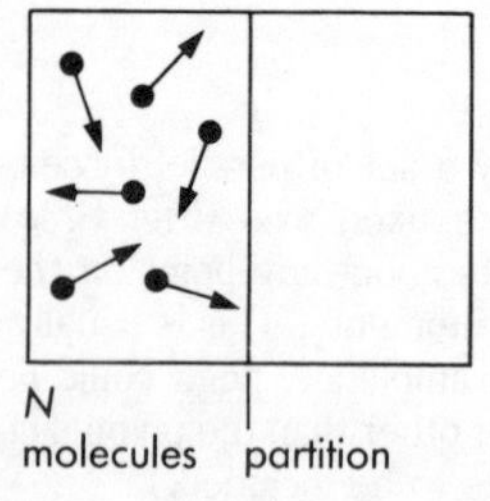

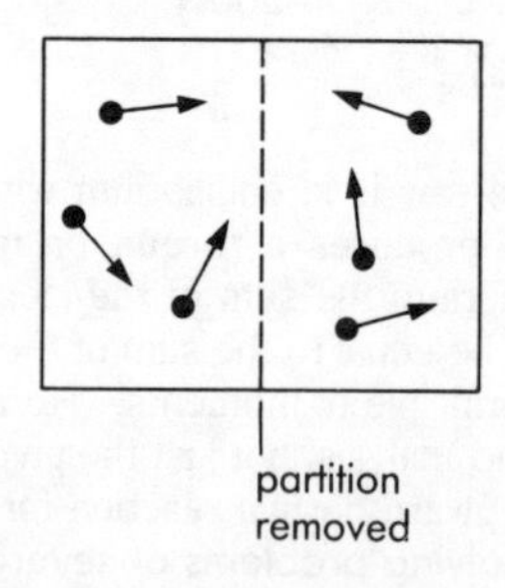

Fig. S.36

Consider an ideal gas of N molecules all contained in the left-hand side of the box shown in Fig. S.36. Once the partition is removed the molecules can move to anywhere in the whole box. The probability of any molecule being where it started, i.e. in the left-hand side of the box, is 1/2. The probability of all of them being in the left-hand side is $(1/2)^N = 1/2^N$, an exceedingly small number. Another way of thinking about this is to consider the change in the ways of arranging the molecules. Once the partition is removed we would have the rare possibility of all the molecules being in the left-hand side, all but one in the left-hand side, all but two in the left-hand side, and so on. Doubling the space open to them increases the ways of rearranging them from 1 to 2^N, assuming they are distinguishable.

The link between the microscopic and the macroscopic is given by the equation for entropy change:

$$\Delta S = k \ln (W'/W)$$

where W' = new number of ways of arranging the molecules, W the old number of ways, and k is the Boltzmann constant.

Entropy, energy and temperature

Some understanding of the role of chance in thermal equilibrium can be achieved by using what is called the *Einstein model of a solid.* In this model each atom is considered to have a set of equally spaced energy levels, the difference between each level being called a quantum of energy ϵ. (It should of course be noted that this model of energy levels is somewhat different from that used to explain the light-emitting properties of atoms in the entry **Energy levels.**) In this model an atom may only have energies of value 0, ϵ, 2ϵ, 3ϵ, 4ϵ,. . . etc., and we can number the corresponding energy levels n = 0, 1, 2, 3, 4,. . . etc. Because of random interactions between atoms, the energy can be constantly redistributed between them. Some ways of distributing four quanta, each of energy ϵ among three atoms are shown in Fig. S.37.

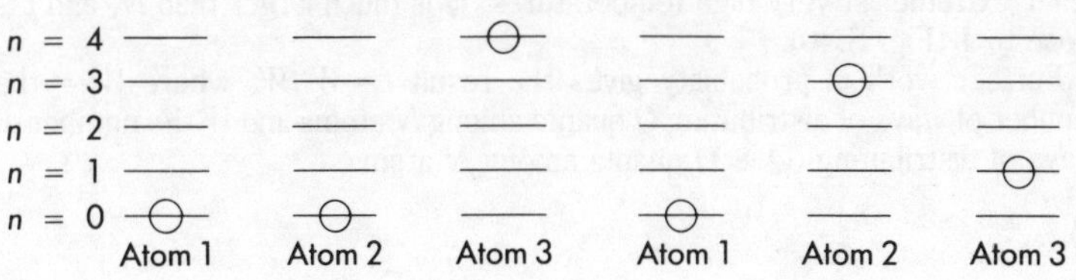

Fig. S.37

We could write all these combinations out: 400, 040, 004, 310, 301, 130, 031, 103, 013, 220, 202, 022, 211, 121, 112. Note that the combination of 3ϵ in one atom, 1ϵ in another and 0 in the third occurs more frequently than any other. With large amounts of energy and large numbers of atoms this pattern, i.e. of one combination occurring more frequently than any others, is even more pronounced. This combination is, of course, the equilibrium distribution. It can be represented by the histogram as shown in Fig. S.38. Y is the number of atoms holding n quanta of energy. The graph is for 305 quanta distributed among 102 atoms. The histogram shows an exponential decrease, i.e. a

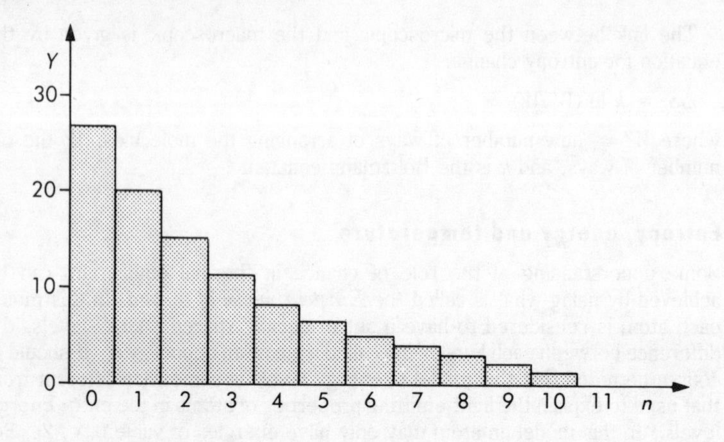

Fig. S.38 Histogram of number of atoms (*Y*) against quanta of energy (*n*)

constant ratio, f, between adjacent bars. $f =$ the number of atoms with n quanta. The number of atoms with $(n-1)$ quanta is

$$\frac{Q}{Q+N}$$

where Q is the total number of quanta and N the total number of atoms (if both Q and N are large).

At low temperatures Q is small, making f very small (Fig. S.39). At the other extreme, at very high temperatures, Q is much larger than N, and f is close to 1 (Fig. S.40).

Further work in probability gives the result $f = W'/W$, where $W' =$ the number of ways of distributing Q quanta among N atoms and W the number of ways of distributing $(Q + 1)$ quanta among N atoms.

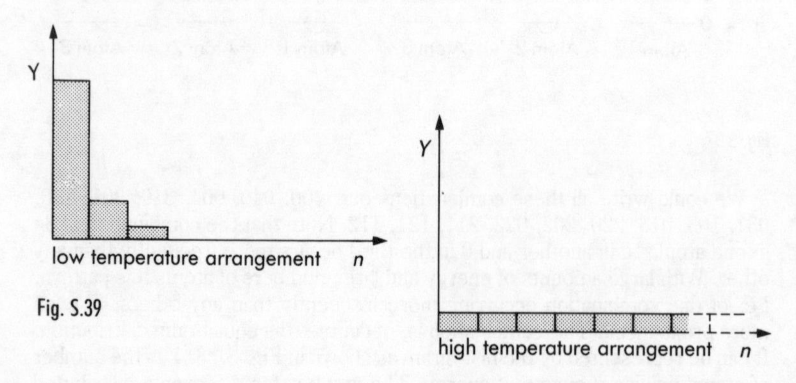

Fig. S.39

Fig. S.40

This result allows the derivation of further results linking energy, entropy and temperature. We shall simply summarise them here. The entropy change associated with the addition of one quantum ϵ is

$$\Delta S = \epsilon/T$$
$$\ln f = -\epsilon/kT$$
$$\text{or } f = e^{-\epsilon/kT}$$

where f is often referred to as the *Boltzmann factor*.

Note that doing statistical calculations from first principles is a hard task. The point of these various formulae is that they allow us to consider the effects of chance and change at a microscopic level without having to do probability calculations each time. It should also be noted that the arguments of the Einstein model generalise to other forms of matter where the energy levels are not equispaced. Some examples are considered below.

Evaporation

This takes place when a sizeable number of the molecules of a liquid acquire energy to escape as a result of random collision processes. The Boltzmann factor $f = e^{-\epsilon/kT}$ is a good guide to the temperature-dependence of the process. Evaporation is of course related to vapour pressure, and here a similar formula describes the temperature-dependence of vapour pressure.

If E is the energy needed to eject a molecule from the liquid, then $E = L/N_A$, where L is the number of joules per mole needed to vaporise a liquid and N_A is the Avogadro number. The fraction of molecules in the vapour is indicated by the vapour pressure, p, and so $p \propto e^{-L/N_A kT}$ or $\ln p = \text{constant} - L/N_A kT$ (Fig. S.41).

Two other examples are:

a) The current in a thermistor, or other semiconductor, where the current I is given by $I \propto e^{-E/kT}$ or $\ln I = \text{const} - E/kT$, where E is the energy needed to 'free' an electron into a conducting state (Fig. S.42);
b) Viscosity in liquids. Here flow rate $\propto e^{-E/kT}$ where E is the energy needed to push aside neighbouring molecules (Fig. S.43).

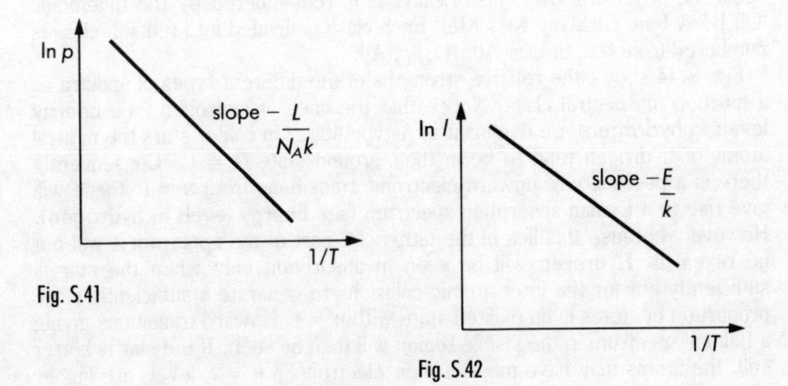

Fig. S.41

Fig. S.42

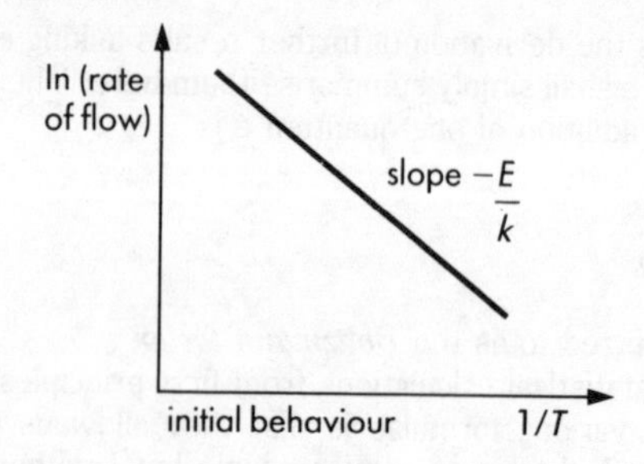

Fig. S.43

STEFAN'S LAW

◀ Thermal radiation ▶

STELLAR CLASSIFICATION

Stars are classified on the basis of the appearance of their spectra. The spectra are largely **absorption spectra** and are obtained by using a prism in the objective system of a telescope when a photograph of the sky is taken (a sky survey). Instead of a point image, each star than produces a small spectrum on the plate. Very high-resolution film is used, so that these images can be subsequently enlarged in order to obtain information about the spectra.

The spectra are governed mainly by the stellar surface temperatures. An unusual chemical composition has a big effect on the spectra, but as most stars are like the sun, containing mostly hydrogen and helium, it is the temperature which has the greatest effect.

The spectra are classified into seven main groups which form a sequence from hot to cold. The sequence is O, B, A, F, G, K, M. This rather odd sequence of letters arose historically. It is remembered by the mnemonic 'Oh Be A Fine Girl/Guy Kiss Me!' Each class is divided into ten sub-classes numbered from 0 to 9, e.g. A0, A1,. . . A9.

Fig. S.44 shows the relative strengths of the different types of spectra as a function of spectral class. Notice that the lines of hydrogen (see **Energy levels in hydrogen**) are dominant in A-type stars. In colder stars the neutral atoms of hydrogen tend to be in their ground state ($n = 1$). Consequently there is a possibility of upward electronic transitions from $n = 1$: these will give rise to a Lyman absorption spectrum (see **Energy levels in hydrogen**). However, because this lies in the ultraviolet part of the spectrum it will not be revealed. Hydrogen will be seen in absorption only when the star is sufficiently hot for the inter-atomic collisions to generate a sufficiently large proportion of atoms in an excited state with $n = 1$. Upward transitions giving a Balmer spectrum in the visible region will then be seen. If the star is hotter still, the atoms may have most of their electrons in $n = 2$; levels are higher

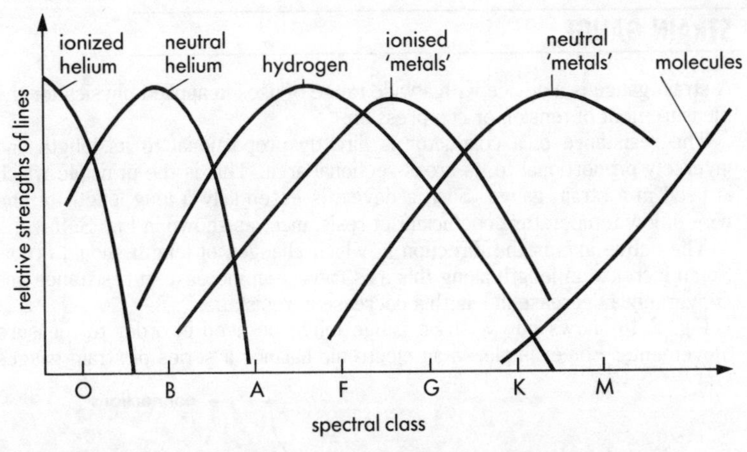

Fig. S.44 The progression of selected spectral properties through the sequence of spectral classes

and so the Balmer (visible) spectrum will not be seen. Really hot stars will contain ionised hydrogen which has no absorption spectrum. A similar story can be told for other components of the stellar atmosphere: there is always a particular and limited range of temperature in which a spectral type is dominant.

Note the term 'metals' in Fig. S.44. In astrophysics any element other than hydrogen and helium is referred to as a 'metal'.

STERADIAN

◄ Solid angle ►

STOKE'S LAW

◄ Millikan's experiment ►

STRAIN

Strain is the ratio of the extension of a material to its original length. It is a term used in the physics of materials to measure the extent to which a material is extended or compressed by a **stress**. It is used in preference to plain extension (or compression) because it takes into account the effect of the size of the sample. It is formally defined by:

Strain = e/l

where e is the extension and l the original length.

Because it is a ratio of distances it is dimensionless.

◄ Hooke's Law, Solids, properties of, Stress–strain characteristics ►

STRAIN GAUGE

A strain gauge is a device with a wide range of uses in applied physics for the measurement of tension or compression.

The resistance of a conductor is directly proportional to its length and inversely proportional to its cross-sectional area. This is the principle which is used in a strain gauge. Such a device is essentially a long length of fine wire of low temperature coefficient of resistance, as shown in Fig. S.45.

The active axis is the direction in which changes of length should occur. So an increase in length along this axis causes an increase in resistance and conversely a decrease in length a decrease in resistance.

Fig. S.46 shows how a strain gauge might be used in order to measure movements. For example, in an electronic balance a series of strain gauges

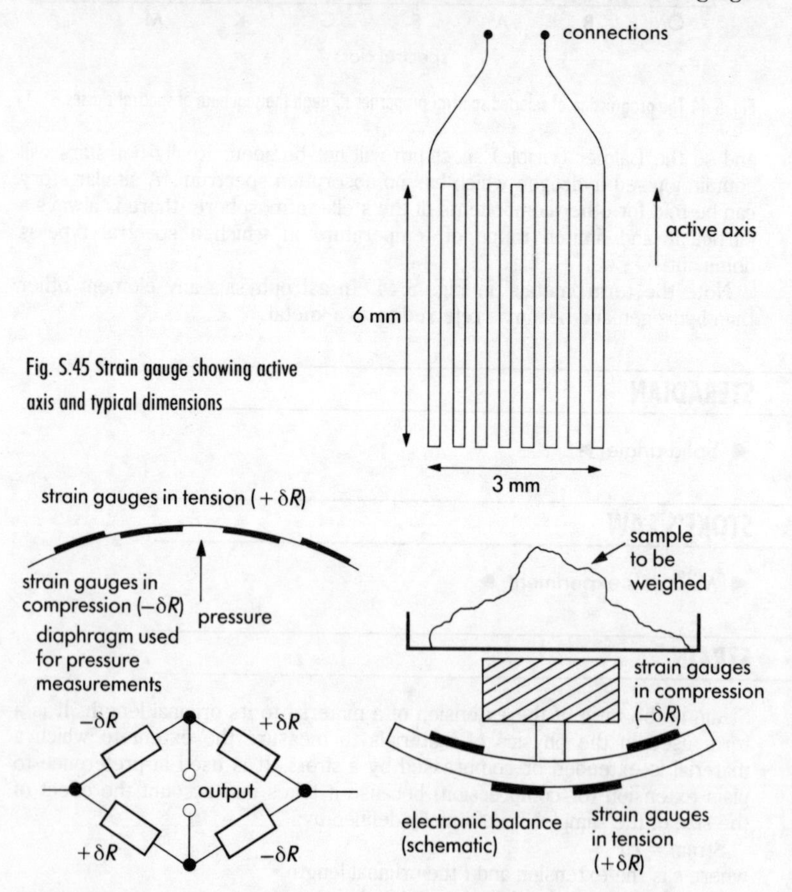

Fig. S.45 Strain gauge showing active axis and typical dimensions

Fig. S.46 Two uses of strain gauges and a circuit used for providing an output

might be arranged as shown on a deflecting plate, or in medical physics on either side of a diaphragm. When the component flexes, one side is in compression and the other side in tension. The change in resistance may be measured by a bridge circuit as shown in Fig. S.46.

STREAMLINE

This is a term used in the physics of **fluid** flow. In Fig. S.47, ABCD represents the path of a particle in a flowing fluid as time runs on. We say that the flow is streamline flow and that ABCD is a streamline when every particle entering the fluid at A subsequently goes through B, C, D etc. Streamlines can be made visible in the flow of water by injecting dyes into the flow.

Streamline flow contrasts with **turbulent flow.**

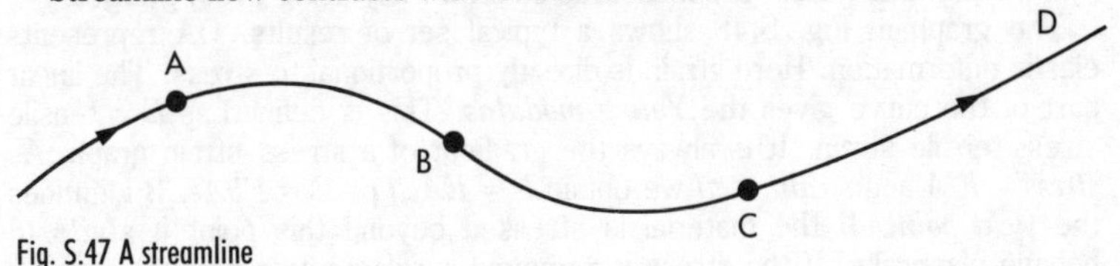

Fig. S.47 A streamline

STRESS

Stress is defined as the force acting on unit cross-sectional area of a material. It is a term used in the physics of materials when a solid material is acted on by **forces** of tension or compression. It is used in preference to force so that the effect of the cross-sectional area of the sample is taken into account.

Formally we define stress by:

Stress = F/A

where F is the force acting on unit cross-sectional area A. (The unit is N m^{-2} or the Pascal, Pa.)

Stress can be either *tensile*, as when the solid is stretched, or *compressive*, if it is compressed.)

Breaking stress is the greatest force per unit area that a material can withstand without fracture.

◀ Hooke's Law, Solids, properties of, Strain, Stress–strain characteristics ▶

STRESS–STRAIN CHARACTERISTICS

In the theory of solids the behaviour of a metal, for example, in the form of a wire can be described in terms of either a force–extension or a stress–strain graph. The advantage of the latter is that it is characteristic of the material, so that direct comparisons between the stress–strain graphs for different materials can be made when the dimensions of the specimens are different, e.g. a steel rod can be compared with a copper wire.

Stress–strain graphs are important in understanding the behaviour of a material and what it might be used for, and in trying to find and achieve a molecular understanding of the material.

Any apparatus used to find the stress–strain characteristics of a material must enable the experimenter to steadily increase the force/stress while simultaneously allowing accurate measurement of the extension/strain. In the school laboratory a metal is usually measured in the form of a thin wire suspended from a rigid support. A tensile force/stress is applied by loading with weights. The extension/strain is measured by means of a **vernier scale** attached to a control wire; this automatically allows for temperature compensation. In industry purpose-built testing rigs are used with forces applied hydraulically and strains are measured electronically using **strain gauges.**

The graph in Fig. S.48 shows a typical set of results. OA represents elastic deformation. Here strain is directly proportional to stress. The linear part of the curve gives the *Young modulus*. This is defined as E = tensile stress/tensile strain. It is always the gradient of a stress–strain graph. As *stress* = F/A and *strain* = e/l we obtain $F = EAe/l$ or $E = Fl/Ae$. B identifies the *yield point*. If the material is stressed beyond this point it starts to behave plastically. If the stress is removed it relaxes to a point O′, having acquired a permanent extension or 'set' represented by OO′.

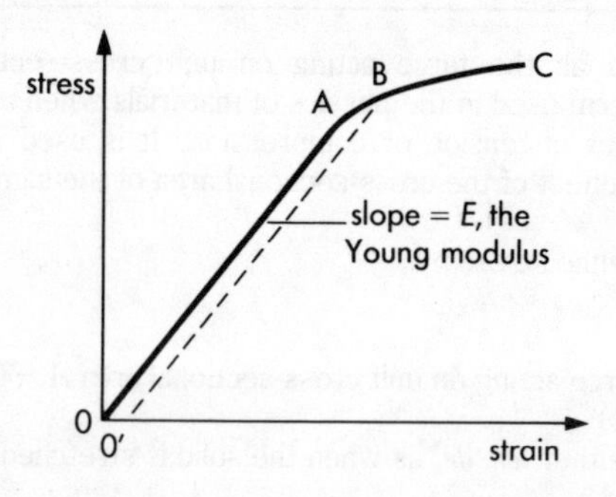

Fig. S.48 Elastic deformation caused by stress

Behaviour of non-metal samples

The types of graph vary considerably. For Figs S.49 and S.50 the curve obtained on unloading is different from that on loading. This is called hysteresis. Rubber regains its original length and is elastic. Polythene becomes permanently stretched, as does plastic.

◀ Hooke's Law ▶

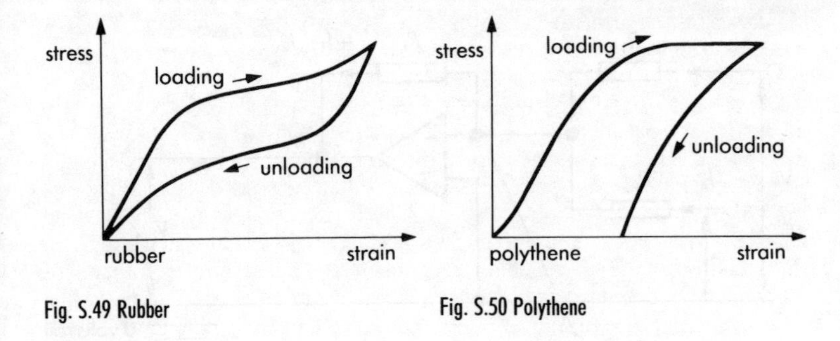

Fig. S.49 Rubber

Fig. S.50 Polythene

STROBOSCOPE

In A-level physics the stroboscope is a device with a xenon flash tube which is driven by an oscillator which sends out electric pulses at very regular intervals. As a result the stroboscope produces a sequence of very short flashes of light at regular intervals. The frequency is the number of flashes per second. The device is used to measure the frequency of vibrating or rotating objects, e.g. insect wings, mechanical vibrations or the speed of an electric motor. The frequency of the strobe is adjusted until it is flashing once per vibration or rotation, so that the object being viewed is always in the same place when it is seen. As a result it appears stationary. In practice there is always some ambiguity in reading a stroboscope because the object may have rotated or vibrated twice or three times between flashes. To resolve the ambiguity it is necessary to make an initial frequency measurement as explained above, and then to double the frequency of the strobe. If the object was truly being illuminated only once per revolution/vibration, at twice the frequency it will appear stationary in two different positions. In this way any ambiguity of measurement can be overcome.

◀ Frequency measurement ▶

STRONG INTERACTION

This is sometimes called the *strong force*. It is the name given to the attractive force that grips **protons** together in the **nucleus** and enables them to overcome their mutual electrostatic repulsion. It is one of the fundamental forces of nature.

SUMMING AMPLIFIER

The **operational amplifier** can be used to add a number of voltages, the voltages being a.c. or d.c., and hence can be used as a 'mixer' in audio-electronics where it is necessary to combine signals from an electric guitar, a pick-up, a microphone, etc.

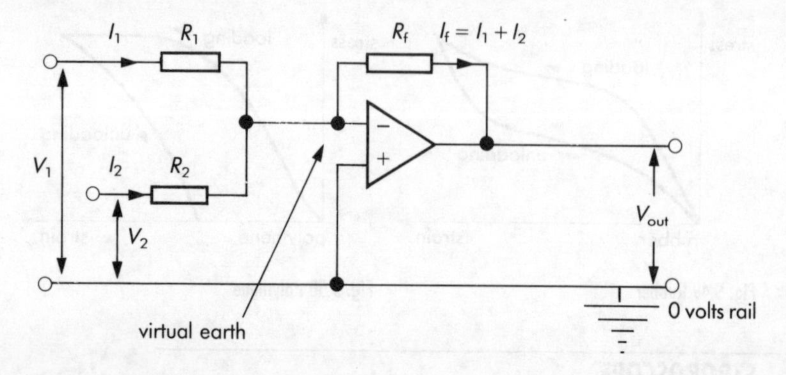

Fig. S.51 Summing amplifier

In Fig. S.51 two input voltages, V_1 and V_2, are applied to the inverting terminal through input resistors, R_1 and R_2. The inverting terminal is a virtual earth and the very high input impedance of the operational amplifier is such that the two input currents, I_1 and I_2, join together and flow through the feedback resistance, R_f. Note that if V_1 and V_2 are above earth potential, V_{out} is negative, i.e. the amplifier is in an inverting mode.

$I_f = I_1 + I_2$. Because of the virtual earth we have $I_1 = V_1/R_1$, $I_2 = V_2/R_2$, $I_f = -V_{out}/R_f$.

$$\text{Hence } -\frac{V_{out}}{R_f} = \frac{V_1}{R_1} + \frac{V_2}{R_2}$$

$$\text{Hence } V_{out} = -\left(\frac{R_f}{R_1}V_1 + \frac{R_f}{R_2}V_2\right)$$

Provided the feedback resistor is greater than each of the two input resistors, the two input voltages are added and amplified. Note that by using different input resistors the amplification factor for the two voltages may be different.

One useful property of the amplifier is that each input is isolated from the other, so that each behaves as if the other did not exist and neither feeds the input of the other even though both the resistors are connected at the inverting input. The circuit described may be made even more sophisticated by having additional inputs into the inverting terminal.

◀ Musical instruments ▶

SUPERCONDUCTIVITY

Below a certain temperature the electrical resistance of some metallic conductors completely vanishes. Such behaviour is called superconductivity.

The highest temperature at which superconductivity occurs is called the critical temperature, T_c. Values of T_c for a number of metals which are superconductors are given in the table.

Element	T_c/K	B_o/tesla
Aluminium	1.19	0.010
Lead	7.18	0.080
Mercury	4.15	0.041
Niobium	9.46	0.19
Tin	3.72	0.030
Zinc	0.88	0.005

At any temperature T, below T_c, superconductivity will cease and normal conductivity will be restored by placing the specimen in a magnetic field of sufficiently large flux density. The minimum value of the external flux density for this to occur is called the *critical flux density,* B_c. B_c varies with T according to

$$B_c = B_o\left[1-\left(\frac{T}{T_c}\right)^2\right]$$

where B_o is the value of B_c when T is 0 K. This relation holds for all metals which exhibit superconductivity. Values for B_o for some of these are shown in the table.

Clearly this effect causes difficulties if superconducting coils are used in an electromagnet, as the very existence of the field requires a lower temperature for superconductivity.

Superconductivity has recently been discovered in a number of substances which are not pure metals and at significantly higher temperatures than those in the table.

SUPERPOSITION PRINCIPLE

The superposition principle is the underlying principle of all **interference** problems in wave theory. It was the first outlined by Young, who was also the first to show that light was a wave motion by the **Young's slits** experiments. The superposition principle states that the resultant displacement of a point in a medium carrying a wave is equal to the sum of the displacements of separate and individual waves passing through the medium at that point. Note that in adding the displacements together account has to be taken of the sign of the displacement. So a positive displacement of, say, 3 cm added to a negative displacement of 2 cm leaves a net displacement of 3 – 2, or 1 cm. The superposition principle lies behind the statement in waves physics that wave plus wave can equal something or wave plus wave can equal nothing.

SURFACE TENSION

Water behaves as if it has a skin on its surface. As a result it is possible to overfill a tumbler with water, and with great care to 'float' a needle on the surface of the water. In both cases the water surface behaves like a stretched 'skin' or like a stretched membrane of rubber. This effect is called surface tension. Clearly the surface has properties which are different from those of the liquid as a whole.

Surface tension can be understood in terms of the **binding energy** ϵ_o of pairs of individual molecules.

Consider what happens if we were to make a surface in the middle of a liquid. Suppose as in Fig. S.52 that a volume of liquid is somehow 'split' apart along a surface PP′. Two new surfaces are formed corresponding to the now separate liquids X and Y. If the new surface area is S and if there are A molecules per unit area of surface, there are SA molecules on each surface. As a first approximation it can be assumed that for each surface molecule half its neighbours have been pulled away in forming the surface. With n nearest neighbours an energy per molecule of $\frac{1}{2}n\epsilon_o$ is needed. Thus a total energy of approximately $SA\frac{1}{2}n\epsilon_o$ is needed to create a total new surface area of $2S$. Hence we can define γ as the energy per unit area of the surface, and hence γ is $\frac{1}{4}nA\epsilon_o$

γ can be defined in other ways, as we can show. Thinking of the 'skin'-like properties of a liquid surface, consider a film of liquid stretched across a horizontal wire frame ABCD (Fig. S.53). Because of the stretched liquid surface there will be a sideways force say on BC. Suppose BC has a length l and x is the force per unit length. Then the force on BC is $2xl$. The factor of

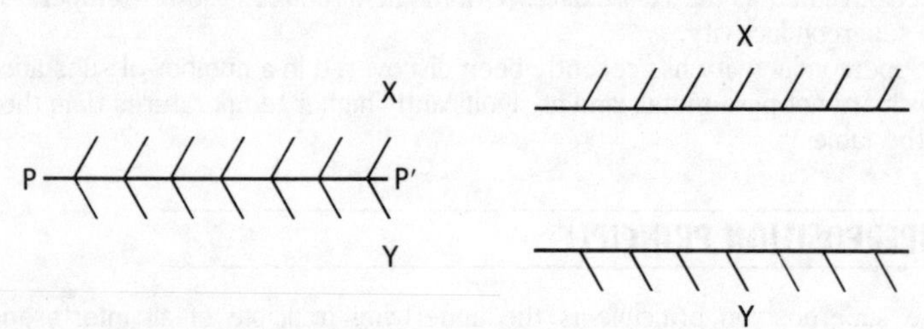

Fig. S.52 'Splitting' a liquid into two parts

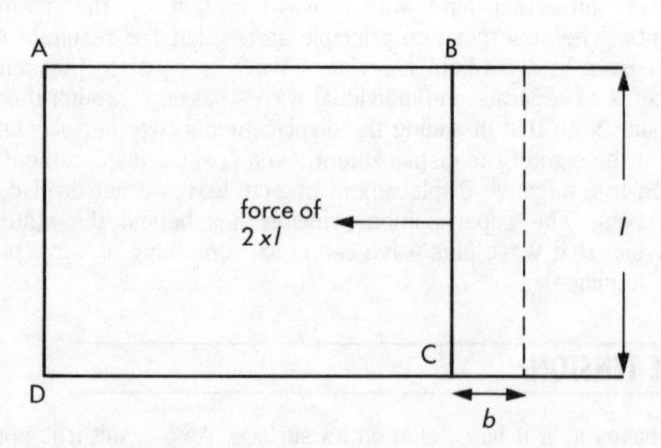

Fig. S.53 Liquid exerting surface tension stretched across a wire frame

2 arises because there are two surfaces to the liquid, one at the top and one at the bottom. Suppose BC is now moved a distance b. Then usually there will be a drop in temperature as the surface tension changes. But supposing that the surface area increases under isothermal conditions so that the surface tension remains the same. In this case the work done in enlarging the surface is $2xl \times b$. In this expression $2lb$ is the increase in area, again there being top and bottom surfaces. But γ is the energy for an increase in unit area of the surface. Hence $\gamma = x$.

So γ can be given several meanings. It is:

a) The work done per unit area in increasing the surface area of a liquid under isothermal conditions.
b) The free surface energy – the mechanical work that could be done when the surface contracts.
c) The force per unit length acting in the surface at right angles to one side of a line drawn in the surface.

There is also a relation between L the molar **latent heat of vaporisation** and γ. $L = \frac{1}{2}N_A n \epsilon_o$ where N_A is the Avogadro number. So as $\gamma = \frac{1}{4}nA\epsilon_o$, $L/\gamma = 2N_A/A$.

◀ Interatomic forces ▶

TELEPHOTO LENS

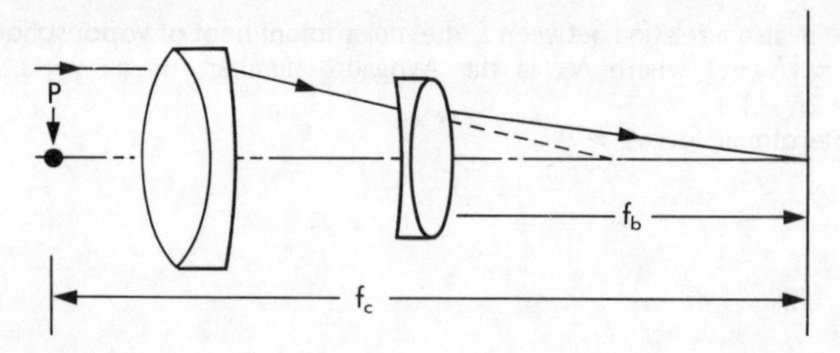

Fig. T.1 Telephoto lens

The telephoto lens is used in cameras in order to produce a large image of a distant object without having to use a lens of very long focal length which would make the camera like a telescope. It consists of a combination of a **converging lens** with a weaker **diverging lens** located near the film (Fig. T.1). As far as the light reaching the film is concerned, the system behaves as if it were being focused by a single lens of focal length f_c located at P. The ratio f_c/f_b is called the telephoto magnification. Lenses are usually corrected for chromatic aberration.

In movie or video photography it is sometimes useful to go from a distance view to a close-up continuously and without allowing the picture to go badly out of focus. The *zoom lenses* used for this purpose are combinations whose focal length is changed by altering the positions of some of the components in such a way that the distance of the image from the fixed components is unchanged while the magnification of the telephoto system changes from a value near unity to a much higher value.

TEMPERATURE

Simply, the temperature of something is how hot it is. At a scientific level it is not possible to talk about temperature without having the notion of a scale, i.e. a set of numbers by which the degree of 'hotness' can be measured.

Before the invention of thermometers and temperature scales, people were able to record how hot or cold it was only by their subjective impressions or by the effect on certain critical material phenomena. By critical we mean here something which happens only when a certain degree of hotness (or coldness) is reached. For example in a particularly bad winter in Norfolk in the eighteenth century, a diarist called Parson Woodforde noted that it was cold enough for the urine in his bedroom chamber pot to freeze. Thermometers and temperature scales were invented so that numbers could be assigned to particular degrees of hotness (or coldness).

All systems use two fixed points. Before 1954 the fixed points were the ice point (labelled 0°C on the Celsius scale) and the steam point (labelled 100°C). A particular material property which changes with temperature is then used to give numerical values to temperatures. Graphically this is done as shown in Fig. T.2. It should be noted that the expression 'temperature scale' as used here refers to the particular material property (thermometric property) used, e.g. the expansion of mercury. It should not be confused with the scale notation e.g. Celsius, Kelvin, etc.

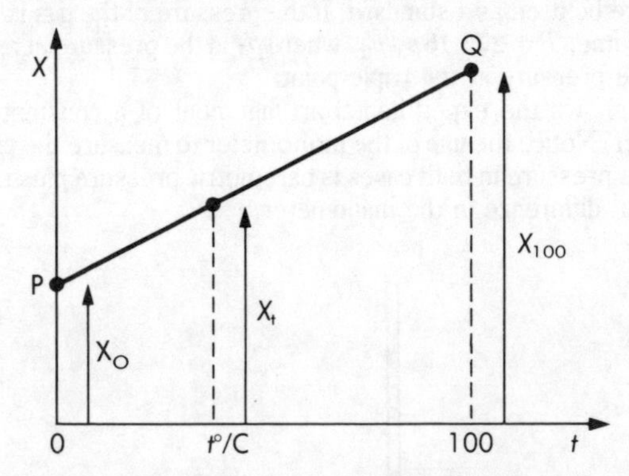

Fig. T.2

At 0°C, the value X_0 of the material property X_p is found and plotted at the point P. At 100°C the value X_{100} is found and plotted at Q. At another temperature t°C, X_t is measured. A straight-line graph is drawn through P and Q, and the temperature t°C read off. Notice how the straight-line graph locks the temperature scale on to the change in the material property between the fixed points. By comparing similar triangles on the diagram we get:

$$\frac{X_t - X_0}{t - 0} = \frac{X_{100} - X_0}{100 - 0}$$

This gives:

$$\frac{t\text{°C}}{100} = \frac{X_t - X_0}{X_{100} - X_0}$$

See the entry **Thermometers** (mercury-in-glass, gas pressure, platinum resistance and thermocouple (i.e. e.m.f.) thermometers), where this formula is used.

Use of the triple point of water

Since 1954 the two fixed points have been the absolute zero of temperature 0 K, and the triple point of water (the temperature at which ice, liquid water and water vapour co-exist) 273.16 K (nearly 0.01 C). Then $T = 273.16\, X_T/X_{tr}$, where T is the temperature on the Kelvin scale, X_T the value of the material property at this temperature and X_{tr} the value at the triple point of water.

Absolute temperature scale

Kelvin proposed that there should be an absolute scale of temperature based upon the behaviour of gases at low pressure. Gases like this obey the general gas equation, $pV = n\,RT$, and are like **ideal gases**. This makes the scale effectively independent of the properties of any particular material (gas) and it can therefore be used as a standard. If the pressure of the gas is measured at constant volume, $T = 273.16\, p_T/p_{tr}$, where p_T is the pressure at a temperature T and p_{tr} the pressure at the triple point.

Fig. T.3 shows the experimental arrangement of a constant-volume gas thermometer. Notice the use of the **manometer** to measure the pressure, and note that the pressure in both cases is barometric pressure plus that indicated by the height difference in the manometer.

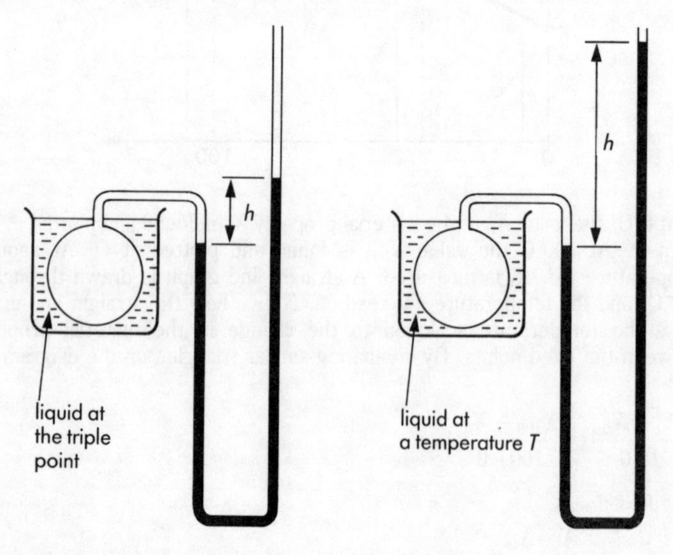

Fig. T.3 Constant-volume gas thermometer

Alternatively if only the mass of gas is held constant, i.e. the volume can vary, the formula

$$T = 273.16 \frac{(pV)_T}{(pV)_{tr}}$$

is used. This absolute scale is also known by other names: absolute thermodynamic scale, gas scale, ideal gas scale.

Conversion from the Kelvin to the Celsius notation is obtained using

$$t°C = \frac{T}{K} - 273.15$$

TEMPERATURE GRADIENT

◀ Thermal conductivity ▶

TERMINAL VELOCITY

This is a name given to the maximum velocity a body acquires when falling through a viscous liquid under the action of a constant force, for example gravity.

The value of terminal velocity depends upon the viscosity of the fluid, the shape of the falling body and the downward force. For example, if a man falls out of an aircraft, the terminal velocity is about 120 miles per hour, but with a parachute his velocity is reduced to less than 10 miles per hour.

THERMAL CONDUCTIVITY

Conduction is one of the three ways in which heat is transferred from one place to another in a substance. The other two ways are by **convection**, a process which is not applicable to solids, and by **radiation**, a process which requires no intervening medium. In the conduction process the internal energy of a hot part of a substance is energy of the oscillations of atoms or molecules making up the material. A molecule which is 'hotter' than its neighbours exerts a force on its neighbours through the force that links it to them. So they receive some of the hot molecule's energy. They too are then able to 'heat up' other neighbours and so on.

In A-level physics the mechanism for thermal conduction is not considered. Instead an experimental approach is ádopted. Fig. T.4 shows an example of thermal conduction in a solid. Here there is a perfectly lagged metal bar connected to a chamber through which steam can be passed. The graph in Fig. T.5 shows the temperature θ as a function of the distance x along the bar a short time after steam is passed. The rate at which heat passes down the bar, $\frac{dQ}{dt}$, is proportional to the magnitude of the slope of the temperature/

distance curve known as the *temperature gradient*, i.e.

$$\frac{dQ}{dt} \propto \frac{-d\theta}{dx}$$

The minus sign is a consequence of heat always flowing from a hot body to a cold body. Some authors and textbooks avoid the use of terms like 'heat flow', preferring instead 'transfer of thermal energy'.

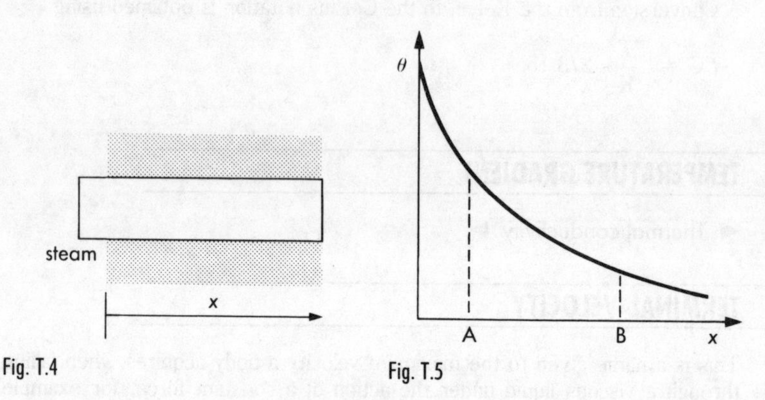

Fig. T.4

Fig. T.5

The rate of flow of heat at A is much greater than at B. This is obvious and implies a net flow of heat into the region between A and B. Eventually, as heat is conducted into the bar, a steady state is reached as shown in Fig. T.6, where the rate of flow of heat is the same at all points along the bar. All the heat entering at one end is ultimately conducted through the bar. The rate of flow of heat is proportional to the area of cross-section A and depends upon the material of the bar. The equation

$$\frac{dQ}{dt} = -kA\frac{d\theta}{dx}$$

describes the phenomenon. k is coefficient of thermal conductivity with the units of $W\,m^{-1}K^{-1}$.

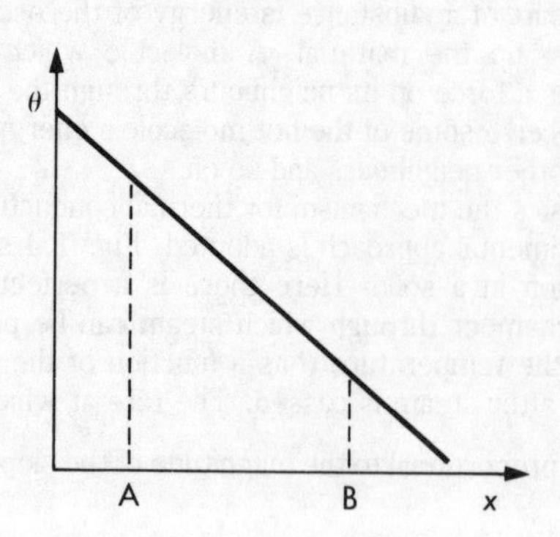

Fig. T.6

In a steady-state situation, one which results when everything has settled down and when no point is going to get any hotter, we have for a perfectly lagged bar,

$$\frac{dQ}{dt} = kA\,\frac{(\theta_1 - \theta_2)}{l}$$

where l is the length of the bar and θ_1 and θ_2 the temperatures of the ends.

The steady-state case of a perfectly lagged bar is one in which all the heat entering at one end leaves from the other. In experiments to measure the thermal conductivity of a *good* conductor this formula is in fact used. The bar is well lagged and it is assumed that the rate of transfer of heat along it is very much greater than the heat lost from the sides (Fig. T.7). Perfect lagging is difficult to achieve and in reality there will be some loss of heat along the bar (Fig. T.8).

Of course just having heat flowing through one substance is a fairly idealised situation. In the situations of heat engineering it is much more likely that heat

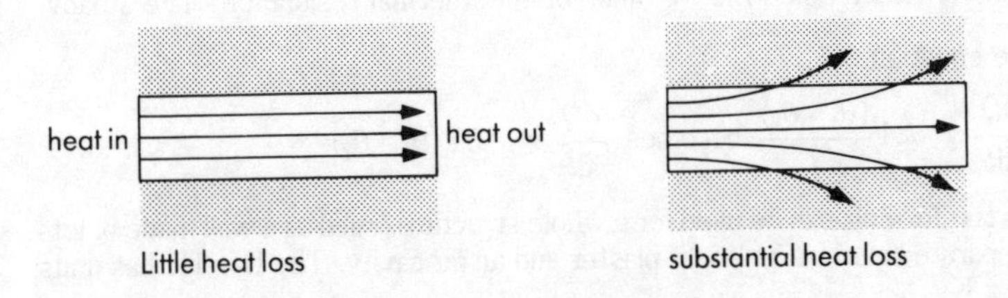

Fig. T.7

Fig. T.8

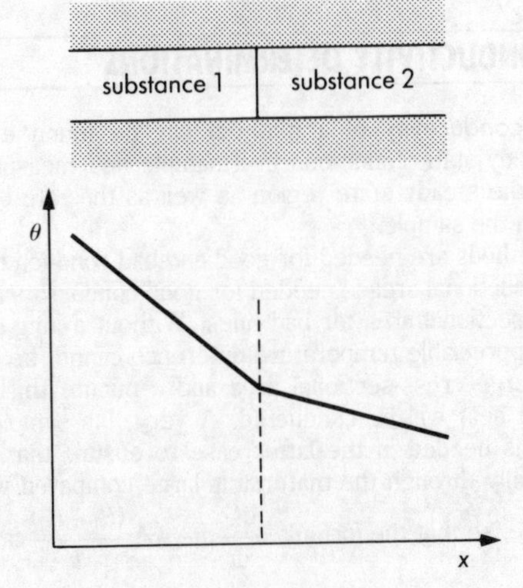

Fig. T.9

passes through one material and then through another. We need to know about what happens at a boundary between two substances. At A-level this condition is only ever considered in the special case of lagged steady-state conditions (Fig. T.9). As a result the temperature gradient $d\theta/dx$ changes abruptly at the interface. The key concept is that the rate of flow of heat, $\frac{dQ}{dt}$, on either side of the boundary is the same. Hence the relationship between the temperature gradient is

$$k_1 \frac{d\theta_1}{dx} = k_2 \frac{d\theta_2}{dx}$$

Another approach which is adopted in heat transfer through several layers is to treat the collection of layers all as one substance and to use a quantity called the 'U-value' instead of lots of different values of k. This is of course only helpful when the U-values are known. U-value calculations are commonly done in calculating the heat losses from houses.

In a calculation of that kind for a single layer U is written for the quantity $\frac{k}{l}$, and is either called the 'U-value' or the 'thermal resistance'. The steady-state equation

$$\frac{dQ}{dt} = kA \frac{(\theta_1 - \theta_2)}{l} \text{ becomes } \frac{dQ}{dt} = UA\,(\theta_1 - \theta_2)$$

This last formula can be used for a whole structure, such as a wall made of lots of separate layers, e.g. brick, plaster and an air cavity. The U-value has units $Wm^{-2}\,K^{-1}$.

For the experimental methods used for the determination of coefficients of thermal conductivity, see **Thermal conductivity determinations**.

◀ Conductivities of metals ▶

THERMAL CONDUCTIVITY DETERMINATIONS

The **thermal conductivity** of a material can be found experimentally by setting up steady-state conditions in a sample and measuring the temperatures across the steady state region as well as the rate of flow of thermal energy through the sample.

Different methods are needed for good and bad conductors. A long sample of small cross-sectional area is needed for good conductors and a thin sample of large cross-sectional area for bad ones. Without a long sample of a good conductor an appreciable temperature difference cannot be obtained, whereas without a large cross-sectional area and a minute thickness for a poor conductor little heat will be conducted. A very thin sample of large cross-sectional area is needed in the latter case to ensure that the rate of heat transferred axially through the material is large compared with the heat lost through its edge, so that the formula $\frac{dQ}{dt} = kA \frac{(\theta_1 - \theta_2)}{l}$ can be used.

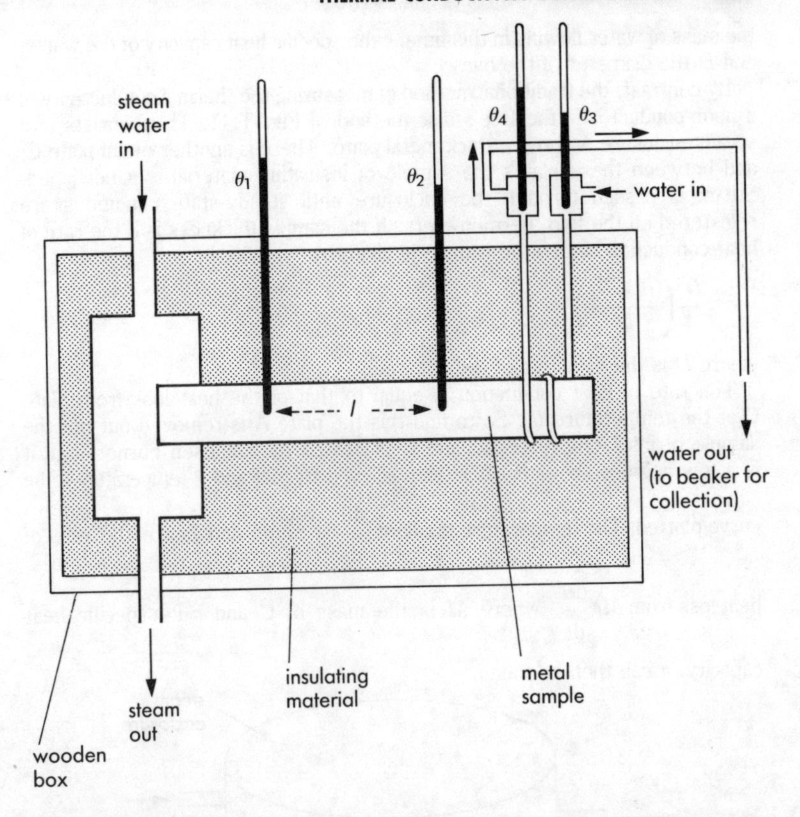

Fig. T.10 Searle's bar

The traditional method of measuring the thermal conductivity of a good conductor is therefore the Searle's bar method of Fig. T.10. Heat is supplied from a steam chest at one end. The metal sample is a fairly large bar from which heat is extracted at the cold end by means of a copper tube through which a supply of cold water at a steady rate flows. The temperatures of this water on entering and leaving, θ_3 and θ_4, are noted. Two holes are drilled in the bar distance l apart in which are placed two thermometers to measure the temperatures θ_1 and θ_2. These thermometers dip into mercury or oil in order to make good thermal contact with the bar. Once steady-state temperatures are established the experiment is run for a number of minutes during which the water passing through the cooling tubes is measured. The thermal conductivity k is then found from

$$Mc\ (\theta_3 - \theta_4)/t = k\pi \frac{D^2}{4} \frac{(\theta_1 - \theta_2)}{l}$$

where t is the time duration of the steady-state part of the experiment, M is the mass of water flowing in this time, c the specific heat capacity of the water, and D the diameter of the bar.

By contrast, the traditional method of measuring the thermal conductivity of a poor conductor is the Lee's disc method of Fig. T.11. This consists of a steam enclosure A above a thick metal plate. There is another metal plate C, and between these plates the sample of insulating material is sandwiched. Steam is passed through the enclosure until steady-state conditions are registered on the two thermometers. If the sample thickness is d the rate of heat conduction across the sample is given by

$$k\pi \frac{D^2}{4}\left(\frac{\theta_1 - \theta_2}{d}\right)$$

where D is the diameter of the apparatus.

The rate of heat conduction is equal to that of the heat loss from plate C at the temperature θ_2. So to find this the plate A is removed but not the sample of insulating material, and C is heated by a bunsen burner until it is a few degrees above θ_2. It is then allowed to cool and a temperature–time curve plotted. The temperature gradient $\frac{d\theta}{dt}$ is found and hence the rate of heat loss from $Mc\frac{d\theta}{dt}$, where M is the mass of C and c its specific heat capacity. k can then be found.

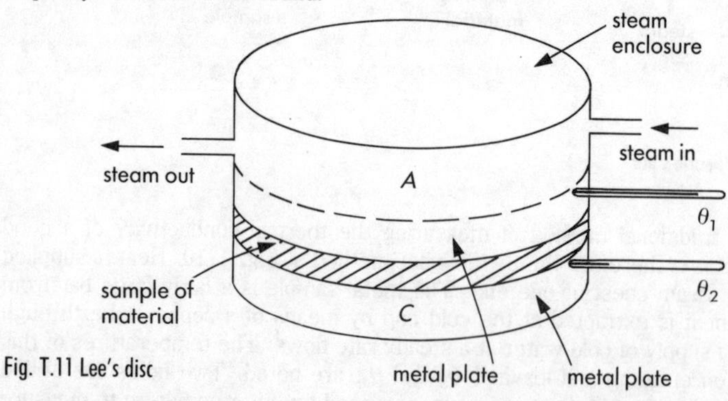

Fig. T.11 Lee's disc

THERMAL RADIATION

Thermal radiation is one of the three ways in which heat is transferred from one body to another, the other ways being convection and conduction. It is electromagnetic radiation with a broad-band spectrum, and needs no medium for its transmission. For example if you hold the glass of a vacuum-filled electric light bulb and switch it on your hand immediately feels very hot. This is because energy is being immediately transferred through the vacuum of the bulb.

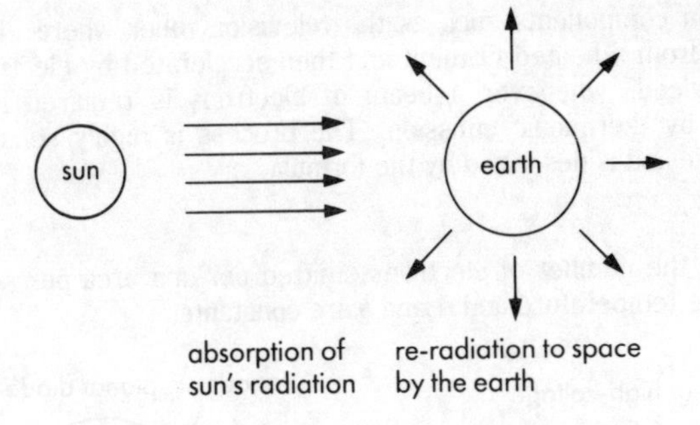

Fig. T.12

All bodies absorb and emit radiation. For example the earth absorbs radiation from the sun (Fig. T.12). It also emits radiation into space and remains in equilibrium at a temperature where the rate at which it gains energy is equal to the rate at which it loses it.

◀ Wien displacement law ▶

THERMIONIC EMISSION

This is the phenomenon whereby free electrons close to the surface escape from a metal if it is heated to a sufficiently high temperature.

Electrons were originally discovered during experiments involving the passage of electric currents either through gases or in an evacuated tube. An electron is normally held captive in a metal by attractive electrostatic forces resulting from the lattice of positive ions. The electron needs to be given energy in order to escape and for a particular metal there is a minimum amount of energy, called the work function, ϕ, which an electron needs in order to escape. Removing electrons from a metal in this way is very similar to the process of evaporation in liquids. A liquid molecule has to have energy to escape from the liquid surface in order to become part of the vapour surrounding it. The molecules in a liquid are in constant random motion according to the kinetic theory, colliding with one another and as a result having a very wide range of energies. Those molecules with sufficiently high energies can reach the surface and escape in the process known as evaporation. Some of the more loosely bound electrons in metals, the so-called free or conduction electrons, the ones responsible for conducting electricity, behave rather similarly. However, in most metals at normal temperatures they rarely acquire enough energy to be emitted in a similar fashion. On the other hand if the metal is heated to a sufficiently high temperature the atoms and the electrons have considerably more kinetic energy, so that free electrons near the surface can escape. This phenomenon is known as thermionic emission.

Thermionic emission formed the basis of the technology of electronics which predated **transistors**, i.e. that of thermionic valves. This technology is still used in components such as the television tube, where electrons are generated from a heated filament and then accelerated by electrodes to the screen. Indeed, whenever a beam of electrons is required it is usually generated by thermionic emission. The process is highly sensitive to the temperature and is described by the formula

$$n = A\,T^2 e^{-b/T}$$

where n is the number of electrons emitted per unit area per second, T is the absolute temperature and A and b are constants.

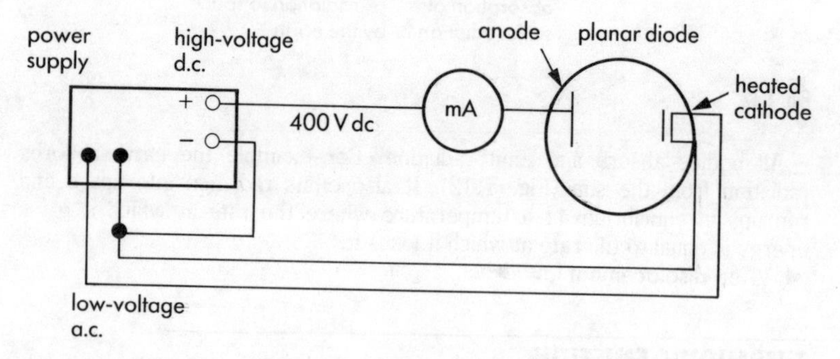

Fig. T.13 Apparatus for exploring thermionic emission with a planar diode

Fig. T.13 shows the kind of apparatus used in school or college laboratories for demonstrating thermionic emission. It consists of a planar diode, i.e. an anode (positive plate) which is flat (planar), and a cathode heated by a filament a few centimetres away. The electrons produced by thermionic emission are accelerated by the electric field between the filament and the anode. If the potential difference between the filament and the anode is V, an electron will gain energy eV, which will be converted into kinetic energy $\frac{1}{2}mv^2$. Hence

$$eV = \tfrac{1}{2}mv^2$$

Fig. T.14 shows the results of experimentation with this apparatus. If the anode voltage is negative no current is observed on the milliameter. This shows that the electrons are negatively charged and are only attracted to the anode if it is positively charged with respect to the cathode. It is this which makes the device a diode valve: it only lets electricity pass one way. Notice the form of the curve. Eventually the graph of anode current forms a plateau. This is because eventually all the electrons being generated from the cathode per second are being drawn by the electric field to the anode. Anode currents can be generated by increasing the filament current, by raising the temperature of the filament.

If there were no field between the anode and the cathode the escaping electrons would simply form a cloud of charge round the cathode. As more and more of them got thrown off it would become progressively more difficult for others to escape, because of the net positive charge acquired by the cathode.

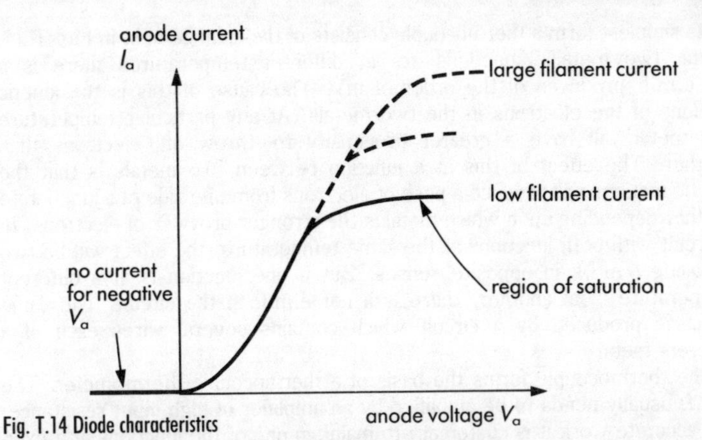

Fig. T.14 Diode characteristics

Because of the positive charge on the cathode, electrons thrown off would be eventually pulled back and the situation would be very analogous to the equilibrium of a liquid and its vapour in a sealed vessel.

◀ Electron volt ▶

THERMISTOR

A thermistor is a component of electronics of semiconducting material whose resistance is very sharply dependent upon temperature. Most thermistors have the property that their resistance falls very rapidly but non-linearly with an increase in temperature. These are sometimes called n.t.c. (negative temperature cooefficient) thermistors. However, there are some newer thermistors available whose resistance increases with temperature.

THERMOCOUPLE

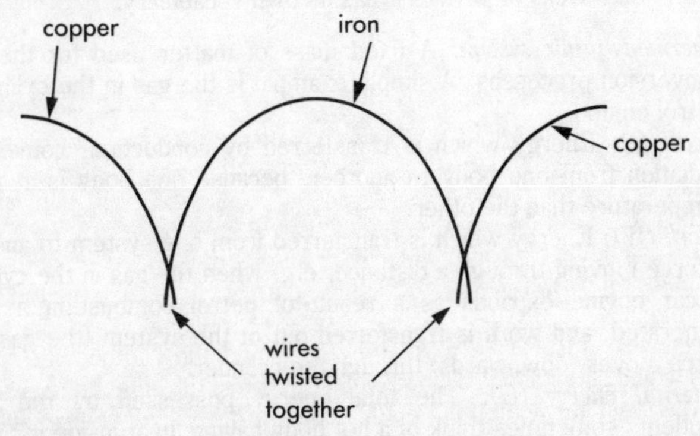

Fig. T.15 Thermocouple

In its simplest form a thermocouple consists of the arrangement in Fig. T.15. If the two metallic junctions are at different temperatures there is a net e.m.f. produced of the order of mV. The cause of this is the kinetic motions of the electrons in the two metals. At any particular temperature one metal will have a greater propensity to 'throw off' electrons than another. The effect of this at a junction between two metals is that the kinetic motions will produce a push of electrons from one side of a junction to another depending upon which metal is the stronger provider of electrons. In a circuit with both junctions at the same temperature, the effect will be two opposing e.m.f.s in opposite senses. But if one junction is at a different temperature from another, there is a net e.m.f. in the circuit. The same effect is produced by a circuit which contains several wires each of a different metal.

The thermocouple forms the basis of a thermocouple **thermometer**. The e.m.f. usually needs to be amplified by an amplifier of high input resistance. For accurate work it is customary to maintain one of the junctions at a fixed temperature, e.g. to keep it in a mixture of ice and water.

◀ Potentiometer ▶

THERMODYNAMICS

In everyday life, motion is usually obtained by a cycle of events which starts with the combustion of fuel. The conversion of 'heat' to 'work' in this way is crucial to our civilisation. Thermodynamics is the name given to this branch of science. It is concerned with processes in which heat flows in or out of a 'system', while work is done on or by the 'system'.

Thermodynamics is now an important branch of both physics and chemistry. In the last century it began when engineers were trying to understand how they might improve the efficiency of heat engines. Nowadays its engineering importance is largely in the design of power stations, diesel and petrol engines, and in the large chemical processing plants used in the chemical and oil industries.

As with other areas of physics it has its own vocabulary:

- *Thermodynamic system:* A fixed mass of matter used for the energy conversion processes. A simple example is the gas in the cylinder of a petrol engine.
- *Heat (Q):* Energy which is transferred by conduction, convection or radiation from one body to another, because one body is at a higher temperature than the other.
- *Work (W):* Energy which is transferred from one system to another by a force moving through a distance; e.g. when the gas in the cylinder of a car engine expands as a result of petrol combustion a force is generated, and work is transferred out of the system (the gas) as the force moves (downwards) through the cylinder.
- *Internal energy (U):* The total energy possessed by the system. Students sometimes think of a hot body having 'heat inside it'. This is a

misuse of the term heat: they should say that a hot body has internal energy and its internal energy increases when it is supplied with heat.

◀ Laws of thermodynamics, Statistical thermodynamics ▶

THERMOMETERS

The common household mercury or spirit thermometer works only for a limited range of temperature, and by the standards of modern instrumentation is large and clumsy. So many other types are used. These are summarised and compared in the table below:

Type and thermometric property	*Temperature range*	*Advantages*	*Disadvantages*	*Other points*
Mercury-in-glass (length of mercury column)	–39°C to 450°C	Fast response Direct reading	Fragile Large heat capacity Limited range	Useful for everyday lab. work and can be calibrated against constant volume gas thermometer Unsuitable for interfacing with electronic equipment
Spirit-in-glass (length of spirit column)	Depends upon the liquid used, approx. –40°C to 150°C	Fast response Direct reading	As above	As above
Constant-volume gas thermometer (pressure of a gas of fixed volume)	–270°C to about 1500°C	Accurate Sensitive Wide temperature range Standard results	Slow response and inconvenient	Standard thermometer against which others are calibrated (see Fig. T.3, p.386)
Platinum-resistance (electrical resistance of a platinum coil measured with a **Wheatstone bridge**)	Approx. –200°C to 1100°C	Accurate Wide range	Slow response and large heat capacity	Good for steady temperature differences Used as a standard on IPTS between –183°C and 630°C Can be interfaced with electronic equipment
Radiation pyrometer (colour (i.e. peak wavelength) of radiation emitted by a hot body)	Above 1000°C	Does not have to make contact with the hot body	Cumbersome Readings are only indirect	Used as IPTS standard above 1063°C

Type and thermometric property	*Temperature range*	*Advantages*	*Disadvantages*	*Other points*
Thermocouple (e.m.f. produced between junctions of dissimilar metals which are at different temperatures)	−250°C to 1150°C	Very fast response Low heat capacity	Needs careful circuitry because of very small e.m.f.s., i.e. high impedance amplifier or sensitive **potentiometer** circuit	Used as IPTS standard between 630°C and 1063°C Can easily be interfaced with electronics equipment
Thermistor (resistance of thermistor)	Approximately − 30°C to 200°C	Small heat capacity Fast response	Needs calibration	Can easily be interfaced with electronic equipment

Note that a thermometer which has a small heat capacity, such as a thermocouple, will respond to rapid temperature changes. This is because little thermal energy is required to change the temperature, a point which should underline the difference between 'heat' and temperature.

Note also that the IPTS scale is the International Practical Temperature Scale. This is a system for accurate scientific work which uses different thermometers in different temperature ranges rather than the constant-volume gas thermometer throughout. This is because thermometers other than the constant-volume gas thermometer are more practical. The IPTS thermometers are summarised in the table below.

Temperature range	*Thermometer*
Below −183°C	Constant-volume gas thermometer
−183°C to 630°C	Platinum-resistance thermometer
630°C to 1063°C	Thermocouple
Above 1063°C	Radiation pyrometer

◀ Temperature ▶

THIN-FILM INTERFERENCE

When light is reflected off an oily road surface, or off oil resting on the surface of water, colours are often seen. This is one example of an **interference** phenomenon in light caused by the existence of a thin film of material. Other examples which may be encountered in advanced physics are Newton's rings and the small-angle air wedge.

Fig. T.16 shows a light beam incident on a thin film of thickness t and of **refractive index** n. Some of the light is reflected at B, forming the beam BF. Other light is refracted along BC and of this some is reflected again at C to come back to the point D and some transmitted out of the film to G. The pattern of transmission and reflection at each interface between the air and the film repeats itself. It turns out that the beam BF and the beam DE have approximately equal amplitudes. Thus if they were brought together by the focusing action of a lens, or the eye, there is constructive or destructive interference depending upon the optical path difference between the two beams. Fig. T.16 has shown the general case of a beam of light AB which is

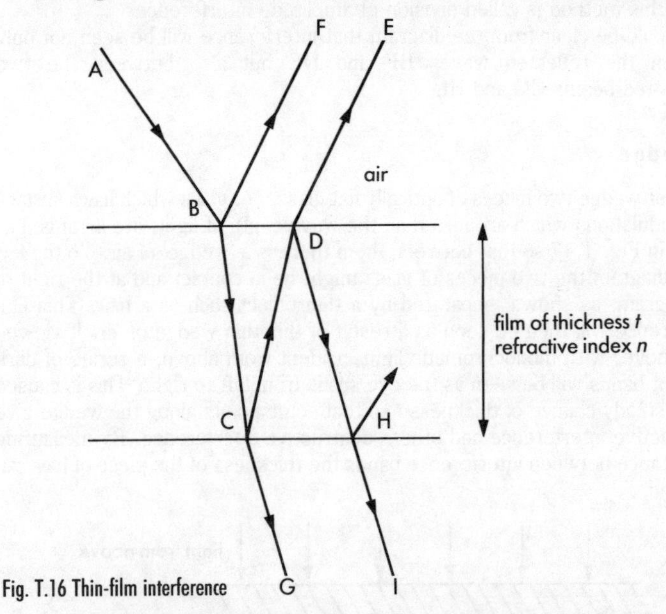

Fig. T.16 Thin-film interference

incident at an angle at the surface of the film. In A-level physics only cases of normal incidence, that is AB normal to the surface of the film, need to be considered. Nevertheless, Fig. T.16 shows clearly how one beam is related to another. In the normal incident case a diagram would be confusing, because all the rays would lie along the same line normal to the interface.

Nevertheless, the theory is particularly simple in the case of normal incidence. The beam equivalent to BCDE travels an extra distance compared with the beam BF of $2t$, i.e. twice the thickness of the film. But as light travels more slowly in the thin film, the effect of extra length traversed, the **optical path length**, is $2nt$. So in normal incidence it would be expected that there would be constructive interference between the beam equivalent to BF and that equivalent to DE, provided $2nt$ was a whole number of wavelengths. But in fact when light is reflected from a material of higher refractive index there is a $\pi/2$ phase change. Such a phase change occurs at B but not at C. Thus the condition for constructive interference is

$$2nt = \left(m + \tfrac{1}{2}\right)\lambda$$

where $m = 0, 1, 2, 3$, etc., and for destructive interference

$$2nt = m\lambda$$

It should be noted that this kind of interference is different from that in Young's slits. There, two parts of a wavefront arrive at the same place after travelling by different routes, and the method is called division of wavefront. In this case it is the same point on the wavefront which is divided, with one part going by a different route from the other before the two meet again. Hence this method is called division of amplitude interference.

It should be clear from the diagram that interference will be seen not only between the reflected waves BF and DE but also between the two transmitted beams CG and HI.

Air wedge

In the air wedge two pieces of optically flat glass, i.e. glass which has a surface with undulations which are less than the wavelength of light, are arranged as shown in Fig. T.17 so that between them there is a 'wedge' of air. To the left of the diagram the two pieces of glass might be in contact and at the right of the diagram, as shown, separated by a thin object such as a hair. Thin-film interference will then be seen as a result of this thin wedge of air. If viewed from above, with monochromatic light incident from above, a series of dark and light bands will be seen as the eye scans from left to right. This is caused by the steady change of thickness t so that some points along the wedge give constructive interference and others destructive interference. By measuring the distance between interference bands the thickness of the piece of hair can be found.

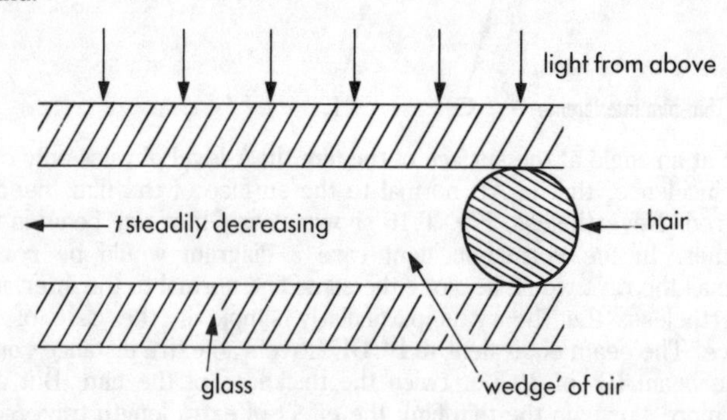

Fig. T.17 Air wedge

Newton's rings

Fig. T.18 shows a glass lens standing upon an optically flat surface. The air between the glass lens and the flat surface forms a thin film, and so circular interference fringes can be seen if illuminated by monochromatic source from above. If the system is viewed by reflected light from above, the centre of the fringe system is dark provided there is true contact between the lens and the optically flat surface. This is a result of the phase change on reflection from the bottom surface of the lens. Fringes can also be observed by viewing from

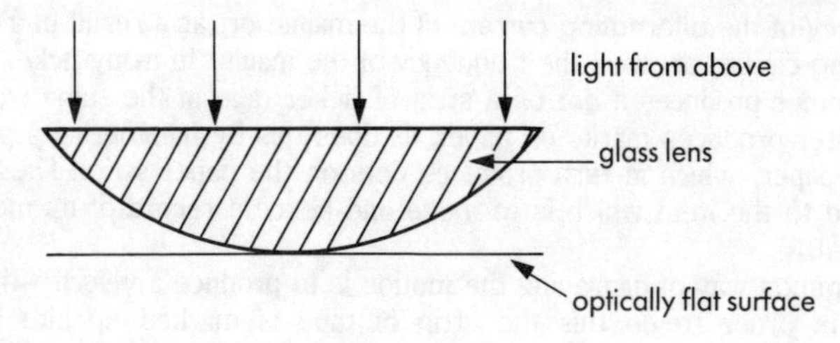

Fig. T.18 Newton's rings

underneath the optically flat surface. There are formed by transmitted light and in this case the central fringe is bright. These fringes are lower in contrast than those viewed by reflection.

There is a simple relationship between the diameter of the *m*th dark ring and the diameter *d* of that ring. This relationship is

$$d_m{}^2 = 4R\lambda m$$

where R is the radius of curvature of the surface of the lens in contact with the optical flat.

In this way Newton's rings can be used for determining the radius of curvature of a lens surface, and also by inspection of the circularity of the fringes to determine whether a lens which has been manufactured is spherically symmetrical.

THREE-PHASE A.C.

This is the method used for generating electricity in the national grid. The generators at the power station have coils which produce three separate supplies of a.c., each leading one of the other supplies in phase by 120° and lagging behind the other by 120°. Heavy-duty machinery in factories and workshops is usually run on a three-phase supply. A domestic household has only one phase supplied to it. Neighbouring houses will be on one of the other two phases.

A generator with a single phase produces and supplies power unevenly. When the voltage is at a maximum, the power supplied is at a maximum, but when the voltage is zero no power is being supplied. In a three-phase system there is much more evenness to the overall rate of supply of power. The method is also much more efficient in the use of transmission cables.

◀ Alternating current ▶

TICKER TIMER

The ticker timer is the instrument used in elementary physics to record the motion of a moving object. It consists of a hammer which is driven at the frequency of the **alternating current** of the mains, or, as a result of a **bridge rectifying** circuit, at twice the frequency of the mains. In many ticker timers the hammer produces a dot on a strip of ticker tape in the same way as a typewriter produces marks on paper. It does this by hammering a piece of carbon paper, which in turn produces dots on the paper strip. The tape is attached to the item which is to move and hence a record of its motion is recorded.

A common way of displaying the motion is to produce a velocity–time bar chart. In order to do this the strip of tape is marked up into lengths corresponding to a particular multiple of the time between strikes of the tape. Fig. T.19 shows the kind of bar chart produced by allowing a mass to pull a tape under gravity, the tape passing through a ticker timer. The timer operated at fifty strikes per second and thus produced dots every 0.02 s The tape was marked up into lengths which corresponded to five intervals of this time, i.e. 0.1 s. The tapes were then assembled into the chart as shown.

In this example 7.6 cm of tape was drawn out in the first 0.1 s, indicating that the mass travelled this distance in this time interval. As a result of gravitational acceleration the mass speeded up, so that during the final time interval 47.5 cm of tape was drawn out. Bar charts of this form are very useful for quickly showing a velocity–time profile.

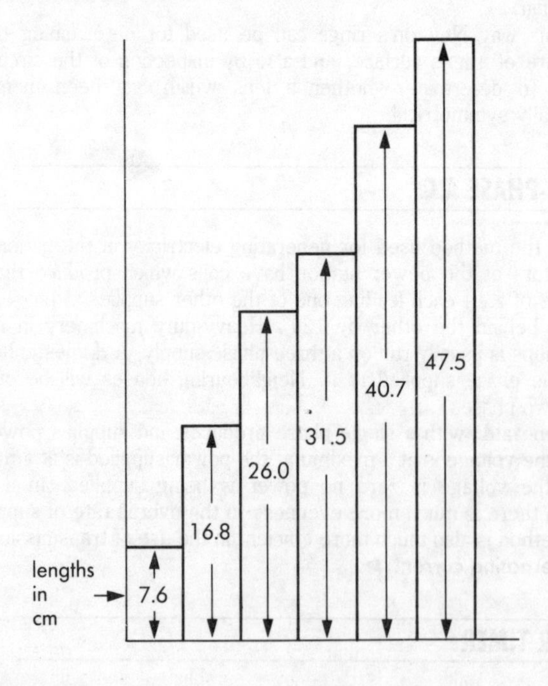

Fig. T.19 Velocity–time bar chart for a mass falling under gravity

Calculation of acceleration

The acceleration of the falling mass can be calculated from the bar chart as follows.

The final velocity in this experiment, v,

$$= \frac{47.5\,\text{cm}}{0.1\,\text{s}} = 475\,\text{cm s}^{-1}$$

$$= 4.75\,\text{m s}^{-1}$$

The initial velocity, u,

$$= \frac{7.6\,\text{cm}}{0.1\,\text{s}} = 76\,\text{cm s}^{-1} = 0.76\,\text{m s}^{-1}$$

The time interval, t, between these measurements is 5×0.1 s. (Note that it is five intervals and not six. This is because each strip represents an average velocity and we can regard the average velocities recorded as being equal to the instantaneous velocities at about half-way through each time interval.) So the mass acquires the initial velocity of $0.76\,\text{m s}^{-1}$ 0.05 s after the start of the motion and reaches the velocity $4.75\,\text{m s}^{-1}$ 0.55 s after the start of the motion. Hence t is 0.50 s. Using the formula $v = u + at$ we get

$$a = \frac{4.75 - 0.76\,\text{m s}^{-1}}{0.5\,\text{s}}$$

$$= \frac{3.99\,\text{m s}^{-1}}{0.5\,\text{s}}$$

$$= 7.98\,\text{m s}^{-2}$$

This value is well below the accepted value of $9.81\,\text{m s}^{-2}$ because of the **friction** imposed by the ticker timer on the tape. It is one reason why the ticker timer is a poor method for exact work.

TIMBRE

Timbre is a term used in music and is the subjective description of the waveform of a note as it appears to a listener.

Two notes may be of the same frequency but may have different waveforms, and the waveforms themselves may change during the duration of the playing of the note. For example, if a note is keyed on a typical electronic organ the profile may well be sinusoidal and of constant amplitude. By contrast a note, particularly a very low note keyed on a pipe organ, will take several milliseconds to become established and will then have a fairly constant amplitude. A note keyed on a piano will steadily die away.

◀ Fourier methods, Musical instruments ▶

TIME CONSTANT

A measure of the rate of discharge of a capacitor circuit, often denoted by the symbol τ.

◀ Charging a capacitor through a resistor, Discharge of a capacitor ▶

TORQUE

This a term used in physics to refer to the turning effect of some agent. In the case of a force acting at a distance from an axis it is usually called the moment of the force. However, the term torque is a more general one which is used when it is not always easy or even possible to identify the forces involved.

For example, we could have a turbine held in a flow of fluid, as in a diesel hydraulic locomotive, or a windmill driven by a flow of air. In both these cases it is hard to pin-point the individual forces. But it is still possible to measure the turning effect and we call this the torque. The units of torque are newton metres.

TOTAL INTERNAL REFLECTION

This is a term used in ray optics and in ray theory generally when light is incident at a surface on the far side of which the refractive index is greater, and at an angle greater than the **critical angle**. Under such circumstances the light is reflected from the surface rather than refracted. Under the conditions of ordinary reflection at a mirror surface there is some absorption. The amount depends upon the angle of incidence. But in the case of total internal reflection 100 per cent of the light is reflected and there is no absorption at all.

Total internal reflection is used in **optical fibres**.

TRANSFORMER

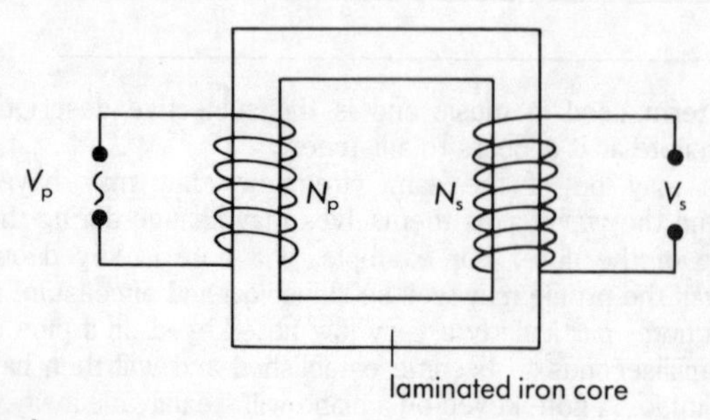

Fig. T.20 Transformer

The transformer is a device designed to change an alternating voltage of one value to another of greater or smaller value.

Fig. T.20 shows the essential features of a transformer drawn schematically. It consists of a central closed loop of material of high magnetic permeability, usually soft iron. This is usually made out of laminated sections rather than being formed from one solid piece. There are two coils of wire wound round it, one called the primary coil and the other the secondary coil. When an alternating e.m.f. E_{ext} is applied to the primary coil an alternating e.m.f. will be generated across the secondary. The physics of this is as follows:

a) The applied alternating e.m.f. will drive an alternating current through the primary coil. A p.d., V_p, will be produced across the primary terminals. V_p is of course equal to E_{ext}.
b) The alternating current in the primary produces an alternating magnetic flux in the core.
c) Because of the high magnetic permeability of the core, a closed loop of magnetic flux is produced, and all this flux is linked by the secondary coil and so by Faraday's and Lenz's Laws (see **Electromagnetic induction**) an alternating e.m.f. is induced in the secondary.
d) The secondary e.m.f. drives alternating current in a completed secondary circuit. The magnitude of the induced e.m.f. in the secondary coil depends upon the magnitude of the primary p.d. and also on the ratio of the number of turns in the secondary coil to the number of turns in the primary. Alternatively one can write this

$$\frac{E_s}{V_p} = \frac{N_s}{N_p}$$

where V_p = the primary p.d., E_s = the secondary e.m.f., N_p = the number of primary turns; and N_s = the number of secondary turns.

The complete theory of even an ideal transformer is complicated. Only a simple version is given here, together with some pointers to the difficulties which a more sophisticated treatment must explain.

Consider an ideal transformer, i.e. one in which the primary coil has a negligible resistance, and in which all the flux created by the primary coil is linked by the secondary windings. Suppose too that the load attached to the secondary circuit is very large, so that the current taken from it is very small. A simple experiment with a real transformer will demonstrate that in this circumstance the current in the primary coil will also be very small. This is due to the fact that a back e.m.f. is induced in the primary coil and its magnitude is almost equal to that of the applied e.m.f. If ϕ is the flux in the core at time t caused by the current in the primary when an external e.m.f., E_{ext}, is applied to it, then the back e.m.f. induced in the primary, caused by the self-inductance of the primary, is given by

$$E_p = \frac{-\mathrm{d}}{\mathrm{d}t}(N_p\,\phi) = -N_p\frac{\mathrm{d}\phi}{\mathrm{d}t}$$

and here $-E_p = E_{ext}$ so that the net e.m.f. in the primary circuit, $E_{ext} + (-E_p)$, is zero. (Note that were it not so a large current would flow). Hence

$$E_{ext} = N_p \frac{d\phi}{dt}$$

The e.m.f. E_s induced in the secondary of N_s turns by the same flux in the coil is given by

$$E_s = \frac{-d}{dt}(N_s \phi) = -N_s \frac{d\phi}{dt}$$

Because of the very high resistance of the load we have

$$E_s = V_s$$

where V_s is the p.d. across the load. We have, therefore,

$$V_s = -N_s \frac{d\phi}{dt}$$

and hence for magnitudes at least

$$\frac{V_s}{V_p} = \frac{N_s}{N_p}$$

Reducing the resistance across the secondary increases the load upon it, i.e. the current taken is greater. This increased secondary current itself produces a flux in the core, and the action of the secondary current is to tend to reduce that flux. This is because the secondary current tends to oppose the change producing it. There is, therefore, a smaller back e.m.f in the primary coil and so the external e.m.f. exceeds the back e.m.f. by a greater amount and hence the primary current increases. The effect of this is to restore the flux to its previous value. The net effect of the whole process is an increase in the primary current and, in energy terms, an increase in the energy transferred from the primary to the secondary. A sophisticated theory is needed to explain this complicated process by which there is feedback from the secondary to the primary. Note also that in a good transformer all the flux is trapped in the core. Although the secondary coil links the flux, no field lines actually cross the wires of the secondary coil. A sophisticated theory is needed to explain how the field away from the core interacts with the electrons in the core of the secondary.

Transformer efficiency

A real transformer does not transfer all the energy supplied to the primary into the secondary. There are four main causes for the loss in efficiency:

a) Energy is converted into internal energy (heat) in the coils. The rate of heating is given by I^2R. The use of insulated low-resistance wire helps minimise this loss of energy.

b) Heating of the core by eddy currents. The core is a magnetic conductor but also a conductor of electricity. The changing magnetic field in the core will induce e.m.f.s in the core, causing whirlpools (eddies) of currents and hence producing I^2R heating. Laminating the core reduces this effect by increasing the resistance in the loops taken by these eddies.

c) Loss of magnetic flux. In an ideal transformer all the flux generated by the primary circulates through (is linked by) the secondary. However, in practice not all the field lines produced by the primary may link the secondary and so the efficiency of energy transfer is reduced.

d) Hysteresis in the core. As the magnetic field in the core oscillates there is a loss of energy caused by magnetic hysteresis. Soft iron suffers less from this than other substances such as steel, and therefore is the most appropriate as the core material.

◀ Direct current power supplies, Electromotive force, Potential difference ▶

TRANSIENTS

◀ Forced oscillations, Musical instruments ▶

TRANSISTOR

The transistor is a three-terminal semiconductor device which can be used as a switch or as a current amplifier.

Of the various kinds of transistor the only one likely to be encountered in A-level study is the npn junction (or bipolar) transistor. This consists of two semiconductor **diodes** laid back to back. A thin slice of doped p-type semiconductor, usually silicon, i.e. one in which conduction is effectively by positive charges, is sandwiched between two thicker n-type materials (i.e. materials in which conduction is by negative charges, that is electrons). The three parts of the sandwich have lead connections and these are called the base, collector and emitter (Fig. T.21).

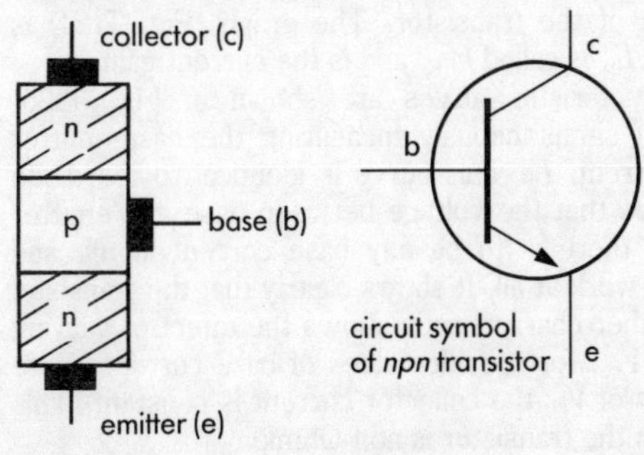

Fig. T.21

Fig. T.22

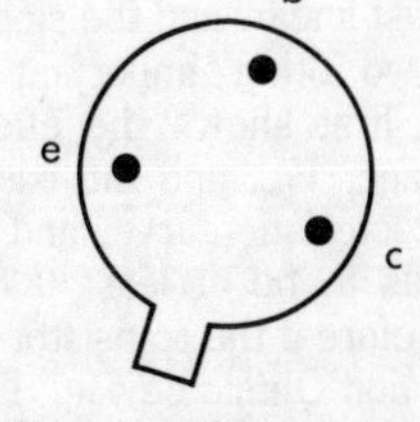

Pin connections on a typical *npn* transistor, a BFY 51 type, as viewed from below

The physical mechanisms underlying the operation of the transistor are not required at A-level, but a knowledge of the circuit properties may be. In most elementary work the transistor is used with its emitter connected to the ground or 0 volt rail of a circuit. This is called common emitter working. A typical circuit for exploring the behaviour of the transistor is shown in Fig. T.23.

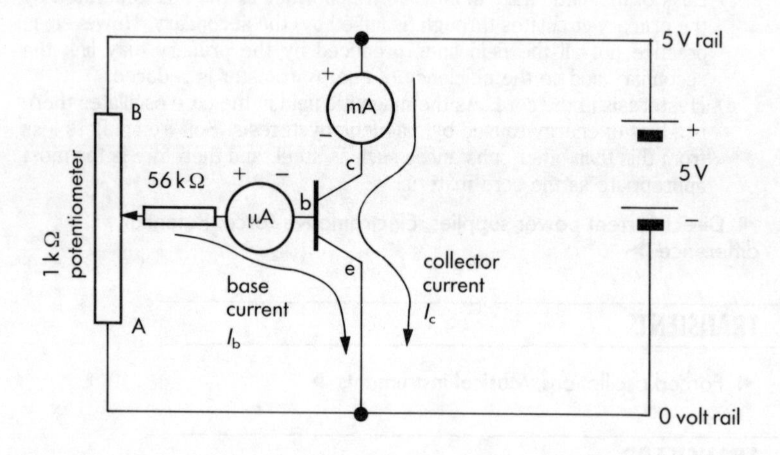

Fig. T.23

There are two currents through the transistor, a small base-emitter current (usually called the base current, I_b) and a collector-emitter current (usually called the collector current, I_c). I_b is usually of the order of tens of microamperes, and I_c is typically a hundred times bigger. The basic action of the transistor is that of a current amplifier, and in this respect it contrasts with the **operational amplifier**, the basic action of which is that of a voltage amplifier. By moving the potentiometer slider in the circuit above, I_b can be changed and I_c measured. The result of doing this is called the current transfer characteristic of the transistor. The graph (Fig. T.24) is almost linear, and the slope, I_c/I_b, is called h_{FE}, and is the current gain.

Two other important characteristic curves are shown in Fig. T.25. The first shows the effect of simultaneously measuring the base-emitter voltage, V_{be}, and the base current, I_b. This curve is identical to the diode characteristic curve, and shows that the voltage between base and emitter needs to be at least 0.7 V if there is to be any base current at all, and therefore if the transistor is to work at all. It shows clearly that the transistor is a non-Ohmic device. The other characteristic shows the effect of varying the collector-emitter voltage, V_{ce}, for specific values of base current. Note that for a large range of values of V_{ce} the collector current is constant. This shows the second way in which the transistor is non-Ohmic.

◀ Transistor switching circuits ▶

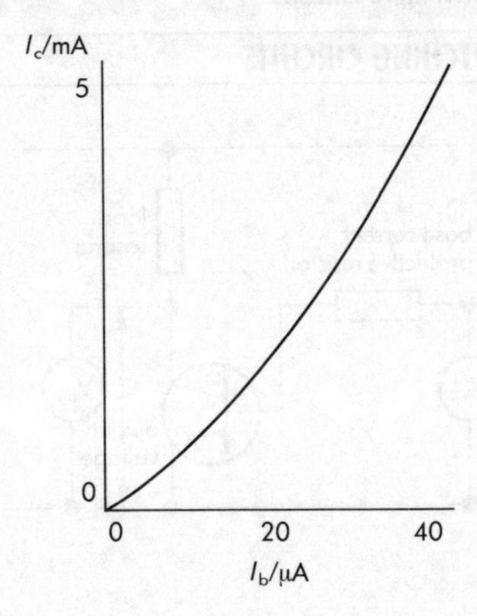

Fig. T.24 Typical graph of I_c as a function of I_b for an npn transistor (BFY 51). Slope is h_{FE}' the current gain

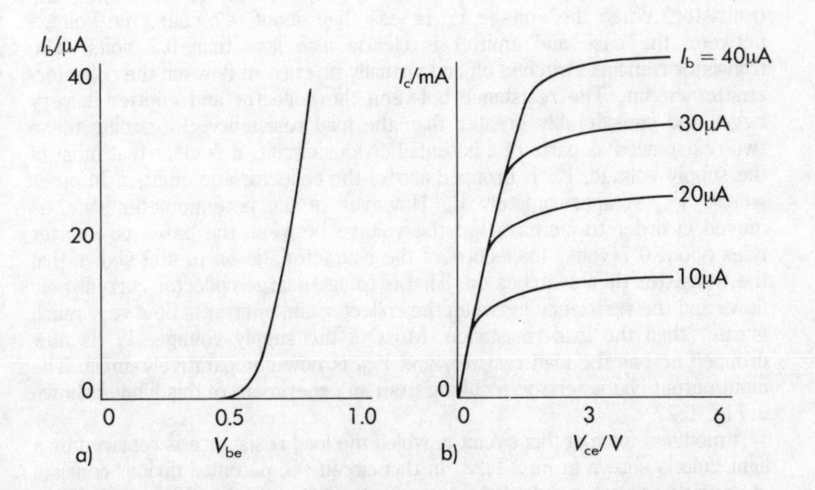

Fig. T.25 a) Base current as a function of base-emitter voltage V_{be} b) Collector current as a function of collector-emitter voltage V_{ce} for various values of base current I_b

TRANSISTOR SWITCHING CIRCUITS

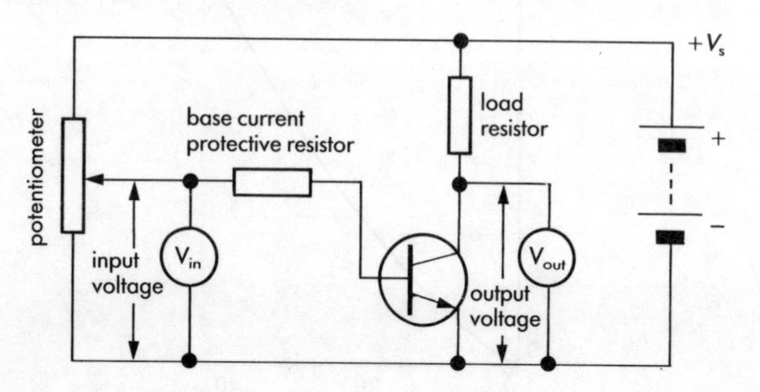

Fig. T.26

The circuit in Fig. T.26 can be used to show experimentally the **transistor**'s switch action. A transistor input voltage can be supplied by moving the slider of the potentiometer up and down. A resistor is placed between the collector of the transistor and the positive pole of the supply. The supply voltage, V_s, is then divided between this resistor, sometimes called the load resistor, and the collector and emitter terminals of the transistor. Note that the circuit incorporates a protective resistance for the base current. This is to avoid too large a base current flowing at any time and therefore destroying the transistor. When the voltage V_{in} is less than about 0.7 volts, the voltage between the base and emitter is clearly also less than 0.7 volts. The transistor remains switched off and virtually no current flows in the collector-emitter circuit. The resistance between the collector and emitter is very large, and considerably greater than the load resistance. Regarding these two resistances as parts of a potential divider circuit, it is clear that most of the supply voltage, V_s, is dropped across the collector and emitter. In other words, V_{out} is approximately V_s. However, if the potentiometer slider is moved in order to increase V_{in}, the voltage between the base and emitter rises about 0.7 volts. Inspection of the characteristic on p. 409 shows that the transistor then switches on. That is to say a large collector current now flows and the resistance between the collector and emitter is now very much greater than the load resistance. Most of the supply voltage, V_s, is now dropped across the load resistor, and V_{out} is now comparatively small. The input/output characteristic resulting from an experiment of this kind is shown in Fig. T.27.

A modified form of this circuit in which the load resistance is replaced by a light bulb is shown in Fig. T.28. In this circuit the potential divider consists of a variable resistor and a light-dependent resistor (LDR). When the LDR is in darkness it has a very high resistance, perhaps of the order of 2 MΩ. V_{in} is then comparatively high, the transistor is on, and a large collector current flows, illuminating the bulb. If on the other hand the LDR is illuminated its

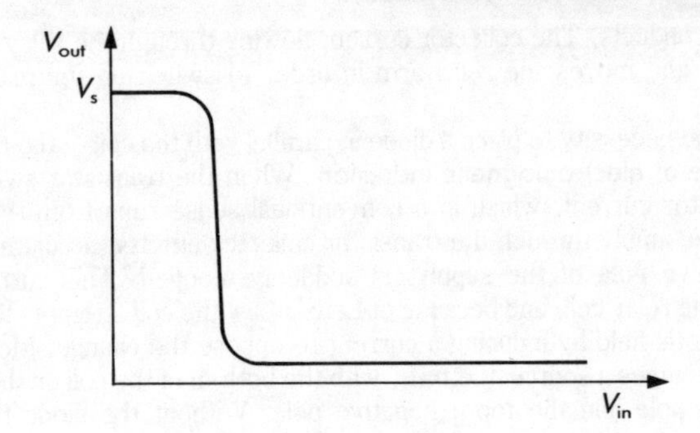

Fig. T.27

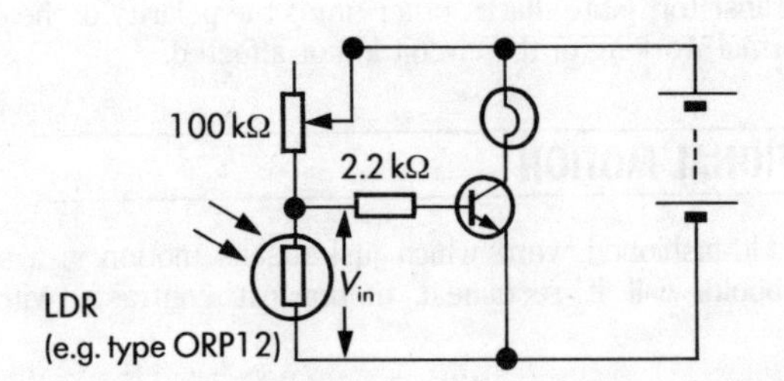

Fig. T.28

resistance is comparatively small, and if the voltage between the base and emitter is less than 0.7 volts the transistor will not conduct and the bulb will stay off. A circuit used in this way is clearly acting as a switch. A small base current determines whether or not the transistor is on or off, and therefore whether the bulb is on or off.

The circuit in Fig. T.29 is a much more sophisticated switching circuit. Here two transistors are used. The effect of this is to sharpen the switching action considerably. And in this case a relay is placed in the collector circuit of the second transistor. When the LDR is illuminated the first transistor conducts, a current passes through the 680 Ω resistor and so the voltage at the base of the second transistor is raised above the critical 0.7 V value, and

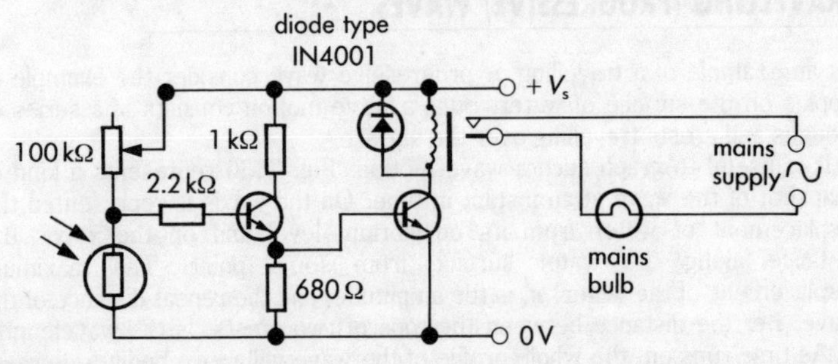

Fig. T.29

so it too conducts. The collector current flowing through the relay energises the **relay** and moves the relay-arm in order to switch on the mains-driven bulb.

Note the necessity to place a diode in parallel with the coil of the relay. This is because of **electromagnetic induction**. When the transistor switches off, the collector current, which in a conventional sense runs from the positive pole of the supply through the transistor collector-emitter circuit and back to the negative pole of the supply, is suddenly stopped. This current flows through the relay coil, and because of Lenz's Law the coil attempts to maintain this magnetic field by inducing a current to oppose the change. Momentarily the coil becomes a source of e.m.f., with the bottom of the coil on the diagram a positive pole and the top a negative pole. Without the diode this would generate a very large potential difference across the transistor and destroy it. The diode provides a short-circuit produced by this sudden e.m.f. and hence saves the transistor. Note that at other times the polarity of the diode is such that the normal working of the circuit is not affected.

TRANSLATIONAL MOTION

This is an old-fashioned word which just means motion in a straight line. Some textbooks call it rectilinear motion. It contrasts with **rotational motion**.

TRANSVERSE WAVES

Transverse waves are waves in which the local displacements of the medium in which the wave travels are perpendicular to the direction in which the wave travels (propagates). All electromagnetic waves, including light, are transverse. Transverse waves can be polarised. They contrast with longitudinal (compressional) waves in which the local motion is a to-and-fro motion along the direction of travel.

◀ Travelling (progressive) waves ▶

TRAVELLING (PROGRESSIVE) WAVES

As an example of a travelling or progressive wave consider the example of ripples on the surface of water. Such a wave motion consists of a series of troughs and crests travelling over the surface.

It is useful to graph such a wave motion. Fig. T.30 represents a kind of snapshot of the wave at an instant in time. On the y-axis is represented the displacement of water from its equilibrium level and on the x-axis the distance along the water surface from some point. The maximum displacement of the water, a, is the amplitude, and the repeat distance of the wave, i.e. the distance between the tops of two crests, is the wavelength, λ. As time runs on, the whole profile of the wave will move bodily sideways. At any particular point on the surface, e.g. at P, there will be a local

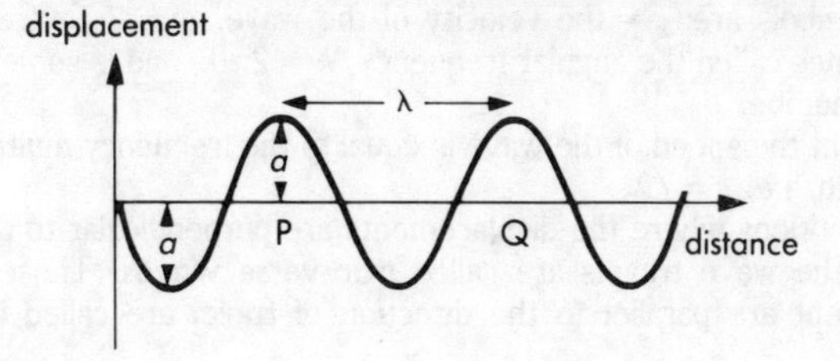

Fig. T.30 Ripples on water

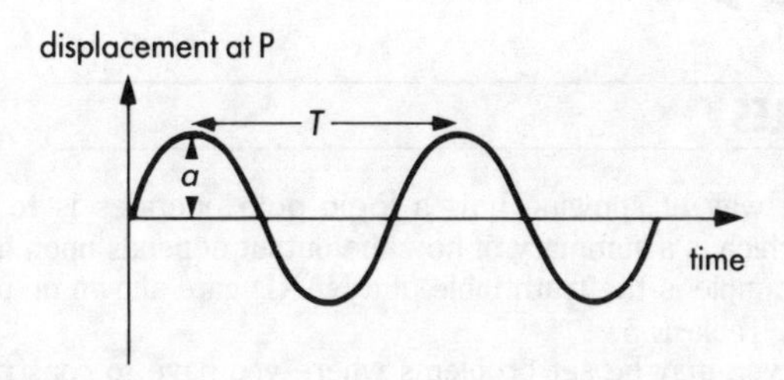

Fig. T.31 Displacement against time

up-and-down oscillation with a regular frequency. Fig. T.31 shows the graph of the displacement of the water surface at P against time. T is the period, but not this is sometimes represented by τ.

Some syllabuses require one or other of the formulae for the propagation of a sinusoidal wave. Sinusoidal waves are the easiest kinds of waves for the physicist to analyse, but it must be remembered that they are not the only kind of wave, others being square, stepped, etc. in form. As the name suggests, sinusoidal waves are waves whose graphs are sinusoidal in form. The equations of a travelling sinusoidal wave are one of the following forms:

$$y = a \sin \frac{2\pi}{\lambda}(x - c\,t)$$

$$\text{or } y = a \sin (k\,x - \omega t)$$

$$\text{or } y = a \sin 2\pi \left(\frac{x}{\lambda} - \frac{t}{\tau} \right)$$

Note that these are descriptions of waves travelling in a direction of increasing x. Waves travelling in the opposite direction have the form:

$$y = a \sin \frac{2\pi}{\lambda}(x + ct) \text{ etc.}$$

The symbols are: c = the velocity of the wave, $\omega = 2\pi \times$ frequency and is sometimes called the angular frequency, $k = 2\pi/\lambda$, and is sometimes called the wavenumber.

Note that the speed of the wave is equal to the frequency multiplied by the wavelength, i.e. $c = f\lambda$.

Wave motions where the displacements are perpendicular to the direction in which the wave travels are called **transverse waves**. Those where the displacement are parallel to the direction of travel are called **longitudinal waves**.

TRIMMER

◀ Capacitors ▶

TRUTH TABLES

The common way of showing how a **logic gate** operates is to produce a truth table, which is a summary of how the output depends upon the input or inputs. An example is the truth table of a NAND gate shown on page 222 in Fig. L.13 and Table L.5.

At A-level you may be set problems where you have to construct a truth table for a series of interconnecting gates in sequence. To do this, simply set out a grid so that each input and output is listed and work through from left to right. Remember to check whether the gate has any kind of inverting function (e.g. NOR rather than OR). Note the 'blob' on the symbols which indicate this function.

TTL

◀ Digital logic ▶

TURBULENT FLOW

This is a term used in the flow of fluids to describe the irregular pattern of flow which occurs when the flow rate is comparatively high. It is important in the physics of **musical instruments** because it provides a mechanism for the setting-up of **standing waves** in organ pipes, whistles, etc.

Consider the flow of a fluid past a blunt object. If the flow-speed is steadily increased, eventually fluid friction fails to control the movement. The **streamlines** diverge as they meet the object but they do not close in again behind it. Instead they curl up behind the object in a series of circulating eddies, sometimes called *vortices*. Large drag forces are produced when this happens. Consequently, in the flow of air past a car or water past a ship, eddy formation can result in strong and unwanted frictional forces.

The eddies are usually shed first to one side and then to the other (at positions A and B in Fig. T.32). The resultant quasi-regular pressure pattern can cause the object to experience **forced vibrations.** When air flows at speed past a telephone wire the vibrations are at an audio frequency and people speak of the telephone wires 'singing'.

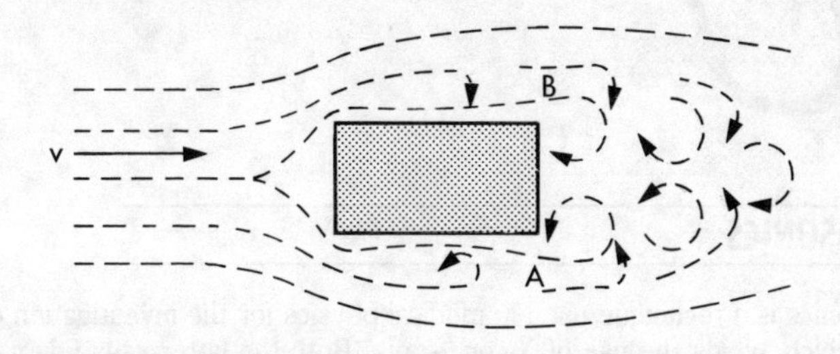

Fig. T.32 Turbulent flow past a blunt object

ULTRASONICS

Ultrasonics is a technique used in medical physics for the investigation of the body which avoids the use of X- or γ-rays. Both the latter cause damage to biological tissue and are referred to as *invasive techniques*. Where possible doctors will always prefer a method of analysis which is harmless to the body.

Ultrasonic waves are sound waves with frequencies above the audible range. In medical physics frequencies between 1 and 5 MHz are used. It is a central feature of wave physics that when there is a boundary between two media some of the wave is transmitted on into the new medium and some is reflected. The only exception to this process is total internal reflection, where there is no transmitted wave. So if an ultrasonic pulse crosses an interface between two media there will be an echo produced. The size of the echo depends upon the difference between what is called the acoustic impedance of the two materials. Acoustic impedance, Z, is defined as ρv, where ρ is the density of the medium and v the velocity of sound in that medium. The table below shows some values for v, ρ, and Z.

Material	$v/\mathrm{m\,s^{-1}}$	$\rho/\mathrm{kg\,m^{-3}}$	$Z/\mathrm{kg\,m^{-2}\,s^{-1}} \times 10^6$
Air	330	1.3	4.29×10^{-4}
Water	1500	1000	1.50
Bone	4080	1908	7.78
Oil	1500	950	1.42
Brain	1540	1025	1.58
Muscle	1580	1075	1.70
Liver	1585	1042	1.65
Fat	1450	952	1.38

It can be shown that

$$I_r/I_i = \left(\frac{Z_2 - Z_1}{Z_2 + Z_1}\right)^2$$

where I_i = incident intensity in the first medium whose Z value is Z_1 and I_r = reflected intensity. Z_2 is the second medium.

So that for a muscle/fat interface $I_r/I_i = 0.0107$, or 1.07 per cent, and for muscle to air, or from air to muscle, $I_r/I_i = 0.998$, or 99.8 per cent, showing that in this case almost all the incident energy is reflected. This shows that ultrasound in the body cannot penetrate beyond passages containing air, such as the lungs. It also shows the difficulty of transmitting ultrasound from air into the body. So in ultrasound examination a transducer which produces ultrasound from electrical pulses has to be placed on the surface of the body under examination. This is said to ensure good 'acoustic coupling' between the transducer and the body.

There are several methods of analysing the echos which are received from the body. One way is to handle them in the same way as depth sounding is used in oceanographic surveying. In this method the echoes are shown on an oscilloscope screen as shown in Fig. U.1. The positions of the peaks on the screen correspond to different echoes, and these peaks have to be interpreted against the possible geometry of the body to be examined. This method can for example be used to monitor the growth of a foetus in a pregnant mother.

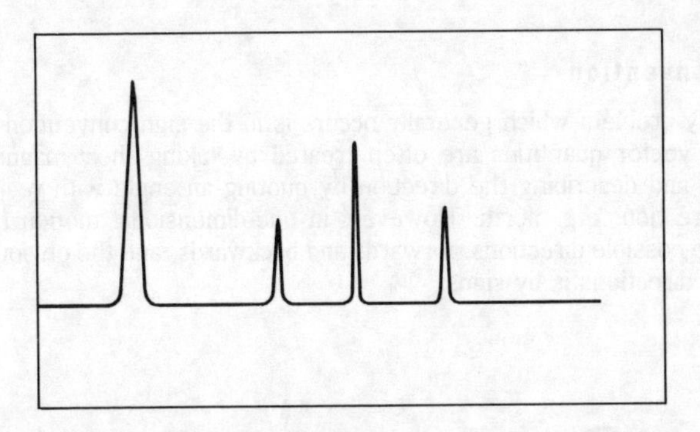

Fig. U.1 Oscilloscope trace of echoes in an ultrasound scan

UNCERTAINTY PRINCIPLE

In order to measure both position and velocity simultaneously two measurements are required. In the subatomic world of quantum mechanics it is considered that the act of performing the first measurement will disturb a particle and so create uncertainty in the second. As a result it is not possible to measure both position and velocity, for example, to perfect accuracy. The disturbance is so very small that it can be ignored in the macroscopic world of everyday life, but it is of considerable importance in the physics of subatomic particles.

UNIFORM ACCELERATION IN A STRAIGHT LINE

This is an important special case of **kinematics**, the most common of which is the uniform **acceleration** of a body under gravity. If the **velocity** of a body increases from an initial value u to a final value v, with a constant acceleration a, in a time t, then $a = \dfrac{v-u}{t}$, giving

$$v = u + at$$

and if the displacement is s, then the equations

$$s = \frac{(u+v)}{2}t$$

$$s = ut + \tfrac{1}{2}at^2$$

and $v^2 = u^2 + 2as$ can be derived.

Take care with units when using these equations. Units are s(m), v(m s^{-1}), a(m s^{-2}), t(s).

Sign convention

The only problem which generally occurs is in the sign convention used. In physics **vector** quantities are often treated by taking their magnitudes as positive and describing the direction by quoting an angle with respect to a fixed direction, e.g. north. However, in one-dimensional motion there are only two possible directions, forwards and backwards, and the obvious way to indicate directions is by signs.

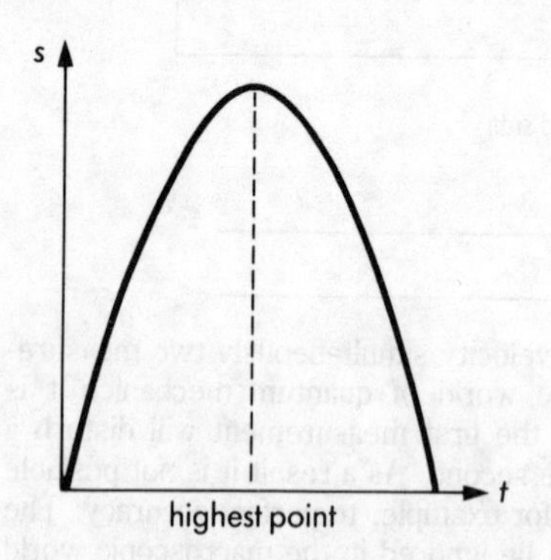

Fig. U.2 Graph of displacement against time

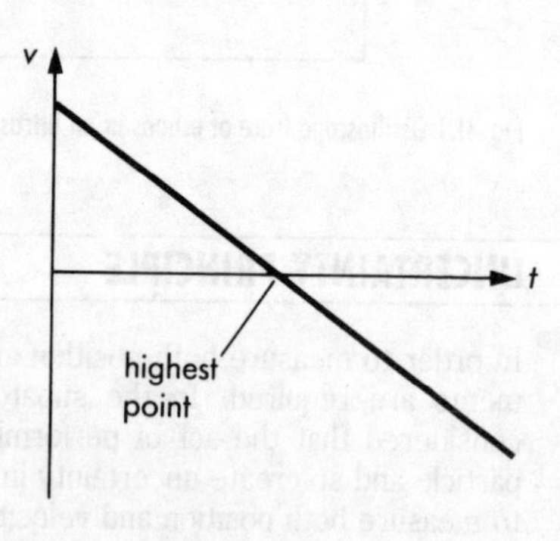

Fig. U.3 Graph of velocity against time

The graphs in Figs U.2 and U.3 show **displacement** and **velocity** for a stone thrown in the air. Here upward is taken as positive and so when v goes negative it implies the stone is moving downwards. With this sign convention the acceleration a is constant at -9.8 m s^{-2}.

◀ Ticker timer ▶

UNIFORM ELECTRIC FIELD

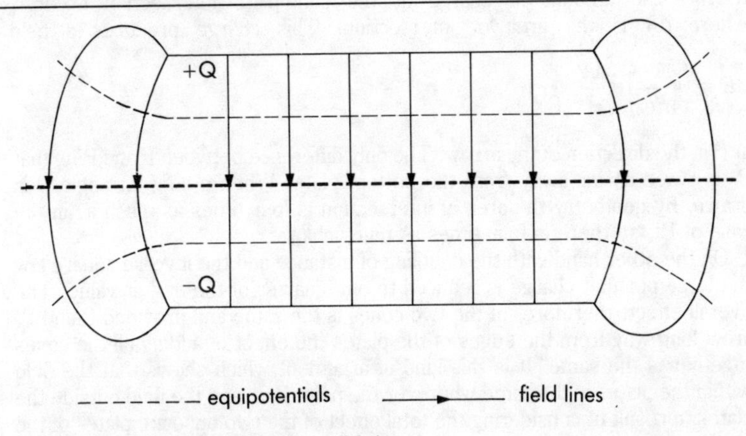

Fig. U.4 Uniform field between charged parallel plates

The electric field between two parallel plates is uniform, i.e. the field strength is the same at all points between the plates. Thus the lines of equipotential are parallel to the plates. Fig. U.4 shows a cross-sectional field and equipotential diagram of a parallel-plate system. Note that at the ends of the plates there is a 'fringing' effect, and that above and below the plates the field is zero.

As in the case of the zero field within a charged sphere (see **Radial electric fields**), the key to both the uniform field between the plates, and the zero field beyond them, lies in the inverse square law nature of Coulomb's Law.

Consider, for example, Fig. U.5. A cone has been drawn from the two points P and P′ towards the bottom plate at an angle, θ. The charge is

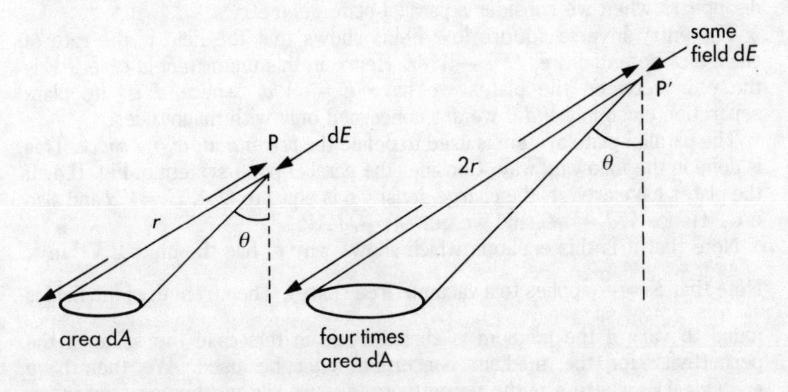

Fig. U.5 The field at points above the plate of a capacitor

uniformly distributed on the bottom plate, and if the density of charge is $\sigma\,\mathrm{C\,m^{-2}}$ the amount of charge at the cone/plate intersection is σdA, where dA is the area of intersection. This charge produces a field

$$dE = \left(\frac{1}{4\pi\epsilon_0}\right)\sigma\frac{dA}{r^2}$$

at P in the direction of the arrow. The only difference between P and P′ is that P′ is twice as far away from the bottom plate. When a cone at angle θ is drawn, by geometry the area of intersection is four times as much as in the case of P′, so there is four times as much charge.

On the other hand with the doubling of distance and the inverse square law the force per unit charge is reduced to one quarter of the earlier value. The overall effect, therefore, of the two cones is the same and provided P and P′ are a long way from the edges of the plates the effect of adding all the cones together is the same. It is this kind of argument which shows that the field within the plates is the same wherever the point P is, and the field outside the plates, a result of considering the total effect of the two opposite plates of the charge, is zero.

To calculate the total field E at a point P it is necessary to integrate the expression for dE. That is to say it is necessary to consider all the possible cones in three-dimensional space and to vectorially add up the components dE that each produces.

When this is done the $1/4\pi$ factor disappears and the result is

$$E = \frac{\sigma}{2\epsilon_0}$$

Note that this is independent of the distance r, as indicated earlier. Note also that if we were considering the field within a parallel-plate system we would have to consider the sum of both the field of the positive charge on one plate and that of the negative charge on the other. We would then get $E = \sigma/\epsilon_0$. Note how the awkward constant $(1/4\pi\epsilon_0)$ which occurs in Coulomb's law disappears when we consider a parallel-plate geometry.

The entry **Inverse square law fields** shows that the field is the rate of change of potential, i.e. $E = -dV/dr$. Hence in this uniform field case if V is the p.d. between the plates we have $E = -V/d$, where d is the plate separation or simply V/d if we are concerned only with magnitudes.

The parallel-plate system is used to define the *permittivity of free space*. This is done in the following way. Consider the parallel-plate system of Fig. P.4. If the plates have area A, the charge density σ is equal to Q/A. $E = V/d$ and also σ/ϵ_0. Hence $V/d = \sigma/\epsilon_0$ and we get $\epsilon_0 = Qd/AV$.

Note that it is this equation which shows why ϵ_0 has the units $\mathrm{C\,V^{-1}\,m^{-1}}$.

Note that $E = \dfrac{\sigma}{\epsilon_0}$ applies to a vacuum (free space). The strength of the field is found to vary if the medium is changed and in this case the value of the permittivity for the medium concerned must be used. We then have $\epsilon = Qd/AV$, where ϵ is the permittivity. ϵ is usually written $\epsilon_r\epsilon_0$, where ϵ_r is called the relative permittivity of the medium.

The formula for the capacitance of the system is $C = Q/V$, and hence using the results we have obtained we get the formula for the capacitance of a parallel plate capacitor, $C = A\epsilon_0\epsilon_r/d$.

◀ Radial electric fields ▶

UNIFORM FIELD THEORY

◀ Fields ▶

UNIT CELL

The unit cell is a term used in the physics and chemistry of crystals. It is the smallest convenient and suitable repeat unit within the lattice. It is usually chosen so that it has the symmetry of the structure. The lattice, the 'framework' of the structure, is then obtained by translating (moving from side to side or up and down) the unit cell in the three directions of space (see Fig. U.6).

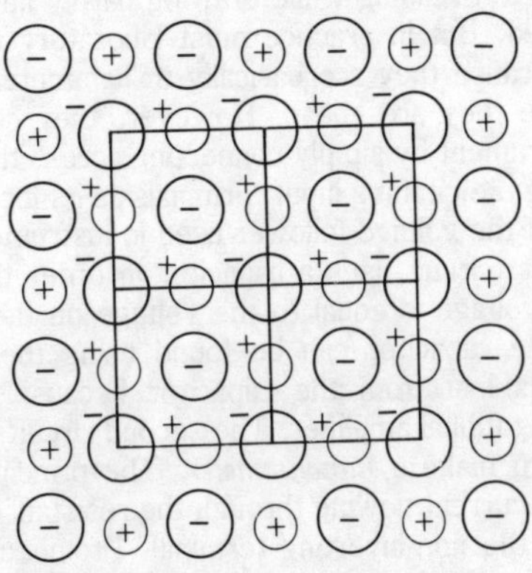

Fig. U.6 Ionic structure of sodium chloride showing unit cells

UNITS

◀ Physical quantities in the SI system ▶

UNITY GAIN VOLTAGE FOLLOWER

This is a special case of the **operational amplifier** used in the non-inverting amplifier mode. In this special case 100 per cent negative feedback is obtained by connecting the output directly to the inverting terminal, as shown in Fig. U.7.

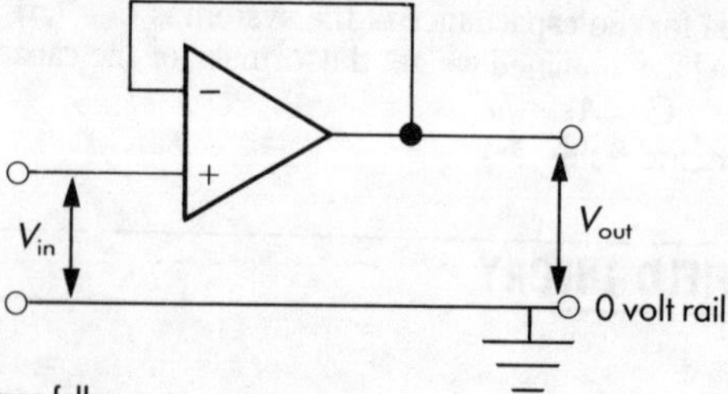

Fig. U.7 Unity gain voltage follower

It will be seen that this is the form of the circuit on p. 265 with $R_f = 0$ and R_i infinite. Applying the amplification formulae for the non-inverting amplifier we see that the gain here is unity. That is to say, the output voltage is the same as the input voltage to within approximately 70 μV. The circuit is called a voltage follower because the output follows the input.

The usefulness of the circuit is that it has an extremely high input impedance and a very low output impedance. A perfect voltmeter has just this property: it gives a reading while drawing hardly any current from the input being measured. But in practice most laboratory voltmeters are not like this. This is because they are basically milliammeters in series with a high resistor. Hence they are cheap. However, they can be made into a high-impedance instrument by simply connecting across the output terminals of Fig. U.8 and using the circuit's input terminals as its input.

Other examples of the voltage follower used in instrumentation are shown in Fig. U.8. The first circuit uses a capacitor in order to make a coulomb meter. The output voltage is equal to the voltage on the capacitor. Hence the charge Q on the capacitor can be found using the formula $Q = VC$. Almost no charge is lost from the capacitor because of the high input impedance of the operational amplifier. The second circuit shows the use of a high-value resistor to make a *nanoammeter*. The principle is the same as before. A very small current flowing through the resistance R will generate a voltage, IR, across the non-inverting terminal. Provided the resistor R is considerably less than the input resistance of the operational amplifier, in practice less than $10^{11}\Omega$, then all the current in the circuit passes through the resistance R. The current is found using the formula $I = V/R$.

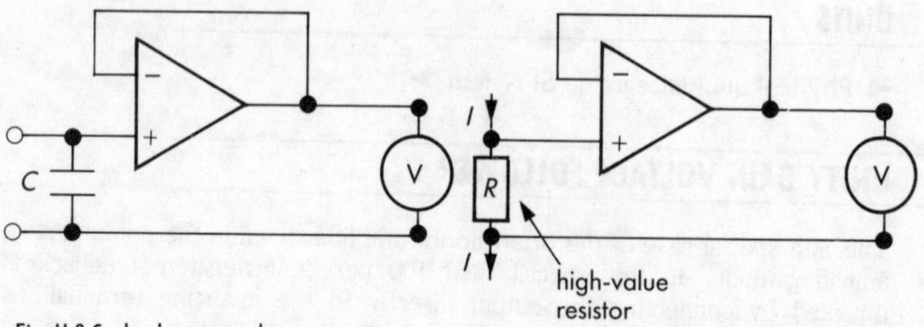

Fig. U.8 Coulomb meter and nanoammeter

UNSATURATED VAPOUR

◀ Saturated vapour ▶

UPTHRUST

This is a term used in the physics of **fluids** to describe the net upward force experienced when an object is wholly or partially immersed in the fluid.

The 'object' might for example be a submarine and the 'fluid' the sea. The submarine might be on the surface and therefore only partiallly immersed or under the water and hence completely immersed.

An object immersed in a fluid experiences a net force which tends to push it upwards and, if possible, out of the fluid (Fig. U.9). This resultant force arises from the fact that the pressure in a fluid increases with depth.

Archimedes' principle states that the upthrust is equal to the weight of fluid displaced. The object may, of course, be only partially immersed in the fluid.

In Fig. U.10, the drum floating in a liquid of density ρ displaces a volume of liquid Ad and hence a mass of $Ad\rho$ and a weight of $Ad\rho g$. For a floating object the weight of the object equals the weight of liquid displaced. This is called *buoyancy*.

◀ Hydrometer ▶

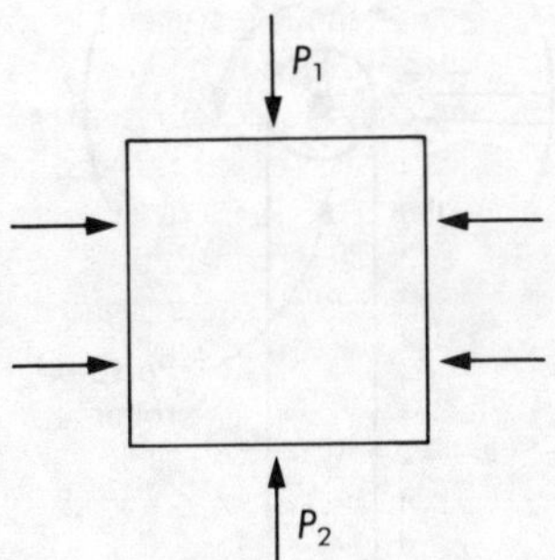

Fig. U.9 Fully immersed object

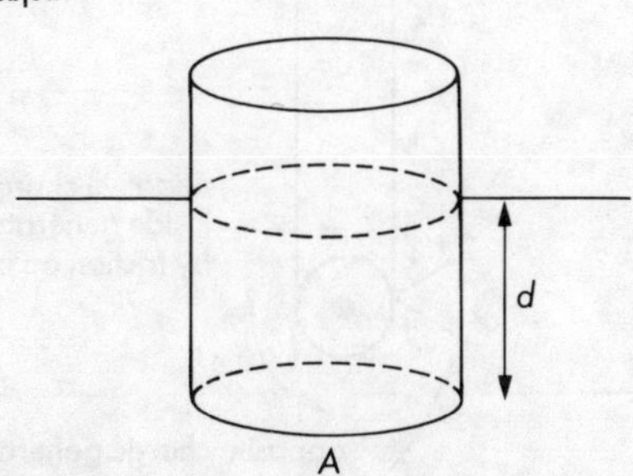

Fig. U.10 Partially immersed object

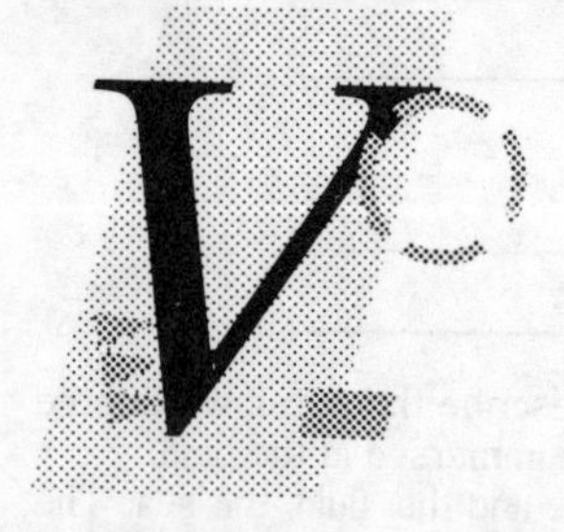

VAN DE GRAAFF GENERATOR

The van de Graaff generator is a very efficient electrostatic charge generator which was invented following the discovery that charge delivered to the inside of a hollow conductor is all transferred to the outside (see **Faraday's ice-pail experiments**).

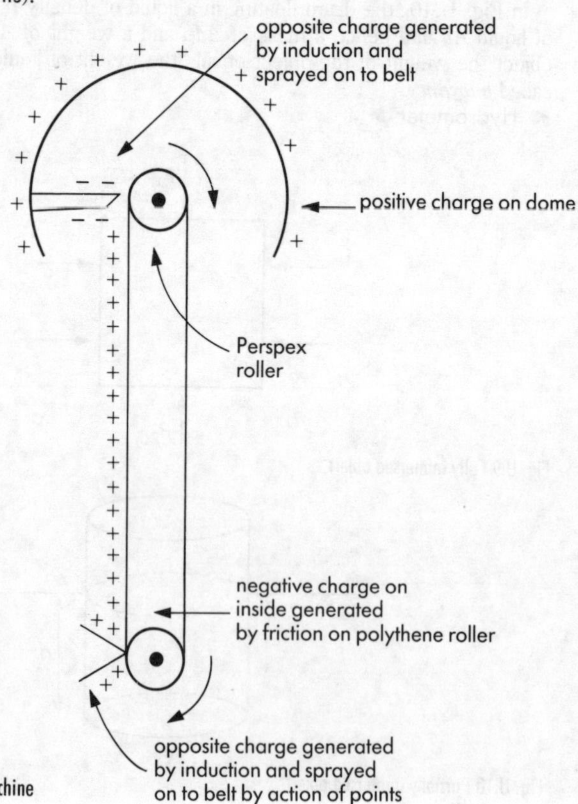

Fig. V.1 Van de Graaff machine

In the van de Graaff generator (Fig. V.1) the charge is generated on a polythene roller which is hand- or motor-driven. This charge is generated by friction. Opposite the roller is a series of points set out like a comb. Because negative charge is generated by rubbing polythene, the opposite charge generated on the comb, by induction, is positive. By the **action of points**, this charge is sprayed on to the outside of the moving rubber belt. At the top of the belt is another comb, where again an inductive process coupled with the action of points takes place. Here electrons, negative charge, are induced on the comb and sprayed on to the belt, first neutralising the positive charge. The net effect is the accumulation of positive charge on the metal dome. This charge accumulates on its outside. In energy terms there is a build-up of electrostatic energy by the increasing charge stored on the dome. In order to do this, positive charges have to be brought up the rotating rubber belt and work has to be done to raise them up and to oppose the repulsive forces caused by the charge already on the dome.

In order to avoid the production of positive charge by induction on the belt at the top, the upper roller is made of Perspex. If the position of the polythene and Perspex rollers are exhanged the dome becomes negatively charged.

Small van de Graaff machines are found in schools and colleges. However, very large machines have been built for experiments in nuclear and particle physics where a source of extremely high voltage is required.

◀ Charge distribution, Electrostatic phenomena ▶

VAN DER WAALS' EQUATION

Van der Waals' equation is an equation of state for gases which approximates better to their actual behaviour at low temperatures and high pressures than the **ideal gas** equation. By an equation of state we mean an equation which relates pressure p, volume V and temperature T. The equation is

$$\left(p + \frac{a}{V^2}\right)(V - b) = RT$$

where the equation is written for 1 mole. V is therefore the volume occupied by 1 mole. However, the actual volume of the gas molecules is less than this and b represents this volume. Hence $(V - b)$ represents the free volume in which random molecular motion can take place. This is the first correction to the ideal gas formula. The second correction, a/V^2, is a correction term which allows for the effect of attractive forces between the molecules.

Fig. V.2 shows graphs of p against V for a gas which obeys the Van der Waals' model. For large values of V, a/V^2 is negligible, as is b compared with V. Therefore the equation reduces in this case to the ideal gas equation. Otherwise the curves for constant temperature resemble those for real gases except for the part of the curve labelled PQR, which cannot be realised experimentally.

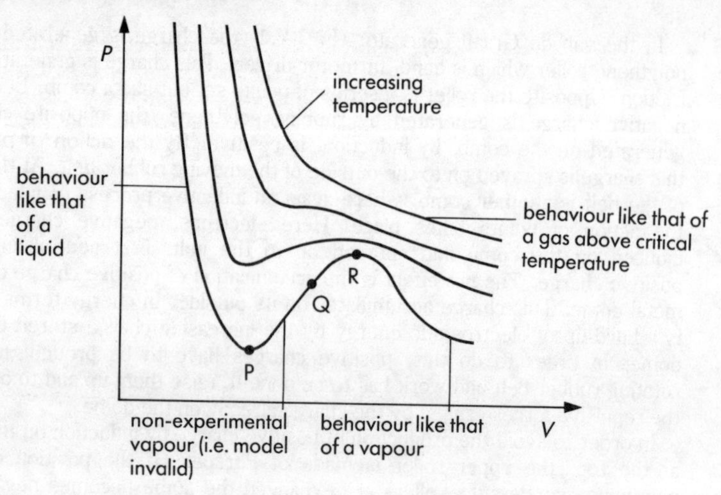

Fig. V.2 Curves of *p* against *V* at constant temperature for a gas obeying a Van der Waals model

VAN DER WAALS' FORCES

◀ Solids ▶

VAPOURS

◀ Gases, liquids, Vapours and plasmas, Saturated vapours ▶

VECTOR

A vector quantity in physics is a quantity which can be completely specified only by quoting both a magnitude and a direction. It contrasts with a **scalar** quantity, for which only the specification of a magnitude is necessary.

Force and **momentum** are examples of vector quantities. For example, it is insufficient to say a force is, say, 23.5 newtons: it is also necessary to state the direction of the force. This is because vector quantities do not add up by the ordinary laws of arithmetic but by the rule of the **parallelogram of vectors**. So two forces of 10 N and 10 N newtons may add up to anything from zero to 20 N depending on the relative directions of each.

VELOCITY

This is speed in a particular direction. Thus, as both magnitude and direction have to be specified, it is a **vector**. (If no direction is specified it is better to use the term speed, usually thought of as a **scalar**.)

Consider a girl on a roundabout (Fig. V.3). Her speed may be constant at, say, $4\,\text{m s}^{-1}$. But velocity is speed in a particular direction and the velocity is constantly changing because the child's direction of motion is changing. At one instant her velocity is $4\,\text{m s}^{-1}$ due east. Half a revolution later it is $4\,\text{m s}^{-1}$ due west.

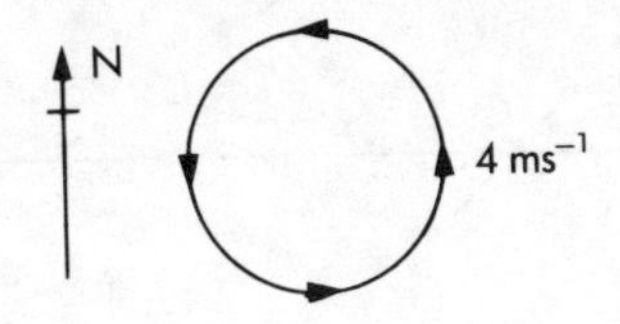

Fig. V.3

Velocity is strictly defined as the rate of change of **displacement**. It is useful to distinguish between average and instantaneous velocity:

$$\text{Average velocity} = \frac{\text{final displacement} - \text{initial displacement}}{\text{total time}}$$

Instantaneous velocity is defined by $v = \Delta s/\Delta t$, where Δs is the small change in displacement which occurs in a small instant of time Δt. More strictly, using the notation of the calculus,

$$v = \lim_{\Delta t \to 0}\left(\frac{\Delta s}{\Delta t}\right) = \mathrm{d}s/\mathrm{d}t$$

Graphically $\mathrm{d}s/\mathrm{d}t$ is the slope of an s, t graph at the particular instant in time.

VELOCITY-DEPENDENT DAMPING

◀ Damped s.h.m. ▶

VELOCITY OF ELECTROMAGNETIC WAVES

The velocity of electromagnetic waves, $c = 3 \times 10^8\,\text{m s}^{-1}$, is a universal and **fundamental constant** in physics and therefore its direct measurement is of some importance.

In the school or college laboratory the speed of visible light can be measured by the use of the apparatus by shown in Fig. V.4. This method relies on some sophisticated electronics which modulates the light beam emitted by a light-emitting diode (LED). The modulation is done with a very high-frequency sinusoidal signal. The beam is focused on a photodiode, where the modulated light signal is converted back into a sinusoidal voltage. The signals at the emitter and the detector will not be in phase because of the time of propagation from the emitter to the detector. This phase difference is measured either using a direct reading instrument, called a phase-sensitive detector, or by supplying one of the signals to the Y-plates of an **oscilloscope** and the other to the X-plates. If the modulation frequency

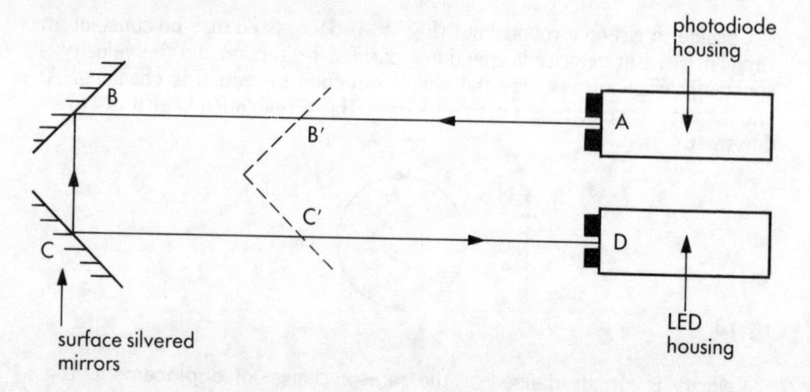

Fig. V.4 Method for determining c using electronics technology in a college laboratory. The mirrors and housings are mounted on an optical bench. The path travelled by the beam is d = ABCD and can be reduced by moving the mirrors as shown

is f, and the phase difference between the two signals is ϕ then it can be shown that

$$c = \frac{2\pi}{\phi} df$$

where d is the distance of propagation.

Another experiment which can be performed in the school or college laboratory is the measurement of the speed of electromagnetic waves down a coaxial cable. Using a 200 kHz pulse generator voltage spikes or pulses are generated at one end of a long cable and their arrival at the far end are detected. An oscilloscope with a very fast time base is used to measure the time taken for the pulse to travel the length of the cable. In this case the speed is about $2 \times 10^8\,\mathrm{m\,s^{-1}}$. The speed is reduced from c because of the polythene insulation between the inner and outer conductors of the coaxial cable.

Both these college/school experiments illustrate the principles of a direct measurement of the speed of electromagnetic waves, but are not accurate. The classic experiment for accurately measuring the speed of light was performed by the American physicist, Michelson. This method is an example of a **null method.** Michelson used an eight-sided rotating mirror which was mounted near the top of Mount Wilson in the USA. Fig. V.5 shows schematically the arrangement adopted in the 1927 version of his experiment.

Light from a powerful source L was directed on to the octagonal mirror M_1 which reflected the beam in turn at plane mirrors M_2 and M_3 such that eventually it was reflected from the large concave mirror M_4. This directed the beam to a point on Mount San Antonio, 35 km away, on which there was another concave reflector M_5. The light was reflected back from San Antonio to the eight-sided mirror via M_6 M_4 M_7 and M_8 to be detected by an observer at E. The mirror speed was varied so that for the light to be detected by the eyepiece it must have rotated by one eighth of a turn. That is to say one face

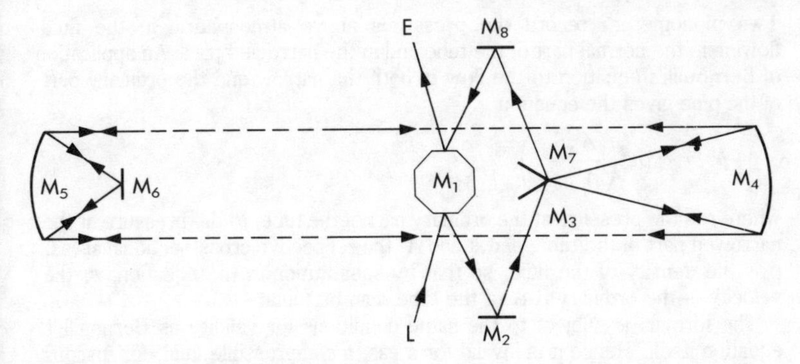

Fig. V.5 Michelson's method for the speed of light

of the prism must have replaced its predecessor in the time it took the light to travel to Mount Wilson to Mount San Antonio and back again. If d is the total distance to be travelled and n the number of revolutions per second then: $c = 8nd$.

The distance between the two mountains was measured to high precision by the US Admiralty. Michelson's mean result for c was 299,798 km s^{-1}. Michelson wanted to repeat the experiment with an evacuated tube, but died before he could do so. His collaborators completed this work with a tube 1 mile long using repeated reflections to obtain a value of d of 13 km, but with no improvement in accuracy on Michelson's earlier method.

VENTURI METER

The venturi meter is a method of measuring the rate of flow of a liquid through a pipe. It consists of a horizontal pipe with a constriction (Fig. V.6).

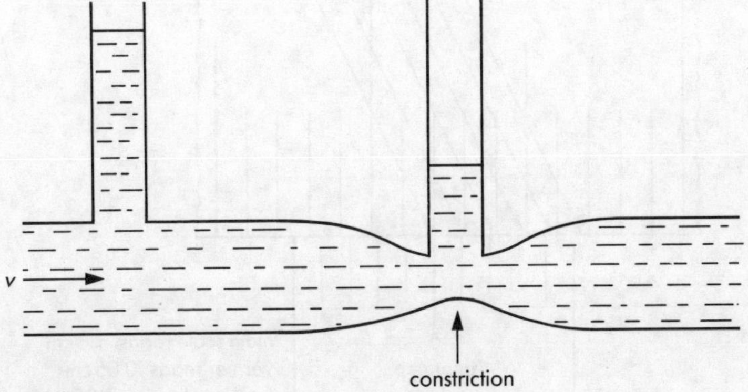

Fig. V.6 Venturi meter

Two monometers record the pressures above atmospheric in the fluid flowing in the normal part of the tube and in the narrowed part. An application of **Bernouilli's** equation to the flow in both the narrow and the ordinary part of the pipe gives the equation

$$p - p' = \tfrac{1}{2}\rho v^2\left(\frac{A^2}{A'^2} - 1\right)$$

where p is the pressure at the ordinary part of the tube, p' the pressure at the narrowed part of the tube, and A and A' the respective cross-sectional areas. ρ is the density of the fluid, so that by substitution in the equation, v, the velocity in the ordinary part of the tube, can be found.

The formula is subject to the same conditions for validity as Bernouilli's equation itself. Hence it is invalid for a gas, a compressible fluid, for viscous liquids in which there may be energy losses through the narrower part of the tube, through friction, and for very rapid flow in which there may be turbulence.

◀ Pitot static tube ▶

VERNIER SCALE

A vernier scale is found on a pair of **callipers.** Verniers are also commonly found on travelling microscopes, and in a different form (to measure minutes of arc) on a **spectrometer** scale.

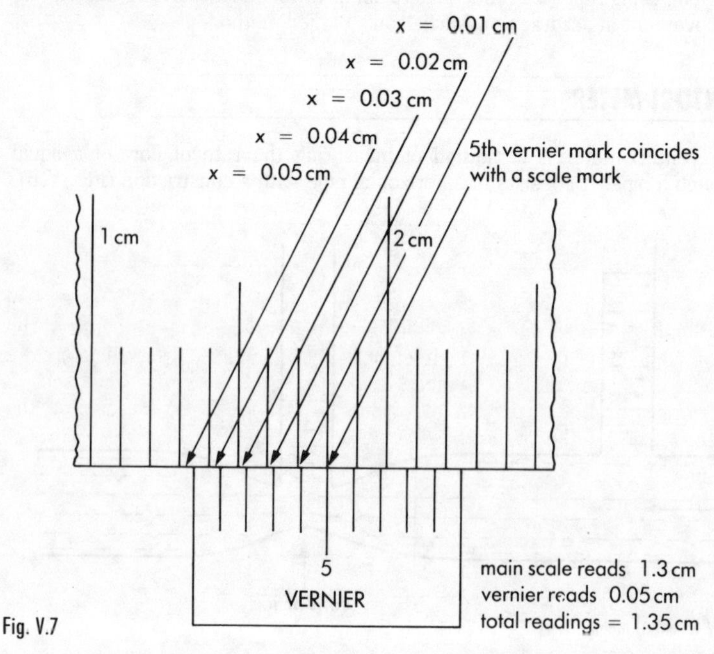

Fig. V.7

The vernier scale itself is the short scale of ten divisions on say the sliding jaw of a pair of callipers. It enables the accurate determination of the second decimal place without having to estimate factions of the division by eye. Usually the vernier is 9 mm long divided into ten equal parts, so that the difference in length between a vernier division and a scale division is 0.1 mm or 0.01 cm. Fig. V.7 shows a scale and vernier giving a reading of 1.35 cm. The fraction of a scale division shown as x is given by a second decimal place. Note that the fifth vernier mark coincides with a scale mark. The second decimal place in the measurement made is given by the number of a vernier mark which coincides with the scale mark.

VIBRATION MAGNETOMETER

◀ Magnetic flux density measurement ▶

VIRTUAL EARTH

◀ Operational amplifier ▶

VIRTUAL IMAGE

This is a term used in ray optics to describe a point from which rays appear to come. It contrasts with the term **real image**, which is a point through which rays converge but actually pass through as well.

VISION

◀ Eye, Defects of vision ▶

VOLTAGE COMPARATOR

If two voltages are applied simultaneously to both inputs of an **operational amplifier** the output voltage is either high or low depending on which of the input voltages is the greater. It effectively behaves as a digital two-state device, comparing the two voltages.

Consider an op. amp. with two inputs and no feedback. Because of the large gain A, the operational amplifier saturates. If $V_+ > V_-$, V_{out}

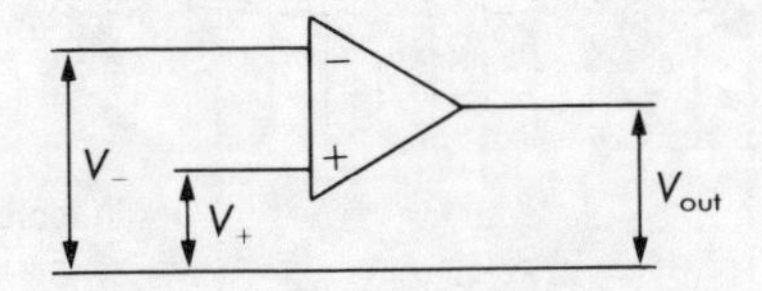

Fig. V.8

becomes $+V_s$, the positive supply voltage. When $V_+ < V_-$, V_{out} 'flips' to $-V_s$. Only if V_+ is within about 60 μV of V_- will the output be anything other than $+V_s$. Regarding $+V_s$ as logic state 1 and $-V_s$ as logic state 0, and the non-inverting and inverting inputs as inputs A and B, the system can be described by the statement:

IF A > B THEN OUTPUT = 1
IF B < A THEN OUTPUT = 0

The comparator is commonly used in sensing circuits where a temperature or light-dependent device is arranged in a potential divider circuit.

The circuit in Fig. V.9 is a typical example. When the light-dependent resistor is dark it has a very high resistance and the variable resistor is adjusted so that $V_+ > V_-$, so that V_{out} is high. On the other hand when a light shines on the LDR its resistance falls. V_+ is now less than V_- and so the output is now low. Sufficient current can be drawn from the output for it to be able to drive other circuitry. The output could, for example, be sent to a relay to control, indirectly, a mains-driven lamp.

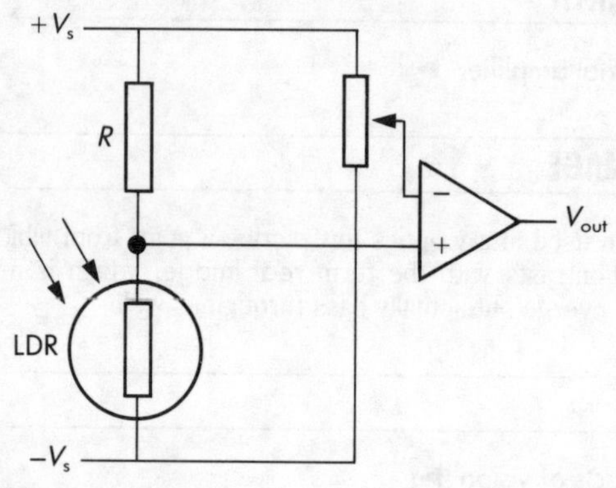

Fig. V.9 Light switch using a comparator

VOLTMETER

◀ Ammeters and voltmeters ▶

VORTICES

◀ Turbulent flow ▶

WAVE

◀ Standing waves, Travelling (progressive) waves ▶

WAVE MECHANICS

◀ Quantum mechanical model of the atom ▶

WAVE NUMBER

This is a term used in wave physics and also in spectroscopy. It is one of the few terms in physics where there is an ambiguity.

In the physics of mechanical waves wave number is denoted by k, and $k = 2\pi/\lambda$.

In spectroscopy wave number is also denoted by k but is equal to the reciprocal of wavelength. Hence $k = 1/\lambda$.

In both cases the units are m^{-1}.

◀ Travelling (progressive) waves ▶

WAVEFRONT

The term wavefront is used in the physics of waves in situations where waves travel in a two-dimensional medium, e.g. ripples on the surface of water, where at an elementary level it is usually used to refer to the line of a crest or a trough.

In more advanced physics it is applied to two- or three-dimensional situations. An example of the latter would be sound waves travelling through the air from a localised source. All the points on a wavefront have the same phase of oscillation. So for example in the case of ripples on water the wavefront could, as in elementary physics, be the line joining all the points of a wave which form a crest, i.e. the point for which the amplitude is locally a maximum. But equally the wavefront could be chosen to be a line linking points which are at a constant phase angle ϕ from a crest, where ϕ is anything from 0 to 2π. In simple wave theory the wavefront is always at right angles to the direction of propagation of the wave.

The term wavefront is often used in the theory of light, and especially in order to make a link between a description of light in terms of **rays** and a description in terms of waves. The wavefront is perpendicular to the ray direction, i.e. the direction of propagation. If the waves are plane waves then the rays are parallel.

WAVELENGTH

◀ Travelling (progressive) waves ▶

WEAK INTERACTION

This is one of the four fundamental forces of nature. It is the cause, among other things, of β-decay.

WEIGHT

Weight is the downward force on a body due to gravity. It acts towards the centre of the earth. Because it is a **force** it is not to be confused with **mass**, which is independent of the presence or absence of the earth. It is measured in newtons.

WHEATSTONE BRIDGE

This is a circuit used for measuring **resistance**.

Like the **pontentiometer**, the Wheatstone bridge is a **null method**, in this case used for measuring the resistance of an unknown resistor. The circuit is shown in Fig. W.1.

Four resistances are used, one of them being an unknown resistor. In practical terms R_3 and R_4 are formed by two sections of a meter resistance wire, as shown in Fig. W.2.

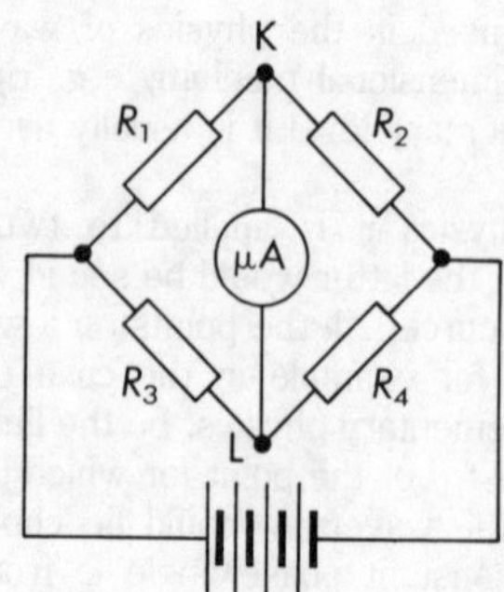

Fig. W.1 Wheatstone bridge

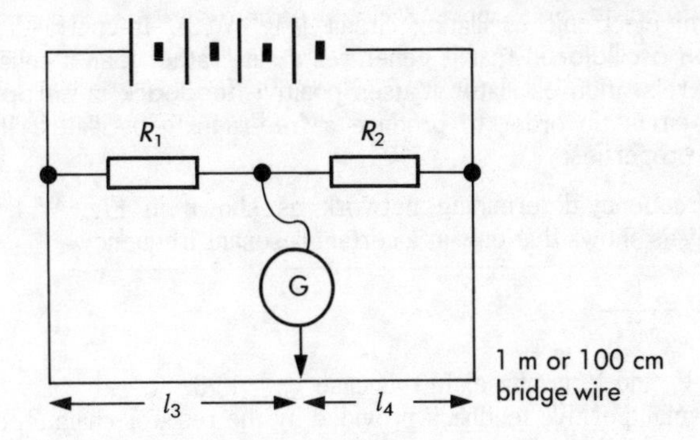

Fig. W.2 Wheatstone bridge using a slide wire arrangement

In use, the p.d. across l_3 is equal to the p.d. across R_1, and the p.d. across l_4 is equal to the p.d. across R_2. If I_w is the current in the resistance wire, I is the current in R_1 and R_2, and r is the resistance per unit length of the bridge wire, then we have $I_w r l_3 = IR_1$ and $I_w r l_4 = IR_2$, giving

$$\frac{l_3}{l_4} = \frac{R_1}{R_2}$$

Hence the unknown resistance can be found.

WHOLE-WAVE RECTIFIER

◀ Direct current power supplies ▶

WIEN BRIDGE OSCILLATOR

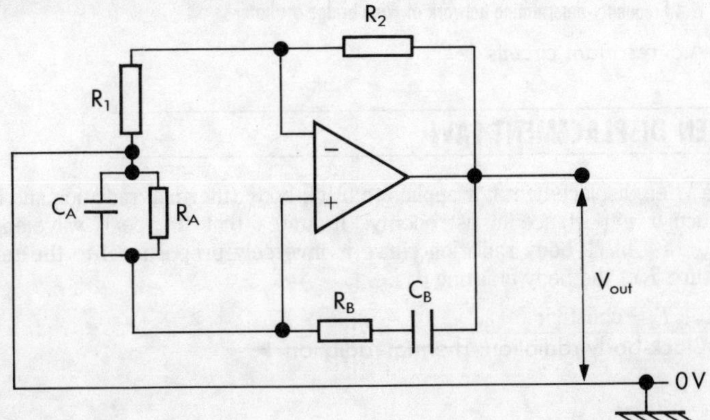

Fig. W.3 Wien bridge oscillator

This is an electronic oscillating circuit (Fig. W.3). It contrasts with the **relaxation oscillator** in that it generates a sine rather than a square wave. Like the relaxation oscillator it uses positive **feedback** in an **operational amplifer** circuit in order to produce a free-running oscillator. It has the following properties:

i) A frequency-determining network as shown in Fig. W.4. An a.c. analysis shows that only at a certain resonant frequency

$$f = \frac{1}{2\pi RC}$$

are V_0 and V_r in phase. In this case $V_0 = V_r/3$.

ii) A small positive feedback provided by the resistor chain R_1 and R_2 to sustain this oscillation.

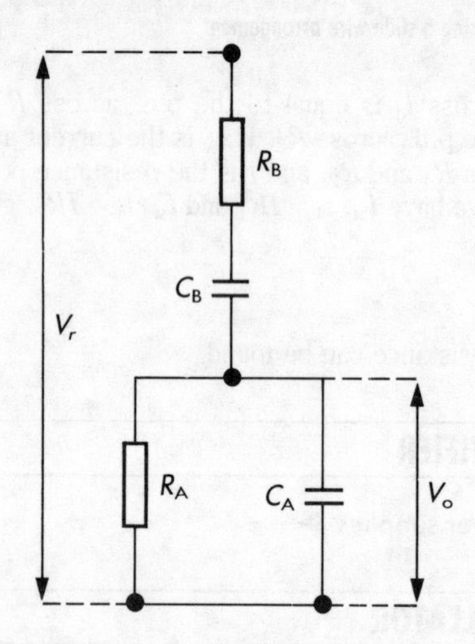

Fig. W.4 Frequency-determining network of Wien bridge oscillator

◀ A.c. resonant circuits ▶

WIEN DISPLACEMENT LAW

The Wien displacement law applies to black-body (thermal) radiation and is of particular importance in astronomy. It states that the peak wavelength, λ_{max}, of a black-body radiation curve is inversely proportional to the temperature T of the body emitting it, i.e.

$$\lambda_{max} T = \text{constant}$$

◀ Black-body radiation, Thermal radiation ▶

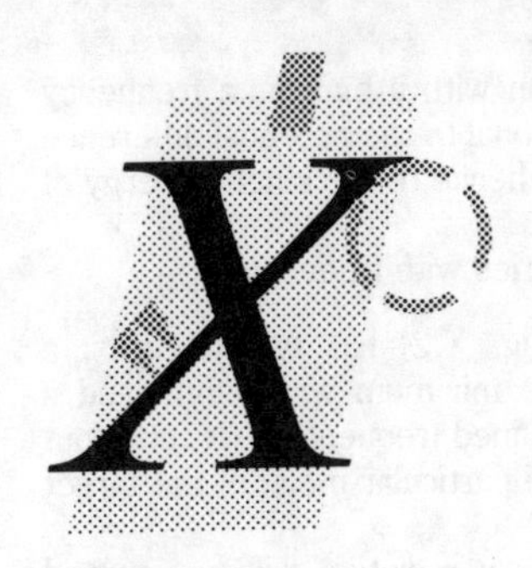

X-RAYS

X-rays are electromagnetic waves with a wavelength of about 10^{-10} m, which result from the collision of high-speed electrons with metals. They are able to penetrate matter and so have been used since their discovery at the end of the nineteenth century to 'see' inside the body. In material science and in biology the **diffraction** of X-rays, using the regular arrays of atoms in matter as **diffraction gratings**, is used to work out molecular and crystal structures.

X-rays are produced using a tube similar to that shown in Fig. X.1. Inside the evacuated glass tube is a metal filament which heats a cathode indirectly. The anode is usually made of tungsten metal. Electrons thrown off from the filament by **thermionic emission** are accelerated towards the anode by a potential difference of between 30 kV and 100 kV. When they strike the anode the electrons are suddenly decelerated, releasing their energy. Part of this is converted into X-rays and is emitted from the tube through a 'window' in the tube, i.e. a comparatively thin part of the glass envelope.

Experimentally it has been found that:

i) The greater the filament current the greater is the intensity of the X-radiation.

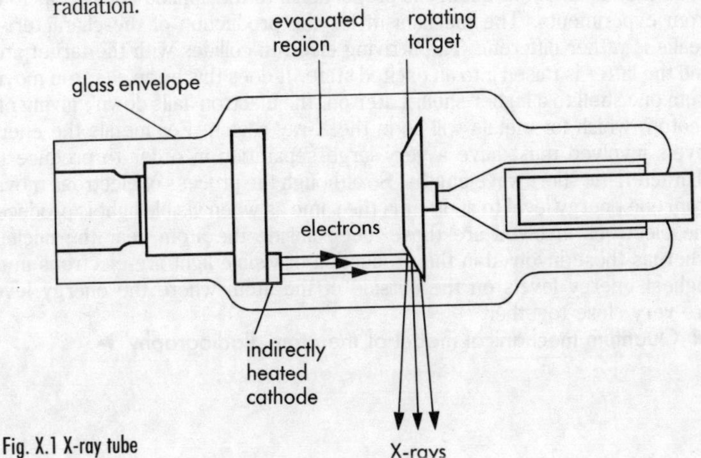

Fig. X.1 X-ray tube

ii) There is a continuous range of radiation with a maximum frequency (minimum wavelength) which is proportional to the potential difference between the cathode and the anode and hence to the kinetic energy of the incident electrons.
iii) The intensity of the emitted radiation varies with frequency.

The graph of intensity against frequency (Fig. X.2) has two features: a continuous spectrum which terminates at the minimum wavelength and a number of peaks in the curve at a few well-defined frequencies. It turns out that these frequencies are characteristic of the particular metal of the target but independent of the accelerating voltage.

According to classical electromagnetic theory radiation will be emitted whenever an electron is accelerated. Thus when an accelerated electron passes close to a nucleus of a target and is deflected, there is an accompanying emission of radiation and a change in speed and therefore kinetic energy. This is called **Bremsstrahlung**, a German word meaning rays produced by braking (deceleration). In quantum mechanical terms the radiation consists of **photons** of energy with each photon having a definite energy. The equation describing this is $hf = \Delta(\frac{1}{2}mv^2)$, where h is the Planck constant, f the frequency of the radiation, and $\Delta(\frac{1}{2}mv^2)$ the change in kinetic energy of the electron. Photons of radiation of various frequencies are produced. The maximum photon frequency (minimum wavelength) is achieved when the electron is brought to a complete standstill, so that $\frac{1}{2}mv^2 = hf_{\text{max}}$. As a result the frequencies of the radiation will vary continuously up to a maximum, where there will be an abrupt cut-off. Now, $\frac{1}{2}mv^2 = eV$, where e is the charge on the electron and V the potential difference between the cathode and the anode. Hence we get

$$eV = hf_{\text{max}}$$

$$\text{or } f_{\text{max}} = \frac{eV}{h}$$

Thus the maximum frequency is proportional to the applied voltage, as found from experiments. The mechanism for the production of the characteristic peaks is rather different. The arriving electron collides with the target atom and the latter is raised into an excited state. It does this by an electron moving from one **shell** to a higher shell. Later on, the electron 'falls down', giving off a photon, which for metals will lie in the X-ray region. For metals the energy levels involved must have a very large separation in order to produce the characteristic short wavelengths. So although the process of electrons moving from one energy level to another is the same as when visible light is produced, the electrons involved are those 'deep' inside the atom near the nucleus, whereas those involved in the production of visible light are electrons in the highest energy levels on the outside of the atom where the energy levels are very close together.

◀ Quantum mechanical model of the atom, Radiography ▶

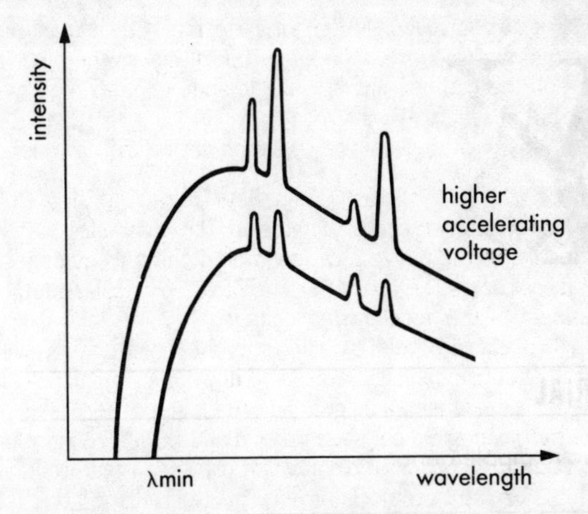

Fig. X.2 Typical X-ray spectrum showing peaks and continuous spectrum

YAGI AERIAL

◀ Half-wave dipole aerial ▶

YIELD POINT

◀ Stress–strain characteristics ▶

YOUNG MODULUS

◀ Stress–strain characteristics ▶

YOUNG'S SLITS

This is the simplest method of producing an overall **interference** pattern from a source of light. The method produces two coherent sources of light from one source by simply using two slits to divide the wavefront.

The experimental arrangement is shown in Fig. Y.1. The diagram is not to scale. It is usual to use a source *S* of monochromatic radiation. A single slit is placed in front of the source in order to ensure that the wave arriving at the two slits further on is part of the same wavefront. This first slit is usually

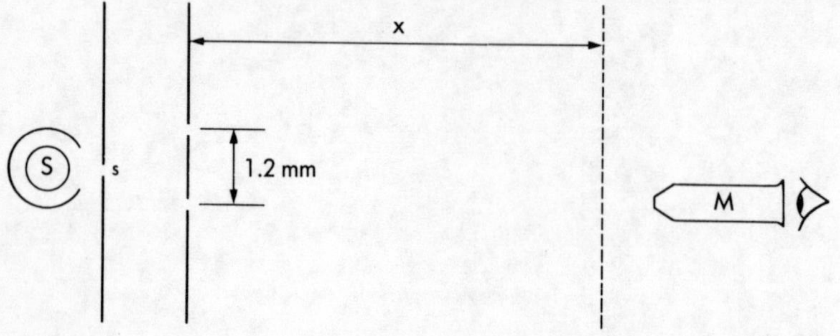

Fig. Y.1

kept about a metre behind the two slits. This ensures that when the wave gets to the two slits it is a plane wave. The single slit is not necessary if a laser is used as the light source because light from all parts of a laser source is coherent.

Because of the effect of diffraction the wave from the single slit spreads out and then is subsequently diffracted again from each of the two slits (Fig. Y.2). There is an area of overlap of the two waves and it is here that an intereference pattern can be observed, either on a screen or by looking towards the two slits through an eyepiece as shown in Fig. Y.1.

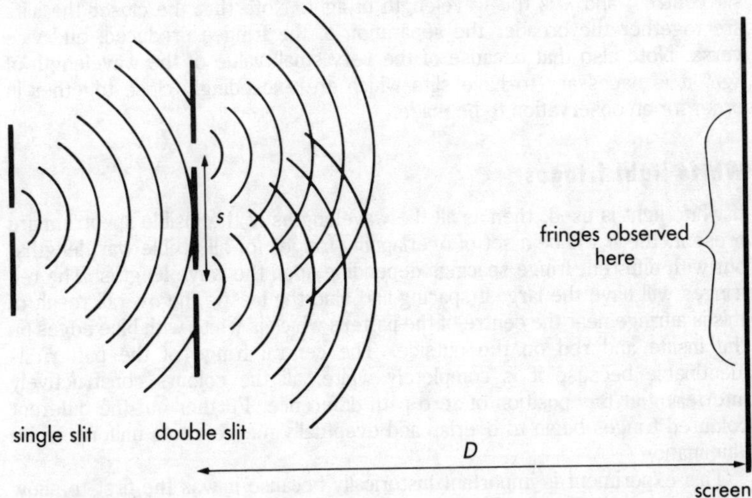

Fig. Y.2 Young's slits

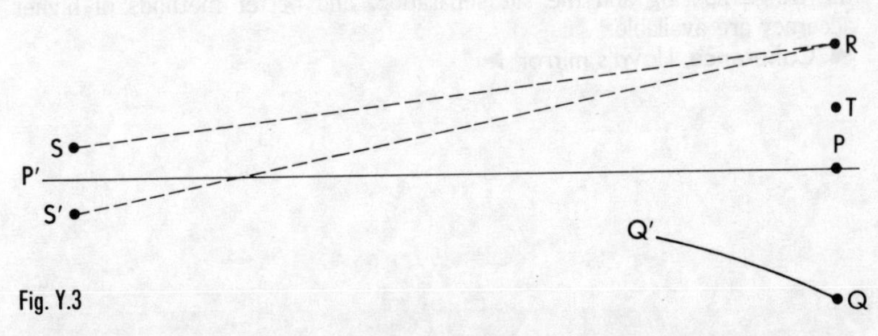

Fig. Y.3

The formation of the pattern can be considered as follows. At the two slits S and S′, as shown in Fig. Y.3, the oscillations of the light are in phase: that is, wave crests are produced at the same time and as these crests travel at the same speed, they will arrive at an equidistant point P at the same time. As a result there will be constructive interference anywhere along the line PP′. There will also be constructive interference along QQ′, any point along this line being one wavelength further from S than S′. Constructive interference occurs wherever the path difference SR – S′R is a whole number of wavelengths. Similarly destructive interference will occur where there is a path difference of an odd number of half wavelengths, e.g. at T, ST – ST′ being half a wavelength. The intensity of the light observed is proportional to the square of the net wave amplitude. Constructive interference results in bright fringes and destructive interference in dark fringes. The interference pattern is described by the formula $x = D\lambda/S$, where x is the distance between two adjacent bright fringes, D is the distance from the double slit to the plane of observation, S is the slit separation, i.e. the distance between slit centres, and λ is the wavelength of light. Note that the closer the slits are together the broader the separation of the fringes produced, and vice versa. Note also that because of the very small value of the wavelength of light it is necessary to have slits which are exceedingly close together in order for an observation to be made.

White light fringes

If white light is used, then as all the wavelengths of the visible spectrum are present, there will be a set of overlapping fringes for all visible wavelengths, but with different fringe spacings depending upon the wave lengths. The red fringes will have the largest spacing and blue the least. The overall result of this is a fringe near the centre of the pattern which is white with blue edges on the inside and red on the outside. The central fringe of the pattern is identifiable because it is completely white, all the colours constructively interfering at this position of zero path difference. Further out the different coloured fringes begin to overlap and eventually merge into a uniform white illumination.

This experiment is important historically because it was the first to show clearly the wave nature of light. The method can be used for wavelength determination, but the accuracy is limited by uncertainties in measurements of the fringe spacing and the slit separation, and better methods of higher accuracy are available.

◀ Coherence, Lloyd's mirror ▶

ZENER DIODE

If a reverse voltage is imposed upon an ordinary **diode** it will not conduct. However, if a very large reverse voltage is imposed conduction will begin and the diode will suffer permanent damage. A Zener diode on the other hand is made to be used in this breakdown region provided that a series resistor is used in order to limit the current. The characteristic and the symbol is shown in Fig. Z.1.

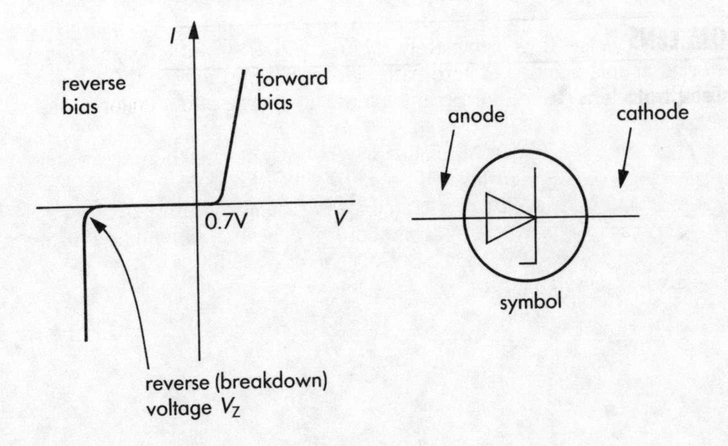

Fig. Z.1 Zener diode: characteristic and symbol

As can be seen, as the reverse voltage is increased there is a negligible current until the breakdown voltage V_Z is found. The current then increases in magnitude very rapidly, the characteristic curve being almost vertical. The main use of the Zener diode is in voltage stabilising circuits (see Fig. Z.2).

Provided the external supply exceeds the breakdown voltage of the diode and because the voltage across the diode, when conducting, is virtually independent of the current passing through it, the voltage across the diode remains steady. However, it is important in circuits of this kind to ensure that the quoted power rating of the diode is not exceeded. Zener diodes are manufactured in a range of values, e.g. 3.0 V, 3.9 V, 6.2 V, etc.

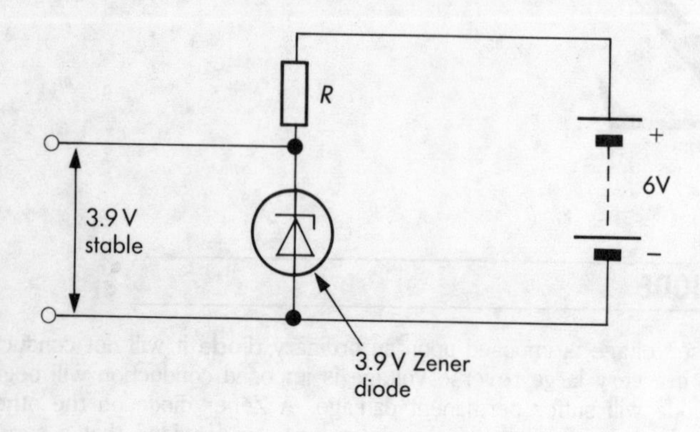

Fig. Z.2 Circuit using a Zener diode to generate 3.9 V from a 6 V supply

ZOOM LENS

◀ Telephoto lens ▶